Vital Directions
for Health & Health Care

An Initiative of the National Academy of Medicine

Victor J. Dzau, Mark B. McClellan, J. Michael McGinnis,
and Elizabeth M. Finkelman, *Editors*

NATIONAL ACADEMY OF MEDICINE

WASHINGTON, DC
NAM.EDU

NATIONAL ACADEMY OF MEDICINE • 500 FIFTH STREET, NW • WASHINGTON, DC 20001

NOTICE: This publication has undergone peer review according to procedures established by the National Academy of Medicine (NAM). Publication by the NAM signifies that it is the product of a carefully considered process and is a useful contribution worthy of public attention, but does not represent formal endorsement of conclusions and recommendations by the NAM. The views presented in this publication are those of individual authors and do not represent formal consensus positions of the NAM; the National Academies of Sciences, Engineering, and Medicine; or the authors' organizations.

Support for the NAM's Vital Directions for Health & Health Care Initiative was provided by the California Health Care Foundation, The Commonwealth Fund, the Gordon and Betty Moore Foundation, The John A. Hartford Foundation, the Josiah Macy Jr. Foundation, the Robert Wood Johnson Foundation, and the NAM's Harvey V. Fineberg Impact Fund.

Library of Congress Cataloging-in-Publication Data

Names: Dzau, Victor J., editor. | McClellan, Mark B., editor. | McGinnis, J.
   Michael, editor. | Finkelman, Elizabeth, editor. | National Academy of
   Medicine (U.S.), issuing body.
Title: Vital directions for health and health care : an initiative of the
   National Academy of Medicine / Victor J. Dzau, Mark McClellan, J. Michael
   McGinnis, Elizabeth Finkelman, editors.
Description: Washington, DC : National Academy of Medicine, [2017] | Includes
   bibliographical references.
Identifiers: LCCN 2017034965 (print) | LCCN 2017036005 (ebook) | ISBN
   9781947103016 (ebook) | ISBN 9781947103009 (pbk.)
Subjects: | MESH: Health Policy | United States
Classification: LCC RA418 (ebook) | LCC RA418 (print) | NLM WA 540 AA1 | DDC
   362.1--dc23
LC record available at https://lccn.loc.gov/2017034965

Printed in the United States of America.

Suggested citation: Dzau, V. J., M. McClellan, J. M. McGinnis, and E. M. Finkelman, editors. 2017. *Vital directions for health & health care: An initiative of the National Academy of Medicine.* Washington, DC: National Academy of Medicine.

"Knowing is not enough; we must apply.
Willing is not enough; we must do."

—GOETHE

LEADERSHIP

IMPACT

for a healthier future

NATIONAL ACADEMY OF MEDICINE

ABOUT THE NATIONAL ACADEMY OF MEDICINE

The **National Academy of Medicine** is one of three Academies constituting the National Academies of Sciences, Engineering, and Medicine (the National Academies). The National Academies provide independent, objective analysis and advice to the nation and conduct other activities to solve complex problems and inform public policy decisions. The National Academies also encourage education and research, recognize outstanding contributions to knowledge, and increase public understanding in matters of science, engineering, and medicine.

The **National Academy of Sciences** was established in 1863 by an Act of Congress, signed by President Lincoln, as a private, nongovernmental institution to advise the nation on issues related to science and technology. Members are elected by their peers for outstanding contributions to research. Dr. Marcia McNutt is president.

The **National Academy of Engineering** was established in 1964 under the charter of the National Academy of Sciences to bring the practices of engineering to advising the nation. Members are elected by their peers for extraordinary contributions to engineering. Dr. C. D. Mote, Jr., is president.

The **National Academy of Medicine** (formerly the Institute of Medicine) was established in 1970 under the charter of the National Academy of Sciences to advise the nation on issues of health, medical care, and biomedical science and technology. Members are elected by their peers for distinguished contributions to medicine and health. Dr. Victor J. Dzau is president.

Learn more about the National Academy of Medicine at NAM.edu.

VITAL DIRECTIONS FOR HEALTH & HEALTH CARE

Steering Committee

VICTOR J. DZAU, MD, National Academy of Medicine (*Co-Chair*)
MARK B. McCLELLAN, MD, PhD, Duke Margolis Health Policy Center (*Co-Chair*)
SHEILA P. BURKE, MPA, RN, Harvard Kennedy School
MOLLY J. COYE, MD, AVIA
THE HONORABLE THOMAS A. DASCHLE, The Daschle Group
ANGELA DIAZ, MD, PhD, MPH, Mount Sinai School of Medicine
THE HONORABLE WILLIAM H. FRIST, MD, Vanderbilt University
MARTHA E. GAINES, JD, LM, University of Wisconsin Law School
MARGARET A. HAMBURG, MD, National Academy of Medicine
JANE E. HENNEY, MD, National Academy of Medicine
SHIRIKI K. KUMANYIKA, PhD, MPH, University of Pennsylvania
THE HONORABLE MICHAEL O. LEAVITT, Leavitt Partners
J. MICHAEL MCGINNIS, MD, MPP, National Academy of Medicine
RUTH M. PARKER, MD, Emory University School of Medicine
LEWIS G. SANDY, MD, UnitedHealth Group
LEONARD D. SCHAEFFER, University of Southern California
GLENN D. STEELE, JR., MD, PhD, xG Health Solutions
PAMELA THOMPSON, MS, RN, American Hospital Association (ret.)
ELIAS A. ZERHOUNI, MD, Sanofi

NAM Staff

Development of this publication was facilitated by contributions of the following NAM staff, under the guidance of J. Michael McGinnis, MD, MPP, NAM Leonard D. Schaeffer Executive Officer and Executive Director of the Leadership Consortium for a Value and Science-Driven Health System.

ELIZABETH M. FINKELMAN, MPP, Project Director
MORGAN KANAREK, Chief of Staff, President's Office

LAURA HARBOLD DeSTEFANO, Director of Communications
KYRA E. CAPPELUCCI, Communications Specialist
MOLLY DOYLE, Communications Specialist
CELYNNE BALATBAT, Special Assistant to the President

REVIEWERS

The papers in this volume were reviewed in draft form by individuals chosen for their diverse perspectives and technical expertise, in accordance with review procedures established by the National Academy of Medicine. We wish to thank the following individuals for their review of the papers in this volume:

DAVID ALTSHULER, MD, PhD, Massachusetts Institute of Technology

JOSEPH ANTOS, PhD, American Enterprise Institute

MICHAEL J. BARRY, MD, Massachusetts General Hospital

PETER BASCH, MD, MACP, MedStar Health

JO IVEY BOUFFORD, MD, New York Academy of Medicine

PAULA BRAVEMAN, MD, MPH, University of California, San Francisco

JEFFREY BRENNER, MD, Camden Coalition of Healthcare Providers

ATUL BUTTE, MD, PhD, University of California, San Francisco

DAVE A. CHOKSHI, MD, MSc, FACP, New York University

KENNETH L. DAVIS, MD, The Mount Sinai Hospital

JACK E. DIXON, PhD, University of California, San Diego

MARK FISHMAN, MD, Harvard University

ROBERT GALVIN, MD, Blackstone

PAUL GINSBURG, PhD, University of Southern California

GARY L. GOTTLIEB, MD, Partners in Health

JAMES S. HOUSE, PhD, University of Michigan

ROBERT HUGHES, PhD, Missouri Foundation for Health

THOMAS R. INSEL, MD, Verily Life Sciences *(through May 2017)*

SHERMAN JAMES, PhD, Emory University

CRAIG JONES, MD, Vermont Blueprint for Health *(through June 2016)*

MARY E. KERR, PhD, RN, FAAN, Case Western Reserve University

DARREL G. KIRCH, Association of American Medical Colleges

WILLIAM E. KIRWAN, University System of Maryland *(through June 2015)*

ISAAC KOHANE, MD, PhD, Harvard Medical School

JEFFREY P. KOPLAN, MD, MPH, Emory University

Although the reviewers listed above provided many constructive comments and
suggestions, they were not asked to endorse the content of the papers, nor did
they see the final drafts before publication. Review of these papers was overseen
by **Elizabeth M. Finkelman, MPP,** Associate Program Officer, NAM; and
J. Michael McGinnis, MD, MPP, Leonard D. Schaeffer Executive Officer,
NAM. Responsibility for the final content of these papers rests entirely with
the authors and the NAM.

PREFACE

In summer 2015—nearly 18 months before America elected its new president and health reform resumed center stage in the policy arena—the National Academy of Medicine (NAM, formerly the Institute of Medicine) launched *Vital Directions for Health and Health Care*, a major policy initiative that brought together leading experts from across the nation to identify the most promising opportunities to improve health and health care in the United States. The initiative was born out of anticipation of a new administration and recognition that health and health care in the United States, while having achieved significant recent advancements—including reduced overall mortality, accelerated technological innovation, and a record-low uninsured rate—still faces critical challenges. Perhaps most notably, health care costs are rising at an unsustainable rate. The United States spends more than $10,000 per person per year on health care, amounting to a total of $3.2 trillion, or 18 percent of national GDP. Unsurprisingly, studies continue to indicate that our health system is inefficient; in 2013, the Institute of Medicine estimated that upwards of $750 billion of health care spending could be attributed to excess costs. And, evidence is mounting that inefficient health care spending is crowding out investments in critical social services and other priority areas for improving population health. So, despite our great investment, we fail to see a corresponding improvement in health outcomes; in fact, we fall measurably behind our international peers across important measures of access, equity, and efficiency. This concerning trend has been acknowledged and written about for years, and there is a great need for a strategic framework to help policymakers tackle these issues.

As America's most trusted health advisor, the NAM is committed to illuminating pressing issues that require attention and remediation, and to guiding and informing health leaders and policymakers about the best possible solutions. Past reports from the National Academies have helped shape the nation's health agenda—from the response to the AIDS epidemic to the crisis of medical error, from recommended dietary intakes to a safe vaccine schedule for children. We launched *Vital Directions* in keeping with this valued tradition. Under the leadership of an 18-member, nonpartisan steering committee, we commissioned over 150 of our nation's best researchers and health policy experts to assess 19 prominent areas in health, health care, and biomedical science. In completing their assessments, authors were asked to go beyond simply describing the pressing challenges and issues, and instead to focus on identifying the most promising and tangible policy opportunities to achieve progress. In keeping with the charge, they proposed approximately 68 recommendations across the 19 expert papers contained in this volume.

The steering committee next undertook the task of synthesizing and prioritizing the experts' recommendations. The committee found four key action priorities—*pay for value, empower people, activate communities,* and *connect care*—and four essential infrastructure needs—*measure what matters most, modernize skills, accelerate real-world evidence,* and *advance science*—that resonated across the papers as the most essential levers for advancing American health, health care, and scientific progress. Nonpartisan and rooted in an extensive evidence base, these eight vital directions constitute a comprehensive and succinct framework for improving health that spans well beyond the current discussions and debates around insurance coverage. And, while very important, reforming coverage alone cannot drive the change that is needed. For coverage to have value, the health system must work toward attaining its fullest potential. As such, these eight directions are essential to future health policy legislation and related program activities, and represent the fundamental principles around which any approach to health reform should be structured.

Finally, the importance of the *Vital Directions* initiative in the existing policy context cannot be overstated. Health reform is currently the subject of intense political polarization and scrutiny—discussions sometimes so sharp that they obscure focus on the issues that matter most in improving health and health care. In taking on this initiative and executing its work, the NAM strove to rise above the partisan rhetoric and debate to provide independent, impartial, and strong evidence-based policy guidance, and to refocus needed attention on shared goals and common principles. Beyond presenting a blueprint to drive needed progress toward better health care and lower costs, the initiative has sought to provide an avenue for bipartisan leadership and policymaking in health.

We are at a critical inflection point for health and health care in the United States. The challenges are great, but the opportunities to achieve progress are even greater. Altogether, the evidence suggests that refocusing is essential, and that our health policy framework must evolve to fully capitalize on the knowledge and capacity we now have to improve health and more efficiently deliver care.

We hope that our colleagues, community and health leaders, and policymakers at all levels will use and implement the *Vital Directions* framework as they seek to drive meaningful change and achieve better health for all.

—**VICTOR J. DZAU AND MARK B. MCCLELLAN**
Co-Chairs, *Vital Directions for Health & Health Care*
May 2017

ACKNOWLEDGMENTS

The *Vital Directions for Health and Health Care* initiative would not have been possible without the insights, contributions, and time invested by so many. From its inception to the completion of this final publication, the initiative was a collaborative effort in the truest sense, and we wish to recognize its contributors and thank them for their hard work and dedication.

First, we would like to thank the sponsors of the initiative, whose support made the work possible: the California Health Care Foundation, The Commonwealth Fund, the Gordon and Betty Moore Foundation, the John A. Hartford Foundation, the Josiah Macy, Jr. Foundation, The Robert Wood Johnson Foundation, and the National Academy of Medicine's Harvey V. Fineberg Impact Fund.

Members of the initiative's steering committee did a superb job guiding and overseeing the initiative. Their perspectives, experience, and wisdom were integral to making every step a success, and we are so deeply appreciative of the knowledge and time they invested in driving this effort over its 18-month duration.

Of course, the steering committee and the NAM alike are most grateful for the participation and contributions of the authors of the 19 discussion papers—over 150 people who collaborated for 9 months writing and revising the individual perspectives. Their work is at the heart of this initiative, and the final products reflect the extensive time and knowledge they invested. Special recognition must be paid to the papers' lead authors, who played key roles not only in the drafting of the work but also in coordinating and guiding their writing teams.

We would also like to thank those who participated and spoke at the September 2016 symposium, "Vital Directions for Health and Health Care: A National Conversation," and the public release event in March 2017. In particular, the conversations and feedback gathered at the symposium helped inform the final versions of the 19 discussion papers, as well as the steering committee's synthesis paper.

We must also express our sincere appreciation and gratitude to Howard Bauchner, Stacy Christiansen, Phil Fontanarosa, and the staff at the *Journal of the American Medical Association* (*JAMA*) for their sterling collaboration and wise counsel. Their cooperation and meticulous coordination ensured a seamlessly smooth process. Altogether, *JAMA* published 20 Viewpoints, 3 editorials, and a Special Communication related to the *Vital Directions* initiative.

Finally, we would like to thank the staff in the National Academy of Medicine and those in other offices at the National Academies for their contributions over the course of the initiative. In the NAM: Adrienne Anzanello, Celynne Balatbat, Bruce Block, and Morgan Kanarek. In the Office of News and Public Information: Molly Galvin and Jennifer Walsh. In the Office of Development: Julie Ische. In the National Academies' Research Center: Rebecca Morgan. And, a final, special thanks to the initiative's core staff, whose tremendous work and efforts were crucial to its success: J. Michael McGinnis, who oversaw the work of the initiative; Elizabeth Finkelman, who closely managed the initiative and production of its core products; Laura DeStefano, who led communications and publishing; Kyra Cappelucci, who provided critical production, communications, and event support; and Molly Doyle, who assisted with special communications projects.

CONTENTS

1. Vital Directions for Health and Health Care: Priorities from a National Academy of Medicine Initiative 1

   Victor J. Dzau, MD, Mark B. McClellan, MD, PhD, Sheila P. Burke, MPA, RN, Molly J. Coye, MD, The Honorable Thomas A. Daschle, Angela Diaz, MD, PhD, MPH, The Honorable William H. Frist, MD, Martha E. Gaines, JD, LLM, Margaret A. Hamburg, MD, Jane E. Henney, MD, Shiriki K. Kumanyika, PhD, The Honorable Michael O. Leavitt, J. Michael McGinnis, MD, MPP, Ruth M. Parker, MD, Lewis G. Sandy, MD, Leonard D. Schaeffer, Glenn D. Steele, Jr., MD, PhD, Pamela Thompson, MS, RN, and Elias A. Zerhouni, MD

PART I: BETTER HEALTH AND WELL-BEING

2. Systems Strategies for Better Health Throughout the Life Course 43

   J. Michael McGinnis, MD, MPP, Donald M. Berwick, MD, The Honorable Thomas A. Daschle, Angela Diaz, MD, PhD, MPH, Harvey V. Fineberg, MD, PhD, The Honorable William H. Frist, MD, Atul Gawande, MD, MPH, Neal Halfon, MD, MPH, and Risa Lavizzo-Mourey, MD, MBA

3. Addressing Social Determinants of Health and Health Disparities 71

   Nancy E. Adler, PhD, David M. Cutler, PhD, Jonathan E. Fielding, MD, MPH, Sandro Galea, MD, DrPH, Maria Glymour, ScD, Howard K. Koh, MD, MPH, and David Satcher, MD, PhD

4. Preparing for Better Health and Health Care for an Aging Population 97

   John W. Rowe, MD, Lisa F. Berkman, PhD, Linda P. Fried, MD, MPH, Terry T. Fulmer, PhD, RN, FAAN, James S. Jackson, PhD, Mary D. Naylor, PhD, RN, FAAN, William D. Novelli, MA, S. Jay Olshansky, PhD, MPH, and Robyn Stone, DrPH

5. Chronic Disease Prevention: Tobacco, Physical Activity, and Nutrition for a Healthy Start 111

   William H. Dietz, MD, PhD, Ross C. Brownson, PhD, Clifford E. Douglas, JD, John J. Dreyzehner, MD, MPH, FACO, Ron Z. Goetzel, PhD, Steven L. Gortmaker, PhD, James S. Marks, MD, MPH, Kathleen A. Merrigan, PhD, Russell R. Pate, PhD, Lisa M. Powell, PhD, and Mary Story, PhD, RD

6. Improving Access to Effective Care for People Who Have Mental Health and Substance Use Disorders. 135

James R. Knickman, PhD, K. Ranga Rama Krishnan, MB, ChB, Harold A. Pincus, MD, Carlos Blanco, MD, PhD, Dan. G. Blazer, MD, PhD, MPH, Molly J. Coye, MD, MPH, John H. Krystal, MD, Scott L. Rauch, MD, Gregory E. Simon, MD, MPH, and Benedetto Vitiello, MD

7. Advancing the Health of Communities and Populations 153

Lynn R. Goldman, MD, MPH, Georges C. Benjamin, MD, Sandra R. Hernández, MD, David A. Kindig, MD, PhD, Shiriki K. Kumanyika, PhD, MPH, Carmen R. Nevarez, MD, MPH, Nirav R. Shah, MD, MPH, and Winston F. Wong, MD

PART II: HIGH-VALUE HEALTH CARE

8. Benefit Design to Promote Effective, Efficient, and Affordable Care 175

Michael E. Chernew, PhD, A. Mark Fendrick, MD, Sherry A. Glied, PhD, Karen Ignagni, MBA, Stephen T. Parente, PhD, Jamie C. Robinson, PhD, MPH, and Gail R. Wilensky, PhD

9. Payment Reform for Better Value and Medical Innovation 191

Mark B. McClellan, MD, PhD, David T Feinberg, MD, MBA, Peter B. Bach, MD, Paul Chew, MD, Patrick H. Conway, MD, Nick Leschly, MBA, Gregory D. Marchand, Michael A. Mussallem, and Dorothy Teeter, MHA

10. Competencies and Tools to Shift Payments from Volume to Value 221

The Honorable Michael O. Leavitt, Mark B. McClellan, MD, PhD, Susan D. Devore, Elliott S. Fisher, MD, MPH, Richard J. Gilfillan, MD, H. Stephen Lieber, CAE, Richard Merkin, MD, Jeffrey A. Rideout, MD, and Kent J. Thiry, MBA

11. Tailoring Complex-Care Management, Coordination, and Integration for High-Need, High-Cost Patients. 233

David Blumenthal, MD, Gerard F. Anderson, PhD, Sheila P. Burke, MPA, RN, Terry Fulmer, PhD, RN, Ashish K. Jha, MD, MPH, and Peter Long, PhD

12. Realizing the Full Potential of Precision Medicine in Health and Health Care 249

Victor J. Dzau, MD, Geoffrey S. Ginsburg, MD, PhD, Aneesh P. Chopra, MPP, Dana P. Goldman, PhD, Eric D. Green, MD, PhD, Debra G.B. Leonard, MD, PhD, Mark B. McClellan, MD, PhD, Andrew S. Plump, MD, PhD, Sharon F. Terry, MA, and Keith R. Yamamoto, PhD

13. Fostering Transparency in Outcomes, Quality, Safety, and Costs **269**

   Peter J. Pronovost, MD, PhD, FCCM, J. Matthew Austin, PhD, MS, Christine K. Cassel, MD, Suzanne F. Delbanco, PhD, Ashish K. Jha, MD, MPH, Bob Kocher, MD, Elizabeth A. McGlynn, PhD, Lewis G. Sandy, MD, FACP, and John Santa, MD, MPH

14. The Democratization of Health Care **289**

   Paul C. Tang, MD, MS, Mark D. Smith, MD, MBA, Julia Adler-Milstein, PhD, Tom Delbanco, MD, Stephen J. Downs, SM, Giridhar G. Mallya, MD, MS, Debra L. Ness, MS, Ruth M. Parker, MD, and Danny Z. Sands, MD, MPH

15. Workforce for 21st-Century Health and Health Care **301**

   Steven H. Lipstein, MHA, Arthur L. Kellermann, MD, MPH, Bobbie B. Berkowitz, PhD, RN, Robert Phillips, MD, MSPH, David P. Sklar, MD, Glenn D. Steele Jr., MD, PhD, and George E. Thibault, MD

PART III: STRONG SCIENCE AND TECHNOLOGY

16. Information Technology Interoperability and Use for Better Care and Evidence **319**

   Jonathan B. Perlin, MD, PhD, Dixie B. Baker, PhD, David J. Brailer, MD, PhD, Douglas B. Fridsma, MD, PhD, Mark E. Frisse, MD, John. D. Halamka, MD, PhD, Jeffrey Levi, PhD, Kenneth D. Mandl, MD, MPH, Janet M. Marchibroda, MBA, Richard Platt, MD, MS, and Paul C. Tang, MD, MS

17. Data Acquisition, Curation, and Use for a Continuously Learning Health System. **345**

   Harlan M. Krumholz, MD, SM, Philip E. Bourne, PhD, Richard E. Kuntz, MD, MSc, Harold L. Paz, MD, MS, Sharon F. Terry, MA, and Joanne Waldstreicher, MD

18. Innovation in Development, Regulatory Review, and Use of Clinical Advances **369**

   Michael Rosenblatt, MD, Christopher P. Austin, MD, Marc M. Boutin, JD, William W. Chin, MD, Steven K. Galson, MD, MPH, Sachin H. Jain, MD, MBA, Michelle McMurry-Heath, MD, PhD, Samuel R. Nussbaum, MD, John Orloff, MD, Steven E. Weinberger, MD, and Janet Woodcock, MD

19. Targeted Research: Brain Disorders as an Example **395**

   Alan I. Leshner, PhD, Steven E. Hyman, MD, and Story C. Landis, PhD

20. Training the Workforce for 21st-Century Science **407**

   Elias A. Zerhouni, MD, Jeremy P. Berg, PhD, Freeman A. Hrabowski, PhD, Raynard S. Kington, MD, PhD, and Story C. Landis, PhD

APPENDIXES

A. Vital Directions Steering Committee Biographies. 433

B. Related Publications from the National Academies of Sciences,
Engineering, and Medicine 449

C. "Vital Directions for Health & Health Care: A National Conversation"
Symposium Agenda (September 26, 2016) 469

1

VITAL DIRECTIONS FOR HEALTH AND HEALTH CARE: PRIORITIES FROM A NATIONAL ACADEMY OF MEDICINE INITIATIVE

Victor J. Dzau, MD, Mark B. McClellan, MD, PhD, Sheila P. Burke, MPA, RN, Molly J. Coye, MD, The Honorable Thomas A. Daschle, Angela Diaz, MD, PhD, MPH, The Honorable William H. Frist, MD, Martha E. Gaines, JD, LLM, Margaret A. Hamburg, MD, Jane E. Henney, MD, Shiriki K. Kumanyika, PhD, MPH, The Honorable Michael O. Leavitt, J. Michael McGinnis, MD, MPP, Ruth M. Parker, MD, Lewis G. Sandy, MD, Leonard D. Schaeffer, Glenn D. Steele, Jr., MD, PhD, Pamela Thompson, MS, RN, and Elias A. Zerhouni, MD

The United States is poised at a critical juncture in health and health care. Powerful new insights are emerging on the potential of disease and disability, but the translation of that knowledge to action is hampered by debate focused on elements of the Affordable Care Act that, while very important, will have relatively limited impact on the overall health of the population without attention to broader challenges and opportunities. The National Academy of Medicine has identified priorities central to helping the nation achieve better health at lower cost.

CONTEXT: FUNDAMENTAL CHALLENGES

Health care today is marked by structural inefficiencies, unprecedented costs, and fragmented care delivery, all of which place increasing pressure and burden on individuals and families, providers, businesses, and entire communities. The consequent health shortfalls are experienced across the whole population, but disproportionately impact our most vulnerable citizens due to their complex health and social circumstances. This is evidenced by the growing income-related gap in life expectancy for both men and women (*Figures 1-1 and 1-2*). Today, higher-income men can expect to live longer than they did 20 years ago, while life expectancy for low-income males has not changed. Higher-income women are also anticipated to live longer, but life expectancy for low-income women is projected to decline.

Beyond systemic and structural issues, this country is faced with serious public health challenges and threats: emerging infectious diseases; an evolving opioid epidemic; alarming rates of tobacco use, obesity, and related chronic diseases;

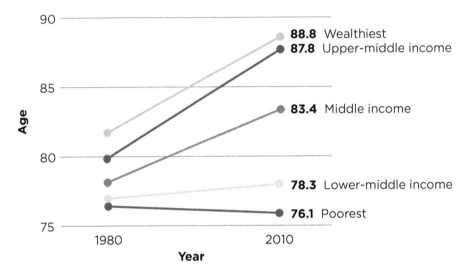

FIGURE 1-1 | Widening inequality in life expectancy for men in the United States.
SOURCE: Data from NASEM, 2015.

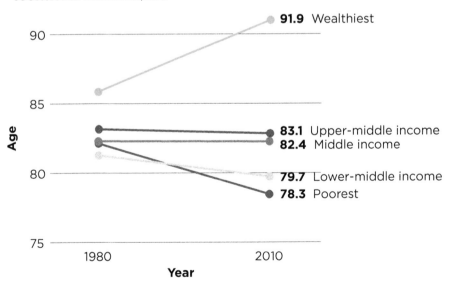

FIGURE 1-2 | Widening inequality in life expectancy for women in the United States.
SOURCE: Data from NASEM, 2015.

and a rapidly aging population that requires great support from our health care delivery and financing systems. Following are summarized fundamental challenges with which our health and health care system must be better prepared to contend.

Persistent Inequities in Health

In spite of the United States' great investment in health care services and the state-of-the-art health care technology available, inequities in health care access and status persist across the population and are more widespread than in peer nations (Lasser et al., 2006; Avendano, 2009; van Hedel et al., 2014; Siddiqi et al., 2015). Over the past 15 years, individuals in the upper income brackets have seen gains in life expectancy, while those in the lowest income brackets have seen modest to no gains (Chetty et al., 2016). And, while health inequities are seen most acutely across socioeconomic and racial/ethnic lines, they also emerge when comparing other characteristics such as age, life stage, gender, geography, and sexual orientation (Braveman et al., 2010; Artiga, 2016). However, health status is not predetermined; rather, is the result of the interplay for individuals and populations of genetics, social circumstances, physical environments, behavioral patterns, and health care access (McGinnis et al., 2002). Similarly, inequities in health are not inevitable (Adler et al., 2016; McGinnis et al. 2016); efforts to lessen social disadvantage, prevent destructive health behaviors, and improve built environments could have important health benefits.

Rapidly Aging Population

By 2060, the number of older persons (ages 65 years or older) is expected to rise to 98 million, more than double the 46 million today; in total population terms, the percentage of older adults will rise from 15 percent to nearly 24 percent (Mather et al., 2015; ACL, 2016). This trend is explained by the fact that people are living longer and the baby boomers are entering old age. The aging population is placing increasing demand on our health care delivery, financing, and workforce systems, including informal and family caregivers. As more and more people age, rates of physical and cognitive disability, chronic disease, and comorbidities are anticipated to rise, increasing the complexity and cost of delivering or receiving care. In particular, Medicare enrollments and related spending will rise, as will Medicaid and out-of-pocket spending for long-term care services not provided under Medicare (CMS 2016a; ACL, 2016). Ensuring that the elderly can be adequately cared for and supported will require greater understanding of their social, medical, and long-term needs, as well as workforce skills and care delivery models that can provide complex care (Rowe et al., 2016).

New and Emerging Health Threats

US public health and preparedness has been strained by a number of recent high-profile challenges, such as lead-contaminated drinking water in several of our cities; antibiotic resistance; mosquito-borne illnesses such as Zika, Dengue, and Chikungunya; diseases of animal origin, including HIV, influenzas, Severe Acute Respiratory Syndrome (SARS), Middle East Respiratory Syndrome-Coronavirus (MERS-CoV), and Ebola; and devastating natural disasters, such as hurricanes Sandy and Katrina (Morens and Fauci, 2013). The emergence of these threats, and in some cases the related responses, highlights the need for the public health system to better equip communities to better identify and respond to these threats.

Persisting Care Fragmentation and Discontinuity

While recent efforts on payment reform have aimed to advance coordinated care models, much of health care delivery still remains fragmented and siloed. This is particularly true for complex, high-cost patients—those with fundamentally complex medical, behavioral, and social needs. Complex care patients include the frail elderly, those who are disabled and under 65 years old, those with advanced illness, and people that have multiple chronic conditions (Blumenthal et al, 2016). High-need, high-cost patients comprise about 5 percent of the patient population, but drive roughly 50 percent of health care spending (Cohen and Yu, 2012). Individuals with chronic illness and/or behavioral health conditions often experience uncoordinated care which has been shown to result in lower quality care, poorer health outcomes, and higher health care costs (Druss and Walker, 2011; Frandsen et al., 2015).

Health Expenditure Costs and Waste

It is widely acknowledged that the United States is experiencing unsustainable cost growth in health care: spending is higher, coverage costs are higher, and the costs associated with gaining access to the best treatments and medical technologies are similarly increasing. In 2015, health care spending—including spending by the federal government, state and local governments, households, and private businesses—grew 5.8%, totaling $3.2 trillion or close to 5.8 percent, of GDP. Of that, it has been estimated that approximately 30 percent can be attributed to wasteful or excess costs, including costs associated with unnecessary services, inefficiently delivered services, excess administrative costs, prices that are too high, missed prevention opportunities, and fraud (IOM 2010, 2013). Resources consumed in this way represent significant opportunity costs both in terms of higher-value care that could be pursued, and in terms of the social, behavioral, and other essential services necessary for effective care and good outcomes. *Figure*

1-3 shows how rising federal spending on health care programs, as a percentage of GDP, is outpacing and compressing other parts of the federal budget.

Constrained Innovation Due to Outmoded Approaches

The United States has long been a global leader in biomedical innovation, but our edge is increasingly at risk due to outdated regulatory, education, and training models. In the drug and medical device review and approval process, uncertainty and unpredictability around approval expectations adds complication, delay, and expense to the research and development process, and can translate to a disincentive to investors (Battelle, 2010). Simultaneously, there are concerns that the movement toward population-based payment models may stifle innovation and patient access by placing excessive burden on manufacturers to demonstrate the value of their products upfront in approval and reimbursement decisions. Further, our biomedical education and scientific training pathways are outdated and fragmented (Kruse, 2013; Zerhouni et al., 2016). Talented young scientists are increasingly discouraged from pursuing careers in biomedical research due to rising educational requirements and tuition costs combined with uncertain career pathways.

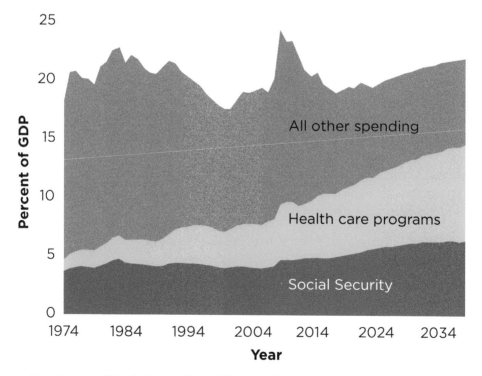

FIGURE 1-3 Historical and projected federal spending: health care and other programs.
SOURCE: Data from Congressional Budget Office.

CONTEXT: REALISTIC TOOLS

The good news is that the nation is equipped to tackle these formidable challenges from a position of unprecedented knowledge and substantial capacity. Locally and nationally, new models of care delivery and payment are emerging that seek to reduce waste by rewarding value over volume, are more patient-centric, and are driving better care coordination and integration. The rise of digital health technology has opened the door to enhanced health care and provider access, greater patient engagement, as well as data and tools to support more personalized and tailored health care. Further, increased recognition of the importance of community and population health strategies has helped foster a greater system-wide focus on prevention and overall health promotion opportunities. And, thanks to major advancements and continued innovation in biomedicine and technology, diagnostic capabilities and treatments have expanded greatly, allowing Americans to live longer, more productive lives. Following are several of the crosscutting opportunities for progress identified over the course of the initiative and its work.

A New Paradigm of Health Care Delivery and Financing

Against the backdrop of fee-for-service payment models that can incentivize unnecessary or duplicative care, progress is underway toward a more value-based, person-centric approach. This transformation represents a common effort stemming from the initiative from many quarters—health care leaders, providers, policymakers, and academic experts—responding to rising health care costs, deficiencies in care quality, and inefficient spending. Under fee-for-service, health care services are paid for by individual units, incentivizing providers to order more tests and administer more procedures, sometimes irrespective of need or expected benefit to the patient. In contrast, value-based, alternative payment models (APMs) incentivize providers to maintain or improve the health of their patients, while reducing excess costs by delivering coordinated, cost-effective, and evidence-based care.

Fully Embracing the Centrality of Population and Community Health

With the increasing emphasis on value-based care, and with increasing recognition that factors outside of health care are among the strongest determinants of the health and health care needs of individuals and population segments, efforts are growing to strengthen the activities, tools, and impact related to community health in US health care today (Kindig and Stoddart, 2003). It is increasingly acknowledged that effective measures to improve health status and health outcomes over groups and over time require tending to the conditions and factors that affect individual and population health over the life course, including social, behavioral, and environmental determinants. While health care in the United States has developed on a track substantially apart from, and generally uncoordinated with, programs directed to the other determinants (Goldman et al., 2016), great gains stand to be achieved if they are more effectively integrated into care delivery and planning.

Increased Focus on Individual and Family Engagement

While calls to more effectively and meaningfully engage patients and their families in care design and decisions are not new, the awareness of the importance to clinical outcomes has increased substantially, as have the tools to facilitate that engagement (Topol, 2015). Today, there is increased focus on expanding the roles of individuals and families in not only designing and executing health care regimens, but in measuring progress, and in developing and testing new and innovative treatments. Across the care continuum, there is greater recognition that patients and families—as the end-users of the services provided—are an integral part of the decision process, whose engagement, understanding, and support is imperative to individual health and well-being, as well as system efficiency, quality, and overall performance.

Biomedical Innovation, Precision Medicine, and New Diagnostic Capabilities

Biomedical science and innovation has accelerated at a tremendous pace, and, with increasing knowledge, available treatments, and technologies to combat illness and disease, Americans are able to live longer, healthier lives. Since the 1980s, nearly 300 novel human therapeutics have been approved covering more than 200 indications (Evens and Kaitin, 2015). Breakthroughs in biotechnology have generated new treatments and cures for diseases that were previously untreatable or could only be symptomatically managed, such as cardiovascular disease, HIV, and hepatitis C. Diagnostics have also become more sophisticated and precise, as diagnostic capabilities have expanded. Today, the field of precision medicine is emerging and has the potential to transform medicine by tailoring diagnostics, therapeutics, and prevention measures to individual patients (Dzau et al., 2016). Precision medicine has great promise to improve care quality by delivering more accurate and targeted treatments, and increase care efficiency by reducing the use of multiple and/or ineffective tests and therapies.

Advances in Digital Technology and Telemedicine

The ability exists to build a continuously learning health system (IOM, 2007; 2013). Health and health care are being fundamentally transformed by the development of digital technology with the potential to deliver information, link care processes, generate new evidence, and monitor health progress (Perlin et al., 2016). Health information technology includes electronic health records (EHRs), personal health records, e-prescribing, and mHealth (mobile health) tools, including personal health tools, such as personal wellness devices and smartphone apps, and online peer support communities (ONC, 2013). All of these technologies are changing the way the health system operates, how individuals interact with the health system and one another, and the data available to monitor and improve health and make care decisions. Technological advances in the health arena have also enabled the rise of telemedicine, which allows patients and clinicians to interact with one another remotely.

Promise of "Big Data" to Drive Scientific Progress

Rapid advancement in cost-effective sensing and the expansion of data-collecting devices have enabled massive datasets to be continuously produced, assembled, and stored. The amount of high-dimensional data available is unprecedented and will only continue to grow. If effectively harnessed and curated, big data could enable science to "extend beyond its reach" and allow technology to become more "adaptive, personalized, and robust" (NRC, 2013). In particular, these large-scale data stores have the potential to reveal and further our understanding of subtle population patterns, heterogeneities, and commonalities that are inaccessible in smaller data (Fan et al., 2014). Using big data, we can learn more about disease causes and outcomes, advance precision medicine by creating more precise drug targets, and better predict and prevent disease occurrence or onset (Khoury and Ioannidis, 2014).

THE NATIONAL ACADEMY OF MEDICINE INITIATIVE

In 2015, mindful of the 2017 transition in the US presidency, the National Academy of Medicine (NAM, formerly the Institute of Medicine) launched an initiative to marshal and make available the best possible health and health care expertise and counsel for the incoming administration, policymakers, and health leaders across the country. In doing so, the NAM is responding to the chartered mandate of the National Academies and its long-standing record of providing trusted and independent counsel. Appropriate to the centrality of the issues, this initiative is named *Vital Directions for Health & Health Care*. This paper synthesizes the range of compelling opportunities identified over the course of the initiative and presents strategic priorities for the next administration and the nation's health leaders to undertake now and in the years ahead.

To guide the initiative, the NAM convened a Steering Committee of respected leaders from the health, health care, science, and policy communities (*Box 1-1*). Although the activity is expressly nonpartisan, participants include those who have held cabinet-level posts and key legislative responsibilities under both major parties.

BOX 1–1
Vital Directions Steering Committee Members

Victor J. Dzau, MD, National Academy of Medicine *(Co-Chair)*
Mark B. McClellan, MD, PhD, Duke Margolis Health Policy Center *(Co-Chair)*
Sheila P. Burke, MPA, RN, Harvard Kennedy School
Molly J. Coye, MD, AVIA
The Honorable Thomas A. Daschle, The Daschle Group
Angela Diaz, MD, PhD, MPH, Mount Sinai School of Medicine
The Honorable William H. Frist, MD, Vanderbilt University
Martha E. Gaines, JD, LLM, University of Wisconsin Law School
Margaret A. Hamburg, MD, National Academy of Medicine
Jane E. Henney, MD, National Academy of Medicine
Shiriki K. Kumanyika, PhD, MPH, University of Pennsylvania
The Honorable Michael O. Leavitt, Leavitt Partners
J. Michael McGinnis, MD, MPP, National Academy of Medicine
Ruth M. Parker, MD, Emory University School of Medicine
Lewis G. Sandy, MD, UnitedHealth Group
Leonard D. Schaeffer, University of Southern California
Glenn D. Steele, Jr., MD, PhD, xG Health Solutions
Pamela Thompson, MS, RN, American Hospital Association *(ret.)*
Elias A. Zerhouni, MD, Sanofi

The *Vital Directions* initiative is rooted in a vision of a health system that performs optimally in promoting, protecting, and restoring the health of individuals and populations, and helps each person reach their full potential for health and well-being (*Figure 1-4*). To achieve this vision requires simultaneously pursuing three core goals for the nation—better health and well-being, high-value health care, and strong science and technology—through advancing strategic action priorities and essential infrastructure needs.

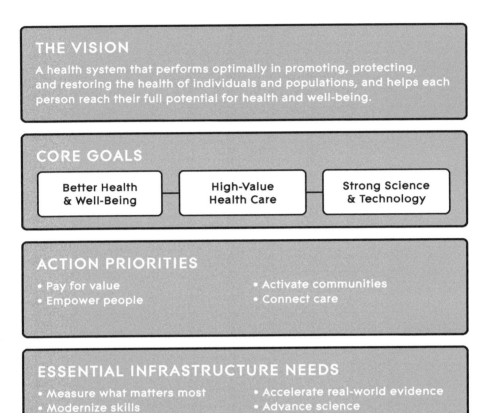

THE VISION
A health system that performs optimally in promoting, protecting, and restoring the health of individuals and populations, and helps each person reach their full potential for health and well-being.

CORE GOALS

| Better Health & Well-Being | High-Value Health Care | Strong Science & Technology |

ACTION PRIORITIES
- Pay for value
- Empower people
- Activate communities
- Connect care

ESSENTIAL INFRASTRUCTURE NEEDS
- Measure what matters most
- Modernize skills
- Accelerate real-world evidence
- Advance science

FIGURE 1-4 | Vital Directions framework.

Based on invited suggestions from the public, health and health care communities, and their own collective evaluation, the steering committee identified for assessment the most important issues to realizing the nation's health prospects, now and in the years ahead, ultimately selecting 19 issue areas across the 3 goals (*Box 1-2*). More than 150 of the best-respected health leaders and scholars in the nation were invited to analyze the 19 issue areas in the form of expert discussion papers. For each issue area, authors were asked to identify the key challenges and strategic opportunities for progress—recommended *vital directions*—and to offer suggestions on effective ways for policymakers to act on those opportunities.

Each paper underwent a rigorous peer review and revision process before being posted on the NAM website for public review and comment, and then published in final form. In addition, summaries of the papers were published as Viewpoints in the *Journal of the American Medical Association* (*JAMA*). On September 26, 2016, the NAM hosted a public symposium—"A National Conversation"—to discuss and receive stakeholder feedback on the recommendations proposed in the discussion papers, to explore crosscutting themes and priorities, and identify outstanding issues and questions. The comments received at the symposium, in response to the web posting, and in response to the *JAMA* publication informed the final versions of the papers, and were a resource for our identification of the priorities presented below.

VITAL DIRECTIONS FOR HEALTH AND HEALTH CARE: THE PRIORITIES

Across the total of 68 recommended vital directions identified by the 19 author groups—each important to progress in health, health care, and biomedical science—certain elements are clearly common to each. It is those elements that we present as the nation's most compelling health priorities. To achieve and sustain a health and health care system that is most effective in helping all people reach their full potentials for health and well-being, to better secure our fiscal future, and to provide the global leadership that is expected from the United States, it is essential that all levels of leadership act on four action priorities and four essential infrastructure needs for health and health care.

Action Priorities

These priorities address what are, in many ways, the greatest contributors to deficiencies in health system performance but are among the most tangible opportunities to make substantial impact and progress.

- *Pay for value*—deliver better health and better results for all
- *Empower people*—democratize action for health
- *Activate communities*—collaborate to mobilize resources for health progress
- *Connect care*—implement seamless digital interfaces for best care

Essential Infrastructure Needs

The necessary underpinnings for an accountable, efficient, and modern health system that will strengthen the impact and better ensure the success of the action priorities.

- *Measure what matters most*—use consistent core metrics to sharpen focus and performance

- *Modernize skills*—train the workforce for 21st-century health care and bio-medical science
- *Accelerate real-world evidence*—derive evidence from each care experience
- *Advance science*—forge innovation-ready clinical research processes and partnerships

---

BOX 1–2
Vital Directions Issue Areas

Better health and well-being

- Systems strategies for better health throughout the life course
- Addressing social determinants of health and health disparities
- Preparing for better health and health care for an aging population
- Chronic disease prevention: tobacco, physical activity, and nutrition for a healthy start
- Improving access to effective care for people who have mental health and substance use disorders
- Advancing the health of communities and populations

High-value health care

- Benefit design to promote effective, efficient, and affordable care
- Payment reform for better value and medical innovation
- Competencies and tools to shift payments from volume to value
- Tailoring complex care management, coordination, and integration for high-need, high-cost patients
- Realizing the full potential of precision medicine in health and health care
- Fostering transparency in outcomes, quality, safety, and costs
- The democratization of health care
- Workforce for 21st-century health and health care

Strong science and technology

- Information technology interoperability and use for better care and evidence
- Data acquisition, curation, and use for a continuously learning health system
- Innovation in development, regulatory review, and use of clinical advances
- Targeted research: brain disorders as an example
- Training the workforce for 21st-century science

THE ACTION PRIORITIES

Four crosscutting action priorities are clearly evident: pay for value, empower people, activate communities, and connect care. Whether from the perspective of the need to reduce the causes and improve the management of heart disease, cancer, or diabetes; to prevent, identify, and treat people with problems of mental health and addiction; or to streamline and improve access to the range of services needed, these four strategic directions are indeed vital. Much greater advantage needs to be taken of what has been learned about the importance of helping people take more personal control of their health and health care, strengthening locally-based efforts and resources, reducing the fragmentation of care processes, and focusing payments on the quality of the results achieved. New insights about their successful engagement underscore the importance of these strategies, but because they represent a substantial departure from current trends, their advancement requires strong commitment and leadership.

Pay for Value—Deliver Better Health and Better Results for All

Design and promote health financing strategies, policies, and payments that support the best results—the best value—for individuals and the populations of which they are a part.

Health expenditures in the United States are far above those in other countries, in part because, when it comes to payments, the notion of "health" has been explicitly linked to the provision and consumption of discrete health care services, and sometimes without consideration of necessity, effectiveness, or efficiency (IOM, 2013). In the traditional fee-for-service model of health care payment, providers are paid according to the number and type of health care services they provide. This approach to payment can incentivize unnecessary procedures and duplicative services, contributing to avoidable waste and inefficiency. Further, treatments are frequently prescribed without enough consideration of the social, behavioral, and environmental factors that are significant determinants of health (Chetty et al., 2016; Cullen et al., 2012; McGinnis and Foege, 1993; McGinnis et al., 2016; Mokdad et al., 2004). Although contributions vary across population groups, medical treatment has a relatively small effect on the overall health and well-being of the population with shortfalls in medical care accounting for only about 10 percent of premature deaths overall, while behavioral patterns, genetic predispositions, social circumstances, and environmental exposures account for roughly 40 percent, 30 percent, 15 percent, and 5 percent of early deaths respectively (*Figure 1-5*) (McGinnis et al., 2002). Yet, most health expenditures are devotedly exclusively to treatment. With evidence mounting, it is becoming better understood that achieving better care and better value requires more active engagement of these broader factors in the care process and beyond.

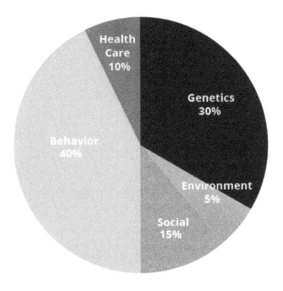

FIGURE 1-5 | Schematic of health determinants.
SOURCE: Adapted from McGinnis, 2002.

To further advance value-based care, policy reforms should:

- **Drive health care payment innovation providing incentives for outcomes and value**. New payment and delivery models are being introduced that aim to reduce waste, increase value, and improve outcomes by advancing tailored, coordinated, and integrated care. Population-based payment models—the most comprehensive among alternative payment models—hold providers accountable for delivering patient-centered care for a designated population over a specified timeframe and across the entire spectrum of care (E. Mitchell, 2016). For providers to deliver care in this way, strong financial incentives must be in place, which require payers (beyond Medicare and Medicaid) to support and carry out payment reforms. Transition to value-based and population-oriented payment models will require different approaches to structuring economic rewards for population-wide progress, and well as harmonized measures used to assess results and reward accountability for system-wide performance (McClellan et al., 2016).
- **Help clinicians develop the core competencies required for new payment models**. More evidence is needed not only on the features and elements

that determine the success of certain payment models, but also on which core competencies providers need to be successful in payment models. Evidence is accumulating in these areas but is spreading slowly. More timely and efficient evaluations of successful models are needed for Medicare payment reform pilots, as well as those being implemented in public and private programs (McClellan et al., 2016). Further, increased support and greater participation in public-private collaborations would be very helpful for providers in identifying the core competencies they need to succeed (Leavitt et al., 2016).

- **Remove barriers to integration of social services with medical services.** There is mounting evidence that US under-investments in social services relative to health care services may be contributing to the country's poor health performance (Bradley and Taylor, 2013; Bradley et al., 2011; IOM and NRC, 2013). Integrating clinical care services and nonmedical services (i.e., housing, food, transportation, and income assistance), combined with some reinvestment of existing health care dollars into social services has great potential to achieve better outcomes, reduce inequality, and increase cost savings (Taylor et al., 2015). Although more research is needed to better understand the policy, payment, and regulatory options that could facilitate integration, some private health systems and health plans are already well positioned to pilot more of these efforts (Abrams et al., 2015).

Example policy initiatives from the Vital Directions discussion papers:

- Sustain and accelerate the implementation, demonstration, and assessment of alternative payment models supported by public and private health care payers to reward value and improve outcomes and health (McClellan et al., 2016).
- Reward measurement streamlining that helps identify and reward innovation and outcomes delivering value at system-wide and population levels (population-based payments) (McClellan et al., 2016).
- Support public-private collaborations among industry and government, (e.g., the Accountable Care Learning Collaborative), which help clinicians and other provider groups identify and develop the core competencies necessary for success in the execution and use of alternative payment models (McClellan and Leavitt, 2016).
- Implement successful payment and delivery models for health and social services integration. For example, pursue funding stream integration, such that Medicaid managed care plans can coordinate with social and community interventions proven effective in improving outcomes and reducing costs (Adler et al., 2016).

Develop coordinated multiagency strategies at the federal, state, and local levels to demonstrate the scale and spread of models that sucessfully link and deliver integrated health and social services.

Empower People—Democratize Action for Health

Ensure that people, including patients and their families, are fully informed, engaged, and empowered as partners in health and health care choices, and that care matches well with patient goals.

Improving the patient experience, improving population health, and reducing the per capita cost of health care cannot be achieved without effectively engaging and empowering patients and families across the care continuum—in effect, the quadruple aim of health and health care. However, too frequently, patients are insufficiently involved in their own care decisions, sometimes resulting in care that does not take into account the greater context of their lives or their individual goals. To be effective, policy reforms must do more than simply achieve engaged patients—rather, reforms need to ensure that patients and their families are fully informed and able to participate as partners in determining outcomes and values for their own health and health care. Further, empowering individuals to lead their own health care decisions requires giving them ownership of their personal health data. Doing so would better enable individuals to use, act on, and obtain personal value from their health information (Krumholz et al., 1999).

To empower people, policy reforms should:

- **Link care and personal context**. Identifying the "best" or "most appropriate" treatment goes beyond health factors and measures alone. Health care regimens and treatments must not only be safe and efficacious, but must work in the context of the patient's life and goals (Braddock et al., 2016; Covinsky et al., 2000; Legare and Witteman, 2013; Turnbull et al., 2016). Providers with their patients and the patients' families need to engage in integrated assessments of clinical and social goals, and reach mutual care decisions.
- **Communicate in a way appropriate to literacy.** Shared decision making relies on people's ability to gain access to, process, and understand basic health information. Policymakers and health leaders should focus on increasing the amount of information available and making the information more understandable and useful for everyone. These actions will help foster trust and lead to a more actively involved and health-literate public.
- **Promote effective telehealth tools**. Telehealth technologies—ways of delivering health-related information or services through the internet, phone,

and other methods—can increase patient access to medical care, particularly in remote or underserved areas, and reduce costs (Berman and Fenaughty, 2005; Hailey et al., 2002; Keely et al., 2013). State-by-state regulatory barriers inhibiting the adoption of these technologies should be reduced. These barriers include reimbursement ineligibility and variations and restrictions in state-by-state licensure rules, which prevent physicians from practicing medicine outside of the state(s) in which they were licensed (Tang et al., 2016).

- **Ensure patient data access, ownership, and privacy**. Individuals' health information is stored in numerous, often siloed, locations and most frequently in EHRs, from which data can been very difficult to access. Further, ownership of individuals' health data is typically assigned to physicians and hospitals (Kish and Topol, 2015). Empowering individuals to make informed, personal health decisions requires giving them ownership of their own health data, and offering every assurance that their data are held privately and securely.

Example policy initiatives from the Vital Directions discussion papers:

- Develop incentives, along with clinical practice guidelines and decision support tools to encourage physicians to engage with each patient on their personal context and goals in making care decisions (Tang et al., 2016).
- Expand health literacy services to ensure that information, processes, and delivery of health care in all settings align with the skills and abilities of all people.
- Support patient communication research on and decision-making strategies to determine the most effective approaches to relaying information on care, cost, and quality (Pronovost et al., 2016). For example, the Patient-Centered Outcomes Research Institute (PCORI) Communication and Dissemination Research program, focusing on approaches to communicate and disseminate health information and research findings to patients (PCORI, 2017).
- Harmonize telemedicine reimbursement standards across payers, and establish common national licensure for telehealth practitioners, so that telehealth clinicians may provide services across state lines (Tang et al., 2016).

Activate Communities—Collaborate to Mobilize Resources for Health Progress

Equip and empower communities to build and maintain conditions that support good health, link health and social services where possible, and identify and respond to health threats locally.

Health is rooted in communities, where people live, work, eat, learn, and play—a person's ZIP code is perhaps the strongest predictor of health outcomes and life expectancy (Heiman and Artiga, 2016; RWJF, 2009). Related, a person's health is very much a product of the available social supports within their community, their surrounding physical environment and local characteristics, and personal behavior, which is highly influenced by these factors. In this way, while some communities are healthy and thriving, others are struggling, as reflected in the widening gap in lifespans between the rich and poor (Chetty et al., 2016; NASEM, 2015), and persisting discrepancies in quality and health care access between urban and rural areas (Stanford School of Medicine, 2010). Underscoring the potential for community-driven initiative to effect social and cultural change, a recent report from the National Academies examined efforts in nine communities to address social, economic, or environmental health determinants, finding that, with the right mix of evidence-based attention to growing community capacity, and multisectoral collaboration, communities can put forward solutions to promote health equity (NASEM, 2017). However, when comparing relative investments in health care and social services, the United States continues to invest far less in community-based social services than its peers (Bradley and Taylor, 2013) (*Figure 1-6*).

Communities have essential roles to play in combating the nation's most pressing health threats, such as the chronic disease and substance abuse epidemics. If activated with the sufficient resources and capacity, community health leaders—health care organizations, hospitals, municipal public health departments, and community standards-setting agencies—are capable of driving critical change by promoting healthy environments and behaviors, and by fostering a culture of continuous health improvement (Goldman et al., 2016). To be successful, community solutions require a supportive policy and resource environment to facilitate community efforts.

To activate communities, policy reforms should:

- **Invest in local leadership and infrastructure capacity for public health initiatives**. Transformative change in health and health care requires a culture shift spearheaded by leadership and action within communities. Notably, achieving optimal health for all will necessitate a "Health in All Policies Approach," including collaborations and support from leaders in all sectors, such as business, education, housing, and transportation, in defining and achieving health goals. Buy-in should be built on the premise that all sectors have an interest in creating and sustaining livable communities that are healthy, thriving, and prosperous.
- **Expand community-based strategies targeting high-need individuals**. High-need patients are typically among the sickest, with multiple comorbidities

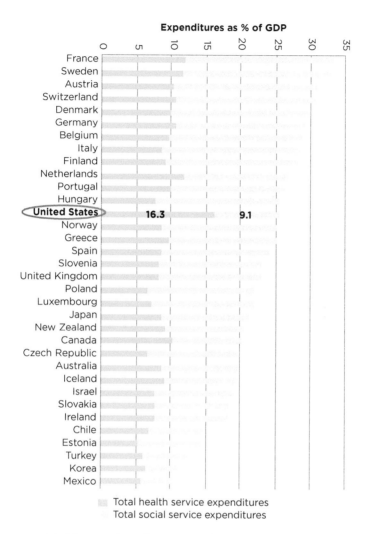

Health care and social services spending (%GDP) across OECD countries.
SOURCE: Adapted from Bradley and Taylor, 2013. Used with permission.

and the most complex health needs. These individuals constitute about 5 percent of all patients but drive roughly 50 percent of health care costs (E. M. Mitchell, 2016) (*Figure 1-7*). Achieving better health outcomes and greater efficiency within this patient segment requires close coordination and integration of medical and social services. Expanded community-based strategies are needed to ensure that high-need, high-cost individuals receive the social supports essential to the success of their health care and health outcomes, including food, housing, transportation, and income assistance. Ultimately, close links between health care and community-based services will be essential to achieving better health outcomes and greater system efficiency.

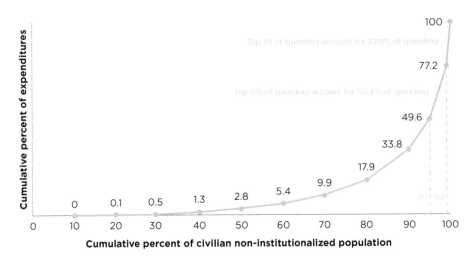

FIGURE 1-7 | Distribution of health care spending, US civilian, non-institutionalized population, 2014.
SOURCE: Data from E. M. Mitchell, 2016.

- **Provide strong state-based capacity for guidance, assistance, and synergy for local health efforts**. States are often considered the "laboratories" for health and health care, and should be looked to as a resource to scale existing community health innovations. Useful case examples and best practices should be identified and disseminated for other communities to learn from and tailor for their own purposes.

Example policy initiatives from the Vital Directions discussion papers:

- Strengthen local level infrastructure and capacity for multisectoral health initiatives, using resources marshaled from federal grant programs, tax incentives, health insurance payments linked to population health, and public-private partnerships (Goldman et al., 2016). For example, require that tax exempt health organizations meeting IRS requirements for community benefit work through coordinated, community-wide, public-private partnerships and multi-sectoral initiatives.
- Invest in the nation's physical infrastructure with an eye on health. For example, a multisectoral strategy targeting jurisdictions with older physical infrastructures to assess infrastructure weak spots and to facilitate with community structural improvements—leveraging not only health assets but labor, housing, transportation, and other relevant department efforts.
- Support states' flexible use of grant funds to provide guidance, technical assistance, and strategic resources for local leadership and collaborative action

to identify and target their most important health challenges (Goldman et al., 2016).

- Identify best practices from pilot programs launched through Center for Medicare & Medicaid Innovation (CMMI) on approaches linking relevant health, education, social service, and legal system activities and resources to address individuals at highest risk and with the greatest needs (Adler et al., 2016; Goldman et al., 2016).
- Give states flexibility to use Medicaid funds to implement best practices in targeting the most effective efforts for high-risk, vulnerable children (e.g., prenatal to age 3), as well as adults at particular risk with complex, multifactorial conditions (Adler et al., 2016; McGinnis et al., 2016).

Connect Care—Implement Seamless Digital Interfaces for Best Care

Develop standards, specifications, regulatory policies, and interfaces to ensure that patient care data and services are seamlessly and securely integrated, and that patient experience is captured in real-time for continuous system-wide learning and improvement.

Health information technology (HIT) has had tremendous impact on health care, driving greater accountability and value, enhanced public engagement and purpose, improved public health surveillance, and more rapid development and diffusion of new therapies. Yet, critical challenges remain, including the ability of providers to amass and share electronic health record (EHR) data for individual patients longitudinally, which is essential to harnessing the economic and clinical benefits of EHRs (Perlin et al., 2016). Despite the rapid advancement and broadening technical capacity of digital technology for health, digital interoperability—the extent to which systems can share and make use of data—remains extraordinarily limited. The consequences are adverse in several ways: care continuity between clinicians and over time is impeded; gaps and duplications in efforts are undiscovered; device incompatibility predisposes to patient harm, clinician stress is compounded, and end-user costs are higher as systems try to cobble together temporary fixes. Interoperable information technology and generated data are foundational to the promise of a continuously learning health system, in which data are continuously contributed, shared, and analyzed to support better health, more effective care, and better value.

To achieve connected care, policy reforms should:

- **Make necessary infrastructure and regulatory changes for clinical data accessibility and use**. Specific infrastructure and regulatory barriers exist to clinical data accessibility and use that require attention and remediation.

Among the most critical are: specifications for data that have been developed but not adopted; commercially protective coding practices; proprietary data ownership and use restrictions; and misinterpretation of control requirements for use of clinical data as a resource for new knowledge. The recently passed 21st Century Cures Act does include provisions to encourage and facilitate sharing and use of clinical data, but those provisions will still require local action and leadership.

- **Create principles and standards for end-to-end interoperability**. Either through federally-facilitated or mandated efforts, or through direct federal action, specific standards need to be supported for end-to-end (system/clinician/patient) interoperability, so as to allow private and secure data transmission among EHRs and FDA-approved medical devices, and to provide a path toward data exchange with consumer health technologies.
- **Identify information technology and data strategies that support continuous learning**. The technical capacity exists for continuous communication and learning throughout health care, ranging from the activities of different clinicians and institutions, to the operation and interplay among relevant medical devices, to readings from mobile biomonitoring devices. Taking full advantage of this transformative capacity requires comprehensive strategy and action to strengthen data infrastructure, build public trust around data privacy and security, and harmonize inconsistent state and local policies on data use and sharing.

Example policy initiatives from the Vital Directions discussion papers:

- Use HHS regulatory and reimbursement mechanisms to enforce existing interoperability standards for interoperability across EHRs and medical devices (Perlin et al., 2016).
- Support a voluntary national patient identifier whereby patients could opt in to be assigned a unique identification number, which would facilitate patient-data matching, as well as overall data aggregation (Perlin et al., 2016).
- Continue escalation of EHR use as a condition of participation in federal health care programs, such as Medicare, to better allow understanding of national disease burden, health resource planning, and auditing for prevention of fraud, waste, and abuse (Perlin et al., 2016).
- Through HHS, sponsor a public-private standards organization to commission the necessary additional standards, such as open, standardized application programming interfaces (APIs) to support continuously improving, standardized, service-oriented architecture for interoperability and clinical decision support.
- Streamline inconsistent state and local security and privacy policies related to data exchange and use (e.g., federal guideline enabling states and localities to

harmonize data use policies and reciprocal support agreements). Simultaneously, consider safe harbor provisions against civil penalties for data-sponsored attacks and "hacktivists" (Perlin et al., 2016).

- Building on the principle of patient ownership of data, foster active patient access and use of their own data for care and evidence improvement (Krumholz et al., 2016).

ESSENTIAL INFRASTRUCTURE NEEDS

Successful engagement of these action priorities and their considerable potential for progress requires the simultaneous pursuit of four essential infrastructure needs: measure what matters most, modernize skills, accelerate real-world evidence, and advance science. The significance of these essential infrastructures is clear. At population, community, and individual levels, the pace of health progress will depend on effective measures that can drive better understanding and action focused on the issues that matter most in health and health care. Modern skillsets for the health care workforce will be necessary to provide integrated care for an increasingly complex patient population. Similarly, new training approaches and skills for the biomedical workforce will be needed to realize the most cutting-edge research and technological advancements that will support innovative care. Related, continued innovation in tools and approaches for improving health and health care will require taking advantage of expanding capacities to learn, collect, and share real-world clinical data. Finally, sustained investment in scientific research combined with streamlined regulatory pathways will enable more rapid translation of the most effective and promising medical treatments and tools that will help drive better health outcomes.

Measure What Matters Most—Use Consistent Core Metrics to Sharpen Focus and Performance

Standards, specifications, and governance strategies should be developed to accelerate the identification, refinement, harmonization, and implementation of a parsimonious set of core measures that 1) best reflect national, state, local, and organizational system performance on issues that matter most to health care, and 2) guide the development of related measures, not for reporting but for quality improvement.

Within the past two decades, greater demand for accountability and information on system performance has translated into the proliferation of performance measures and related data. While performance measurement and public reporting have been beneficial to increasing system accountability and performance, concerns are growing about the time, cost, validity, generalizability, and overall burden of clinical measurement (Pronovost et al., 2016). For example, performance measures are often produced and applied by numerous organizations in a variety of ways, creating inconsistencies and reducing the measures' value and usefulness. And, while it is critical to be transparent by reporting outcomes and performance, the results become meaningless if the measure and its application lack validity, reliability, and generalizability. Further, as the volume of performance measures becomes burdensome and time-consuming for providers, measurement reporting has the unintended effect of driving up costs and adding to existing inefficiencies.

To achieve meaningful measurement, policy reforms should:

- **Focus reliably and consistently on factors most important to better health and health care**. A standard set of core measures, available at national, state, local, and institutional levels, would offer benchmarks for targeting and assessing problems and interventions, as well as providing baseline reference points to improve the reliability of broader measurement, evaluation, accountability, and research efforts. The National Academies report *Vital Signs: Core Metrics for Health and Health Care Progress* presents a framework for 15 such measures of health, care quality, value, engagement, and public communication (IOM, 2015a).
- **Create the national capacity for identifying, standardizing, implementing, and revising core measures**. On the assumption that measures employed as a baseline, multilevel performance assessment instrument should be developed, tested, and refined through a broad, independent process involving multiple stakeholders, the *Vital Signs* committee recommended that the Secretary of Health & Human Services identify a lead organization for each of the 15 core measures, which would, in turn, engage related stakeholder organizations in the refinement process. The committee also recommended creating an ongoing, independent capacity to guide and oversee the revision process long-term.
- **Invest in the science of performance measurement**. Currently, there is no consensus on how best to measure care delivery and performance. More research is needed on the development of performance measures, including how to create and maintain a standardized, scientific approach to performance measurement (Pronovost et al., 2016).

Example policy initiatives from the Vital Directions discussion papers:

- Initiate HHS process to refine and implement the *Vital Signs* core measures nationally, beginning with the federal categorical and health care funding programs, including a variation to be used by states in return for Medicaid management flexibility (McGinnis et al., 2016).

- Provide waivers from Medicare reporting requirements for health care organizations working in multiorganization collaboratives to implement and report on core system-wide performance measures (McGinnis et al., 2016).
- Through an initiative or taskforce, explore the design of an independent, standards-setting body for reports on health care performance measures. The Financial Accounting Standards Board (FASB) could be referenced as a model—the FASB establishes financial accounting and reporting standards for companies and nonprofit organizations (Pronovost et al., 2016).
- Create a multiagency, collaborative research initiative on the science of performance measurement, including how best to develop, test, evaluate, and improve measures (Pronovost et al., 2016).

Modernize Skills—Train the Workforce for 21st-Century Health Care and Biomedical Science

Foster modern skillsets through integrated and innovative education and training approaches that can meet the rapidly evolving demands of health care, biomedical science, and industry.

Ensuring the talent and motivation of the nation's human capital pool is a central determinant of national competitiveness (Zerhouni et al., 2016). Investing in and strengthening the capacity of our health care and biomedical science workforces is critical to our nation's health, economic and physical security, and global leadership in research and innovation. But, new directions in training are needed. The health care workforce of the 21st century must be able to effectively manage and treat increasingly complex patient and population health profiles and circumstances, particularly with a rapidly aging population and rising burden of chronic disease. Simultaneously, health care workers must be adept at keeping healthy patients healthy through preventive therapies and guidance, while harnessing and applying rapidly advancing health information technology and innovation. Supporting the biomedical science workforce of the 21st century will also require modern education and training approaches. Existing training models and pathways are outdated and fragmented (Kruse, 2013), have become longer and more expensive, and no longer assure stable, successful careers (Zerhouni et al., 2016).

To modernize skills, policy reforms should:

- **Reform health care education and training approaches to meet our nation's complex health needs**. For the health care workforce, adapting training and practice to coordinated team-based approaches is essential to care delivery in our ever-evolving and complex care environment. To deliver efficient and high-quality care, a next generation health care workforce needs to be recruited, educated, and trained to work collaboratively in interdisciplinary teams, become technically skilled, and be facile with the full use of health information technology (Lipstein et al., 2016). In particular, clinical workforce skills and capabilities will need to evolve and advance alongside the rapid innovations in HIT. In addition to using information technology, health care practitioners will need to understand how the data are collected, analyzed, and applied. To facilitate, informatics requirements should be integrated into existing graduate medical education (GME) and training programs, including the federal GME program.

- **Create and support new education and training pathways for the science workforce**. Training the science workforce for the future will require new models, new partners, and cross-disciplinary thinking. Our new workforce will need to be diverse, multidisciplinary, team-oriented, and possess strong skills in data analytics and informatics. Recruiting and retaining the most talented will necessitate innovative education pathways and programs to assemble and support a cutting-edge, biomedical science workforce.

Example policy initiatives from the Vital Directions discussion papers:

- Engage the scientific community, private foundations, state higher education officials, federal health professions payers in proposing a public-private national initiative on health professions education that is team-based, collaborative, multidisciplinary, and skilled in HIT and informatics (Lipstein et al., 2016).
- Leverage eligibility requirements for Medicare alternative payment models to require that providers include a description of their plans for augmented use of systems engineers and HIT coaching and expertise (Perlin et al., 2016).
- Launch a visible, high-level initiative to attract the most talented students and researchers into biomedical research careers (e.g., a NextGen Opportunity Fund, as described by Zerhouni et al., 2016).

Accelerate Real-World Evidence—Derive Evidence from Each Care Experience

Accelerate clinical research that enlists patients as partners, takes advantage of big data, and collects real-world data on care or program experience for continuous learning, improving, and tailoring of care.

Harnessing the full power of a learning health system will remain more an aspiration than a consistent achievement until fully leveraging available data becomes a practical possibility (Krumholz, 2016). The existing ability to collect enormous swaths of real-world, clinical and health-related data holds immense promise for improving clinical care by better informing clinical choice, improving drug and medical device safety, effectiveness assessment, and scientific discovery. However, technical, regulatory, and cultural barriers to harnessing these data for societal benefit persist—notably, an outdated clinical research paradigm and inadequate data-sharing incentive structure. With respect to the latter, data-sharing is neither simple, nor an established norm in health care and clinical research. In fact, much of the data generated over the course of a clinical trial is never published or made easily accessible (IOM, 2015b).

Related to clinical research, the complexity of many medical products being developed today is exceeding traditional evaluation models, such as randomized clinical controlled trials (RCTs). Roughly 85 percent of therapies fail early during clinical development, and of those that survive phase III trials, about 50 percent actually get approved (Ledford, 2011). The traditional paradigm of clinical research that was instituted in the 1960s was based on single trials that occurred at one site, and were designed to answer one question. Today, trials are much larger, occurring in multiple sites, and seeking to solve more complex problems. RCTs, while still the gold standard of clinical research, can be limited in their generalizability and ability to reflect real-world results. And, as we enter the era of precision medicine, RCTs alone will be unable to produce enough data to support this new paradigm (BPC, 2016). Alongside RCTs, learning health system models of evaluation are emerging that use real-world evidence (or digital health information) captured in EHRs and other digital platforms that continuously collect and distribute clinical data. The 21st Century Cures Act includes provisions supporting the inclusion of real-world evidence in approving new indications for drugs. Demonstrative real-world evidence combined with the rigor of clinical trial data could yield important and powerful opportunities to enhance care and improve outcomes.

To accelerate reliable evidence, policy reforms should:

- **Advance continuous learning clinical research drawing on real-world evidence**. Complementing controlled studies, the ability to collect data from clinical practice presents a great opportunity to gain new, possibly more accurate insights about the efficacy and safety of drugs and medical devices. These data could offer nuanced information and findings that would be otherwise unattainable in a standard RCT. Beyond complementing traditional RCTs, initial applications of clinical practice data could include testing supplemental applications of approved medicines. In the future, select pilots could be pursued using a continuously learning approach to evaluate real-world evidence in both preapproval and postapproval contexts (Rosenblatt et al., 2016).

- **Foster a culture of data sharing by strengthening incentives and standards**. As with routine clinical data, research participants should have presumptive ownership and the right to access and share their own health information. In addition, researchers should more broadly accept that strong science and "good scientific citizenship" require individual level data to be more accessible for evaluation and reuse, with the necessary safety and privacy precautions in place (Krumholz et al., 2016). For data sharing to become a more accepted norm, a cultural shift in health care might be facilitated through financial and professional incentives, as well as strengthened standards for data ownership and sharing protocols.
- **Partner with patients and families to support evidence generation and sharing**. Partnering with patients, and simultaneously taking steps to better ensure their privacy and trust, is a prerequisite to effective evidence generation and data sharing for care improvement and learning. Engaging patients throughout the research process can help identify unmet care needs, future research priorities, and help realize better clinical outcomes. Initiatives on patient engagement should address how best to incorporate patient input; how to effectively build patient skillsets for engagement; and how to define value, so that it better reflects the patient perspective (Rosenblatt et al., 2016).

Example policy initiatives from the Vital Directions discussion papers:

- Support public-private partnerships to build on existing pilot studies to assess and expand real-world evidence development in both preapproval and postapproval settings (Rosenblatt et al., 2016).
- Continue to promote and harmonize federal standards relevant to data-sharing, as well as to ownership, security, and privacy of health-care data (Krumholz et al., 2016).
- Incentivize data-sharing; for example, create a reimbursement benefit for health systems that facilitates data access and sharing between patients and researchers (Krumholz et al., 2016).
- Establish initiatives to build patient skill-sets for engagement. In addition, better define value in terms that reflect the patient perspective, and assess and identify measures for patient trustworthiness and participation (Dzau et al., 2016).

Advance Science—Forge Innovation-Ready Clinical Research Processes and Partnerships

Redesign training, financial support, and research and regulatory policies to enable and encourage transformative innovation in science and its translation.

The United States has long been at the forefront of biomedical science and innovation, but in recent years, its lead has been challenged by rising competition from other countries. Cumbersome and outdated regulatory review processes are making it more difficult to bring promising therapies and devices to market. In addition, the cost of drug and device development has risen substantially—some estimate the cost of bringing a new drug to market to be $2.6 billion (TSCDD, 2015). The slowing pace and rising cost of biomedical innovation are fueling calls for new discovery, development, production, and commercialization models (Rosenblatt et al., 2016), as well as more collaborative partnerships capable of driving rapid innovation.

To advance the pace of innovation, policy reforms should:

- **Promote the conditions for scientific innovation**. Advancing science first and foremost requires investment. Necessary conditions for success are commitment to funding and support for basic and applied research, and the acceleration in translation. Furthermore, taking advantage of datasets rapidly growing to very large sizes, new forms of science, technology, and evidence development can boost clinical care research. Opportunities include making greater use of real-world evidence and cognitive computing to better understand and ensure the most effective and appropriate interventions for the best possible clinical outcomes (Rosenblatt et al., 2016).
- **Support an adaptive and patient-oriented regulatory framework**. Outdated models of discovery, development, and approval need to be adapted to a more forward-looking paradigm promoting efficiency, continuous innovation, and patient centricity. Recent efforts by the FDA to implement expedited regulatory approval tracks represent good progress, but other opportunities to improve efficiency exist. Aligning discovery and development with current needs will require patient input and partnership in all stages of research and development; multidisciplinary, cross-sector collaborations to achieve needed breakthroughs in combating complex diseases; more efficient clinical trials with adaptive designs; and greater experimentation with and use of real-world evidence, in addition to data produced during RCTs.
- **Foster cross-disciplinary and public-private partnerships**. Existing silos across disciplines and sectors are counterproductive to progress. Greater collaboration among scientists in the government, academia, and industry is needed to advance innovation. Cross-disciplinary partnerships will be essential, with basic scientists, translational scientists, and clinical scientists working together to achieve breakthroughs in the most challenging therapeutic areas, including autoimmune, neurodegenerative, and inflammatory diseases (Rosenblatt et al., 2016).

Example policy initiatives from the Vital Directions *discussion papers:*

- Ensure research funding for basic and applied sciences.
- Support public-private programs to invest in and advance the science and related applications of big data analysis, such as cognitive computing (Rosenblatt et al., 2016).
- Develop and apply a strategy for engaging patients as active partners in the advancement of innovative approaches to clinical research, including their support for expanded use of clinical data for discovery and for appropriate communication and experience feedback between industry and patients throughout the discovery and development processes (Rosenblatt et al., 2016).
- Support precompetitive collaborations including industry, government, and academia—such as the Accelerating Medicines Partnership—to achieve needed breakthroughs in the most challenging therapeutic areas that cannot be done by any sector alone (Rosenblatt et al., 2016), such as the Accelerating Medicines Partnership (NIH, 2017).

THE PATH FORWARD

Despite the intense debate that surrounds many health policy issues today, we have found strong agreement on the critical challenges as well as the vital directions required to achieve progress. As policymakers consider the next chapter of health reform, no matter the fate of the ACA, the priority actions and essential infrastructures identified here represent the basic principles around which we can attain better health and well-being, higher-value care, and the strong science and innovation that will drive better health outcomes, efficiency, and quality. In particular, we see substantial prospects if we can capture the potential from greater empowerment of people in their care processes; activate communities to promote and sustain the health of their residents; harness the potentially transformative connectivity of our digital infrastructure; and accelerate the movement toward a payment system based on value and results. Just a decade ago, these strategic prospects were scarcely more than conceptual notions, but today we see evidence of their promise, including the essential infrastructures needed to support them.

The potential for progress hinges on strong leadership at all levels—organizational, local, state, and federal—as well as strategic investment across these priorities. At the federal level, leadership opportunities exist on multiple fronts: creating and supporting program partnerships that enhance the flexibility of state and local leaders to rally community-wide engagement around agreed upon priorities and targets; developing public-private stakeholder groups working together on strategies, benchmarks, training, and resources; introducing accountability measures and tracking that focus on results rather than processes; and offering flexibility and incentives for cross-sector alliances and activities.

Similarly, leadership at the state and local levels is vital to ensure that individual communities are healthy, thriving, and promoting the strength of the cooperative community-wide initiatives important to progress. As noted earlier, health begins where people live, work, eat, learn, and play. Community-led programs and initiatives are critical to identifying and mitigating socioeconomic and environmental factors that contribute to health disparities; developing models and best practices for preventing disease; creating health-promoting infrastructure and local environments; and mitigating some of our most pressing health threats.

Beyond strong leadership, strategic investment of existing resources across the priorities indicated will be required to achieve the better outcomes we have long sought. As a nation, we have the world's largest observable discrepancy between the amount spent on health care and the impact of that expenditure on the nation's health—but we are poised with real prospects for improvement, if we deploy our resources wisely. And, if we can redirect even a relatively small portion of the approximately $1 trillion now spent unnecessarily on health care to the high-priority investment opportunities described here, the health and productivity benefits will extend far beyond the health sector. Notably, prioritizing our nation's health through strong leadership and strategic investment will yield greater prosperity, security, global leadership, and competitiveness for the country. These are vital directions for every American.

REFERENCES

Abrams, M. K., and D. Moulds. 2015. *Integrating Medical and Social Services: A Pressing Priority for Health Systems and Payers.* http://healthaffairs.org/blog/2016/07/05/integrating-medical-and-social-services-a-pressing-priority-for-health-systems-and-payers (accessed March 15, 2017).

Adler, N. E., D. M. Cutler, J. E. Jonathan, S. Galea, M. Glymour, H. K. Koh, and D. Satcher. 2016. *Addressing Social Determinants of Health and Health Disparities.* Discussion Paper, Vital Directions for Health and Health Care Series. National Academy of Medicine, Washington, DC. https://nam.edu/wp-content/uploads/2016/09/addressing-social-determinants-of-health-and-health-disparities.pdf.

Administration for Community Living (ACL). 2016. *Administration on Aging: Aging Statistics*. http://www.aoa.acl.gov/aging_statistics/index.aspx (accessed March 14, 2017).

Artiga, S. 2016. *Disparities in Health and Health Care: Five Key Questions and Answers*. http://kff.org/disparities-policy/issue-brief/disparities-in-health-and-health-care-five-key-questions-and-answers/#endnote_link_195310-9 (accessed March 14, 2017).

Avendano, M., M. M. Glymour, J. Banks and J. P. Mackenbach. 2009. Health Disadvantage in US Adults Aged 50 to 74 Years: A Comparison of the Health of Rich and Poor Americans With That of Europeans. *American Journal of Public Health* 99(3):540–548.

Battelle Technology Partnership Practice. 2010. *Gone Tomorrow? A Call to Promote Medical Innovation, Create Jobs, and Find Cures in America*.

Berman, M. and A. Fenaughty. 2005. Technology and managed care: Patient benefits of telemedicine in a rural health care network. *Health Economics* 14(6):559–573. doi:10.1002/hec.952.

Bipartisan Policy Center (BPC). 2016. *Using Real-World Evidence to Accelerate Safe and Effective Cures*. http://cdn.bipartisanpolicy.org/wp-content/uploads/2016/06/BPC-Health-Innovation-Safe-Effective-Cures.pdf (accessed March 15, 2017)

Blumenthal, D., Anderson, G., Burke, S.P., Fulmer, T., Jha, A.K., Long, P. 2016. *Tailoring Complex-Care Management, Coordination, and Integration for High-Need, High-Cost Patients*. 2016. Vital Directions for Health and Health Care Series. Discussion Paper, National Academy of Medicine, Washington, DC. https://nam.edu/wp-content/uploads/2016/09/tailoring-complex-care-management-coordination-and-integration-for-high-need-high-cost-patients.pdf.

Braddock III, C.H., K.A. Edwards, N.M. Hasenberg, T.L. Laidley, and W. Levinson. 1999. Informed Decision Making in Outpatient Practice Time to Get Back to Basics. *Journal of the American Medical Association* 282(24):2313–2320. doi:10.1001/jama.282.24.2313.

Bradley, E.H., B.R. Elkins, J. Herrin, and B. Elbel. 2011. Health and social services expenditures: associations with health outcomes. *BMJ Quality and Safety* 20(10): 826–831. doi: 10.1136/bmjqs.2010.048363.

Bradley, E. and Taylor, L. A. 2013. *The American Health Care Paradox: Why Spending More is Getting Us Less*. New York, NY: PublicAffairs.

Braveman, P.A., C. Cubbin, S. Egerter, D.R. Williams, and E. Pamuk. 2010. Socioeconomic Disparities in Health in the United States: What the Patterns Tell Us. *American Journal of Public Health*. 100(Suppl 1):S186-S196. doi:10.2105/AJPH.2009.166082.

Centers for Medicare and Medicaid Services (CMS). 2016a. *Analysis of Medicaid per enrollee spending by age group is available from Centers for Medicare & Medicaid Services, Table 25, Medicaid Per-enrollee Spending by Gender and Age Group, Calendar Years 2002, 2004, 2006, 2008, 2010.* https://www.cms.gov/research-statistics-data-and-systems/statistics-trends-and-reports/nationalhealthexpenddata/nhe-fact-sheet.html (accessed March 14, 2017).

Centers for Medicare and Medicaid Services (CMS) 2016b. *National Health Expenditure Data—Historical.* https://www.cms.gov/Research-Statistics-Data-and-Systems/Statistics-Trends-and-Reports/NationalHealthExpendData/NationalHealthAccountsHistorical.html (accessed March 14, 2017).

Chetty, R., M. Stepner, S. Abraham, S. Lin, B. Scuderi, N. Turner, A. Bergeron, D. Cutler. 2016. The Association Between Income and Life Expectancy in the United States, 2001–2014. *Journal of the American Medical Association.* 315(16):1750–1766. doi:10.1001/jama.2016.4226.

Cohen, S. and W. Yu. 2012. *The concentration and persistence in the level of health expenditures over time: Estimates for the U.S. Population, 2008–2009.* Rockville, MD: Agency for Healthcare Research and Quality.

Congressional Budget Office (CBO). *Historical Budget Data March 2016* [Data Table]. https://www.cbo.gov/sites/default/files/recurringdata/51134–2016-03-historicalbudgetdata.xlsx (accessed March 15, 2017).

Congressional Budget Office (CBO). *Long-Term Budget Projections July 2016* [Data Table]. https://www.cbo.gov/sites/default/files/recurringdata/51119–2016-07-ltbo-4.xlsx (accessed March 15, 2017).

Covinsky, K.E., J.D. Fuller, K. Yaffe, et al. 2000. Communication and decision-making in seriously ill patients: Findings of the SUPPORT project. *Journal of the American Geriatrics Society* 48(S1):S187–S193. doi:10.1111/j.1532–5415.2000.tb03131.x.

Cubanski, J., C. Swoope, A. Damico, and T. Neuman. 2014. *How Much Is Enough? Out-of-Pocket Spending Among Medicare Beneficiaries: A Chartbook.* http://kff.org/health-costs/report/how-much-is-enough-out-of-pocket-spending-among-medicare-beneficiaries-a-chartbook (accessed March 14, 2017).

Cullen, M. R., C. Cummins, V. R. Fuchs. 2012. Geographic and Racial Variation in Premature Mortality in the U.S.: Analyzing the Disparities. *PLoS ONE* 7(4): e32930. doi:10.1371/journal.pone.0032930.

Druss, B. G. and E. R. Walker. 2011. *Mental disorders and medical comorbidity.* Princeton, NJ: Robert Wood Johnson Foundation.

Dzau, V.J., G. S. Ginsburg, A. Chopra, D. Goldman, E. D. Green, D. G. B. Leonard, M. McClellan, A. Plump, S. F. Terry, and K. R. Yamamoto. 2016. *Realizing the Full Potential of Precision Medicine in Health and Health Care.* Vital

Directions for Health and Health Care Series. Discussion Paper, National Academy of Medicine, Washington, DC. https://nam.edu/wp-content/uploads/2016/09/realizing-the-full-potential-of-precision-medicine-in-health-and-health-care.pdf.

Evens, R. and K. Kaitin. 2015. The evolution of biotechnology and its impact on health care. *Health Affairs* 34(2):210–219. doi:10.1377/hlthaff.2014.1023.

Fan, J., F. Han, and H. Liu. 2014. Challenges of big data analysis. *National Science Review* 1(2):293–314. doi:10.1093/nsr/nwt032.

Frandsen, B. R., K. E. Joynt, J. B. Rebitzer, and A. K. Jha. 2015. Care fragmentation, quality, and costs among chronically ill patients. *American Journal of Managed Care* 21(5):355–62.

Goldman, L., G.C. Benjamin, S. Hernández, D. A. Kindig, S. Kumanyika, C. Nevarez, N. R. Shah, and W. F. Wong. 2016. *Advancing the health of communities and populations.* Discussion Paper, Vital Directions for Health and Health Care Series. National Academy of Medicine, Washington, DC. https://nam.edu/wpcontent/uploads/2016/09/advancing-the-health-of-communities-and-populations.pdf.

Hailey, D., R. Roine, and A. Ohinmaa. 2002. Systematic review of evidence for the benefits of telemedicine. *Journal of Telemedicine and Telecare* 8(suppl 1):1–7. doi:10.1258/1357633021937604.

Heiman, H. J. and S. Artiga. 2016. *Beyond Health Care: The Role of Social Determinants in Promoting Health and Health Equity.* The Henry J. Kaiser Family Foundation. http://kff.org/disparities-policy/issue-brief/beyond-health-care-the-role-of-social-determinants-in-promoting-health-and-health-equity (accessed March 15, 2017).

Institute of Medicine (IOM). 2007. *The learning healthcare system: Workshop summary.* Washington, DC: National Academies Press.

Institute of Medicine (IOM). 2010. *The healthcare imperative: Lowering costs and improving outcomes: Workshop series summary.* Washington, DC: The National Academies Press.

Institute of Medicine (IOM). 2013. *Best Care at Lower Cost: The Path to Continuously Learning Health Care in America.* Washington, DC: The National Academies Press. doi:10.17226/13444.

Institute of Medicine (IOM). 2015a. *Vital Signs: Core Metrics for Health and Health Care Progress.* Washington, DC: The National Academies Press. doi: 10.17226/19402.

Institute of Medicine and National Research Council (IOM and NRC). 2013. *U.S. Health in International Perspective: Shorter Lives, Poorer Health.* Washington, DC: The National Academies Press. doi: 10.17226/13497.

Keely, E., C. Liddy, and A. Afkham. 2013. Utilization, benefits, and impact of an e-consultation service across diverse specialties and primary care providers. *Telemedicine and e-Health* 19(10):733–738. doi:10.1089/tmj.2013.0007.

Kindig, D. and G. Stoddart. 2003. What is population health? *American Journal of Public Health* 93(3):380–383. doi:10.2105/ajph.93.3.380.

Kish, L. J., and E. J. Topol. 2015. Unpatients—why patients should own their medical data. *Nature Biotechnology* 33(9):921–924. doi:10.1038/nbt.3340.

Khoury, M. J., and J. P. A. Ioannidis. 2014. Big data meets public health. *Science* 346(6213):1054–1055. doi:10.1126/science.aaa2709.

Krumholz, H.M., P. E. Bourne, R. E. Kuntz, M. B. McClellan, H. L. Paz, S. F. Terry, and J. Waldstreicher. 2016. *Data Acquisition, Curation, and Use for a Continuously Learning Health System*. Vital Directions for Health and Health Care Series. Discussion Paper, National Academy of Medicine, Washington, DC. http://nam.edu/wp-content/uploads/2016/09/data-acquisition-curation-and-use-for-a-continuously-learning-health-system.pdf.

Kruse, J. 2013. Fragmentation in US medical education, research, and practice: The need for system wide defrag. *Family Medicine* 45(1):54–57.

Lasser, K. E., D. U. Himmelstein, and S. Woolhandler. 2006. Access to care, health status, and health disparities in the United States and Canada: Results of a cross-national population-based survey. *American Journal of Public Health* 96(7): 1300–1307.

Leavitt, M., M. McClellan, S. D. DeVore, E. Fisher, R. J. Gilfillan, H. S. Lieber, R. Merkin, J. Rideout, and K. J. Thiry. 2016. *Competencies and Tools to Shift Payments from Volume to Value*. Vital Directions for Health and Health Care Series. Discussion Paper, National Academy of Medicine, Washington, DC. https://nam.edu/wp-content/uploads/2016/09/competencies-and-tools-to-shift-payments-from-volume-to-value.pdf.

Ledford, H. 2011. Translational research: 4 ways to fix the clinical trial. *Nature* 477:526–528. http://www.nature.com/news/2011/110928/full/477526a.html (accessed March 15, 2017)

Legare, F. and H.O. Witteman. 2013. Shared decision making: Examining key elements and barriers to adoption into routine clinical practice. *Health Affairs.* 32(2):276–284. doi:10.1377/hlthaff.2012.1078.

Lipstein, S.H., A.L. Kellermann, B. Berkowitz, R. Phillips, D. Sklar, G.D. Steele, and G.E. Thibault. 2016. *Workforce for 21st Century Health and Health Care*. Vital Directions for Health and Health Care Series. Discussion Paper, National Academy of Medicine, Washington, DC. https://nam.edu/wp-content/uploads/2016/09/workforce-for-21st-century-health-and-health-care.pdf.

Institute of Medicine (IOM). 2015b. *Sharing Clinical Trial Data: Maximizing Benefits, Minimizing Risk.* Washington, DC: The National Academies Press. doi: 10.17226/18998.

Mather, M.., L. A. Jacobsen, and K. M. Pollard. 2015. Aging in the United States. *Population Bulletin* 70(2).

McClellan, M., D. T. Fienberg, P. B. Bach, P. Chew, P. Conway, N. Leschly, G. Marchand, M. A. Mussallem, and D. Teeter. 2016. *Payment Reform for Better Value and Medical Innovation.* Vital Directions for Health and Health Care Series. Discussion Paper, National Academy of Medicine, Washington, DC. https://nam.edu/wp-content/uploads/2017/03/Payment-Reform-for-Better-Value-and-Medical-Innovation.pdf.

McClellan, M. B. and M. O. Leavitt. 2016. Competencies and Tools to Shift Payments from Volume to Value. *Journal of the American Medical Association* 316(16):1655–1656. doi:10.1001/jama.2016.14205

McGinnis, J. M., and W. H. Foege. 1993. Actual Causes of Death in the United States. *Journal of the American Medical Association.* 270(18):2207–2212. doi:10.1001/jama.1993.03510180077038

McGinnis, J. M., P. Williams-Russo, and T. R. Knickman. 2002. The case for more active policy attention to health promotion. *Health Affairs* 21(2):78–93. doi:10.1377/hlthaff.21.2.78.

McGinnis, J. M., Berwick, D.M., Dascle, T.A., Diaz, A., Fineberg, H.V., Frist, W.H., Gawande, A., Halfon, N., Lavizzo-Mourey, R. 2016. *Systems Strategies for Health throughout the Life Course.* Discussion Paper, Vital Directions for Health and Health Care Series. National Academy of Medicine, Washington, DC. https://nam.edu/wp-content/uploads/2016/09/systems-strategies-for-health-throughout-the-life-course.pdf.

Mitchell, E. 2016. *Population-Based Payment Models: Overcoming Barriers, Accelerating Adoption.* https://hcp-lan.org/2016/05/pbp-models-overcoming-barriers-accelerating-adoption (accessed March 14, 2017).

Mitchell, E. M. November 2016. *AHRQ Statistical Brief #497: Concentration of Health Expenditures in the U.S. Civilian Noninstitutionalized Population, 2014.* https://meps.ahrq.gov/data_files/publications/st497/stat497.shtml (accessed February 2, 2017)

Mokdad, A. H., J. S. Marks, D. F. Stroup, and J. L. Gerberding. 2004. Actual Causes of Death in the United States, 2000. *Journal of the American Medical Association* 291(10):1238–1245. doi:10.1001/jama.291.10.1238.

Morens, D. M., and A. S. Fauci. 2013. Emerging Infectious Diseases: Threats to Human Health and Global Stability. *PLoS Pathogens* 9(7): e1003467. doi:10.1371/journal.ppat.1003467.

National Academies of Sciences, Engineering, and Medicine (NASEM). 2015. *The Growing Gap in Life Expectancy by Income: Implications for Federal Programs and*

Policy Responses. Washington, DC: The National Academies Press. doi:https://doi.org/10.17226/19015.

National Academies of Sciences, Engineering, and Medicine (NASEM). 2017. *Communities in Action: Pathways to Health Equity.* Washington, DC: The National Academies Press. doi:https://doi.org/10.17226/24624.

National Institutes of Health (NIH). 2017. *Accelerating Medicines Partnership (AMP).* https://www.nih.gov/research-training/accelerating-medicines-partnership-amp (accessed March 15, 2017).

National Research Council (NRC). 2013. *Frontiers in Massive Data Analysis.* Washington, DC: The National Academies Press. doi:10.17226/18374.

Office of the National Coordinator for Health Information Technology (ONC). 2013. *Basics of Health IT.* https://www.healthit.gov/patients-families/basics-health-it (accessed March 14, 2017).

Patient-Centered Outcomes Research Institute (PCORI). 2017. *Communication and Dissemination Research.* http://www.pcori.org/about-us/our-programs/communication-and-dissemination-research (accessed January 27, 2017).

Perlin, J.B., Baker, D.B., Brailer, D.J., Fridma, D.B., Frisse, M.E., Halamka, J.D., Levi, J., Mandl, K.D., Marchibroda, J.M., Platt, R., Tang, P.C. 2016. *Information Technology Interoperability and Use for Better Care and Evidence.* Vital Directions for Health and Health Care Series. Discussion Paper, National Academy of Medicine, Washington, DC. https://nam.edu/wp-content/uploads/2016/09/information-technology-interoperability-and-use-for-better-care-and-evidence.pdf.

Pronovost, P.J., J.M. Austin, C.K. Cassel, S.F. Delbanco, A.K. Jha, B. Kocher, E.A. McGlynn, L.G. Sandy, and J. Santa. 2016. *Fostering Transparency in Outcomes, Quality, Safety, and Costs.* Vital Directions for Health and Health Care Series. Discussion Paper, National Academy of Medicine, Washington, DC. https://nam.edu/wp-content/uploads/2016/09/fostering-transparency-in-outcomes-quality-safety-and-costs.pdf.

Robert Wood Johnson Foundation (RWJF) Commission to Build a Healthier America. 2009. *Beyond health care: new directions to a healthier America.* Washington (DC): The Commission. http://www.rwjf.org/en/library/research/2009/04/beyond-health-care.html (accessed December 7, 2016).

Rosenblatt, M., C.P. Austin, M. Boutin, W. Chin, S.K. Galson, S.H. Jain, M. McMurry-Heath, S.R. Nussbaum, J. Orloff, S.E. Weinberger, and J. Woodcock. 2016. *Innovation in Development, Regulatory Review, and Use of Clinical Advances.* Vital Directions for Health and Health Care Series. Discussion Paper, National Academy of Medicine, Washington, DC. https://nam.edu/wp-content/uploads/2016/09/innovation-in-development-regulatory-review-and-use-of-clinical-advances.pdf.

Rowe, J., Berkman, L., Fried, L., Fulmer, T., Jackson, J., Naylor, M., Novelli, W., Olshansky, J., and Stone, R. 2016. *Preparing for better health and health care for an aging population.* Discussion Paper, Vital Directions for Health and Health Care Series. National Academy of Medicine, Washington, DC. https://nam.edu/wp-content/uploads/2016/09/preparing-for-better-health-and-health-care-for-an-aging-population.pdf

Siddiqi, A., R. Brown, Q. C. Nguyen, R. Loopstra and I. Kawachi. 2015. Cross-national comparison of socioeconomic inequalities in obesity in the United States and Canada. *International Journal for Equity in Health* 14(1):1.

Stanford School of Medicine. 2010. *Healthcare disparities & barriers to health care—rural health fact sheet.* http://ruralhealth.stanford.edu/health-pros/factsheets/downloads/rural_fact_sheet_5.pdf (accessed January 31, 2017).

Tang, P.C., M. Smith, J. Adler-Milstein, T. L. Delbanco, S. J. Downs, D. L. Ness, R. M. Parker, and D. Z. Sands. 2016. *The Democratization of Health Care.* Discussion Paper, Vital Directions for Health and Health Care Series. National Academy of Medicine, Washington, DC. https://nam.edu/wp-content/uploads/2016/09/the-democratization-of-health-care.pdf.

Taylor, L.A., C.E. Coyle, C. Ndumele, E. Rogan, M. Canavan, L. Curry, and E.H. Bradley. June 2015. *Leveraging the Social Determinants of Health: What Works?* Boston, MA: Blue Cross Blue Shield of Massachusetts Foundation. http://bluecrossfoundation.org/sites/default/files/download/publication/Social_Equity_Report_Final.pdf (accessed March 15, 2017)

Topol, E. 2015. *The patient will see you now: The future of medicine is in your hands.* Basic Books.

Tufts Center for the Study of Drug Development (TSCDD). 2015. *Outlook 2015.* Tufts University: Boston, MA.

Turnbull, A.E., S.K. Sahetya, D.M. and Needham. 2016. Aligning critical care interventions with patient goals: A modified Delphi study. *Heart & Lung: The Journal of Acute and Critical Care* 45(6):517–524. doi:10.1016/j.hrtlng.2016.07.011.

van Hedel, K., M. Avendano, L. F. Berkman, M. Bopp, P. Deboosere, O. Lundberg, P. Martikainen, G. Menville, F. J. van Lenthe and J. P. Mackenbach. 2014. The contribution of national disparities to international differences in mortality between the United States and 7 European countries. *American Journal of Public Health* 105(4): e112–e119.

Zerhouni, E., Berg, J. M., Hrabowski, F. A., Kington, R., and Landis, S. C. R. 2016. *Training the workforce for 21st century science.* Discussion Paper, Vital Directions for Health and Health Care Series. National Academy of Medicine, Washington, DC. https://nam.edu/wp-content/uploads/2016/09/training-the-workforce-for-21st-century-science.pdf.

AUTHOR INFORMATION

Sheila P. Burke, MPA, RN, is Adjunct Lecturer in Public Policy at Harvard Kennedy School's Malcolm Wiener Center for Social Policy. **Molly J. Coye, MD,** is Executive in Residence at AVIA. **The Honorable Thomas A. Daschle** is Founder and CEO of The Daschle Group, A Public Policy Advisory of Baker Donelson. **Angela Diaz, MD, PhD, MPH,** is the Jean C. and James W. Crystal Professor of Pediatrics and Preventive Medicine at the Icahn School of Medicine at Mount Sinai. **Victor J. Dzau, MD,** is President of the National Academy of Medicine. **The Honorable William H. Frist, MD,** is a nationally-acclaimed heart and lung transplant surgeon, former US Senate Majority Leader, and chairman of the Executive Board of the health service private equity firm Cressey & Company. **Martha E. Gaines, JD, LLM,** is Distinguished Clinical Professor and founder and director of the interdisciplinary Center for Patient Partnerships at the University of Wisconsin Schools of Law, Medicine, Nursing & Pharmacy. **Margaret A. Hamburg, MD,** former Commissioner of the US Food and Drug Administration, is Foreign Secretary of the National Academy of Medicine. **Jane E. Henney, MD,** former Commissioner of the US Food and Drug Administration, is Home Secretary of the National Academy of Medicine. **Shiriki K. Kumanyika, PhD, MPH,** is emeritus professor of epidemiology in the Department of Biostatistics and Epidemiology at the University of Pennsylvania Perelman School Of Medicine. **The Honorable Michael O. Leavitt** is the founder and chairman of Leavitt Partners, where he helps clients navigate the future as they transition to new and better models of care. **Mark B. McClellan, MD, PhD,** is the Robert J. Margolis Professor of Business, Medicine, and Policy, and Director of the Duke-Margolis Center for Health Policy at Duke University with offices at Duke and in Washington, DC. **J. Michael McGinnis, MD, MPP,** is the Leonard D. Schaeffer Executive Officer and Senior Scholar and Executive Director of the Leadership Consortium for a Value & Science-Driven Health System at the National Academy of Medicine. **Ruth M. Parker, MD,** is Professor of Medicine, Pediatrics and Public Health at Emory University in Atlanta, Georgia. **Lewis G. Sandy, MD,** is Executive Vice President, Clinical Advancement, UnitedHealth Group (a Fortune 25 diversified health and well-being company dedicated to helping people live healthier lives). **Leonard D. Schaeffer** is the founding Chairman & CEO of WellPoint, the nation's largest health benefits company by membership. **Glenn D. Steele, Jr., MD, PhD,** is the Chairman of xG Health Solutions. **Pamela Thompson, MS, RN,** is chief executive officer emeritus of the American Organization of Nurse Executives. **Elias A. Zerhouni, MD,** is President, Global R&D, at Sanofi.

PART I

BETTER HEALTH AND WELL-BEING

2

SYSTEMS STRATEGIES FOR BETTER HEALTH THROUGHOUT THE LIFE COURSE

J. Michael McGinnis, MD, MPP, Donald M. Berwick, MD, The Honorable Thomas A. Daschle, Angela Diaz, MD, PhD, MPH, Harvey V. Fineberg, MD, PhD, The Honorable William H. Frist, MD, Atul Gawande, MD, MPH, Neal Halfon, MD, MPH, and Risa Lavizzo-Mourey, MD, MBA

Health and health care outcomes for Americans should be better for most, and much better for some. This should be possible with currently available knowledge and resources. Capturing the potential will require adapting our strategies and approaches to the reality that health is not immutably determined at birth, but shaped by different factors over time. Similarly, caring for health cannot be confined to singular interactions within the walls of the health care system, but must fully engage powerful determining influences residing in other systems—e.g., education, employment, justice, transportation—which are natural parts of our lives. Exploring the nature and strategic opportunities inherent in these intersecting influences is the focus of this paper, and the implications for societal attention and resources suggest the promise of shifting emphases across the life span, across systems, and within the health care system.

Our assessment begins with an overview of the prominent health and health care challenges for Americans, and they are many. US life expectancy at birth ranks 43rd in the global community, and has even recently declined among some specific groups (IOM, 2014b). Unacceptable disparities in health outcomes and access persist among certain populations, in particular African Americans and Native Americans (Pearcy and Keppel, 2002). The US health system ranked in a World Health Organization assessment only 37th in performance among 191 member nations (WHO, 2001), and in a recent study of 11 highly industrialized Organisation for Economic Co-operation and Development nations, the United States ranked last (Davis et al., 2014). These deficiencies are all the more glaring in the face of health expenditures that are clearly the highest in the

43

world, about 50 percent higher than the country next behind us, and requiring investment of nearly 18 percent of our total economic productivity (GDP) in 2015 (Squires and Anderson, 2015). Why are we performing so poorly relative to our potential? A major reason lies in the fact that the primary foci of our attention, our resources (Murray, 2013) and our incentives, are too narrow and too late: despite an increasingly strong and specific understanding of the preventable elements in the development of many of our health challenges—social, behavioral, environmental—our investments are primarily directed to their biomedical manifestations, well after the problems have taken root.

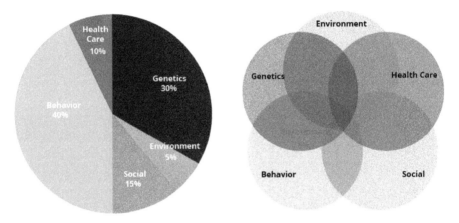

FIGURE 2-1 | Schematics of factors influencing health, their association with premature death, and their intersections.
SOURCE: Adapted from McGinnis et al., 2002.

Health is the product of our experiences layered onto the biological matrices we inherit. Those experiences begin at conception, and, through the intersecting influences of genetics, environment, social circumstances, behaviors, and medical care, health emerges and takes form. *Figure 2-1* presents schematics of the relative overall impact throughout the population of each major health determinant domain on the occurrence of early deaths (McGinnis et al., 2002). The specific impact of each domain varies by individual, and most important are the dynamics at the domain intersections for each individual.

Each of us represents, in essence, a complex system in constant and dynamic interface with other systems that shape our fates in manners great and small. The process is not linear, but one in which similar experiences may exert variable influences at different points. In this paper, we explore the implications of these dynamics for efforts to improve health prospects throughout those interwoven influences at various stages over the course of people's lives (Halfon and

Hochstein, 2002). Because emerging health problems and potential required solutions span well beyond a single determining factor or single point in time and place, it is necessary to take a systems-oriented perspective (Emanuel et al., 2012). In doing so, we respect the simple fact that optimal health will not be achievable or affordable—for society or individuals—without attention to the effectiveness, efficiency, and availability of essential services within and among the various sectors important to health outcomes.

Fortunately, transformational insights, tools, and initiatives are emerging that offer practical prospects for dramatic advances in the ability to mobilize information, cooperation, and collaborative action for more effective and efficient progress from the national down to the community and individual levels, on behalf of better health throughout the life course. We review these prospects by touching briefly on several questions:

- What are the most common health threats at each stage throughout life?
- What are the root sources of diseases, disability, and death most prominent among Americans?
- Why do we spend so much and get so little for our national health system investment?
- Which systems and partner stakeholders must be seamlessly engaged?
- How can financing, accountability, technology, and culture be aligned to foster system-wide transformation for better health over the life course?

HEALTH AND DISEASE OVER THE LIFE COURSE

What are the most common health threats at each stage throughout life?

In terms of morbidity and mortality rates, health profiles vary substantially by life stage. Four of every 10 childhood deaths before age 15 occur among babies in their first 28 days of life (WHO, 2011), about half due to congenital malformations, disorders related to short gestation and low birth weight, and maternal complications during pregnancy (CDC, 2016). Throughout infancy—the first year of life—the major causes of death are complications related to birth and birth defects, sudden infant death syndrome, and unintentional injury (CDC, 2014a). After age 1, injuries take over as the leading cause of death among children (Consumer Federation of America, 2013), and hold that position until age 44, followed by heart disease, cancer, and homicide, at different times and ages. Among adolescents and young adults, ages 15–24, suicide and homicide appear among the leading killers (CDC, 2006), ranking number 2 and 3, respectively, among this age group. In adults ages 35–65, the major causes of death are cancers and heart disease (CDC, 2014a), and after age 65, heart disease is the leading cause of death, followed by cancer and respiratory disease (CDC, 2006).

But, illnesses and injuries that are counted most easily are often not the experiences most important to health prospects. Life expectancy at birth in the United States is now more than 81 years for females and 76 years for males, and for most of those years health status is more a reflection of the presence or absence of illness or injury, consequent level of function, sense of well-being, or predispositions, circumstances, or experiences that influence future profiles on these dimensions (Xu et al., 2016). Although death is the most striking, definitive, and tragic reflection of health status, it is far too limiting as a measure of the health of a population (Fineberg, 2013). In the United States in 2013, for example, there were fewer than 33,000 total deaths among the more than 61 million children under age 15 (Xu et al., 2016), but nearly 25 million children were overweight or obese, more than 30 million lived in low-income families and 15 million in poverty, in the range of some 5 million lived in a household touched by violence (Child Witness to Violence Project; Child Trends, 2016), and more than 1 million were the victims of child abuse and neglect (IOM, 2014a), with the highest rates among the youngest (Child Maltreatment, 2015; Wight et al., 2010). In 2015, about 1.1 million people under age 75 died, but those who suffer from diabetes, depression, and alcohol abuse amount to 18, 11, and 15 times that number, respectively (CDC, 2014b; Center for Behavioral Health Statistics and Quality, 2015).

In this respect, the most important overall childhood determinants of health over the life course are at least as much those related to the caring, social, environmental, and behavioral experiences as to health services they receive. This is especially the case for ages 0–3, when central nervous system development occurs at such a rapid rate, with ongoing development of physical stature and physiologic function. Advances in neuroscience have provided a much deeper understanding of brain development in the early years, as well as the remolding during adolescence that sets the stage for issues with lifelong consequences—e.g., overweight and obesity, substance abuse, and psychological disorders (Wise, 2016). It is often assumed that children are generally healthy and, if they suffer a health problem or developmental delay, they will grow out of it. However, while children can be resilient, adversity during these sensitive developmental periods is often embedded, only to emerge years later as a source of disability and ill health (Boyce et al., 2012; Essex et al., 2013; Halfon and Hochstein, 2002). The role of attention and nurturing as an influence on health status, nearly always a relevant determinant, may not be again as relatively important a focus until the final years of a natural life span (Gawande, 2016).

Over a lifetime, acute infections represent the most frequent sources of short-term functional limitation among all age groups, with asthma and short-term injuries increasing in later childhood, and obesity and depression occurring at higher rates as children move into adolescence (Gordon et al., 2016). In adolescents and young adults, substance abuse emerges as a more common near- and longer-term health threat (Blum and Qureshi, 2011), as does risky sexual behavior and violence in some populations. In the past 15 years, opioid addiction rates have rapidly increased, particularly in white, rural communities, in part as a result of neglectful prescribing behavior among clinicians, in part as a result of segmenting and marginalizing the treatment strategies for those with pain and behavioral health problems (Rudd et al., 2015). Addiction rates among active duty military personnel, which had previously been on the decline, tripled from 2005 to 2008, and rates of depression and suicide and posttraumatic stress disorder also increased (Office of National Drug Control Policy, 2010; Tanielian and Jaycox, 2008).

Throughout adulthood, various exposures, experiences, and lifestyles contribute increasingly to disease and injury, the rate and impact compounded by growing cooccurrence of multiple diseases and conditions. Among those over age 50, nearly half suffer from arthritis, 28 percent have heart disease, approximately 25 percent are overweight or obese, 22 percent have cancer, and 6.5 percent have lung disease (CDC, 2013). Approximately 45 percent of those over 50, and 75 percent of those over 65, report multiple co-occurring conditions that restrict their activities in some fashion (HHS, 2010). Among people over age 75, approximately 14 percent suffer from some form of dementia. Crippling societal impact is resulting from the increased occurrences of obesity, diabetes, depression, and dementia (Alzheimer's Association, 2015). Successfully reducing the occurrence of most of these conditions, and the extent of incapacities imposed, requires multifaceted, life course–oriented strategies.

Health Disparities

Some people—and some groups—differ substantially from the aggregate profile. Differences occur among various race, ethnic, and socioeconomic groups, but the largest overall disparities occur among African Americans relative to whites. For example, despite the relative safety of gestation and birth in the United States, African American babies are more than twice as likely to be born with a low birth weight or to die in their first year of life (Collins et al., 2004; Reichman, 2005). Interestingly, babies born to mothers who are immigrants from Africa experience low birth weight and related problems at rates similar to whites, suggesting the existence of other factors or stressors for African Americans (Braveman, 2008).

Beginning at birth, the experience of disparities tends to accumulate and widen over time. Black children are twice as likely as white children to have asthma, and obesity is twice as common among American Indian children compared to their white and Asian counterparts (CDC, 2016b). Obesity disparities emerge as early as preschool (Anderson and Whitaker, 2009), and the prevalence of overweight and obesity among black girls ages 2–19 is about 6 percent higher than for their white counterparts (Skinner and Skelton, 2014). Because obese children are at higher risk for obesity and cardiovascular disease as adults, the disadvantage extends into adulthood.

Almost one-half of black adults suffer from hypertension, the highest population-specific prevalence in the world (Freedman et al., 2009). The annual incidences of stroke and heart disease among African Americans in the United States are about 2 and 1.5 times, respectively, than those among whites (Mozaffarian et al., 2015). Although the yearly cancer incidence among African Americans is about the same as whites, cancer death rates projected through 2018 for African Americans are expected to be about 14 percent higher for women and 27 percent higher for men (American Cancer Society, 2016). Rates of Alzheimer's disease and other dementias among African Americans range in estimates from 14 percent to 100 percent higher (Alzheimer's Association, 2002). Life expectancies are shorter for African Americans by about 3 years for women, and 5 years for men (CDC, 2011a). On the other hand, for those who reach age 75, the difference in life expectancy between whites and blacks is only about 0.4 years (Xu et al., 2016).

THE DETERMINANTS OF HEALTH

What are the root sources of disease, disability, and death most prominent among Americans?

Why do different groups and individuals demonstrate such different health profiles? A great deal has been learned in the relatively recent past about the answer to these questions, and the answer is not "fate." As noted earlier, health is the measure of our functional capacity that results from the interplay of factors in five domains shaping our life courses: our biological predispositions, social circumstances, physical environments, behavioral patterns, and access to the health care we need (McGinnis et al., 2002). *Figure 2-2* presents a schematic of how some of these factors might play out to shape health status and health prospects at various times and in various circumstances (Halfon et al., 2014a).

Biologic Predispositions

Point: It is not all about genes. The starting point is indeed with our genes, the predispositions we inherit from our parents. Although very few diseases can be classified as purely genetic in nature, work throughout the world daily identifies new associations between known conditions and specific gene profiles. Importantly, however, more is continuously being learned about epigenetics, the multiple cellular and molecular mechanisms by which genes can be turned on or off and the information modified as it is expressed in cells by different exposures and experiences, and even how experience-related epigenetic modifications can be passed on to subsequent generations. As insights deepen about sensitive periods of health development and the impact of the interactions of our individual gene compositions with our physical, social, and behavioral environments, the better equipped we will be to act on that knowledge in ways that buffer impacts and optimize health development over the life course.

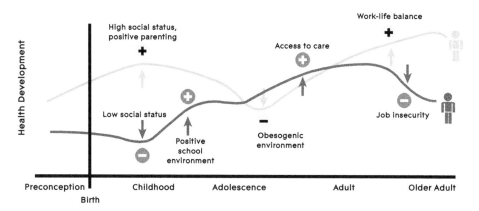

FIGURE 2-2 | Schematic of variable life stage influences.
SOURCE: Halfon et al., 2014a.

Medical Treatment

Point: It also is not all about medical care, unless one is ill or injured. In 2015, total US expenditures for health were about $3 trillion, with medical treatment receiving more than 90 percent of the total. Yet, the impact of those expenditures on the aggregate health of the population was very limited (Lu, 2010). They were not expenditures aimed at the factors most important to the nation's health profile. Shortfalls in the access or quality of medical care are especially surprising in the context of the high US expenditures, and require remediation, but other approaches are required for better health. Illustrative is the fact that approaches to improve birth outcomes and address disparities that have primarily focused on enhancing access to prenatal care have proven insufficient in achieving the gains possible (McGinnis and Foege, 1993; Mokdad et al., 2004). Addressing barriers to care access is a basic social responsibility, but effective engagement of health improvement opportunities requires strategies and investments that are broad and multisystem in nature.

Behavioral Patterns

Point: Health behaviors are central, but are also more than choice. Among the influences on health, those related to behavioral patterns represent the single most prominent preventable source. Tobacco, dietary factors, physical inactivity, and alcohol misuse account for many preventable deaths among Americans, including from coronary heart disease, stroke, cancers of the colon, breast, and prostate, and diabetes (Mokdad, et al., 2004). Diet and physical activity factors together account for about a third of preventable premature deaths among Americans (CDC, 2014c). Unintended pregnancies significantly impact individual and community health, yet one in three births in the United States is unintended, including most of those born to teens (Mosher et al., 2012; World Bank, 2015). Illicit drug use is one of the few leading causes of death with increasing rates and, along with alcohol abuse, imposes a broad and leading social, morbidity, and mortality burden on Americans and their communities (CDC, 2011b). Behaviors are, however, driven at least as much by external factors as internal, as, for example, in the access and affordability of healthy foods. Behavior patterns reflect culture, access, economics, and other factors such as the quality of early experiences and the central importance of supportive human relationships, underscoring the intersections among the domains of influence that require sustained system-wide strategies across communities.

Social Circumstances

Point: For many, health is substantially about social circumstances. Health is powerfully influenced by our social conditions and services—education, income, employment, housing, neighborhoods, racism, and social networks (Braveman et al., 2011). For the population as a whole, the most consistent predictor of the likelihood of death in any given year is level of education. For those ages 45–64 with limited education, the chance of death in a given year is four times those with graduate degrees (Hummer and Hernandez, 2013). Income levels have consistently been associated with life expectancies, and one measure of income inequality holds that a 1 percent increase in inequality doubles the likelihood of death over a decade (Zheng, 2012), presumably due to disproportionate exposures to neighborhood violence, suboptimal school environments, and unstable households (Addy and Wright, 2012). Also important is that *perceptions* matter—perceptions of income inequality, perceptions of limited choices, perceptions of community cohesion (Chetty et al., 2016). Stress "gets under the skin" and exerts an effect that can grow over the life course (Lu, 2010; McEwen, 1998; Arias, 2016).

Physical Environments

Point: The pace of progress will reflect the integrity of our environ-ments. Environments affect health in myriad ways: silent and invisible inadvertent toxic exposures to workplace and product hazards; zoning and design features of our built environments that structurally impair or facilitate health-promoting or health-degrading life and workstyle patterns; ecosystem changes from human activities that foster novel zoonotic infections (Frist, 2015). Two of the largest and most rapidly occurring epidemics to confront the United States—and the world—in recent years have roots in changes in our physical environments: obesity and HIV. They also underscore the intersecting character of the domain determinants, and the importance of tending simultaneously to the dynamics across systems of influence.

CAUSES AND CONSEQUENCES OF SYSTEM SHORTFALLS

Why do we spend so much and get so little for our national health system investment?

Substantially, this is due to constraints on our lines of sight. Because most health improvement efforts—disease and injury prevention, treatment, and rehabilita-tion—are designed around a single encounter or issue, it is there that they often end. Immunizing a toddler, delivering a baby to a young mother, setting a broken arm, counseling someone depressed, testing a blood sugar level, screening for high blood pressure, treating a leg ulcer, explaining an employee safety program, preparing a school meal plan, scheduling for chemotherapy, preparing a hospital discharge—each represents the dedicated work of a skilled health professional usually delivered with a focused sense of purpose in anticipation of the best result. Yet, the reasons care is needed, and the likelihood of its optimal impact on health prospects, depend on myriad factors beyond a single precipitating event or diagnosis, such as a heart attack, stroke, or diabetic retinopathy—factors that include the interplay of behaviors, environments, socioeconomic status, ethnic and gender biases and prejudices, factors that can course throughout communities and throughout lives. Our aims must clearly orient beyond the singular (Berwick et al., 2008).

On the other hand, our payment and reward systems clearly focus on the singular and the serial—occurrence of an illness and its treatment, sometimes repeatedly. Health care financing is largely structured around separate charges for individual components of services provided for a particular diagnosis, presenting powerful organizational and financial disincentives to the health care stewards we trust to be focused on producing optimal health results for patients and families. Even when focus is turned to results rather than services—value rather than volume, as the saying goes—unless incentives are aimed to present and engage the longer term, multisystem factors often involved, attention will be more naturally drawn to a near term and narrow single condition perspective (Daschle et al., 2013b). A clinical team attempting to help a person manage diabetes will be substantially hindered if the focus is limited to the presenting vital signs and blood chemistry profiles, when the most basic success factors reside in patient distinctions as to medication cost and access, literacy, family circumstances, mobility, digital accessibility, dietary patterns, employment status, and neighborhood character.

Economic Implications

The consequences of short-term and narrowly focused interventions impact more than morbidity and mortality. Performance inefficiencies and shortfalls are expensive. Costs are *personal* for people and their families; they are *collective* for organizations whose efficiency and effectiveness are tightly linked to the health status of those who populate them; and they are *societal* for populations whose aggregate vitality and capacity are sapped both by the economic burden of waste and by the dispiriting and debilitating impacts of unnecessary disparity and marginalization.

Children born in low-income, high-risk circumstances, and who are not seamlessly linked to the support they need, risk being delayed or disabled from the outset. The lifetime costs of the resulting services required and lost productivity experienced will likely far exceed what would have been the cost of the initial investment. Without effective linkage of activities, as indicated, among schools, clinicians, social service, law enforcement, and juvenile justice organizations, teens and young adults who are passing through the challenges natural to that period will be placed at greater risk—and lifelong expense and loss of income potential—from issues such as pregnancy, alcohol and drug abuse, depression, and violence. People who live and work in communities in which the cultural signals, norms, and opportunities are aimed at fostering attention, support, and priority to health and health-promoting strategies are more likely to be healthier, with the attendant personal economic advantages.

At the organizational level, the burden of our failure to capture system-wide opportunities for greater efficiencies can be considerable. In 2011, hospital readmissions due in part to missed opportunities to better manage care coordination at discharge imposed more than an estimated $40 billion (Health Policy Brief, 2012; Hernandez, 2010; Hines et al., 2011; Kasper et al., 2002) The cost of lost productivity due to illness imposes a substantial burden on workplaces, often generating costs well beyond those for health care alone (Loeppke et al., 2008). In the aggregate, the full extent of the economic consequences of our fragmented system are unknown, but the costs are staggering. We do know from various studies that about 30 percent of overall health expenses in the United States are unnecessary—the costs of unneeded services, care delivered inefficiently, charges that are too high, excessive administrative costs, missed prevention opportunities, and fraud (Berwick and Hackbarth, 2012; IOM, 2010). Beyond this are the personal and social costs imposed by unwanted pregnancies, learning disabilities unaddressed, overweight and obesity, alcohol and substance abuse, criminality and incarceration, and others that could potentially be avoided or modified if the interfaces and incentives were aligned for their cooperative engagement. Still more consequences reside in the resulting loss of economic productivity among those affected.

POTENTIALLY TRANSFORMATIVE SYSTEM PARTNERSHIPS

Which systems and partner stakeholders must be more seamlessly engaged?

Harnessing society's full potential for optimizing health outcomes across the lifespan requires reaching out well beyond the health care system, from the earliest days of childhood. That potential is determined by the robustly networked interplay among systems and services that, in diverse ways, have central bearings on health prospects, and for which insights are applicable from other sectors using integrative platform models to manage the flow of goods and services (Parker et al., 2016). Examples follow of some of the relevant stakeholders identified in the discussion of the issues mentioned here.

Clinicians, Health Care Organizations, Pharmacies

Across the board, no country can claim a cadre of health professionals that is more skilled, more dedicated, or more highly resourced than those in the United States. Yet, clinicians and health care organizations often are challenged in addressing issues of great social and developmental importance to patients (Diaz and Manigat, 1999). Prevailing cultures, financing, standards, accountability, accessibility, and organizational structures are largely designed to foster narrow perspectives and poorly coordinated activities, certainly between health care and other systems important to optimizing health prospects, but also among different health care institutions providing relevant services, and even among service units within the same organization. Successful models of team care, linked interventions, and information system platforms indicate not only that the care delivery process itself can feasibly operate in a fashion transformative for near-term and lifelong health prospects, but also that it has the potential to operate as a system that continuously learns and improves (Forrest et al., 2014; Margolis, et al., 2013).

By promoting consistent leadership messaging on health progress, underscoring key trends, identifying groups within their own institutions with disproportionate shortfalls, emphasizing the intersecting system-wide influences, indicating steps to marshal community-based corrections, and monitoring progress within their own communities, effective leaders can move organizations beyond disconnected efforts to implement system-wide strategies for better health.

People and Their Families

Since the appearance of the first village healers, health and health care have operated through a flow of authority and expertise that went in only one direction, from healer to patient. With transformations in access to knowledge and tools, the prospects are at hand for an unprecedented democratization of health and health care decision making and delivery (Fineberg, 2012b). Unimagined a generation ago, the speed at which advancing digital technology has put health improvement potential literally at our fingertips is simply stunning (Frist, 2014). Already possible is support through virtually immediate access to information and assistance, online and real-time advice and counseling for specific circumstances, rapidly growing applications for decision assistance for a variety of health and medical issues, GPS (geographic positioning) tailored care access and care monitoring facilitation, remote site diagnosis and assessment of certain laboratory and physiologic parameters, and even the early stages of remote site therapeutic measures. Patient portals and teleconsults have already improved the quality of information available for ongoing care, reduced the need for outpatient visits in many facilities, and made possible improved care for homebound and geographically distant people. The growing capacity for gathering, assessment, and use of individual clinical data dramatically accelerates to prospects for continuous learning and care that is better tailored to an individual's life-course circumstances. Barriers come not so much from the limits of technology as from inequity in access, the need for greater priority on system interoperability, the development and testing of reference standards to ensure reliability, cross-sector strategies for deployment, and adoption of an operative personal linkage approach to allow the service integration, improvement, life-course tailoring, and learning that is technically feasible.

Social Services

In the spirit of the adage that the advancement of a society can be judged by the way it treats its most vulnerable, some of our most important gains as a nation have come as a result of efforts to reach out and engage the basic needs of the poor and the isolated. As a society, there is substantial common ground on the fundamental notions: that every person has the basic food and shelter they need; that care is available to all pregnant women; that newborns and their mothers have the appropriate services required; that young families contending with unfamiliar experiences and new financial pressures have helpful assistance, including the lifelines and links of home visits, if required; that young children get an early start with positive socialization and educational experiences; that schools and care organizations be alert for social circumstances placing children in jeopardy; that those who are ill, infirm, and homebound have ready access to assistance that meets them where they are; and that those in the late stages of life suffer as little pain, displacement, and as little loss of dignity as possible. Although these are social values around which beliefs are broad, the public and private efforts to act upon them can often be sporadic, disjointed, uncoordinated, with limited follow-through—multiple organizations tending individually to responsibilities for narrow segments of the needs. Promising intersectoral and multi-system models have been demonstrated for high health care utilizers—the so-called "hot spotters" (Gawande, 2014)—through the work of various organizations. The Camden Coalition used targeted and tailored multifaceted services with a group of high-cost, high-utilizer individuals and reported a 50 percent reduction in costs and hospital visits (Green et al., 2010). A community-oriented organization, Health Leads, using a multidisciplinary team-based model to connect high-risk individuals with community-based resources such as employment, health insurance, and food, reported broad-based positive impact in reducing those needs (Garg et al., 2012). The Commonwealth Care Alliance is a not-for-profit delivery system for complex medical need patients served by Medicare and Medicaid. Using multidisciplinary clinical teams, their Senior Care Plan model reported nearly half the rate of hospital stays of those in fee-for-service plans, as well as much lower medical spending growth over 5 years (Meyer, 2011). These promising results suggest the need to deepen the partnership between clinical and social organizations in the interest, first, of the patients served, but clearly as well for community and financial sustainability.

Public Health and Safety Agencies

Public health holds society's front-line responsibility for identification and engagement of health threats to the population. Many of the most important health gains of the past century have come as a result of public health measures ranging from those of sanitation and hygiene to safer food, reductions in deaths among mothers and babies, immunization and infection control programs, and on to campaigns on tobacco and lifestyle issues. The effectiveness of public health has long been dependent on a close relationship with the clinical community, and, if the number and variety of newly emerging diseases is increasing with population expansion and ecosystem change—e.g., Lyme disease, HIV, SARS, Ebola, and Zika, among others—the seamless interface of public health and clinical care systems is essential. Of related importance is the ability of public health to be able to draw upon, and share the results of, emerging laboratory, genetic, GPS, information processing, and crowd-sourced data for strategic community-wide planning and response. Simply stated, public health should be a central steward of system interfaces and strategic direction for better health throughout the life course.

Schools and Preschool Facilities

Virtually every child in the nation attends a school, and, while education has to be the first priority for our schools, for too many children their school is the closest thing they have to an agent with a dedicated interest in their welfare. Beyond the fact that educational level is the most powerful determinant of lifelong health prospects, schools have also served as the anchor locus for community health interventions such as immunizations, drug and alcohol use, teen pregnancy, and health behavior efforts. If schools are to be able to effectively manage their basic educational responsibilities, while also helping advance the agendas of the health and social service sectors, the communication interfaces with those sectors have to be as seamless and fluid as possible, the databases interoperable, and the reward structures fully aligned.

Income and Payment Organizations

Employers have a clear incentive for keeping their workforces healthy, as do those who manage the health care payments for their employees and other stakeholders. Although as a group, no sector may have a greater stake in the long-term health prospects of the population as a whole, whether from a productivity or cost of care perspective, the current payment systems, as well as the rate of turnover among employee groups and beneficiaries, all provide adverse incentives for the longer-term view needed. Shorter-term approaches oriented to value-based and bundled payment models are of interest, as are accountability initiatives tailored to focusing payments on proven interventions. But, for these stakeholders to be able to bring to bear their considerable influence in the interest of system-wide strategies for better health throughout the life course, the prevailing payment system will have to move more directly to one that aims to improve overall population and community-wide health outcomes, with accountability measures directed to and focused on system-wide performance in improving health. Similarly, state flexibility to use Medicaid and other categorical federal funding to improve a shift to population-based care and accountability structures may help reduce fragmentation and stimulate systems-oriented leadership and integration at the community level.

Broadcast and Social Media

The nature of our digital lives is changing so rapidly, it is difficult to know the trajectory of its evolution. But, it is clear that it is a rapidly spreading and global force that is likely to have a very important influence on health-related dynamics over the life course. The use of social media, by virtue of its nature, has the ability to instantly cross lines of previously disparate and separate sectors. Whether from the perspective of the use of communication channels to influence perspectives, or to draw attention to emerging problems, or to rally support for action, or to use crowdsourced data as a research tool, this is an arena of direct relevance for life-course strategies.

Consumer Product Retailers

Marketing is a clearly established accelerant of human behavior, for better or for worse. Television marketing in the 1950s and 1960s drove the ascendance of cigarette use and pushed tobacco to the leading spot among the nation's killers. On the other hand, televised counter-tobacco marketing in the time from 1968 to 1970 yielded the historically steepest decline in tobacco use, and actually led to some relief in the tobacco industry when television advertising—and the mandatory counter-ads—were eliminated. Advertising of food products targeted to children clearly had an impact on their attitudes and food choices, and probably on the rates of childhood obesity. The potential effectiveness of sustained social marketing strategies to facilitate positive behavior change suggests that marketing awareness is clearly relevant to conceptualizing life-course strategies for health improvement (IOM, 2006).

Law Enforcement and the Courts

The nation is currently experiencing a resurgence of addiction, in this case fueled by increased use of opioids by young people. Accordingly, we are reminded of the central role of the law enforcement and the courts in any strategy aimed at effective engagement of those afflicted with addiction. Police have clearly said, "We can't arrest ourselves out of this problem." These circumstances, as well as those in which the first surfacing of childhood endangerment may be in family courts, underscore the critical importance of common agendas and strong and effective communication channels between and among the justice, social services, education, and clinical care systems.

Community Commons Stewards

Sustained multisystem progress for health improvement across the life course starts where people live, work, and play (Lavizzo-Mourey, 2015). In part, health care organization leaders can play a natural role in this respect. Hospitals can advance community-wide strategies for health improvement, and have an economic incentive to do so, via community benefit programs. Municipal public health departments are poised to steward a coordinated agenda linking health, community, and economy in development efforts. Community agencies planning and setting not only standards for food, sanitation, and environmental safety, but also standards for green space, for activity-friendly building designs, for zoning in the placement of fast food and alcohol outlets, and for working with employers in the development of community-wide initiatives, all can have important influences on the extent to which a community culture of continuous health improvement becomes a central element of a community's identity (Lavizzo-Mourey and McGinnis, 2003). Community leadership, with the elected leader at the head, is central to fostering the bridges across sectors, and ensuring the establishment and tracking of key indicators necessary for attention and progress throughout the life course (Inkelas and Bowie, 2014).

VITAL DIRECTIONS

How can financing, accountability, technology, and culture be aligned to foster system-wide transformation for better health over the life course?

With so many issues and stakeholders—in the face of such complexity—how can a life-course, systems-oriented approach be envisioned, much less implemented? Our view is that it is substantially achievable with more effective use of the tools and aggregate resources already available and in use at some level today, but which require the leadership and will to refine, implement, and spread (1) health care financing that supports and rewards health improvement at the population level, in addition to the best care for individuals; (2) a parsimonious set of validated core measures to drive sustained systems-wide focus and accountability for actionable factors most important to health—the vital signs for our vital directions; (3) seamless digital connectivity affording operative real-time interfaces across sectors and across time; and (4) a transformative culture of health equity and continuous health improvement in every community throughout the nation. Each can be accomplished, and is dependent only on strong collaborative-minded public and private leadership at every level—national, state, local, organizational, and individual (Fineberg, 2012a; Halfon et al., 2014b).

Vital Direction: *Shift health care payments to financing that rewards system-wide health improvement.* Basic expenditure principles—personal, private, and public—including knowing what you want, knowing its price, and paying for its delivery. Because for the prevailing health care financing pattern, none of these pertain, our payment model has resulted in substantial system distortions (IOM, 2012). With larger and larger sums in play, health care payments are made not for health outcomes or treatment packages, but for many—sometimes hundreds—of individual components; the prices of either of those individual components or their likely total cost is rarely known until completion of a course of uncertain duration; and, as noted, payments made are often unrelated to delivery of results (Frist and Daschle, 2015). The result is a fragmentation of incentives down to a focus on the smallest possible unit, rather than the overall performance of the system for an individual or a population. We pay for illness, not for health (Daschle, 2009). If we are to forge effective interfaces among the various system elements importantly shaping health outcomes, then payments need to shift to reward overall system performance in delivering those outcomes, including incentives for more effective attention to children at risk (Lavizzo-Mourey, 2016). Some prepaid health plans—e.g., Kaiser Permanente, Group Health, and parts of Geisinger—are based on this philosophy and, as a result, tend to have more prominent community-facing dimensions. The Centers for Medicare & Medicaid Services has initiated a broad-based payment Learning and Action Network with the aim of developing alternative payment models for accelerated transition from payments for individual services, ultimately to a system profile that maximizes payments based on value delivered to a population (Daschle et al., 2013a). By assuming financial responsibility for specific populations, health care organizations have a vested interest in better linking to the community, including local health and social service departments, schools, senior centers, and faith-based institutions. What's required is a substantial acceleration of the progress toward a health financing system that clearly supports and rewards health improvement at the population level, in addition to the best care for individuals.

Vital Direction: *Initiate multilevel standardized measurement of system performance on core health indices.* In order to make progress toward better health, we must know where we stand on representative issues for each of the dimensions most important to health: health care, social circumstances, environment, health behaviors, individual and community engagement, and, of course, health status. The challenge is that if the measures are too numerous and are inconsistently formulated from place to place and time to time, they are ineffective and even counterproductive. There remains an urgent need to align and condense our current measurement approaches to a core set of standardized measures reliably available for broad comparison across institutions and across time. If our restructured payment systems are aimed at a substantially improved focus on results—on the performance of the system in producing better health in the near and the long terms—then our assessment models must be similarly designed to assess system performance. Ironically, as we have become better able to measure clinical activities, and as our focus on accountability has imposed requirements for more measurements, the result has actually been to shift focus away from the performance of the system to the delivery of individual services. Moreover, multiple, often incompatible approaches to measuring delivery of the same service have further complicated the issue. Across clinical care, thousands of individual measures are collected to measure results on hundreds of clinical conditions, and without harmonization the opportunities for reliable cross-institutional or system-wide lessons are highly limited. On the grounds that a small set of standardized and harmonized core measures aimed at system performance should be collected at every level—national, state, communal, and, as indicated, institutional—the Institute of Medicine's recent report *Vital Signs* recommends such a core set. It proposes just 15 core and composite measures of health, health care, costs, and engagement, including measures such as high school graduation rate, teen pregnancy rate, and obesity (IOM, 2015). Additional refinement remains for practical implementation of the 15 measures at all levels, but, again, this is a feasible potential tool to shift attention and action to broader and more effective system interfaces and performance. We need vital signs to assess and direct progress toward our vital directions.

Vital Direction: *Speed development of a universally accessible and interoperable digital health platform.* The most basic element defining a system is the network of nodes important to a functional objective—improving health for a defined population—and basic to the effectiveness of the system's operation is the timeliness and reliability of information flow among those nodes. In a substantial departure from the historical limits, we now have the practical possibility of virtually instantaneous communication among the stakeholders. The barriers that exist to achieving that possibility are formidable, but they are not technically prohibitive. Agreeing to standards for interoperability, ensuring their system-wide application, working out use and privacy protocols, ensuring interface and personal access capacities for individuals, and embedding analytic tools for continuous learning are all feasible and their accomplishment would establish the infrastructure for transformative multisystem, multisectoral initiatives enabling life course–oriented strategies for health improvement. With our rapidly accelerating capacity for real-time linkage and learning, we have in place the potential to establish and grow a continuously learning and improving health system.

Vital Direction: *Foster awareness and action on a community culture of continuous health improvement.* Ultimately, transformative changes in health and health care require transformative leadership and action at the community level. Effective integration, application, and assessment of multisector and multidomain strategies to mobilize the clinical, social service, educational, voluntary, commercial, and related stakeholders—to mobilize the citizenry—on behalf of better health for all, requires leadership to catalyze the emergence of the community-wide vision of the possible. It takes a culture change on many dimensions, away from one that is focused on the narrow and proximate, to one inspired by what is feasible to achieve, and how to achieve it, for the issue that ultimately matters most to people: their health, the health of their families, and the health of their neighbors. This is the aim, for example, of the Culture of Health movement envisioned by the Robert Wood Johnson Foundation (Lavizzo-Mourey, 2015). Building on what has already been demonstrated on the ability to use a well-developed digital platform to improve services and linkages and to accelerate knowledge and evidence development, as well as what has been accomplished by continuous improvement initiatives in health care and elsewhere, the beginnings of a move toward a community culture of continuous health improvement are also in place. Using provisions of the community benefit requirements in the tax code that compel the many nonprofit health care organizations to assess and work toward meeting community needs, tools are available for community leaders to mobilize support and movement toward a transformative community health culture.

CONCLUSION

Especially given the considerable resources available and used in the American health care system, we are substantially underperforming. Yet, compelling and actionable knowledge is now available about the ways health is shaped from its very beginning by factors outside the health system, as well as how engaging those factors more effectively can improve health prospects over a lifetime. With the tools available and the prospect of reinforcing leadership, technical assistance, and policy initiative from the national, state, and private sectors, the possibility should be at hand for better health prospects at the start of life, throughout its course, and at its conclusion. By aligning financial incentives, by employing measures that drive attention and accountability to where it matters most, by taking advantage of the potentially stunning power of the emerging digital platform, and by determined efforts to strengthen community capacity to catalyze necessary changes in community culture and priority, substantial advances in health, health care, and health equity are attainable for Americans.

SUMMARY RECOMMENDATIONS FOR VITAL DIRECTIONS

1. Shift health care payments to financing that rewards system-wide health improvement.
2. Initiate multilevel standardized measurement of system performance on core health indices.
3. Speed development of a universally accessible and interoperable digital health platform.
4. Foster awareness and action on a community culture of continuous health improvement.

REFERENCES

Addy, S., and V. R. Wright. 2012. *Basic facts about low-income children, 2010: Children under 18.* New York: National Center for Children in Poverty, Columbia University.

Alzheimer's Association. 2002. *Report: African Americans and Alzheimer's Disease: The Silent Epidemic.* https://www.alz.org/national/documents/report_afri-canamericanssilentepidemic.pdf.

Alzheimer's Association. 2015. 2015 Alzheimer's disease facts and figures. *Alzheimer's & Dementia* 11(3):332.

American Cancer Society. 2016. *Cancer facts & figures for African Americans 2016–2018.* Atlanta: American Cancer Society.

Anderson, S. E., and R. C. Whitaker. 2009. Prevalence of obesity among US preschool children in different racial and ethnic groups. *Archives of Pediatrics and Adolescent Medicine* 163(4):344–348.

Arias, E. 2016. Changes in Life Expectancy by Race and Hispanic Origin in the United States, 2013–2014. NCHS Data Brief 244. Hyattsville, MD: National Center for Health Statistics.

Berwick D. M. 2016. Era 3 for medicine and health care. *Journal of the American Medical Association* 315(13):1329–1330.

Berwick, D. M., and A. D. Hackbarth. 2012. Eliminating waste in US health care. *Journal of the American Medical Association* 307(14):15131516.

Berwick, D. M., T. W. Nolan, and J. Whittington. 2008. The triple aim: Care, health, and cost. *Health Affairs* 27(3):759–769. doi: 10.1377/hlthaff.27.3.759.

Blum, R. W., and F. Qureshi. 2011. *Morbidity and Mortality among Adolescents and Young Adults in the United States: AstraZeneca Fact Sheet.* Johns Hopkins Bloomberg School of Public Health. Available at http://www.jhsph.edu/research/centers-and-institutes/center-for-adolescent-health/_images/_pre-redesign/az/US%20Fact%20Sheet_FINAL.pdf.

Boyce, W. T., M. B. Sokolowski, and G. E. Robinson. 2012. Toward a new biology of social adversity. *Proceedings of the National Academy of Sciences of the United States of America* 109(Suppl 2):17143–17148.

Braveman, P. 2008. Perspective: Racial disparities at birth: The puzzle persists. *Issues in Science and Technology* 24(2).

Braveman, P, S. Egerter, and D. R. Williams. 2011. The social determinants of health: Coming of age. *Annual Review of Public Health* 32:381–398.

CDC (Centers for Disease Control and Prevention). 2006. *Report: Injury–A risk at any stage of life.* Atlanta, GA: CDC.

CDC. 2011a. *QuickStats: Life Expectancy at Birth, by Sex and Race/Ethnicity—United States.* Available at https://www.cdc.gov/mmwr/preview/mmwrhtml/mm6335a8.htm.

CDC. 2011b. Vital signs: Current cigarette smoking among adults aged > 18 years—United States, 2009–2012. *Morbidity and Mortality Weekly Report* 60(35):1207–1212.

CDC. 2013. *The state of aging and health in America 2013.* Atlanta, GA: CDC.

CDC. 2014a. *National Center for Health Statistics: Leading causes of death.* Atlanta, GA: CDC.

CDC. 2014b. *National diabetes statistics report: Estimates of diabetes and its burden in the United States.* Atlanta, GA: CDC.

CDC. 2014c. Press Release: Up to 40 percent of annual deaths from each of five leading US causes are preventable. Available at http://www.cdc.gov/media/releases/2014/p0501-preventable-deaths.html (accessed September 1, 2016).

CDC. 2016. *Infant Mortality.* Available at https://www.cdc.gov/reproductivehealth/maternalinfanthealth/infantmortality.htm (accessed September 1, 2016).

CDC. 2016b. *Asthma Fact Sheet.* Available at https://www.cdc.gov/asthma/impacts_nation/asthmafactsheet.pdf (accessed September 8, 2016).

Center for Behavioral Health Statistics and Quality. 2015. Behavioral Health Trends in the United States: Results from the 2014 National Survey on Drug Use and Health. *HHS Publication* SMA 15–4927, NSDUH Series H-50. SAMHSA.

Chetty, R., M. Stepner, S. Abraham, S. Lin, B. Scuderi, N. Turner, A. Bergeron, and D. Cutler. 2016. The association between income and life expectancy in the United States, 2001–2004. *Journal of the American Medical Association* 315(16):1750–1766.

Child Maltreatment. 2015. Forum on Child and Family Statistics. Available at http://www.childstats. gov/americaschildren/family7.asp (accessed August 15, 2016).

Child Trends. 2016. Children's Exposure to Violence. Available at http://www.childtrends.org/?indicators=childrens-exposure-to-violence (accessed August 15, 2016).

Child Witness to Violence Project–Fact Sheet. No date. Available at http://www.childwitnesstoviolence.org/facts--myths.html (accessed September 1, 2016).

Collins, J. W., R. J. David, A. Handler, S. Wall, and S. Andes. 2004. Very low birthweight in African American infants: The role of maternal exposure to interpersonal racial discrimination. *American Journal of Public Health* 94(12):2132–2138.

Consumer Federation of America. 2013. *Child poverty, unintentional injuries and foodborne illnesses: Are low-income children at risk?* Underwriters Laboratories Inc.

Daschle, T. 2009. *Moving the focus from illness to wellness.* Medical Laboratory Observator.

Daschle, T., P. Domenici, B. Frist, and A. Rivlin. 2013a. How to build a better health-care system. Washington Post: Washington, DC. https://www.washingtonpost.com/opinions/how-to-build-a-better-health-care-system/2013/04/17/a44dd478-a6d1-11e2-8302-3c7e0ea97057_story.html?utm_term=.481d5d3c8afa.

Daschle, T., P. Domenici, B. Frist, and A. Rivlin. 2013b. Prescription for patient-centered care and cost containment. *New England Journal of Medicine* 369(5):471–474.

Davis, K., K. Stremikis, C. Schoen, and D. Squires. 2014. *Mirror, mirror on the wall, 2014 update: How the U.S. health care system compares internationally.* New York, NY: The Commonwealth Fund.

Diaz, A., and N. Manigat. 1999. The health care provider's role in the disclosure of sexual abuse: The medical interview as the gateway to disclosure. *Children's Health Care* 28(2).

Emanuel, E., N. Tanden, S. Altman, S. Armstrong, D. Berwick, F. deBrantes, M. Calsyn, M. Chernew, J. Colmers, D. Cutler, T. Daschle, P. Egerman, B. Kocher, A. Milstein, E. O. Lee, J. D. Podesta, U. Reinhardt, M. Rosenthal, J. Sharfstein, S. Shortell, A. Stern, P. R. Orszag, and T. Spiro. 2012. A systemic approach to containing health care spending. *New England Journal of Medicine.* 367(10): 949–954.

Essex, M. J., T. Boyce, C. Hertzman, L. L. Lam, J. M. Armstrong, S. Neumann, and M. S. Kobor. 2013. Epigenetic vestiges of early developmental adversity: Childhood stress exposure and DNA methylation in adolescence. *Child Development* 84(1): 58–75.

Fineberg, H. V. 2012a. A successful and sustainable health system—how to get there from here. *New England Journal of Medicine* 366(11):1020–1027.

Fineberg, H. V. 2012b. From shared decision making to patient-centered decision making. *Israel Journal of Health Policy Research* 1:6.

Fineberg, H. V. 2013. The state of health in the United States. *Journal of the American Medical Association* 310(6):585–586.

Forrest, C. B., P. Margolis, M. Seid, and R. B. Colletti. 2014. PEDSnet: How a prototype pediatric learning health system is being expanded into a national network. *Health Affairs* 33(7):1171–1177.

Freedman, D. S., W. H. Dietz, S. R. Srinivasan, and G. S. Berenson. 2009. Risk factors and adult body mass index among overweight children: The Bogalusa Heart Study. *Pediatrics* 123(3):750–757.

Frist, B. 2014. Connected health and the rise of the patient-consumer. *Health Affairs* 33:191–193.

Frist, B. 2015, April 15. Where health and environment converge. Forbes. Available at http://www.forbes.com/sites/billfrist/2015/04/15/where-health-and-environment-converge (accessed July 8, 2016).

Frist, B., and T. Daschle. 2015. Advancing transparency in healthcare: A call to action. The Hill. Available at http://thehill.com/opinion/op-ed/244714-advancing-transparency-in-healthcare-a-call-to-action (accessed August 28, 2016).

Garg, A., M. Marino, A. R. Vikani, and B. Solomon. 2012. Addressing families' unmet social needs within pediatric primary care: The health leads model. *Clinical Pediatrics* 51:1191–1193.

Gawande, A. 2014. The hot spotters. *The New Yorker*. January 24.

Gawande, A. 2016. Quantity and quality of life: Duties of care in life-limiting illness. *Journal of the American Medical Association* 315(3):267–269.

Gordon, L., A. Diaz, C. Soghomonian, A. Nucci-Sack, J. Weiss, H. Strickler, R. Burk, N. Schlecht, and C. Ochner. 2016. Increased body mass index associated with increased risky sexual behaviors. *Journal of Pediatric Adolescent Gynecology* 29(1):42–47.

Green, S. R., V. Singh, and W. O'Byrne. 2010. Hope for New Jersey's city hospitals: The Camden Initiative. *Perspectives in Health Information Management* 7(1).

Halfon, N., and M. Hochstein. 2002. Life course health development: An integrated framework for developing health, policy, and research. *Milbank Quarterly* 80(3):433–479.

Halfon, N., K. Larson, and S. Russ. 2010. Why social determinants. *Healthcare Quarterly* 14(1):1–8.

Halfon, N., K. Larson, M. Lu, E. Tullis, and S. Russ. 2014a. Lifecourse health development: Past, present and future. *Journal of Maternal and Child Health* 18(2):344–365.

Halfon, N., P. Long, D. I. Chang, J. Hester, M. Inkelas, and A. Rodgers. 2014b. Applying a 3.0 transformation framework to guide large-scale health system reform. *Health Affairs* 33(11):2003–2011.

Health Policy Brief: Care Transitions. 2012. *Health Affairs*. Available at http://www.healthaffairs.org/healthpolicybriefs (accessed July 8, 2016).

Hernandez, A. F. 2010. Relationship between early physician follow-up and 30-day readmission among Medicare beneficiaries hospitalized for heart failure. *Journal of the American Medical Association* 303(17):1716–1722.

HHS (U.S. Department of Health and Human Services). 2010. Multiple chronic conditions—a strategic framework: Optimum health and quality of life for individuals with multiple chronic conditions. Washington, DC: HHS.

Hines, A. L., M. L. Barrett, H. J. Jiang, and C. A. Steiner. 2011. Conditions with the Largest Number of Adult Hospital Readmissions by Payer. AHRQ Statistical Brief.

Hummer, R. A., and E.M. Hernandez. 2013. The effect of educational attainment on adult mortality in the United States. *Population Bulletin* 68(1):1–16.

Inkelas, M., and P. Bowie. 2014. The Magnolia Community Initiative: The importance of measurement in improving community well-being. *Community Investments* 26(1):18–24.

IOM (Institute of Medicine). 2006. *Food marketing to children and youth: Threat or opportunity?* Washington, DC: The National Academies Press.

IOM. 2010. *The healthcare imperative: Lowering costs and improving outcomes. Workshop series summary.* Washington, DC: The National Academies Press.

IOM. 2012. *Best care at lower cost: The path to continuously learning health care in America.* Washington, DC: The National Academies Press.

IOM. 2014a. *New directions in child abuse and neglect research.* Washington, DC: The National Academies Press.

IOM. 2014b. *U.S. health in international perspective: Shorter lives, poorer health.* Washington, DC: The National Academies Press. doi: 10.17226/13497.

IOM. 2015. *Vital signs: Core metrics for health and health care progress.* Washington, DC: The National Academies Press.

Kasper, E. K., G. Gerstenblith, and G. Hefter. 2002. A randomized trial of the efficacy of multidisciplinary care in heart failure outpatients at high risk of hospital readmission. *Journal of the American College of Cardiology* 39(3):471–480.

Lavizzo-Mourey, R. 2015. Why we need to build a culture of health in the United States. *Academic Medicine* 90(7):846–848.

Lavizzo-Mourey, R. 2016. Halfway there? Health reform starts now. *Journal of the American Medical Association* 315(13):1335–1336.

Lavizzo-Mourey, R., and J. M. McGinnis. 2003. Making the case for active living communities. *American Journal of Public Health* 93(9):1386–1388.

Loeppke, R., M. Taitel, V. Haufle, T. Parry, R. C. Kessler, and K. Jinnett. 2009. Health and productivity as a business strategy: A multiemployer study. *Journal of Occupational and Environmental Medicine* 51(4):411–428.

Lu, M. C. 2010. We can do better: Improving perinatal health in America. *Journal of Women's Health* 19(3):569–574.

Margolis, P. A., L. E. Peterson, and M. Seid. 2013. Collaborative Chronic Care Networks (C3Ns) to transform chronic illness care. *Pediatrics* 131(Suppl 4):S219–S223.

McEwen, B. S. 1998. Protective and damaging effects of stress mediators. *New England Journal of Medicine* 338(3):171–179.

McGinnis, J. M., and W. H. Foege. 1993. Actual causes of death in the United States. *Journal of the American Medical Association* 270(18):2207–2212.

McGinnis, J. M., P. Williams-Russo, and J. R. Knickman. 2002. The case for more active policy attention to health promotion. *Health Affairs* 21(2).

Meyer, H. 2011. A new care paradigm slashes hospital use and nursing home stays for the elderly and the physically and mentally disabled. *Health Affairs* 30(3):412–415.

Mokdad, A. H., J. S. Marks, D. F. Stroup, and J. L. Gerberding. 2004. Actual causes of death in the United States, 2000. *Journal of the American Medical Association* 291(10):1238–1245.

Mosher, W. D., J. Jones, and J. C. Abma. 2012. Intended and unintended births in the United States: 1982–2010. *National Health Statistics Reports* (55):1–28.

Mozaffarian, D, E. J. Benjamin, A. S. Go, D. K. Arnett, M. J. Blaha, M. Cushman, S. de Ferranti, J. P. Després, H. J. Fullerton, V. J. Howard, M. D. Huffman, S. E. Judd, B. M. Kissela, D. T. Lackland, J. H. Lichtman, L. D. Lisabeth, S. Liu, R. H. Mackey, D. B. Matchar, D. K. McGuire, E. R. Mohler, C. S. Moy, P. Muntner, M. E. Mussolino, K. Nasir, R. W. Neumar, G. Nichol, L. Palaniappan, D. K. Pandey, M. J. Reeves, C. J. Rodriguez, P. D. Sorlie, J. Stein, A. Towfighi, T. N. Turan, S. S. Virani, J. Z. Willey, D. Woo, R. W. Yeh, M. B. Turner MB, and the American Heart Association Statistics Committee and Stroke Statistics Subcommittee. 2015. Heart disease and stroke statistics—2015 update: A report from the American Heart Association. *Circulation* e29-322.

Murray, C. 2013. The state of US health, 1990–2010: Burden of diseases, injuries, and risk factors. *Journal of the American Medical Association* 310(6):591–606.

Newsletter of the Office of National Drug Control Policy. 2010. PsycEXTRA Dataset 1.2: Executive Office of the President.

Parker, G., M. Van Alstyne, and S. Choudary. 2016. *Platform revolution*. New York: W.W. Norton & Company.

Pearcy, J. N., and K. G. Keppel. 2002. A summary measure of health disparity. *Public Health Reports* 117(3):273–280.

Reichman, N. E. 2005. Disparities in low birth weight by race, ethnicity, and nativity. *School Readiness: Closing Racial and Ethnic Gaps* 15(1).

Rudd, R. A., N. Aleshire, J. E. Zibbell, and R. M. Gladden. 2015. Increases in drug and opioid overdose deaths—United States, 2000–2014. *Morbidity and Mortality Weekly Report* 64.50–51(2016):1378–1382.

Skinner, A. C., and J. Skelton. 2014. Prevalence and trends in obesity and severe obesity among children in the United States, 1999–2012. *JAMA Pediatrics* 168(6):561–566.

Squires, D., and C. Anderson. 2015. U.S. Health Care from a Global Perspective: Spending, Use of Services, Prices, and Health in 13 Countries. New York, NY: The Commonwealth Fund.

Tanielian, T., and L. H. Jaycox. 2008. Invisible Wounds of War: Psychological and Cognitive Injuries, Their Consequences, and Services to Assist Recovery. RAND Center for Military Health Policy Report.

WHO (World Health Organization). 2001. The World Health Report 2000: Health systems: Improving performance. *Public Health Reports* 116(3):268–269.

WHO. 2011. Newborn Death and Illness. Available at http://www.who.int/pmnch/media/press_materials/fs/fs_newborndealth_illness/en/ (accessed September 1, 2016).

Wight, V., M. Chau, and Y. Aratani. 2010, January. Who Are America's Poor Children? The Official Story. National Center for Children in Poverty, Columbia University.

Wise, P. H. 2016. Child poverty and the promise of human capacity: Childhood as a foundation for healthy aging. *Academic Pediatrics* 16(3):S37–S45.

World Bank. 2015. Adolescent fertility rate (births per 1,000 women ages 15–19) from 2011–2015. Available at http://data.worldbank.org/indicator/SP.ADO.TFRT (accessed July 9, 2016).

Xu, J. Q., S. L. Murphy, K. D. Kochanek, and B. A. Bastian. 2016. Deaths: Final data for 2013. *National Vital Statistics Reports* 64(2):1. Hyattsville, MD: National Center for Health Statistics.

Zheng, H. 2012. Do people die from income inequality of a decade ago? *Social Science & Medicine* 75(1):36–45.

AUTHOR INFORMATION

J. Michael McGinnis, MD, MPP, is Leonard D. Shaeffer Executive Officer, National Academy of Medicine. **Donald M. Berwick, MD,** is President Emeritus and Senior Fellow for the Institute for Healthcare Improvement, and is a former Administrator for Centers for Medicare and Medicaid Services. **The Honorable Thomas A. Daschle,** is Founder and Chairman of The Daschle Group, and is a former United States Senator. **Angela Diaz, MD, PhD, MPH,** is Jean C. and James W. Crystal Professor of Adolescent Health, Department of Pediatrics, Department of Preventive Medicine at the Icahn School of Medicine at Mount Sinai. **Harvey V. Fineberg, MD, PhD,** is President, Gordon and Betty Moore Foundation. **The Honorable William H. Frist, MD,** is University Distinguished Professor of Health, Owen Graduate School of Medicine, Vanderbilt University, and is a former United States Senator. **Atul Gawande, MD, MPH,** is Surgeon, Brigham and Women's Hospital; Professor, Harvard School of Public Health and Harvard Medical School; and Director, Ariadne Labs. **Neal Halfon, MD, MPH,** is Professor of Pediatrics and Public Health, and is Codirector, Center for Healthier Children, Families, and Communities, University of California, Los Angeles. **Risa Lavizzo-Mourey, MD, MBA,** is President and CEO, Robert Wood Johnson Foundation.

3

ADDRESSING SOCIAL DETERMINANTS OF HEALTH AND HEALTH DISPARITIES

Nancy E. Adler, PhD, David M. Cutler, PhD, Jonathan E. Fielding, MD, MPH, Sandro Galea, MD, DrPH, Maria Glymour, ScD, Howard K. Koh, MD, MPH, and David Satcher, MD, PhD

Despite the powerful effects of social and behavioral factors on health, development, and longevity, US health policy has largely ignored them. The United States spends far more money per capita on medical services than do other nations, while spending less on social services (Bradley et al., 2011). Residents of nations that have higher ratios of spending on social services to spending on health care services have better health and live longer (Bradley and Taylor, 2013; NCR and IOM, 2013a). The relative underinvestment in social services helps to explain why US health indicators lag behind those of many countries (Woolf and Aron, 2013). The best available evidence suggests that a health policy framework addressing social and behavioral determinants of health would achieve better population health, less inequality, and lower costs than our current policies.

OVERVIEW

For over a century, each generation of Americans has lived longer than did their parents because of advances in health care and biotechnology (Nabel and Braunwald, 2012) and progress in public health and health behaviors (Laing and Katz, 2012; Tarone and McLaughlin, 2012). However, although the US population gained 1–2 years of life expectancy in each decade from 1950 to 2010, life expectancy has since then increased by only 0.1 year (Arias, 2015; Murphy et al., 2015), and some researchers predict that it will decrease for the next generation because of the obesity epidemic (Olshansky et al., 2005). Mortality in middle-aged white women is already increasing, most strikingly in residents of the southern United States and in women who lack a high school degree (Case and Deaton, 2015; Gelman and Auerbach, 2015).

In contrast with the United States, many high-income nations continue to achieve major gains in health and life expectancy. Life expectancy of white men and women in the United States is more than 4 years shorter than that in many European countries and even shorter among blacks (National Center for Health Statistics, 2015); indeed, the United States overall ranks 27th among Organisation for Economic Cooperation and Development (OECD) countries in life expectancy at birth.

In addition to the relatively poor health of the overall US population, the burden of ill health is unevenly distributed. Differences in health that are avoidable and unjust—referred to as health disparities or health inequities—are greater in the United States than in peer countries, such as Canada or high-income European countries (Avendano et al., 2009; Lasser et al., 2006; Siddiqi et al., 2015; van Hedel et al., 2014). People in less-advantaged groups have worse health from the moment of birth and throughout life. For example, a 40-year-old American man in the poorest 1 percent of the income distribution will die an average of 14.6 years sooner than a man in the richest 1 percent; the gap for American women is 10.1 years (Chetty et al., 2016). Health disparities also occur in relation to other aspects of socioeconomic status, such as education and occupation, and in relation to race or ethnicity, gender, sexual orientation, and place of residence (Adler and Rehkopf, 2008). To a great extent, socioeconomic disparities underlie other bases of health disparities, but they do not account for them fully. Because socioeconomic factors are major, modifiable contributors to disparities, addressing them is a logical way to reduce disparities in multiple dimensions.

Health disparities are not inevitable; actions that lessen social disadvantage can reduce gaps in health and longevity. For example, progress in reducing health inequities between blacks and whites was achieved in the late 1960s and the 1970s after the passage of major civil rights legislation (Almond et al., 2006; Kaplan et al., 2008; Krieger et al., 2008). Contemporary data suggest that, despite the worrisome evidence on middle-aged and older adults, patterns in younger people are more encouraging (Currie and Schwandt, 2016).

Those three lines of evidence—the relatively poor health status of the US population compared with other countries, the existence of health disparities, and fluctuations in health and health inequalities in relation to policy-driven changes in social conditions—point to the importance of policies that address social determinants. Such policies, although not typically viewed as "health policies," have the potential to improve the health and longevity of all Americans and to reduce health disparities.

KEY ISSUES, COST IMPLICATIONS, AND BARRIERS TO PROGRESS

Powerful drivers of health lie outside the conventional medical care delivery system, so we should not equate investment in *clinical care* with investment in *health*. Investment in clinical care may yield smaller improvements in population health than equivalent investments that address social and behavioral determinants. To the extent that health care investment crowds out social investment, substantial allocation of resources in clinical care may have an adverse effect on overall health, particularly on the health of the socially disadvantaged. Health policies need to expand to address factors outside the medical system that promote or damage health.

To help frame the policy options, we consider several issues of overriding potential to improve health and diminish health disparities:

- *Addressing "upstream" social determinants of health.* Accumulating evidence highlights the individual and collective contributions of education, labor, criminal justice, transportation, economics, and social welfare to health. Policies in those domains are increasingly understood to be health policies.
- *Fostering health-promoting resources and reducing health-damaging risk factors throughout the life course.* Behavioral patterns develop and play out in the context of physiologic and social development, and benefits of early intervention accumulate over one's lifetime. Policies that make it easier and more socially normative to engage in healthy behaviors have proved effective, as have policies that reduce the harm caused by risky behaviors.
- *Improving access to, effects of, and the value of clinical health care services.* Differential access to high-quality health care services can create health disparities. These inequities can be rectified by aligning reimbursement strategies to increase access, by expanding the array of services that are reimbursed, and by improving the quality and efficiency of services. Better links between health care and public health activities could increase the effects of health expenditures.

Although policymaking is necessary, it is not sufficient. Effective implementation is essential and requires continuing attention and coordination among different parts of government. Gaps between policies and practices have diminished the effects of excellent policy initiatives. For example, a number of policies included in the Affordable Care Act (ACA) (US Department of Health and Human Services, 2016) have not been implemented, because funding was not appropriated, not fully allocated, or misallocated. A national prevention strategy

(Shearer, 2010), developed by representatives of 20 federal agencies, provided a comprehensive agenda for prevention and recommended funding starting at $500 million and rising to $2 billion. However, it was never fully funded, and monies have been shifted for other purposes within the Department of Health and Human Services.

We discuss below specific policies or enhanced implementation of existing policies in the three vital directions. Although we frame recommendations in terms of the people who will benefit from them directly, family members may also benefit; for example, financial strain on parents or caregivers may be reduced by nutritional benefits provided to children. We emphasize programs that are likely to trigger beneficial spillovers and improve overall population health. Because disadvantaged and vulnerable people should benefit most from these policies, their enactment and implementation should also reduce health disparities.

Health Disparities and the Upstream Social Determinants of Health

Policies that improve the overall social and economic well-being of individuals and families will reverberate across a variety range of health outcomes and help to achieve health equity. Some examples follow.

Home-visiting programs in pregnancy and for parents of young children. Home-visiting programs, especially during pregnancy and early childhood, have demonstrated multiple benefits. Such programs as Healthy Families America, Nurse–Family Partnership, and Parents as Teachers address threats to social, emotional, and cognitive health in children of low-income families by assessing family needs, educating and supporting parents, and referring and coordinating services as needed. They can help parents and children to build better relationships, strengthen family support networks, and link families to community resources, although results have not been consistently strong across implementations (Olds, 2016). The strongest evidence is related to the Nurse–Family Partnership program, whose rigorous evaluations have shown better cognitive development, lower mortality from preventable causes, reduced arrest rates, reduced child abuse, and fewer days on food stamps (Office of the Surgeon General, 2001; Olds et al., 2002, 2004, 2014). The ACA expanded home visiting by amending Title V of the Social Security Act to create the Maternal, Infant, and Early Childhood Home Visiting Program, allocating $1.5 billion to states, territories, and tribes in FY2010–2015. Funding at $400 million per year was extended through September 2017. Support for evaluation of existing programs and programmatic innovations was built into the ACA mandate, and their effects on parenting behavior, child abuse and neglect, economic self-sufficiency, and child development are now being assessed.

Earned income tax credit. Nearly 30 million families receive earned income tax credit (EITC) benefits, which provide cash transfers to low- to moderate-income working people, particularly those who have children. The federal program costs roughly $70 billion a year and lifts about 9.4 million families above the poverty line (IRS, 2016). About 80 percent of eligible families receive EITC benefits. Rigorous studies indicate that more generous EITC benefits predict improvement in maternal health, improvements in indexes of both physical health (e.g., blood pressure and inflammation markers) and mental health (Evans et al. 2010), reductions in maternal smoking during pregnancy, healthier birth outcomes, decreases in childhood behavioral problems, enriched home environments for children, and better mathematics and reading achievement scores (Dahl et al., 2005; Hamad and Rehkopf, 2015, 2016; Hoynes et al., 2012; Strully et al., 2010). Benefits vary substantially between states, because many states add to the federal benefit package; 12 states increase the federal benefit by 20 percent or more. States with higher benefit rates also enjoy better health returns, and this suggests that greater health could be achieved by increasing the federal benefits to match the more generous states. EITC benefits are quite low for childless workers, including noncustodial parents. Improving benefits for noncustodial parents in New York was associated with higher employment rates and child support payments (Nichols and Rothstein, 2015). Greater health benefits could be achieved by including more people, increasing the benefit rate, and providing higher benefits.

Federal minimum wage. The current federal minimum wage—$7.25 per hour—translates to $14,500 per year for a full-time employee and places a family of three far below the poverty line. Poverty is a strong predictor of poor health and earlier mortality not only of the worker but also of family members. A 2001 modeling analysis of increasing the minimum wage to $11 per hour estimated substantial benefits for low-income families by decreasing the risk of premature death and reducing sick days, disability, and depression and for children in those families by increasing high school completion and reducing early childbirth (Bhatia and Katz, 2001). EITC and minimum-wage increases are complementary (Nichols and Rothstein, 2015).

Although some counties and states have passed laws to raise minimum wages to $15 per hour, smaller increases should still have an effect on health. One of the immediate effects may be a reduction in food insecurity. In contemporary, obesogenic environments, food insecurity is linked to consumption of calorie-rich but nutritionally poor foods and consequent weight gain, especially in girls and women (Burke et al., 2016; Cheung et al., 2015). State comparisons suggest that minimum-wage differences have contributed to about 10 percent of the increase in average body-mass index since 1970 (Meltzer and Chen, 2011). Legislation proposed in the 114th Congress to increase the federal minimum wage to $12 per hour by 2020, phased in by $1 per hour each year, would likely have health benefits, especially among low income workers.

Occupational safety and health. Deaths of US workers on the job and from occupation-related diseases occur disproportionately among those who have limited labor-market opportunities and accept unsafe working conditions. These workers are commonly members of racial or ethnic minorities, immigrants, and people who have little education (Steege et al., 2014). The main agency charged with averting work-related injury and other harm is the Occupational Safety and Health Administration (OSHA), and substantial evidence indicates that OSHA enforcement activities reduce workplace injuries (Michaels, 2012; Tompa et al., 2016). Its capacity to ensure that all workers have safe conditions is impeded by the granting of exemptions to many employers and by inadequate funding for oversight. Employers that have 10 or fewer employees are not required by OSHA to keep injury and illness records unless specifically instructed, and enforcement of occupational-safety regulations on small farms that have paid employees is constrained. At current funding levels, OSHA has one compliance officer for every 59,000 workers and 3,600 worksites (OSHA, 2016). Additional capacity is needed to adequately meet OSHA's current mandate, which should also be expanded to smaller employers and agricultural employees.

Episodes of unusual need throughout the life course. Policies that enable individuals and families to deal with challenging periods and life events may be especially effective. Beyond supporting home visiting during pregnancy and early childhood noted above, several types of policies may buffer job loss and address other temporary periods of family need:

- expanding the Family Medical Leave Act to cover smaller employers, and add paid leave;
- allowing family caregivers to be financially compensated for critical care, and reduce the long-term labor-market effect of family caregiving;
- giving employers incentives to provide paid parental leave and paid sick leave, including for low-wage workers; and
- expanding unemployment insurance, especially for low-wage workers.

Most countries support time spent in caring for family members, and the availability of sick leave and parental leave is associated with better health. Across 141 countries, neonatal, infant, and child mortality is lower in those that offer longer paid maternal leave (Heymann et al., 2011). Children whose parents return sooner to work after birth have lower odds of being immunized against polio and measles (Berger et al., 2005). Dual-earner support policies in Nordic countries that provide child-care support and paid leave for both mothers and fathers are associated with lower poverty levels and infant mortality (Lundberg et al., 2008).

The United States is the only high-income country and one of only eight globally not requiring paid leave for mothers (Gault et al., 2014). The Family and Medical Leave Act of 1993 provided up to 12 weeks of unpaid leave a year to care for new children or seriously ill family members or, for a subset of employees, to recover from their own health conditions. However, an estimated 40 percent of the workforce is not covered by the Act, and many people cannot afford to take unpaid leave (National Partnership for Women and Families, 2016).

Adult family members also commonly require care during episodes of illness or age-related disability. An estimated 17 percent of Americans are providing care for adults, generally spouses or parents. Most caregivers are employed, and 60 percent report having to make a workplace accommodation for caregiving (Weber-Raley and Smith, 2015). Such caregiving is associated with stress and poor health outcomes in the caregivers (Adelman et al., 2014; Capistrant et al., 2011, 2012; Wolff et al., 2016). The growing vacuum of unmet needs calls for policies that ensure coverage for the role that family members increasingly have to play in caring for loved ones.

Vulnerability also comes with becoming unemployed. Unemployment is associated with cardiovascular disease, depression, substance use, and other health problems (Deb et al., 2011; Gallo et al., 2000). Adverse health effects are partially offset by unemployment insurance (Cylus et al., 2014, 2015). The US Department of Labor's unemployment-insurance program provides unemployment benefits to eligible workers in conjunction with individual states' policies. In most states, a worker can receive up to 26 weeks of about half the pay received in their most recent job (Stone and Chen, 2014). That is helpful, but many people do not qualify, benefits differ substantially among states, and those who fail to find a job during the 26-week period may be left without income or a safety net.

Criminal justice and sentencing policies. The US incarceration rate is higher than that of any other country and is five times greater than the worldwide median (Sentencing Project, 2016). Well-documented adverse health effects of incarceration need attention, and longer-term consequences for incarcerated individuals, their families, and communities need to be characterized better to guide future reforms (NRC and IOM, 2013b). Particular attention to effects on youth involved with the justice system is needed for:

- improving prison health care services to reduce infectious-disease transmission and improve care management;
- funding rigorous evaluation of programs to improve the health of people who are involved with the criminal-justice system and their families, including alternative sentencing strategies, family preservation, and reentry programs; and
- strengthening diversion and mental health court pipelines for youth. Incorporate mental health services and women's health services into the juvenile crime system.

Incarceration increases transmission of infectious disease, such as HIV/AIDS, tuberculosis, and viral hepatitis; these diseases are, in turn, transmitted to the communities after prisoners are released (Cloud et al., 2014; Drucker, 2013). Despite greater health needs, health care for the incarcerated is characterized by delays, restrictive prescription formularies, and inadequate availability of acute and specialty medical care, including women's health care (Daniel, 2007; Drucker, 2013; Freudenberg and Heller 2016; Travis et al., 2014). Incarceration has ripple effects on families: as of 2007, black children were 7.5 times more likely and Hispanic children 2.5 times more likely than white children to have an incarcerated parent. Improving health care for incarcerated people is likely to be cost effective and could have spillover benefits to their families and communities (Hammett, 2001).

Juvenile offenders have a higher risk of early and violent death than the general population, and this risk is especially high for black youth (Aalsma et al., 2016; Teplin et al., 2005). Incarcerated youth have greater health needs than their nonincarcerated peers (Prins, 2014), but health care services in the juvenile justice system are inadequate and lack enough mental health and substance-abuse treatment professionals (Braverman and Murray, 2011). The health needs of incarcerated girls, including pregnancy testing and prenatal services, are routinely unmet in a system that is designed primarily for boys (Braverman and Murray 2011). The National Research Council report *Reforming Juvenile Justice: A Developmental Approach* proposed a developmentally informed framework to treat youth fairly, hold them accountable, and prevent further offending (NRC, 2013).

Fostering Health—Promoting Behaviors and Diminishing Risk

To grow up healthy and remain healthy into old age, people need resources that enable healthy behaviors, reduce environmental risks, and improve their capacity to maximize their own health. Investment in early life can form the foundation for better health later and yield enduring benefits. However, since early gains can be undone by adverse environments encountered later in life, attention is needed at every life stage.

Nutrition assistance. Adequate nutrition from a healthy diet is necessary at all stages of life, but especially during pregnancy and in childhood, when growth is most rapid. Large-scale Supplemental Nutrition Assistance Programs (SNAPs) have been causally linked to greater consumption by children of fresh fruits and vegetables, 1 percent milk (a superior alternative to whole milk), and fewer sugar-sweetened beverages (Long et al., 2013). A temporary expansion of SNAP benefits in Massachusetts was linked to reductions in inpatient Medicaid expenditures, which suggests that conventional benefit levels are too low (Sonik, 2016). The Special Supplemental Nutrition Program for Women, Infants, and Children (WIC) targets pregnant women and postpartum mothers who have children 0–5 years old and combines vouchers that encourage consumption of lower-fat milk, fruits, vegetables, and whole grains; nutritional and health counseling, including promotion of breastfeeding; and referrals to health care and social-service providers. Participation in WIC has been associated with better birth outcomes and higher child-immunization rates. SNAP serves roughly 45 million households a month but is thought to miss about 17 percent of eligible participants. Expanded enrollment and greater attention to nutritional impact of benefits is needed.

Children's cognitive and social skills. A child's brain development can be impaired by exposure to adversity and lack of responsive, stimulating environments (Hertzman and Boyce, 2010). Children in low-income families are exposed to fewer words and less-affirming responses, and this results in a more constricted vocabulary and a relative disadvantage by the time they begin formal schooling (Hart and Risley, 2003). Children in such environments benefit from high-quality child care. For example, low-income children randomized to attend a preschool that combined a half-day session with family home visits showed long-term cognitive and social benefits; the program generated a financial return on investment in the form of savings on remedial education, incarceration, and teen pregnancies (Knudsen et al., 2006). The best available evidence indicates that high-quality early education programs have both social and health benefits (Campbell et al., 2014; Community Preventive Services Task Force, 2015; Duncan and Magnuson, 2013). However, although the programs set the stage for success, their gains can be undermined if children do not have access to good K–12 schooling. Racial and socioeconomic differences in school quality may thus translate into health disparities (Duncan and Murnane, 2014; Keating and Simonton, 2008).

The strongest current evidence on early education relies on a relatively small number of rigorously conducted studies. We lack sufficient evidence on how variations in program design may modify short-term and long-term effects.

Programs and school improvements are likely to be phased in over time, allowing for experimentation and continued research to identify opportunities for improvements in program effectiveness and efficiency. Therefore, priorities should be placed on:

- expanding access to high-quality child care and preschool and promoting high-quality primary and secondary schools; and
- supporting research on the effects of child care and education programs on health and development.

Healthy behavior incentives. Health behaviors account for over one-third of premature deaths and are strongly influenced by socioeconomic factors (McGinnis et. al., 2002). Smoking, lack of exercise, and diet are among the most important known determinants of health. Market practices that encourage health-damaging behaviors call for offsetting policies that create disincentives to engage in them, such as:

- supporting FDA regulation to reduce the nicotine in cigarettes to below an addictive threshold;
- encouraging the further adoption and rigorous evaluation of city and state taxes for tobacco and sugar-sweetened beverages with emphasis on using generated funds to support high-priority health programs and inform consideration of a federal tax; and
- encouraging city and state policies to use and evaluate cross-subsidies that increase the costs of foods high in fat, salt, or sugar and decrease costs of other foods in restaurants and grocery stores.

Policies and interventions that target use of combustible cigarettes have resulted in a marked drop in consumption over the last few decades. It is consistent with microeconomic theory that increasing the purchase price of cigarettes through added taxes substantially contributed to the marked decline in use and a later decrease in smoking-related diseases (Colchero et al., 2016). However, tobacco use remains an important contributor to premature mortality: nearly 17 percent of Americans smoke, and rates are higher among those who have lower income and education. Quitting is made harder by the fact that combustible cigarettes are designed with nicotine concentrations that engender physiologic addiction. Reduced-nicotine cigarettes facilitate smoking cessation (Donny et al., 2015). Greater gains in reducing smoking could be made if manufacturers reduced the amount of nicotine in cigarettes to a nonaddictive concentration (Fiore, 2016).

Food marketers, including restaurants, grocery stores, bodegas, and food companies, similarly influence consumption patterns. Some of their actions are contributing to overconsumption and overweight and increasing the risks of diabetes and other chronic conditions (Bartlett et al., 2014). Offsetting actions include making healthier options more salient, easier to access, and less expensive and promoting their selection as a default. Small demonstration programs suggest that increasing the cost of sugar-sweetened beverages could reduce overweight and obesity. Berkeley, California, and Philadelphia, Pennsylvania, are using funds generated by increasing taxes on sugar-sweetened beverages to fund other high-priority health programs (such as universal preschools). One concern is that such a tax is potentially regressive in creating a greater economic burden on low-income consumers. However, the counterargument is that the resulting disincentive would be particularly beneficial to that population by reducing its consumption of a health-damaging product and that it would benefit disproportionately from the services enabled by the revenues.

Firearm safety. Injuries from firearms are an important and preventable source of health disparities, especially for youth and young adults, for whom gun incidents are the second leading cause of death. Homicides are visible and garner attention, but firearm suicides are nearly twice as common as firearm homicides—21,175 versus 11,208 in 2013 (Xu et al., 2016). Their occurrence in the United States is 6 times greater than the average in 23 other high-income OECD countries (Richardson and Hemenway, 2011). In addition, accidental discharges of firearms cause about 500 deaths per year, including deaths involving guns picked up by very young children.

Firearm injury is a public health concern and should be dealt with accordingly. More than is the case with any other health issue, developing and testing effective programs and policies to reduce firearm-related morbidity and mortality are hampered both by a paucity of relevant data and the lack of a coordinated approach to regulation of what is a dangerous consumer product.

Most Americans want such strategies as universal background checks and assault weapons bans (Gallup Surveys, 2016), which could reduce injuries and deaths without curtailing legitimate uses of firearms. Background checks would not only reduce homicides (Rudolph et al., 2015) but lower the number of completed suicides inasmuch as such acts are often impulsive and may be averted owing to the time needed for the background check (Miller and Hemenway, 2008). Firearm manufacturers are not subject to the same design standards as are imposed on other consumer products; such standards could reduce the risk of unintentional harm and the use of firearms against others, including law enforcement personnel.

Pressing firearm safety priorities include

- creating a national research infrastructure that includes sustained funding of the National Violent Death Reporting System to enable more research on public health approaches to promoting gun safety;
- requiring permits, comprehensive background checks, and waiting periods for firearm sales, and require firearms dealers to implement them; and
- encouraging application of federal health and safety oversight to firearm design similar to that involving other dangerous consumer products.

Health Care Financing Strategies to Reduce Health Disparities

The traditional models for financing medical care in the United States deliver less than optimal population health, allow substantial health disparities, and exacerbate the burgeoning cost of medical care. Expenditures on clinical care have an opportunity cost, and the amount of money devoted to health care delivery makes it difficult to provide sufficient support for other kinds of investment that would have greater health benefits. The US medical care system emphasizes treating illness over preventing disease; this is the case for mental health and substance-abuse disorders as well as for physical diseases (Frank and Glied, 2006). Large sums are spent when people are acutely ill; much less is spent to prevent illness or manage chronic disease. Economic incentives underlie the discrepancy (Cutler, 2014). Both public and private payers for medical care generally reimburse physicians on a fee-for-service basis, and payment is based on the volume and intensity of services provided. More acute services are reimbursed better than less acute ones; this reflects, in part, a natural desire to provide help to those in crisis. This financing structure results in extensive care provision in acute settings, insufficient care in less intense situations, and inattention to social causes of disease. Steps that can be taken to rectify that imbalance would improve overall population health and reduce disparities.

Several new initiatives have the potential to increase access to care, reduce the cost of care to free resources for public health priorities, and improve the quality of care. The ACA provides opportunities to link efforts in the clinic with those in the community. As part of moving from a volume-based health system to a value-based health system, current demonstration projects funded by the Department of Health and Human Services are examining whether and how integration of public health activities with clinical care systems can improve population health, enhance quality, and lower costs. Team-based approaches to patient-centered care and prevention are receiving heightened attention. Community-based demonstration projects, such as State Innovation Models and

Accountable Health Communities, offer special opportunities to establish such linkages and address social determinants of health.

Alternative payment models. Two commonly proposed alternative payment mechanisms deviate from the predominant fee-for-service reimbursement model. The first is the pay-for-performance system, in which higher-quality care is reimbursed more than lower-quality care. For example, for a person who has a chronic health problem, the traditional fee-for-service reimbursement model pays the primary care physician or specialist for each visit, whether or not it adequately addresses the patient's needs. In a pay-for-performance system, quality is based on the proportion of a provider's patients with the illness who are receiving appropriate therapy, and on how many acute episodes are prevented. Physicians who adhere to guideline recommendations better and have fewer acute incidents among their patients receive financial bonuses.

A second alternative payment model is a bundled payment or global payment system in which a fixed amount is paid for each patient, depending on the patient's diagnosis and disease severity, regardless of what services are provided. The clinician is responsible for all the costs of care management. For example, a physician who successfully works with a patient to take needed medications and avoids inpatient care would keep the savings from prevented hospitalizations. Bundled payment models generally provide bonus payments for higher quality of care.

Payment mechanisms that value prevention over acute care should encourage providers to address social factors that drive the need for services. However, ill-planned implementation of such policies could backfire if incentives discourage caring for vulnerable populations. Quantifying the costs associated with their care is an important challenge in both bundled payment and pay-for-performance models (NASEM, 2016; Sills et al., 2016). If extra costs associated with caring for impoverished or socially marginalized patient groups are not fully captured in metrics of patient illness (such as number of comorbid conditions), the resulting inadequate adjustment in calculating reimbursement structures could foster discrimination by care providers and financially handicap safety-net providers.

Recent pay-for-performance and bundled payment experiments have had encouraging results (Cutler, 2015). Pay-for-performance systems have been associated with increased care quality but less cost savings. Bundled payment systems are associated with both quality improvements and cost savings (Nyweide et al., 2015; Rajkumar et al., 2014; Swchwartz et al., 2015; Song et al., 2014).The Department of Health and Human Services has proposed expanding the use of alternative payment structures in Medicare with a goal of 30 percent of Medicare payments on an alternative payment basis by 2016 and 50 percent by 2018 and most of the other payments tied to quality. However, more remains to be done to expand the programs, including involvement of private payers, and appropriate targets should be set to accelerate movement to alternative payment models.

Health insurance coverage. People who do not have health insurance receive less care than those who do have health insurance, including preventive care and screening (Baicker et al., 2013; Sommers et al., 2014), and their health may suffer as a result. In 2014, about 33 million Americans were uninsured for at least part of the year. The ACA improved health care access substantially by establishing health insurance exchanges, although enrollment in exchanges varies by state. Universal access to Medicaid was intended for people who had incomes up to 138 percent of the federal poverty line, and subsidies for health insurance for those who had incomes of 138 percent to 400 percent of the poverty line. However, the Supreme Court ruling in *NFIB v. Sebelius* allowed states to opt out of the Medicaid expansion, and about 3 million potentially eligible people live in states that opted out. Nevertheless, about 20 million people have obtained coverage under the ACA. Efforts needed to meet the nation's intent to ensure coverage include

- encouraging states to opt into the Medicaid expansion; and
- determining which areas have relatively low enrollment in health insurance exchanges and target enrollment efforts in these areas.

Chronic disease and oral health. More comprehensive health care coverage contributes to better health. When coverage is narrower, people use fewer services, and quality of care suffers (Brot-Goldberg et al., 2015; Lohr et al., 1986). The ACA limited the cost sharing that can be required in insurance, but the minimum policies are not particularly generous, and greater coverage is needed to enable better care for chronic disease.

Many people suffer from chronic illnesses (such as hypertension, hypercholesterolemia, diabetes, and mental illness) that often can be treated with relatively inexpensive pharmaceuticals, but high cost sharing may inhibit their use. For example, each $10 increase in monthly cost sharing reduces use of chronic care medications by about 5 percent (Goldman et al., 2007). The ACA requires insurers to cover, with no cost-sharing, preventive services that are shown to be effective. That principle can be extended to chronic disease management, starting with therapies that are inexpensive and highly effective.

The services covered by the policies should include dental care (Donoff et al., 2014). Oral health problems, such as inflammation of the gums, can trigger or exacerbate other health problems, such as heart disease, pulmonary disease, and poor perinatal health (HHS, 2000). Health insurance generally omits access to all but emergency dental services and provides less access to dental care than to medical care. Beyond possible overall costs savings from an investment in oral health (Jeffcoat et al., 2014), better oral health is important in its own right and may even have spillover effects on socioeconomic outcomes (Glied and Neidell, 2010). ACA expanded dental coverage for children but not for adults.

Pressing priorities therefore include

- requiring Medicare Part D and exchange health plans to cover chronic disease care that leading bodies certify is highly effective, that has only modest cost, and whose cost is a barrier to using the service;
- expanding Medicare, Medicaid, and exchange health plans to cover dental care; and
- expanding standards for primary care medical homes and other advanced primary care practice designs to allow adequate access to and use of preventive dental care.

CONCLUSION

The emphasis in our health system on medical treatments for acute problems has yielded benefits for some but has failed to achieve the levels of population health and longevity enjoyed by other nations. Overcoming our national health disadvantage will require rebalancing our priorities to focus more on preventing or ameliorating health damaging social conditions and behavioral choices. It is an issue not of how much money is invested in health but of whether the dollars are spent on factors that provide the greatest benefit. Moreover, a number of policies addressing social and behavioral determinants of health would entail little or no additional cost. This paper has presented only a sample of the wide array of policy options that address social and behavioral determinants of health. Such policies typically are not viewed as "health policies" but, in fact, have great potential to reduce health disparities and improve the health and longevity of all Americans.

SUMMARY RECOMMENDATIONS FOR VITAL DIRECTIONS

1. Strengthen assessment and action on health-impacting social policies.
2. Expand policies that increase resources and environments fostering healthy behaviors.
3. Extend the reach and transform the financing of health care services.

REFERENCES

Aalsma, M. C., K. S. Lau, A. J. Perkins, K. Schwartz, W. Tu, S. E. Wiehe, P. Monahan, and M. B. Rosenman. 2016. Mortality of youth offenders along a continuum of justice system involvement. *American Journal of Preventive Medicine* 50(3):303–310.

Adelman, R. D., L. L. Tmanova, D. Delgado, S. Dion, and M. S. Lachs. 2014. Caregiver burden: A clinical review. *Journal of the American Medical Association* 311(10):1052–1060.

Adler, N. E., and D. H. Rehkopf. 2008. US disparities in health: Descriptions, causes, and mechanisms. *Annual Reveiw of Public Health* 29:235–252.

Almond, D., K. Y. Chay, and M. Greenstone. 2006. Civil Rights, the War on Poverty, and Black-White Convergence in Infant Mortality in the Rural South and Mississippi. MIT Department of Economics Working Paper 07–04.

Arias, E. 2015. United States life tables, 2011. *National Vital Statistics Reports* 64.

Avendano, M., M. M. Glymour, J. Banks, and J. P. Mackenbach. 2009. Health disadvantage in US adults aged 50 to 74 years: A comparison of the health of rich and poor Americans with that of Europeans. *American Journal of Public Health* 99(3):540–548.

Baicker, K., S. L. Taubman, H. L. Allen, M. Bernstein, J. H. Gruber, J. P. Newhouse, E. C. Schneider, B. J. Wright, A. M. Zaslavsky, and A. N. Finkelstein. 2013. The Oregon experiment—effects of Medicaid on clinical outcomes. *New England Journal of Medicine* 368(18):1713–1722.

Bartlett, S., J. Klerman, P. Wilde, L. Olsho, C. Logan, M. Blocklin, M. Beauregard, and A. Enver. 2014. Evaluation of the Healthy Incentives Pilot (HIP) Final Report. Washington, DC: USDA.

Berger, L. M., J. Hill, and J. Waldfogel. 2005. Maternity leave, early maternal employment and child health and development in the US. *Economic Journal* 115(501):F29-F47.

Bhatia, R., and M. Katz. 2001. Estimation of health benefits from a local living wage ordinance. *American Journal of Public Health* 91(9):1398–1402.

Bonnie, R., R. Johnson, B. Chemers, and J. E. Schuck, eds. 2013. *Reforming juvenile justice: A developmental approach.* Washington, DC: The National Academies Press.

Bradley, E., and L. Taylor. 2013. *The American health care paradox: Why spending more is getting us less.* New York: PublicAffairs.

Bradley, E. H., B. R. Elkins, J. Herrin, and B. Elbel. 2011. Health and social services expenditures: Associations with health outcomes. *BMJ Quality and Safety.* doi: 10.1136/bmjqs.2010.048363.

Braverman, P., and P. Murray. 2011. Health care for youth in the juvenile justice system. *Pediatrics* 128(6):1219–1235.

Brot-Goldberg, Z. C., A. Chandra, B. R. Handel, and J. T. Kolstad. 2015. What Does a Deductible Do? The Impact of Cost Sharing on Health Care Prices, Quantities, and Spending Dynamics. National Bureau of Economic Research Working Paper 21632.

Burke, M. P., E. A. Frongillo, S. J. Jones, B. B. Bell, and H. Hartline-Grafton. 2016. Household food insecurity is associated with greater growth in body mass index among female children from kindergarten through eighth grade. *Journal of Hunger & Environmental Nutrition* 11(2):227–241.

Campbell, F., G. Conti, J. J. Heckman, S. H. Moon, R. Pinto, E. Pungello, and Y. Pan. 2014. Early childhood investments substantially boost adult health. *Science* 343(6178):1478–1485.

Capistrant, B., J. Moon, L. Berkman, and M. Glymour. 2011. Current and long-term spousal caregiving and onset of cardiovascular disease. *Journal of Epidemiology and Community Health* 66(10):951–956

Capistrant, B. D., J. R. Moon, and M. M. Glymour. 2012. Spousal caregiving and incident hypertension. *American Journal of Hypertension* 25(4):437–443.

Case, A., and A. Deaton. 2015. Rising morbidity and mortality in midlife among white non-Hispanic Americans in the 21st century. *Proceedings of the National Academy of Sciences of the United States of America* 112(49):15078–15083.

Chetty, R., M. Stepner, S. Abraham, S. Lin, B. Scuderi, N. Turner, A. Bergeron, and D. Cutler. 2016. The association between income and life expectancy in the United States, 2001–2014. *Journal of the American Medical Association* 315(16):1750–1766.

Cheung, H. C., A. Shen, S. Oo, H. Tilahun, M. J. Cohen, and S. A. Berkowitz. 2015. Peer reviewed: Food insecurity and body mass index: A longitudinal mixed methods study, Chelsea, MA, 2009–2013. *Preventing Chronic Disease* 12:E125.

Cloud, D. H., J. Parsons, and A. Delany-Brumsey. 2014. Addressing mass incarceration: A clarion call for public health. *American Journal of Public Health* 104(3): 389–391.

Colchero, M. A., B. M. Popkin, J. A. Rivera, and S. W. Ng. 2016. Beverage purchases from stores in Mexico under the excise tax on sugar-sweetened beverages: Observational study. *BMJ* 352:h6704.

Community Preventive Services Task Force. 2015. Promoting health equity through education programs and policies: Center-based early childhood education. *Guide to Community Preventive Services.* Available at http://www.

thecommunityguide.org/healthequity/education/centerbasedprograms.html (accessed May 11, 2016).

Currie, J., and H. Schwandt. 2016. Inequality in mortality decreased among the young while increasing for older adults, 1990–2010. *Science* aaf1437.

Cutler, D. M. 2014. *The quality cure.* Berkeley, CA: University of California Press.

Cutler, D. M. 2015. Payment reform is about to become a reality. *Journal of the American Medical Association* 313(16):1606–1607.

Cylus, J., M. M. Glymour, and M. Avendano. 2014. Do generous unemployment benefit programs reduce suicide rates? A state fixed-effect analysis covering 1968–2008. *American Journal of Epidemiology* 180(1):45–52.

Cylus, J., M. M. Glymour, and M. Avendano. 2015. Health effects of unemployment benefit program generosity. *American Journal of Public Health* 105(2):317–323.

Dahl, G. B., L. Lochner, and National Bureau of Economic Research. 2005. The Impact of Family Income on Child Achievement. NBER Working Paper 11279. Cambridge, MA: National Bureau of Economic Research.

Daniel, A. E. 2007. Care of the mentally ill in prisons: Challenges and solutions. *Journal of the American Academy of Psychiatry and the Law* 35(4):406–410.

Deb, P., W. T. Gallo, P. Ayyagari, J. M. Fletcher, and J. L. Sindelar. 2011. The effect of job loss on overweight and drinking. *Journal of Health Economics* 30(2):317–327.

Donny, E. C., R. L. Denlinger, J. W. Tidey, J. S. Koopmeiners, N. L. Benowitz, R. G. Vandrey, M. al'Absi, S. G. Carmella, P. M. Cinciripini, S. S. Dermody, D. J. Drobes, S. S. Hecht, J. Jensen, T. Lane, C. T. Le, F. J. McClernon, I. D. Montoya, S. E. Murphy, J. D. Robinson, M. L. Stitzer, A. A. Strasser, H. Tindle, and D. K. Hatsukami. 2015. Randomized trial of reduced-nicotine standards for cigarettes. *New England Journal of Medicine* 373(14):1340–1349.

Donoff, B., J. E. McDonough, and C. A. Riedy. 2014. Integrating oral and general health care. *New England Journal of Medicine* 371(24):22–47.

Drucker, E. 2013. *A plague of prisons: The epidemiology of mass incarceration in America.* New York: The New Press.

Duncan, G. J., and K. Magnuson. 2013. Investing in preschool programs. *Journal of Economic Perspectives* 27(2):109.

Duncan, G. J., and R. J. Murnane. 2014. Restoring opportunity: *The crisis of inequality and the challenge for American education.* Cambridge, MA: Harvard Education Press.

Evans, W. N., C. L. Garthwaite, and National Bureau of Economic Research. 2010. Giving Mom a Break: The Impact of Higher EITC Payments on Maternal Health. NBER working Paper 16296. Cambridge, MA: National Bureau of Economic Research.

Fiore, M. C. 2016. Tobacco control in the Obama era: Substantial progress, remaining challenges. *New England Journal of Medicine* 375:1410–1412. doi: 10.1056/NEJMp1607850.

Frank, R. G., and S. A. Glied. 2006. *Better but not well: Mental health policy in the United States since 1950.* Baltimore: Johns Hopkins University Press.

Freudenberg, N., and D. Heller. 2016. A review of opportunities to improve the health of people involved in the criminal justice system in the United States. *Annual Review of Public Health* 37(1):313–333.

Gallo, W. T., E. H. Bradley, M. Siegel, and S. V. Kasl. 2000. Health effects of involuntary job loss among older workers: Findings from the health and retirement survey. *Journals of Gerontology Series B: Psychological Sciences and Social Sciences* 55(3):S131–S140.

Gallup Surveys. 2016. Gallup guns. Available at http://www.gallup.com/poll/1645/guns.aspx (accessed August 11, 2016).

Gault, B., H. Hartmann, A. Hegewisch, J. Milli, and L. Reichlin. 2014. Paid Parental Leave in the United States: What the Data Tell Us About Access, Usage, and Economic and Health Benefits. Institute for Women's Policy Research.

Gelman, A., and J. Auerbach. 2015. Age-aggregation bias in mortality trends. *Proceedings of the National Academy of Sciences of the United States of America* 113(7):E816–E817.

Glied, S., and M. Neidell. 2010. The economic value of teeth. *Journal of Human Resources* 45(2):468–496.

Goldman, D.P., G. F. Joyce, and Y. Zheng. 2007. Prescription drug cost sharing: Associations with medication and medical utilization and spending and health. *Journal of the American Medical Association* 298(1):61–69.

Hamad, R., and D. H. Rehkopf. 2015. Poverty, pregnancy, and birth outcomes: A study of the earned income tax credit. *Paediatric and Perinatal Epidemiology* 29(5):444–452.

Hamad, R., and D. H. Rehkopf. 2016. Poverty and child development: A longitudinal study of the impact of the earned income tax credit. *American Journal of Epidemiology* 183(9):775–784.

Hammett, T. M. 2001. Making the case for health interventions in correctional facilities. *Journal of Urban Health* 78(2):236–240.

Hart, B., and T. R. Risley. 2003. The early catastrophe: The 30 million word gap by age 3. *American Educator* 27(1):4–9.

Hertzman, C., and T. Boyce. 2010. How experience gets under the skin to create gradients in developmental health. *Annual Review of Public Health* 31:329–347.

Heymann, J., A. Raub, and A. Earle. 2011. Creating and using new data sources to analyze the relationship between social policy and global health: The case of maternal leave. *Public Health Reports* 126:127–134.

Hoynes, H. W., D. Miller, and D. Simon. 2012. The effect of the earned income tax credit on infant health. *National Bureau of Economic Research Bulletin on Aging and Health* (3):2.

Internal Revenue Service (IRS). 2016. *About EITC*. https://www.eitc.irs.gov/EITC-Central/abouteitc (accessed September 19, 2016).

Jeffcoat, M. K., R. L. Jeffcoat, P. A. Gladowski, J. B. Bramson, and J. J. Blum. 2014. Impact of periodontal therapy on general health: Evidence from insurance data for five systemic conditions. *American Journal of Preventive Medicine* 47(2):166–174.

Kaplan, G. A., N. Ranjit, and S. Burgard. 2008. Lifting gates, lengthening lives: Did civil rights policies improve the health of African American women in the 1960s and 1970s? Pp. 145–169 in *Making Americans healthier: Social and economic policy as health policy*. New York: Russell Sage Foundation.

Keating, D., and S. Simonton. 2008. Health effects of human development policies. Pp. 61–94 in *Making Americans healthier: Social and economic policy as health policy,* edited by G. A. Kaplan, J. S. House, R. F. Schoeni, and H. A. Pollack. New York: Russell Sage Foundation.

Knudsen, E. I., J. J. Heckman, J. L. Cameron, and J. P. Shonkoff. 2006. Economic, neurobiological, and behavioral perspectives on building America's future workforce. *Proceedings of the National Academy of Sciences of the United States of America* 103(27):10155–10162.

Krieger, N., D. H. Rehkopf, J. T. Chen, P. D. Waterman, E. Marcelli, and M. Kennedy. 2008. The fall and rise of US inequities in premature mortality: 1960–2002. *PLoS Medicine* 5(2):e46.

Laing, Y., and M. Katz. 2012. Coronary arteries, myocardial infarction, and history. *New England Journal of Medicine* 366(13):1258–1260.

Lasser, K. E., D. U. Himmelstein, and S. Woolhandler. 2006. Access to care, health status, and health disparities in the United States and Canada: Results of a cross-national population-based survey. *American Journal of Public Health* 96(7):1300–1307.

Lohr, K. N., R. H. Brook, C. J. Kamberg, G. A. Goldberg, A. Leibowitz, J. Keesey, D. Reboussin, and J. P. New-house. 1986. Use of medical care in the Rand Health Insurance Experiment: Diagnosis- and service-specific analyses in a randomized controlled trial. *Medical Care* 24(9):S1–S87.

Long, V., S. Cates, J. Blitstein, K. Deehy, P. Williams, R. Morgan, J. Fantacone, K. Kosa, L. Bell, and J. Hersey. 2013. Supplemental Nutrition Assistance Program Education and Evaluation Study (Wave II). Prepared by Altarum Institute for the US Department of Agriculture, Food and Nutrition Service.

Lundberg, O., M. A. Yngwe, M. K. Stjarne, J. I. Elstad, T. Ferrarini, O. Kangas, T. Norstrom, J. Palme, and J. Fritzell. 2008. The role of welfare state principles and generosity in social policy programmes for public health: An international comparative study. *Lancet* 372(9650):1633–1640.

McGinnis, J. M., P. Williams-Russo, and J. R. Knickman. 2002. The case for more active policy attention to health promotion. *Health Affairs* 21(2):78–93.

Meltzer, D. O., and Z. Chen. 2011. The impact of minimum wage rates on body weight in the United States. Pp. 17–34 in *Economic aspects of obesity.* Chicago: University of Chicago Press.

Michaels, D. 2012. OSHA does not kill jobs; it helps prevent jobs from killing workers. *American Journal of Industrial Medicine* 55:961–963.

Miller, M., and D. Hemenway. 2008. Guns and suicide in the United States. *New England Journal of Medicine* 359(10):989–991.

Murphy, S., K. Kochanek, J. Xu, and E. Arias. 2015. Mortality in the United States, 2014. NCHS Data Brief 229.

Nabel, E. G., and E. Braunwald. 2012. A tale of coronary artery disease and myocardial infarction. *New England Journal of Medicine* 366(1):54–63.

NASEM (National Academies of Science, Engineering, and Medicine). 2016. *Accounting for social risk factors in Medicare payment: Criteria, factors, and methods.* Washington, DC: The National Academies Press.

National Center for Health Statistics. 2015. Health, United States, 2015—Individual Charts and Tables: Spreadsheet, PDF, and PowerPoint files, Table 14. Available at http://www.cdc.gov/nchs/data/hus/hus15.pdf#014 (accessed April 30, 2016).

National Partnership for Women and Families. 2016. *Family and Medical Leave Act.* http://www.national-partnership.org/issues/work-family/fmla.html (accessed September 19, 2016).

Nichols, A., and J. Rothstein. 2015. The earned income tax credit. In *Economics of means-tested transfer programs in the United States, volume 1.* Chicago: University of Chicago Press.

NRC (National Research Council). 2013. *Reforming juvenile justice: A developmental approach.* Washington, DC: The National Academies Press.

NRC and IOM (Institute of Medicine). 2013a. *U.S. health in international perspective: Shorter lives, poorer health.* Washington, DC: The National Academies Press.

NRC and IOM. 2013b. *Health and incarceration: A workshop summary.* Washington, DC: The National Academies Press. doi:10.17226/18372.

Nyweide, D. J., W. Lee, T. T. Cuerdon, H. H. Pham, M. Cox, R. Rajkumar, and P. H. Conway. 2015. Association of pioneer accountable care organizations vs traditional Medicare fee for service with spending, utilization, and patient experience. *Journal of the American Medical Association* 313(21):2152–2161.

Office of the Surgeon General. 2001. *Youth violence: A report of the Surgeon General.* Rockville, MD, Office of the Surgeon General, National Center for Injury Prevention and Control, National Institute of Mental Health, and Center for Mental Health Services.

Olds, D. 2016. Building evidence to improve maternal and child health. *Lancet* 387(10014):105–107.

Olds, D., H. Kitzman, R. Clole, J. Robinson, K. Sidora, D. W. Luckey, C. R. Henderson, C. Hanks, J. Bondy, and J. Holmberg. 2004. Effect of nurse homevisiting on maternal life course and child development: Age 6 followup results of a randomized trial. *Pediatrics* 114:1550–1559.

Olds, D. L., J. Robinson, R. O'Brien, D. W. Luckey, L. M. Pettitt, C. R. Henderson, Jr., R. K. Ng, K. L. Sheff, J. Korfmacher, S. Hiatt, and A. Talmi. 2002. Home visiting by paraprofessionals and by nurses: A randomized, controlled trial. *Pediatrics* 110(3):486–496.

Olds, D. L., H. Kitzman, M. D. Knudtson, E. Anson, J. A. Smith, and R. Cole. 2014. Effect of home visiting by nurses on maternal and child mortality: Results of a 2-decade follow-up of a randomized clinical trial. *JAMA Pediatrics* 168(9):800–806.

Olshansky, S. J., D. J. Passaro, R. C. Hershow, J. Layden, B. A. Carnes, J. Brody, L. Hayflick, R. N. Butler, D. B. Allison, and D. S. Ludwig. 2005. A potential decline in life expectancy in the United States in the 21st century. *New England Journal of Medicine* 352(11):1138–1145.

OSHA (Occupational Safety and Health Administration). 2016. OSHA Commonly Used Statistics. Available at https://www.osha.gov/oshstats/commonstats.html (accessed August 21, 2016).

Prins, S. J. 2014. Prevalence of mental illnesses in US state prisons: A systematic review. *Psychiatric Services* 65(7):862–872.

Rajkumar, R., P. H. Conway, and M. Tavenner. 2014. CMS—engaging multiple payers in payment reform. *Journal of the American Medical Association* 311(19): 1967–1968.

Richardson, E. G., and D. Hemenway. 2011. Homicide, suicide, and unintentional firearm fatality: Comparing the United States with other high-income countries, 2003. *Journal of Trauma and Acute Care Surgery* 70(1):238–243.

Rudolph, K. E., E. A. Stuart, J. S. Vernick, and D. W. Webster. 2015. Association between Connecticut's permit-to-purchase handgun law and homicides. *American Journal of Public Health* 105(8):e49-e54.

Schwartz, A. L., M. E. Chernew, B. E. Landon, and J. M. McWilliams. 2015. Changes in low-value services in year 1 of the Medicare Pioneer Accountable Care Organization program. *JAMA Internal Medicine* 175(11):1815–1825.

Shearer, G. 2010. Prevention provisions in the Affordable Care Act. American Public Health Association Issue Brief.

Siddiqi, A., R. Brown, Q. C. Nguyen, R. Loopstra, and I. Kawachi. 2015. Cross-national comparison of socio-economic inequalities in obesity in the United States and Canada. *International Journal for Equity in Health* 14(1):1.

Sills, M. R., M. Hall, J. D. Colvin, M. L. Macy, G. J. Cutler, J. L. Bettenhausen, R. B. Morse, K. A. Auger, J. L. Raphael, L. M. Gottlieb, E. S. Fieldston, and S. S. Shah. 2016. Association of social determinants with children's hospitals' preventable readmissions performance. *JAMA Pediatrics* 170(4):350–358.

Sommers, B. D., S. K. Long, and K. Baicker. 2014. Changes in mortality after Massachusetts health care reform: A quasi-experimental study. *Annals of Internal Medicine* 160(9):585–593.

Song, Z., S. Rose, D. G. Safran, B. E. Landon, M. P. Day, and M. E. Chernew. 2014. Changes in health care spending and quality 4 years into global payment. *New England Journal of Medicine* 371(18):1704–1714.

Sonik, R. A. 2016. Massachusetts inpatient Medicaid cost response to increased Supplemental Nutrition Assistance Program benefits. *American Journal of Public Health* 106(3):443–448.

Steege, A. L., S. L. Baron, S. M. Marsh, C. C. Menéndez, and J. R. Myers. 2014. Examining occupational health and safety disparities using national data: A cause for continuing concern. *American Journal of Industrial Medicine* 57(5):527–538.

Stone, C. and W. Chen. 2014. *Introduction to Unemployment Insurance.* http://www.cbpp.org/research/introduction-to-unemployment-insurance (accessed September 19, 2016).

Strully, K. W., D. H. Rehkopf, and Z. Xuan. 2010. Effects of prenatal poverty on infant health: State earned income tax credits and birth weight. *American Sociological Review* 75(4):534–562.

Tarone, R., and J. McLaughlin. 2012. Coronary arteries, myocardial infarction, and history. *New England Journal of Medicine* 366(13):1258–1260.

Teplin, L. A., G. M. McClelland, K. M. Abram, and D. Mileusnic. 2005. Early violent death among delinquent youth: A prospective longitudinal study. *Pediatrics* 115(6):1586–1593.

The Sentencing Project. 2016. *Criminal Justice Facts.* http://www.sentencingproject.org/criminal-justice-facts/ (accessed September 19, 2016).

Tompa, E., C. Kalcevich, M. Foley, C. McLeod, S. Hogg Johnson, K. Cullen, E. MacEachen, Q. Mahood, and E. Irvin. 2016. A systematic literature review of the effectiveness of occupational health and safety regulatory enforcement. *American Journal of Industrial Medicine* 59(11):919–933.

Travis, J., B. Western, and S. Redburn, eds. 2014. *The growth of incarceration in the United States: Exploring causes and consequences.* Washington, DC: The National Academies Press.

US Department of Health and Human Services (HHS). 2000. Oral Health in America: A Report of the Surgeon General. Rockville, MD: US Department of Health and Human Services, National Institute of Dental and Craniofacial Research, National Institutes of Health.

US Department of Health and Human Services. 2016. HHS.gov Health Care. Available at http://www.hhs.gov/healthcare/ (accessed May 15, 2016).

van Hedel, K., M. Avendano, L. F. Berkman, M. Bopp, P. Deboosere, O. Lundberg, P. Martikainen, G. Menvielle, F. J. van Lenthe, and J. P. Mackenbach. 2014. The contribution of national disparities to international differences in mortality between the United States and 7 European countries. *American Journal of Public Health* 105(4):e112–e119.

Weber-Raley, L., and E. Smith. 2015. Caregiving in the U.S.: 2015 Report. National Alliance for Caregiving and the AARP Public Policy Institute.

Wolff, J. L., B. C. Spillman, V. A. Freedman, and J. D. Kasper. 2016. A national profile of family and unpaid caregivers who assist older adults with health care activities. *JAMA Internal Medicine* 176(3):372–379.

Woolf, S. H., and L. Y. Aron. 2013. The US health disadvantage relative to other high-income countries: Findings from a National Research Council/Institute of Medicine report. *Journal of the American Medical Association* 309(8):771–772.

Xu, J., S. Murphy, K. Kochanek, and B. Bastian. 2016. Deaths: Final data for 2013. *National Vital Statistics Reports* 64(2). US Department of Health and Human Services, Centers for Disease Control and Prevention, National Center for Health Statistics.

AUTHOR INFORMATION

Nancy E. Adler, PhD, is Lisa and John Pritzker Professor of Medical Psychology in the Departments of Psychiatry and Pediatrics, and Director, Center for Health and Community, University of California, San Francisco. **David M. Cutler, PhD,** is the Otto Eckstein Professor of Applied Economics, Department of Economics, Harvard University. **Jonathan E. Fielding, MD, MPH,** is Distinguished Professor, School of Public Health, University of California, Los Angeles. **Sandro Galea, MD, DrPH,** is Dean and Robert A Knox Professor, School of Public Health, Boston University. **Maria Glymour, ScD,** is Associate Professor in the Department of Epidemiology and Biostatistics, University of California, San Francisco. **Howard K. Koh,**

MD, MPH, is the Harvey V. Fineberg Professor of the Practice of Public Health Leadership at the Harvard T.H. Chan School of Public Health and Harvard Kennedy School, and is former Assistant Secretary for Health, US Department of Health and Human Services. **David Satcher, MD, PhD,** is Director, Satcher Health Leadership Institute, and is Poussaint-Satcher-Cosby Chair in Mental Health, Louis W. Sullivan National Center for Primary Care, Morehouse School of Medicine.

4

PREPARING FOR BETTER HEALTH AND HEALTH CARE FOR AN AGING POPULATION

John W. Rowe, MD, Lisa F. Berkman, PhD, Linda P. Fried, MD, MPH, Terry T. Fulmer, PhD, RN, FAAN, James S. Jackson, PhD, Mary D. Naylor, PhD, RN, FAAN, William D. Novelli, MA, S. Jay Olshansky, PhD, and Robyn Stone, DrPH

The proportion of the US population over 65 years old is increasing dramatically, and the group over 85 years old, the "oldest old," is the most rapidly growing segment. People who survive into higher ages in America, which itself is an aging society, face a suite of competing forces that will yield healthy life extension for some and life extension accompanied by notable increases in frailty and disability for many. We spend more, for worse outcomes, than many if not all other developed countries, including care for older persons. Looking forward, our health care system is unprepared to provide the medical and support services needed for previously unimagined numbers of sick older persons, and we are not investing in keeping people healthy into their highest ages. This paper summarizes the opportunities for valuable policy advances in several important spheres that are central to the health and well-being of older persons. In all of them, concerns regarding disparities in health and the severe concentration of risk among the poorest and least educated members of our society present special opportunities for progress and these issues are addressed in detail in other papers in the *Vital Directions* series.

KEY TRENDS IN DEMOGRAPHY AND HEALTH EQUITY IN THE 21ST CENTURY

Aging and health intersect both at the level of the individual and at the level of the entire society. For individuals, the extension of life achieved in the past century as a product of advances in public health, socioeconomic development, and medical technology constitutes a monumental achievement for humanity. Most people born today will live past the age of 65 years, and many will survive past the age of 85 years, but life extension comes with a Faustian trade. Modern medical advances will no doubt endure, but it is possible that continued success in attacking fatal diseases could expose the saved population to a higher risk of extreme frailty and disability as disabling diseases accumulate in aging bodies.

The aging of our society, reflecting the rapidly increasing proportion of older people relative to the rest of the population, is a product of two major demographic events: the substantial increase in life expectancy and the baby boom. At the societal level, this population shift will place great pressure on our fragile systems of health care, public health, and other supports for older persons. Past increases in life expectancy are impressive, but the more recent news is not as good in America. In the middle 1980s, life expectancy of women in the United States was about the average of that in Organisation for Economic Co-operation and Development (OECD) countries. Since 2000, we have ranked last, and the gap between the United States and other OECD countries in health status is also widening. Contributors to the absolute increases in poor health experienced by the most disadvantaged Americans, the poor and less educated, include the concentration in these groups of multiple risk factors, including smoking, obesity, gun violence, and increased teenage pregnancy (NASEM, 2015; NRC, 2012; Schroeder, 2016).

As America ages, it becomes more diverse. By 2030, the non-Hispanic white population will be the numerical minority in the United States. Increased longevity is prevalent among several ethnic and racial groups (such as black, Chinese, Japanese, Cuban, and Mexican American). Younger Hispanics, the most rapidly growing group in our population, are generally US-born and have both higher fertility rates and much higher disability rates than older Hispanics, who are more likely to be foreign-born.

As discussed in detail in other discussion papers in the *Vital Directions* series, owing largely to socioeconomic factors, many racial and ethnic groups, especially blacks, are at disproportionate risk for adverse health outcomes over the life course compared with whites. Many factors may contribute to the disparity, including biologic disposition to dietary and lifestyle behaviors and failure to receive adequate health care. Given complex sociohistorical contexts, comparisons between racial and ethnic groups may be less useful than comparisons among people within groups—for example, according to socioeconomic status (SES)—in uncovering specific mechanisms.

SES-based racial and ethnic group disparities exist in both physical and mental well-being, even where access to health care is equal. Although targeted policy considerations regarding disparities are not provided here, it is important to understand that disparities constitute an important target for improvements in each of the key areas we identify for action. Issues of health disparity are addressed more specifically in the *Vital Directions* Perspective on addressing health disparities and the social determinants of health (see Chapter 3; Adler et al., 2016).

KEY OPPORTUNITIES FOR PROGRESS

Enhancing Delivery of Effective Care for Those Who Have Multiple Chronic Conditions

The health care needs of older adults coping with multiple chronic conditions, which account for a vast majority of Medicare expenditures, are poorly managed (MedPAC, 2014). Effective management that engages older adults, family caregivers, and clinicians in collaboratively identifying patients' needs and goals and in implementing individualized care plans is essential to achieve higher-value health care. Evidence-based approaches to care management are available, but the uptake and spread of most models have been sporadic and slow.

Many effective approaches to enhancing delivery of care for older persons have been developed; the problems have generally been in dissemination and implementation, often owing to lack of funding. Examples of such programs are the following:

- *Care options in varied settings: the Transitional Care Model (TCM).* The TCM is an advanced-practice, nurse-coordinated, team-based care model that targets at-risk community-based older adults who have multiple chronic conditions and their family caregivers. In several clinical trials funded by the National Institutes of Health, the TCM has consistently demonstrated improvements in patients' care experiences, health, and quality-of-life outcomes while decreasing total health care costs (Naylor et al., 2004).
- *Care options in nursing homes: the Interventions to Reduce Acute Care Transfers (INTERACT) program.* The INTERACT program includes a variety of communication, decision-support, advance care planning and quality-improvement tools, all designed to support nursing home staff efforts to prevent avoidable rehospitalizations of residents. In a typical 100-bed nursing home, the INTERACT program was estimated to reduce rehospitalizations by an average of 25 per year for a net savings of $117,000 per facility (Ouslander et al., 2011).

- *Care options in the community: home-based primary care.* Programs that deliver team-based primary care in the home for people who have advancing chronic conditions have been shown to be very effective by the Department of Veterans Affairs and in a Medicare demonstration (Independence at Home).

Delivery-of-Care Policy Alternatives

- Widespread adoption of high-value, rigorously evidence-based best practices with demonstrated longer-term value that target older adults, such as those listed above (Naylor et al., 2014), should be encouraged. Resources now targeted to short-term results for older adults who have multiple chronic conditions, such as those focused on reducing 30-day rehospitalizations, should be redirected to longer-term solutions that align closely with the needs and preferences of this population.
- New models of care for older adults in such neglected areas as prevention, long-term care, and palliative care should be developed.
- The Public Health Service should strengthen its efforts, such as the "Healthy People" program, to foster a prevention and health-promotion agenda for longer lives with a deep grounding in socioeconomic determinants of health.
- Robust metrics of effective care management for vulnerable older adults should be developed with emphasis on outcomes that matter to patients and their family caregivers.

STRENGTHENING THE ELDER CARE WORKFORCE

One of the greatest challenges to the capacity of our health care system to deliver needed high-quality services to the growing elderly population resides in the current and likely future inadequacy of our workforce, including both the numbers of workers and the quality of their training.

The Institute of Medicine, now the National Academy of Medicine, drew attention to this issue first in 1978 (IOM, 1978), again in 1987 (Rowe et al., 1987), and more recently in its 2008 report, *Retooling for an Aging America*, which reported an in-depth analysis of the future demand for and the recruitment and retention challenges surrounding all components of the geriatric health care workforce. Despite increased awareness of the impending workforce crisis, the problems persist almost a decade later.

The Professional Health Care Workforce

We have an alarming dearth of adequately prepared geriatricians, nurses, social workers, and public health professionals. The number of board-certified geriatricians, estimated at 7,500, is less than half the estimated need, and the pipeline of geriatricians in training is grossly inadequate. The reasons are many, but a prominent impediment is the substantial financial disadvantage facing geriatricians. Working in fee-for-service systems, which continue to dominate health care payment, internists or family physicians who complete additional training to become geriatricians can expect substantial decreases in their income despite their enhanced expertise. The reason for this is that the care they provide is more time intensive and all their patients will be on Medicare or on Medicare and Medicaid simultaneously ("dual users"), as opposed to the mix of Medicare and commercially insured patients served by most general physicians. The failure of Medicare to acknowledge the value of the enhanced expertise punishes those dedicated to careers in serving the elderly (IOM, 2008). Approaches are needed not only in the fee-for-service system that accounts for most of Medicare but also in increasingly important population-based approaches such as accountable care organizations (ACOs).

Nursing is also deficient in geriatrics. Fewer than 1 percent of registered nurses and fewer than 3 percent of advanced-practice registered nurses are certified in geriatrics. One of the major impediments for nurses is related to the lack of sufficiently trained faculty in geriatric nursing. The same can be said of pharmacists, physical therapists, social workers, occupational therapists, and the full array of allied health disciplines (IOM, 2008).

Besides the insufficient numbers, there is a growing awareness that the greater problem—which may be amenable to more rapid improvement if appropriate policies are put into place—is the lack of sufficient training and competence of all physicians and nurses who treat older patients in the diagnosis and management of common geriatric problems. This issue of geriatric competence of all health care providers may be the number one problem we face in delivering needed care for older persons.

An additional critically important issue is related to the lack of effective coordination of specialists such as geriatricians with primary care providers. Such lack of coordination seems worst in traditional fee-for-service settings and may be less severe in population-based settings, such as ACOs.

Direct Care Workers

Direct care workers—certified nursing assistants (CNAs), home health aides, and home care and personal care aides (1.4 million in 2012)—provide an estimated 70 percent to 80 percent of the paid hands-on care to older adults in nursing homes, assisted-living homes, and other home- and community-based settings (Eldercare Workforce Alliance, 2014). From 2010 to 2020, available jobs in those occupations are expected to grow by 48 percent (in contrast with all occupational growth of just 14 percent) at the same time that the availability of people most likely to fill the occupations is projected to decline (Stone, 2015).

Recruiting and retaining competent, stable, direct care workers are serious problems in many communities around the country. Turnover rates are above 50 percent. Many factors contribute to the turnover, but two major issues are low wages (median hourly wages of CNAs, home health aides, and personal care workers in 2014 were $12.06, $10.28, and $9.83, respectively) (BLS, 2016a,b,c) and inadequate training and supervision. Federal regulations require CNAs and home health aides employed by Medicare- or Medicaid-certified organizations to have at least 75 hours of training; that is less than some states require for crossing guards and dog groomers. There are no federal training requirements for home care and personal care workers.

An important issue related to both the professional and the direct elder care components of the workforce is ensuring competence in the recognition, prevention, and management of elder abuse and neglect—a problem that may be especially critical in underprivileged populations.

Workforce Policy Alternatives

Enhancing Geriatric Competence—Priority Considerations

- Physician and nurse training in all settings where older adults receive care, including nursing homes, assisted-living facilities, and patients' homes.
- Demonstration of competence in the care of older adults as a criterion for all licensure, certification, and maintenance of certification for health care professionals.
- Federal requirements for training of at least 120 hours for CNAs and home health aides and demonstration of competence in the care of older adults as a criterion for certification. States should also establish minimum training requirements for personal care aides.
- Incorporation by the Centers for Medicare & Medicaid Services (CMS) of direct care workers into team-based approaches to caring for chronically disabled older adults.

Increasing Recruitment and Retention—Priority Considerations

- Public and private payers providing financial incentives to increase the number of geriatric specialists in all health professions.
- CMS extending graduate medical education payments to cover costs of residency training to public health physicians and nurses to support their training in geriatric care and health promotion.
- All payers including a specific enhancement of reimbursement for clinical services delivered to older adults by practitioners who have a certification of special expertise in geriatrics.

- The direct care workforce being adequately compensated with a living wage commensurate with the skills and knowledge required to perform high-quality work.
- States and the federal government instituting programs for loan forgiveness, scholarships, and direct financial incentives for professionals who become geriatric specialists. One such mechanism should include the development of a National Geriatric Service Corps, modeled after the National Health Service Corps.
- The Department of Labor and the Department of Health and Human Services (specifically, CMS and the Health Resources and Services Administration) developing apprenticeship opportunities for direct care workers in the whole array of long-term support and service settings.

SOCIAL ENGAGEMENT AND WORK-RELATED STRATEGIES TO ENHANCE HEALTH IN LATE LIFE

It is now widely accepted that social factors play an important role in determining health status. As mentioned previously, the issues of social determinants of health status are addressed in detail in other discussion papers in the *Vital Directions* series. Nonetheless, one aspect of particular importance to older persons deserves attention here. A vast body of research indicates that the degree to which men and women are "connected" to others, including volunteerism and work for pay, is an important determinant of their well-being.

Engagement

The effect of deficient social networks and relationships on mortality is similar to that of other well-identified medical and behavioral risk factors. Conversely, social engagement—through friends, family, volunteering, or continuing to work—has many physical and mental benefits.

Over the past 15–20 years, older people have become more isolated and new cohorts of middle-aged adults, especially those 55–64 years old, have shown a major drop in engagement. In addition, national volunteer efforts—such as Foster Grandparents program, the Retired and Senior Volunteer Program (RSVP), and the Senior Companions program—reach only a small percentage of the eligible target audience and have long waiting lists. Programs with high impact on the volunteers and recipients, such as the Experience Corps, have an inadequate number of high-impact opportunities because of low financing.

Work

An impressive and growing body of evidence suggests that working is health promoting as well as economically beneficial. With overall increasing healthy life expectancy, many Americans will be able to work longer than they do now. Working longer will be health promoting for many Americans, providing not only additional financial security but also continued opportunities for social engagement and participation in society. Leave policies related to employee and family sickness are essential to enable workers to remain in the workforce until retirement and at the same time provide social support for their families.

Work-Related and Engagement-Related Policy Alternatives—Priority Considerations

- Strengthening leave policies related to employee and family sickness.
- Evaluating engagement as a core competence of the care plan for older adults.
- Restoring Medicare as the primary payer for health insurance claims for older workers of all employers, with a major communication effort to bring this to the attention of employers and beneficiaries.
- Incentivizing work redesign to increase schedule control and increase opportunities for work–family balance.
- Providing a choice of retirement options so that people who cannot continue to work full time or in their previous jobs because of functional limitations can remain engaged in flexible, part-time, seasonal, or less demanding roles.
- Strengthening on-the-job and community college training programs to hone skills and assist middle- and later-life workers in continuing to work or in transitioning to new types of jobs.
- Providing business tax credits for reinvestment in skill development.
- Strengthening neighborhoods through transportation and housing policies are needed that aim to keep older men and women engaged in their communities.
- Reengineering federal volunteer programs such as Foster Grandparents, RSVP, and Senior Companions to serve a much larger portion of the potential beneficiaries.
- Broadly disseminating intergenerational volunteer programs, such as Experience Corps, which benefit youth and seniors.

ADVANCED ILLNESS AND END-OF-LIFE CARE

At some point, the vast majority of older people will face advanced illness, which occurs when one or more conditions become serious enough that general health and functioning decline, curative treatment begins to lose its effect, and quality of life increasingly becomes the proper focus of care. Many such people receive care that is uncoordinated, fragmented, and unable to meet their values and preferences. That often results in unnecessary hospitalizations, unwanted treatment, adverse drug reactions, conflicting medical advice, and higher cost of care.

In September 2015, the Institute of Medicine released *Dying in America: Improving Quality and Honoring Individual Preferences Near the End of Life.* The report indicated that there exists a strong body of evidence that can guide valuable improvements in this area, including not only enhancements in the quality and availability of needed care and supports but also strengthening of our overall health system. The report noted a number of important topics to be addressed, including fragmented care, inadequate information, widespread lack of timely referral to palliative care, inadequate advanced care planning, and insufficient clinician–patient discourse about values and preferences in the selection of appropriate treatment to ensure that care is aligned with what matters most to patients.

Regarding support for clinicians, *Dying in America* found that there is insufficient attention to palliative care in medical school and nursing school curricula, that educational silos impede the development of professional teams, and that there are deficits in equipping physicians with communication skills. Since *Dying in America* was issued, there has been progress in many arenas, including the decision by CMS to pay for advance planning discussions by clinicians with their patients and continued development of innovative approaches to the delivery of palliative care, such as that adopted by Aspire Health, but critical gaps persist.

Advanced Illness and End-of-Life Care—Policy Alternatives

- Government and private health insurer coverage for the provision of comprehensive care for people who have advanced serious illness as they near the end of life.
- Access to skilled palliative care for all people who have advanced serious illness, including access to an interdisciplinary team, in all settings where they receive care, with an emphasis on programs based in the community.
- Standards for advanced-care planning that are measurable, actionable, and evidence based, with reimbursement tied to such standards.
- Appropriate training, certification, or licensure requirements for those who provide care for patients for advanced serious illness as they near the end of life.
- Integration of the financing of federal, state, and private medical and social services for people who have advanced serious illness as they near the end of life.
- Public education by public health organizations, the government, faith-based groups, and others about advanced-care planning and informed choice, as well as efforts to engender public support for health system and health policy reform.

- Federally required public reporting on quality measures, outcomes, and costs regarding care near the end of life (e.g., in the last year of life) in programs that it funds or administers (such as Medicare, Medicaid, and the Department of Veterans Affairs).

VITAL DIRECTIONS

We identify four vital directions for improvement in our capacity to enhance well-being and health care for older Americans:

1. *Develop new models of care delivery.* New models can increase efficiency and value of cost delivery in various care settings and are especially needed for the management of patients who have multiple chronic conditions. Many new evidence-based models are available but have not been widely adopted.
2. *Augment the elder care workforce.* There are and will be substantial deficiencies not only in the number of physicians, nurses, and direct care workers who have special training and expertise in geriatrics but in the competence of health care workers generally in the recognition and management of common geriatric problems. Addressing these quantitative and qualitative workforce gaps will increase access to high-quality and more efficient care for older persons.
3. *Promote the social engagement of older persons.* Engagement in society, whether through work for pay or through volunteering, is known to have substantial beneficial effects on several aspects of well-being in late life. Evidence suggests that older persons are becoming less engaged, and vigorous efforts to promote engagement can yield important benefits for them and for the productivity of society.
4. *Transform advanced illness care and care at the end of life.* Many people who have advanced illness and especially those nearing the end of life receive care that is uncoordinated, fragmented, and unable to meet their values and preferences. Wider dissemination of available, proven effective strategies can enhance well-being and dignity while avoiding unnecessary hospitalizations, unwanted treatment, adverse drug reactions, conflicting medical advice, and higher cost of care.

The suggestions offered in this paper are within reach, and none is expected to be associated with great cost. In many cases, they call for support of strategies that have been proved to be effective but have not been disseminated widely because of structural or funding limitations in our system. Useful change in all sectors will probably require several years, so urgent action is required now if we are to be prepared when the "age wave" hits. The price of failure would be great, not only with respect to inefficiency but with respect to continued misuse of precious resources, increases in functional incapacity and morbidity, and loss of dignity.

SUMMARY RECOMMENDATIONS FOR VITAL DIRECTIONS

1. Develop new models of care delivery.
2. Augment the elder care workforce.
3. Promote the social engagement of older persons.
4. Transform advanced illness care and care at the end of life.

REFERENCES

Adler, N., D. M. Cutler, J. E. Jonathan, S. Galea, M. Glymour, H. K. Koh, and D. Satcher. 2016. Addressing social determinants of health and health inequities. Discussion Paper, *Vital Directions for Health and Health Care Series.* Washington, DC: National Academy of Medicine. Available at http://nam. edu/wp-content/uploads/2016/09/addressing-social-determinants-of-health-and-health-inequities.pdf.

BLS (Bureau of Labor Statistics). 2016a. Nursing assistants and orderlies. In *Occupational outlook handbook.* Available at www.bls.gov/ooh/healthcare/nursing-assistants.htm (accessed March 10, 2016).

BLS. 2016b. Home health aides. In *Occupational outlook handbook.* Available at www.bls.gov/ooh/healthcare/home-health-aides.htm (accessed March 10, 2016).

BLS. 2016c. Personal care aides. In *Occupational outlook handbook.* Available at www.bls.gov/oes/current/oes399021.htm (accessed March 10, 2016).

Eldercare Workforce Alliance. 2014. Advanced direct care worker. *Annals of Long-Term Care* 22(12):2–5.

IOM (Institute of Medicine). 1978. *Manpower policy for primary care (78–02).* Washington, DC: National Academy Press.

IOM. 2008. *Retooling for an aging America: Building the health care workforce.* Washington, DC: The National Academies Press.

IOM. 2015. *Dying in America: Improving quality and honoring individual preferences near the end of life.* Washington, DC: The National Academies Press. doi: 10.17226/18748.

MedPAC (Medicare Payment Advisory Commission). 2014. *MedPAC data book.* Washington, DC: Med-PAC. Available at http://www.medpac.gov/documents/publications/jun14databookentirereport. pdf?sfvrsn=1.

NASEM (National Academies of Sciences, Engineering, and Medicine). 2015. *The growing gap in life expectancy by income: Implications for federal programs and policy responses.* Washington, DC: The National Academies Press.

Naylor, M. D., D. A. Brooten, R. L. Campbell, G. Maislin, K. M. McCauley, and J. S. Schwartz. 2004.Transitional care of older adults hospitalized with heart failure: A randomized, controlled trial. *Journal of the American Geriatrics Society* 52(5):675–684.

Naylor, M. D., K. B. Hirschman, A. L. Hanlon, K. H. Bowles, C. Bradway, K. M. McCauley, and M. V. Pauly. 2014. Comparison of evidence-based interventions on outcomes of hospitalized, cognitively impaired older adults. Journal of Comparative Effectiveness Research 3(3):245–257.

NRC. 2012. *Aging and the macroeconomy: Long-term implications of an older population.* Washington, DC: The National Academies Press.

Ouslander, J. G., G. Lamb, R. Tappen, L. Herndon, S. Diaz, B. A. Roos, D. C. Grabowski, and A. Bonner. 2011. Interventions to reduce hospitalizations from nursing homes: Evaluation of the INTERACT II Collaborative Quality Improvement Project. *Journal of the American Geriatrics Society* 59:745–753.

Rowe, J. W., R. Grossman, and E. Bond. 1987. Academic geriatrics for the year 2000: An Institute of Medicine report. *New England Journal of Medicine* 316:1425–1428.

Schroeder, S. 2016. American health improvement depends upon addressing class disparities. *Preventive Medicine* 92:6–15.

Stone, R. I. 2015. Factors affecting the future of family caregiving in the United States. Pp. 57–77 in *Family caregiving in the new normal,* edited by J. Gaughler and R. L. Kane. London: Elsevier.

AUTHOR INFORMATION

John W. Rowe, MD, is Julius B. Richmond Professor, Health Policy and Management, Mailman School of Public Health, Columbia University. **Lisa F. Berkman, PhD,** is Thomas Cabot Professor of Public Policy, Epidemiology, and Population and International Health, Harvard School of Public Health. **Linda P. Fried, MD, MPH,** is Dean, DeLamar Professor of Public Health Practice and Senior Vice President, Columbia University Medical Center. **Terry T. Fulmer, PhD, RN, FAAN,** is President, John A. Hartford Foundation. **James S. Jackson, PhD,** is Director, Research Professor, Institute for Social

Research and Daniel Katz Distinguished University Professor of Psychology, University of Michigan. **Mary D. Naylor, PhD, RN, FAAN,** is Marian S. Ware Professor in Gerontology and is Director, NewCourtland Center for Transitions and Health, University of Pennsylvania School of Nursing. **William D. Novelli, MA,** is Professor, McDonough School of Business, Georgetown University. **S. Jay Olshansky, PhD,** is Professor, Division of Epidemiology and Biostatistics, School of Public Health, University of Illinois at Chicago. **Robyn Stone, DrPH,** is Senior Vice President of Research, Center for Applied Research, LeadingAge.

5

CHRONIC DISEASE PREVENTION: TOBACCO, PHYSICAL ACTIVITY, AND NUTRITION FOR A HEALTHY START

William H. Dietz, MD, PhD, Ross C. Brownson, PhD, Clifford E. Douglas, JD, John J. Dreyzehner, MD, MPH, FACO-EM, Ron Z. Goetzel, PhD, Steven L. Gortmaker, PhD, James S. Marks, MD, MPH, Kathleen A. Merrigan, PhD, Russell R. Pate, PhD, Lisa M. Powell, PhD, and Mary Story, PhD, RD

Smoking, obesity, inactivity, and excess intakes of added sugar, saturated fats, and salt are major contributors to the rates of chronic disease in the United States, and the prevalence and costs of chronic diseases associated with those modifiable behaviors account for a growing share of our gross domestic product. Our medical system has evolved to treat people for diseases that result from these behaviors rather than to prevent the diseases. However, as described in the following sections, the prevalence of the diseases associated with the behaviors greatly exceeds the capacity of our medical system to care for people who have them. Furthermore, few providers are trained to deliver effective behavioral-change strategies that are targeted at the risk factors to prevent their associated diseases. There is a need for broader preventive solutions that focus on the social and environmental determinants of chronic diseases.

A variety of policy and environmental changes have begun to improve those health-related behaviors through deterrents, such as tobacco taxes, or through product reformulation, such as reduction in the sodium content of processed foods. But, the contributions of tobacco use, inactivity, and poor diet to chronic-disease rates remain high, and efforts to prevent and control the cooccurring epidemics of obesity, cardiovascular disease, diabetes, and cancer must be sustained. The success of these efforts requires multicomponent strategies implemented in multiple sectors and settings. Many of the strategies are being undertaken. In the sections that follow, we expand on the magnitude of the challenge, point to successful initiatives that are under way, and identify the most promising opportunities. Perhaps the biggest challenge is in learning how to implement what we know needs to be done.

THE MAGNITUDE OF THE CHALLENGE: KEY ISSUES AND COST IMPLICATIONS

Tobacco

Despite substantial efforts to prevent the onset of smoking and increase rates of smoking cessation, smoking is still a major cause of chronic obstructive pulmonary disease, heart attack, and lung cancer. For every person who dies from smoking, 20 suffer serious smoking-related illnesses. Smoking costs the United States $170 billion in health care expenditures and $156 billion in lost productivity—a total economic impact of $326 billion—per year (CDC, 2016).

Obesity

According to the National Health and Nutrition Examination Survey (NHANES), conducted by the Centers for Disease Control and Prevention (CDC), obesity is present in almost 38 percent of US adults (Ogden et al., 2015), is a major cause of heart disease and type 2 diabetes mellitus, and is associated with 16 percent to 20 percent of adult cancers. Rates of obesity and severe obesity are greatest in Hispanic and black women. A recent estimate suggested that the medical costs of adult obesity in the United States amounted to almost $150 billion per year (Finkelstein et al., 2009).

Some 17 percent of US children and adolescents have obesity. Although national rates of obesity in children 2–5 years old have recently decreased and rates in older children appear to have stabilized (Ogden et al., 2015), rates of severe obesity in children have increased (Ogden et al., 2016). The increase in the prevalence of severe obesity in children and adults suggests that the associated medical costs will increase. Those observations emphasize the need for continued efforts to prevent obesity in children and young adults and to improve the efficacy and cost effectiveness of treatment in these groups. "Issue fatigue" and the cultural normalization of obesity constitute major challenges.

Foods and Beverages That Contibute to Obesity

Patterns of consumption of foods and beverages that contribute to obesity offer opportunities for improvement and help to identify the ethnic differences that contribute to diet-related health inequities. In 2009–2010, highly processed foods accounted for 58 percent of total energy intake (TEI) and 90 percent of energy intake from added sugars (Steele et al., 2016). Sugar drinks (SDs)—sodas, non-100 percent juices, isotonic and energy drinks, and sweetened teas and coffees—are the largest contributors to sugar intake and accounted for about 150 kcal/day in youth and adults in 2009–2010 (Kit et al., 2013). Despite recent reductions in mean SD consumption, the prevalence of sports/energy-drink consumption more than doubled from 1999–2000 to 2007–2008 in all age groups, and the prevalence of heavy SD consumption (≥500 kcal/day) increased in children 2–11 years old and was unchanged in adults (Han and Powell, 2013). The types of SDs consumed vary, but black children and adolescents and low–socioeconomic status children, adolescents, and adults are more likely to be heavy SD consumers (Han and Powell, 2013). Low-cost targeted advertising and the wide availability of SDs contribute to increased consumption by those groups.

Consuming foods away from home (FAFH), particularly from restaurants, has increased in the last few decades. Consumption of FAFH accounted for 18 percent of TEI in 1977–1978 and 34 percent in 2010–2012 (USDA, no date). In 2007–2008, 33 percent, 41 percent, and 36 percent of children, adolescents, and adults, respectively, consumed foods or beverages from fast-food restaurants on a given day, which accounted for an average of 10 percent, 17 percent, and 13 percent of TEI (Powell et al., 2012). Black adolescents and adults are more likely than their white counterparts to consume foods from fast-food restaurants (Powell et al., 2009), in part because of the cost of fast foods and because fast-food restaurants are heavily concentrated in their communities. Both the portion size and the caloric content of FAFH may contribute to the consumption of excess calories and to obesity.

Fruits and Vegetables

Fruit and vegetable consumption continues to fall short of recommended intakes. According to the 2007–2010 NHANES, 75 percent and 87 percent, respectively, of the US population do not meet their sex–age group recommended fruit and vegetable intakes. In particular, 93 percent of children consume less than the recommended intake of vegetables (NCI, 2015). Black men and women consistently report lower vegetable intake than their white counterparts (Kant et al., 2007). In 2013, 22 percent of adults and 39 percent of high school students reported consuming vegetables less than once per day; consumption by blacks and Hispanics was even less frequent. Expense and availability are major barriers to increasing consumption.

Sodium

The average sodium intake in the United States is 3,400 mg/day, well above the 2015 Dietary Guidelines for Americans recommendation of 2,300 mg/day (Dietary Guidelines Advisory Committee, 2015). It is estimated that a 40 percent reduction in US sodium intake would save 280,000–500,000 lives over the next

10 years. Adults who have prehypertension or hypertension, which together affects 32 percent of US adults, or over 70 million people, would benefit from further reduction to 1,500 mg/day (Dietary Guidelines Advisory Committe, 2015). However, because most of the sodium in foods is added during processing by the food and restaurant industry (Dietary Guidelines Advisory Committe, 2015), it is difficult for consumers to regulate their intake. Educational efforts directed at sodium reduction have had limited success. Therefore, policy efforts to reduce sodium and cardiovascular diseases are warranted.

Physical Activity

About 6 percent to 10 percent of all deaths from chronic diseases worldwide can be attributed to physical inactivity. Regular physical activity reduces the risk of premature death and disability from a variety of conditions, including coronary heart disease, diabetes, osteoarthritis, osteoporosis, and some types of cancer. According to CDC, only about 20 percent of US adults and less than 30 percent of high-school students meet the 2008 *Physical Activity Guidelines for Americans* (Physical Activity Guidelines Advisory Committee, 2013). The public health goal is to get people moving—some activity is better than none, and more is better than some.

A wide array of physical activity interventions has proved effective in a variety of populations and geographic settings (IOM, 2013a; Task Force on Community Preventive Services, 2016). The National Physical Activity Plan (NPAP) (2016) has extended the Guidelines in a comprehensive set of evidence-based strategies and tactics to increase physical activity in all segments of the US population. Each of the plan's "societal sectors" articulates multiple strategies, and each strategy includes multiple tactics.

OPPORTUNITIES FOR PROGRESS AND POLICY IMPLICATIONS

The following sections recommend efforts to prevent and control tobacco use, improve levels of physical activity and dietary intake, and reduce obesity, with emphasis on opportunities and policies that will prevent chronic diseases.

Tobacco

Since 1965, the year after publication of the US surgeon general's first report linking cigarette smoking to lung cancer in men (US Public Health Service, 1964), reduction in smoking rates due to the effectiveness of tobacco control advocacy and policy adoption policies, and advocacy efforts has saved about 8 million lives in the United States. Nearly one-third of the 10-year increase in average adult life expectancy since 1965 is due directly to lower smoking rates.

However, cigarette smoking persists as the leading preventable cause of death in the United States, and an estimated 480,000 people die each year from cigarette smoking and exposure to secondhand tobacco smoke. Since 1965, cigarette smoking has taken more than 20 million lives. Tobacco manufacturers have continued to market their products aggressively to the most vulnerable members of our society, particularly those who have less education and lower socioeconomic status, while engineering their products for maximum addictive effect. Another critical aspect of the tobacco epidemic is that people who have mental illnesses have roughly twice the rate of smoking prevalence of the overall population. As many as half the cigarettes smoked in the United States are consumed by people who have co-occurring psychiatric or addictive disorders.

The 50th anniversary report of the surgeon general, published in 2014, states that "the burden of death and disease from tobacco use in the United States is overwhelmingly caused by cigarettes and other combusted tobacco products; rapid elimination of their use will dramatically reduce this burden." Although it is imperative to continue public health efforts to reduce the use of all forms of tobacco, the conventional cigarette remains, by far, the most important target.

Current Successes in Tobacco

Clear guidelines exist for tobacco control. CDC's *Best Practices for Comprehensive Tobacco Control Programs—2014* sets forth a comprehensive, science-based plan to reduce tobacco use, smoking prevalence, and exposure to secondhand tobacco smoke (CDC, 2007). Each of the approaches outlined later has been pursued at both federal and state levels. These policy interventions have proved highly effective in the general population and have also reduced disparities by accelerating reductions in tobacco use by the most vulnerable members of society. The strategies include continued promotion and enforcement of smoke-free environments, increased taxes on tobacco products, aggressive public information campaigns, and carefully targeted litigation against the tobacco industry by the government and the private sector. The Patient Protection and Affordable Care Act (ACA) provides for tobacco dependence treatment for the 70 percent of smokers who wish to quit. Wide availability of such treatment is critical for its success.

Policy Needs in Tobacco

The advent of new nicotine delivery products, such as electronic cigarettes, requires new smoke-free, youth access, and other tobacco-control policies. Nicotine poisoning in children as a result of exposure to the liquid used in these devices is a growing problem. The Food and Drug Administration's Center for Tobacco Products, which was formed pursuant to the Family Smoking Prevention and Tobacco Control Act, should use its authority to order product changes that are designed to render tobacco products less harmful and less addictive or even nonaddictive and to better inform the public about the hazards posed by these products through improved labeling and other communication tools.

As described later, some of the most promising strategies for reducing tobacco use are to increase the age at which cigarettes can be purchased, to increase taxes on tobacco, and to limit access to nicotine-containing products.

Nutrition, Physical Activity, and Obesity: Existing Efforts and Policy Improvements

Early Care and Education: Current Successes in Nutrition and Activity

Most US children, including almost half of those under 6 years old, spend an average of 35 hours a week in nonparental care. Early care and education (ECE) facilities include child-care centers, day-care homes, Head Start programs, and preschool and pre-kindergarten programs and are ideal settings in which to implement nutrition and physical activity strategies to prevent obesity. Interventions in ECE settings that have effectively reduced excess weight gain in young children incorporate both nutrition and physical activity (Dietary Guidelines Advisory Committee, 2015). The interventions include improvements in the nutrition quality of meals and snacks, in the mealtime environment, and in food-service practices; increases in physically active play; reductions in sedentary behaviors, such as watching television; improvements in outdoor play environments; enhancement of classroom education in nutrition and physical activity; and outreach to engage parents about making changes in the home environment. Two Institute of Medicine (IOM) committee reports (2011, 2013b) include recommendations for improving nutrition and physical activity in ECE settings. Nonetheless, more evidence on the effects of these strategies on early childhood obesity is warranted.

Policy Needs in Nutrition and Activity

A variety of existing or emergent policy opportunities can improve nutrition and physical activity in ECE settings. The US Department of Agriculture (USDA) plays a central role. Implementation of the revised Child and Adult Care Food Program (CACFP) will improve nutrition standards and meal requirements. The challenge is in the implementation of the policies and programs. USDA can work with state agencies to increase participation in the CACFP through program simplification, paperwork reduction, and other strategies. In addition, USDA could seek the authority needed to require adequate daily physical activity and limits on television watching as conditions of participation in the CACFP. Within the Department of Health and Human Services (HHS), Head Start performance standards should reflect an increased emphasis on healthy eating and physical activity, including increasing linkages to community resources, staff training, and parent engagement.

Schools

Children and adolescents consume up to 50 percent of their total daily calories in school, and USDA's National School Lunch Program (NSLP) and School Breakfast Program (SBP) are key components of the school food environment. Those programs are important for all youth but are especially important for the more than 21.5 million school-age children in low-income families who receive free or reduced-price school meals.

Current Successes in Schools

The Healthy, Hunger-Free Kids Act (HHFKA) of 2010 directed USDA to update and revise nutrition standards for the NSLP and SBP. The standards, implemented in 2012, were based on recommendations in the IOM report *School Meals: Building Blocks for Healthy Children* (2009) and required schools to offer more servings and more varieties of fruits and vegetables, more whole grains, and less saturated fats and sodium, and to set limits on portion size. Recent studies have shown substantial improvements in the nutritional content of school meals, plate waste has not increased, and student acceptance of the healthier offerings is high and improving (Cohen et al., 2014).

A number of other policies and programs that are now in place can help to improve children's nutrition in school, such as federal school wellness policies, farm-to-school programs that focus on fruits and vegetables, and the Fresh Fruit and Vegetable Program. Those programs foster a healthier food and activity culture, especially in schools in low-income communities.

Policy Needs in Schools

The HHFKA also mandated that free potable water be available where meals are served. However, the recent water crisis in Flint, Michigan, has renewed concerns about water safety, particularly in older schools. A national task force should be formed to address the scope of the issue and possible remedies, including providing funds to health departments for testing water supplies for lead and other contaminants.

In addition to school meals, foods and beverages available to students throughout the school day can contribute to a child's excess calorie intake, such as those sold a la carte in school cafeterias, vending machines, and school stores (competitive foods). The IOM report *Nutrition Standards for Foods in Schools: Leading the Way Toward Healthier Youth* (2007) concluded that school breakfast and lunch programs should be the main source of nutrition in school, that opportunities for competitive foods should be limited, and that if competitive foods are available, they should consist of nutritious fruits, vegetables, whole grains, and nonfat or low-fat milk and dairy products. The 2010 HH-FKA required USDA for the first time to establish minimum nutrition standards for competitive foods (Smart Snacks), which were implemented in 2014.

As with ECE, the challenge is in implementation, such as meeting the increased cost of serving healthier meals (e.g., more fruits, vegetables, and whole grains) and updated kitchen equipment and storage, staff training, and technical assistance. Congress, USDA, and states need to find innovative ways to ensure training and technical assistance that address those needs and the added cost of healthier meals. Adequate resources should be provided to monitor effects and scale up these and other interventions as appropriate.

School wellness policies are an important mechanism for engaging families and communities in schools and thereby for increasing the likelihood of sustaining and expanding the programs. USDA should complete regulations related to local wellness polices and work actively with states and localities on full implementation.

Because most children are enrolled in formal education programs at the pre-K, K–12, or postsecondary level, the education sector offers an important opportunity to increase physical activity. The recent revision of the NPAP includes a number of recommendations for the education sector. The plan recommends that states implement standards to ensure that children in child care and early-childhood education programs are appropriately physically active. Furthermore, as we emphasize in the "vital directions" below, states and local school districts should adopt the Comprehensive School Physical Activity Program (CSPAP) model, including provision of high-quality physical education, in K–12 schools. Opportunities and incentives to adopt and maintain physically active lifestyles should be extended to students and employees in postsecondary education institutions.

Worksites

Workplace health promotion (wellness) programs can potentially reach a large segment of adults who are not otherwise exposed to or engaged in organized health-improvement efforts. Employers have a strong incentive to keep people healthy because healthy and fit workers are absent less often, are more productive in their jobs, have fewer accidents, and consume fewer expensive health care resources than workers who are at risk for or suffering from illness because of their health behaviors. However, most employers lack the skills, knowledge, and resources needed to build and sustain effective wellness programs.

Current Successes in Worksites

Research has demonstrated that properly designed, appropriately implemented, and rigorously evaluated programs can improve workers' health, reduce the rate of increase in health care spending, and improve employee productivity. A 2010 systematic review by CDC's Task Force on Community Preventive Services found that evidence-based wellness programs exert a favorable influence on health behaviors (e.g., with respect to smoking, diet, physical activity, alcohol consumption, and seatbelt use), on such biometric measures as blood pressure and cholesterol, and on organizational outcomes important to employers, such as health care use and worker productivity (Soler et al., 2010). A widely cited meta-analysis of the literature on medical costs, medical cost savings, and absenteeism associated with wellness programs estimated returns on investment averaging $3.27 and $2.70 saved over 3 years, respectively, for every $1.00 invested (Baicker et al., 2010).

Policy Needs in Worksites

The federal government can play an important role in engaging the business community in building and sustaining effective workplace health promotion programs. Because the federal government spends more than $40 billion per year on health care for 8 million employees and annuitants (OPM, 2016), there is potential for substantial cost savings through improvement in government workers' health and well-being and reduced spending. As the nation's largest employer, the federal government should lead by example by implementing evidence-based programs in all federal agency worksites.

The federal government should also improve communication and dissemination of best and promising practices associated with workplace health promotion. The strategies require upfront investment, but they will yield a large return on investment to the federal government and the business community in general. Federal support for the CDC resource center, the *Guide to Community Preventive Services (Community Guide)*, and similar dissemination outlets will ensure that the right audiences learn from best and promising practices. Similar communication and dissemination programs should be established in other agencies, such as the Department of Labor, and nonprofits, including the US Chamber of Commerce, in which ideas, experiences, and resources become available through learning cooperatives, newsletters, webinars, and Wikipedia-like computer applications.

The federal government should also provide incentives to implement high-quality and innovative programs. The ACA authorized $200 million for workplace health-promotion pilot efforts, but the funds were never appropriated. The small amount of funding, $10 million per year, set aside for CDC-supported workplace health promotion programs and research has been eliminated in the federal budget. Those funds should be restored. In addition, "smart" incentive programs should be encouraged. Section 2705 of the ACA allows employers to reduce insurance premiums to employees who participate in wellness programs and, under some conditions, to offer financial incentives for achieving specific health outcomes, such as quitting smoking, losing weight, managing blood pressure or cholesterol concentrations, and lowering blood glucose concentrations. Employees affected by evolving incentive rules should be included in the programs' design to avoid the possibility of cost shifting and discrimination based on preexisting conditions.

Communities

Policy Needs in Communities

Community initiatives to address nutrition, physical activity, and obesity include joint use agreements for the after-hours use of school facilities for physical activity. States and communities can adopt Complete Streets policies to ensure that active modes of transportation are included in the planning, design, and construction of roadways. The National Complete Streets Coalition maintains a database that includes a template for model policies. Implementation of state, regional, and local land use policies, comprehensive plans, subdivision regulations, and zoning codes that support physical activity by encouraging mixed uses and infrastructure for short-distance trips, such as walking or taking public transit from home to work, could substantially increase physical activity and thereby reduce the incidence of a number of chronic diseases.

As indicated earlier, research shows that the consumption of SDs is a major contributor to obesity and diabetes. An SD excise tax of $0.01 per ounce in the United States has emerged as one of the policy changes that can potentially slow the growth in obesity prevalence in children and adults, prevent new cases of obesity, improve quality-adjusted and disability-adjusted life years and mortality, and save much more in health care costs over the next decade than the intervention costs to implement—savings are estimated to be $31 for every dollar spent on the intervention. (Gortmaker et al., 2015).

Early data indicate that excise taxes have reduced consumption of SDs in Berkeley, California, and sales in Mexico, and the recently passed beverage excise tax in Philadelphia, Pennsylvania, will be a substantial source of revenue for the city's pre-K program. State and municipal government procurement policies that specify foods with lower amounts of sodium and added sugars, like those in place in the federal government, will improve the health and productivity of the workforce and ultimately reduce the costs associated with obesity. CDC should work with local and state health departments to identify and disseminate model programs.

HHS initiatives have supported CDC's programs in community health that target obesity, nutrition, physical activity, and tobacco. Over the last 10–15 years, annual funding of over $100 million has supported a variety of programs, such as Racial and Ethnic Approaches to Community Health, the Steps to a Healthier US Initiative (targeting asthma, diabetes, and obesity), Communities Putting Prevention to Work, and Community Transformation Grants (as part of the ACA). Those funds have been substantially reduced, but the growing evidence of the value of social–environmental interventions in communities to improve behavior and health outcomes (Evaluating obesity prevention efforts, 2015) emphasizes that funding for the programs should be restored and sustained.

Medical Settings

Current Successes in Medical Settings

Because people who have severe obesity probably will not achieve substantial weight loss solely in response to the policy and environmental changes outlined here, new effective treatment strategies will be required. The Diabetes Prevention Program (DPP) is a model of care that demonstrated that counseling about nutrition, physical activity, and weight loss in adults who had obesity and prediabetes was more effective than medication in the prevention of the development of type 2 diabetes (Knowler et al., 2002). The DPP was adapted for delivery by trained providers in community settings by the Y-USA, and outcomes were comparable with those observed in the DPP and at lower cost. The DPP in community settings is an ideal example of value-based care inasmuch as payment occurs only if enrollees meet specific attendance and weight-loss goals. The Centers for Medicare & Medicaid Services recently announced that it would expand Medicare to cover programs to prevent diabetes. Like Medicare, state Medicaid programs should expand coverage for the prevention of diabetes that includes the delivery of the DPP in community settings by qualified providers.

Policy Needs in Medical Settings

Lack of a standard of care and lack of payment for obesity treatment are major barriers to the effective medical management of obesity. US Preventive Services Task Force recommendations for treatment for adult and childhood obesity have recommended intensive behavioral interventions, defined as at least 26 hours for children and 6 months of visits every 2 weeks for adults. Both recommendations received a B rating from the task force. Because the DPP constitutes an effective weight-loss program, this weight-loss therapy should be expanded to Medicaid with payment if patients meet identified attendance and weight-loss goals.

Medical solutions alone are inadequate to address diseases as prevalent as obesity, diabetes, and cardiovascular disease. Although incentives to integrate clinical and community services have begun, studies that demonstrate the business case for integration could speed the development and implementation of this approach. The Center for Medicare and Medicaid Innovation should fund studies that explore the effects of delivery of services for chronic diseases that integrate clinical and community services for the prevention and treatment of obesity (Dietz et al., 2015). Such studies should assess how to reimburse community systems when community interventions add health value.

Physicians and other health care providers are trusted advocates of favorable health behaviors, and the health care system has the potential to influence physical activity at the individual and population level. However, assessment of and counseling for both physical activity and dietary intake are not well established in clinical practice in the United States. Only about one-third of patients report receiving such counseling during office visits. In contrast with nutritional counseling, in which registered dietitians constitute an existing workforce, few providers are trained in counseling about physical activity. Because physical activity has such a powerful effect on the prevention and mitigation of many chronic diseases, the NPAP recommended several strategies to enhance the role of health care providers in promotion of physical activity. They included the recommendation that HHS establish physical activity as a "vital sign" that all health care providers assess and discuss with their patients. HHS should also support inclusion of physical activity in clinical guidelines for management of conditions for which there is evidence of health and cost benefits. Organizations that assess the quality of care should review the implementation of these practices in health systems. The lack of reimbursement for providers who help patients to improve their diet and physical-activity level is a major barrier to clinical efforts to prevent and treat for obesity and chronic diseases related to it.

Health in All Policies of State and Local Governments

Multiple community strategies have been developed to address the food environment, but fewer have been directed at increasing physical activity. The principles outlined below are specific to physical activity but also apply to improving nutrition.

Policy Needs in State and Local Health

State and local health departments are essential actors in promoting physical activity interventions because of their ability to assess public health problems, develop appropriate programs and policies, and ensure that the programs and policies are effectively delivered and implemented. Fulfilling their obligation to promote physical activity in a variety of community settings will require several steps. CDC's *Community Guide* has established a number of evidence-based strategies to increase physical activity. They should be widely disseminated.

Leadership, funding, and workforce capacity are important barriers to the implementation of evidence-based recommendations to improve the food environment and increase physical activity. State and local governments should be funded to provide coordinated leadership and support for efforts to promote physical activity, particularly efforts focused on high-risk populations, by increasing resources and strengthening policies in all sectors related to physical activity and nutrition. Improved support for evidence-based programs can be accomplished by identifying new funding opportunities and redirecting existing funding to issues, such as physical inactivity, that result in high health and economic burdens for society. In collaboration with the Association of State and Territorial Health Officers and the National Association of City and County Health Officers, new curricula should be developed in schools and programs in public health, and short courses for practitioners and certification by such groups as the National Physical Activity Society should be developed to help public health practitioners to develop cross-sectoral partnerships and implement evidence-based physical activity interventions. Sectors should include education, parks and recreation, transportation, city planning, business, nonprofit organizations, and health care; all have a role in increasing physical activity. Those steps should be complemented by the development and maintenance of an ethnically diverse, culturally diverse, and sex-diverse public-health workforce with competence in physical activity, nutrition, and health through new curricula in training programs and with scholarship support for underrepresented minority groups and disadvantaged populations.

Federal and Cross-Sector Initiatives

Policy Needs for Federal and Cross-Sector Initiatives

More national, state, and local initiatives have focused on nutrition than on physical activity. Achieving progress in promoting physical activity will involve sectors outside health care and public health. To implement effectively many of the strategies outlined above, a set of diverse sectors needs to be engaged. Promotion of physical activity may not be seen as a primary objective of many sectors (such as schools and transportation), but strategies will often have benefits that resonate with multiple sectors. For example, a strong set of actions to support physical education in schools will increase rates of physical activity and may also improve student achievement (CDC, 2010). In cross-sector efforts, high priority should be given to improving access to physical activity–related services and opportunities, particularly for disadvantaged populations that have limited access (Committee on Prevention of Obesity in Children and Youth, 2005; National Physical Activity Plan Alliance, 2016). In communities that receive support from the Prevention and Public Health Fund (which resulted from the ACA), high priority should be given to the development of infrastructure for underserved populations. CDC should identify successful cross-sector partnerships so that it can identify key elements of success and incorporate them into future physical activity initiatives.

Because physical activity has such benefits for a wide array of chronic diseases, HHS should establish at CDC an Office of Physical Activity and Health and allocate to it the resources needed to provide effective national leadership in identifying, implementing, and monitoring high-impact strategies for promotion of physical activity.

Public–Private Partnerships

Current Successes in Obesity Reduction

The nationwide concern about the obesity epidemic in children and adults has engaged organizations and businesses that want to help, especially with regard to children. Many efforts have been undertaken by single sectors or companies, but there have been several important public–private partnerships, the most notable being the Partnership for a Healthy America (PHA). PHA was founded in 2010 in conjunction with Let's Move! and remains an independent, nonpartisan organization. PHA works with public, private, and nonprofit leaders to make voluntary commitments to address childhood obesity. Large grocery chains have committed to reducing added sugars and sodium in store-brand foods and increasing access to healthy foods in food deserts, hotel and restaurant chains are reducing their calorie footprint, and colleges and hospitals around the country are adopting nutrition and physical activity criteria. Notable in the PHA approach is the third-party validation to collect data, monitor progress, and report findings publicly each year (http://ahealthi-eramerica.org/about/annual-progress-reports [accessed March 30, 2016]). The connection of PHA to the Obama Administration has facilitated improved business practices that affect the health of children and families. PHA's approach should be adopted by the next administration.

The Healthy Food Financing Initiative (HFFI) is a program through which the federal government (Department of the Treasury, USDA, and HHS) has provided financial assistance to local development agencies, such as low-interest loans, to improve food access. The funds have enabled private developers to build supermarkets and convenience stores and to establish farmer's markets in neighborhoods that were formerly classified as food deserts. The HFFI also provides employment opportunities in neighborhoods that have high unemployment rates. States and some cities have established programs for the same purpose that engage the private sector.

Policy Needs in Obesity Reduction

Because access to supermarkets constitutes a major inequity, funding for the HFFI should be sustained. However, some early data suggest that, although new supermarkets provide increased access, dietary intakes may not change; access alone might not improve diets (Dubowitz et al., 2015). Both the short- and the longer-term effects of new supermarkets on dietary intake and health should be evaluated. This funding approach should also be explored relative to other issues, such as the development of small-city green spaces and parks as places to increase opportunities for physical activity.

Such programs as Double Up Food Bucks (2016) double the value of federal nutrition assistance (usually the Supplemental Nutrition Assistance Program, SNAP) used predominantly in farmer's markets, helping low-income people to purchase more locally grown fruits and vegetables. Funds for such programs often come from foundations and the private sector. The return on this investment is threefold: low-income consumers eat more healthful food, local farmers gain new customers and make more money, and more food dollars stay in the local economy.

On the basis of the success of SNAP incentive programs, the 2014 Farm Bill included $100 million for Food Insecurity Nutrition Incentive grants. All the projects funded through these grants include a public–private component through the contribution of matching funds. Support for this program should be sustained and expanded.

Support for programs like the HFFI is closely connected to the growing interest in the linkage between community development, housing, and health led by the Federal Reserve Bank of San Francisco and its sister banks (Moon, 2016). Federal Reserve's interest grew out of the recognition that life expectancy was widely divergent between nearby ZIP codes and that improved housing can directly improve health and well-being. Furthermore, indirectly subsidized housing frees low-income families' resources so that they can buy food, pay for medicine, or support their children's school costs. In addition to its support for low-income housing, Federal Reserve banks help to direct funding for supermarkets in food deserts, and charter and other schools, and additional investments amounting to about $100 billion per year (Erickson and Andrews, 2011; David Erickson, personal communication), and they have urged the inclusion of health benefits in the assessment of community development funding projects.

Few sources of funding for housing projects have used health benefits as a justification for funding, and there are still only early efforts to understand how health improvements can be measured and monetized to capture the added value. Policies that lower the capital costs of developments that include elements to improve health could be expected to influence billions of dollars in new investment each year. Pilot and modeling studies should be funded to identify the most promising strategies and to make the business case their impact on health.

A sustainable food system provides nutritious and safe food while ensuring that ecosystems can provide food for future generations; develops agricultural and production practices that reduce environmental effects and conserve resources; makes healthy food available, accessible, and affordable to all; and is humane and just, protecting farmers and other workers, consumers, and communities. Recognizing that the US food supply chain is deeply interconnected with human and environmental health and with social and economic systems, the IOM convened a public workshop in 2013, "Mapping the Food System and its Effects" (IOM, 2013c), and later released a consensus report, *A Framework for Assessing Effects of the Food System* (IOM, 2015a). Those activities led the 2015 Dietary Guidelines Advisory Committee to link public health, food systems, and sustainability; and for the first time, the committee recommended food system sustainability as part of the *Dietary Guidelines for Americans* (Dietary Guidelines Advisory Committee, 2015). The committee concluded that "a dietary pattern that is higher in plant-based foods, such as vegetables, fruits, whole grains, legumes, nuts and seeds, and lower in animal-based foods is more health promoting and is associated with lesser environmental impact (greenhouse gas emissions and energy, land, and water use) than is the current average US diet." Federal, state, and local governments should develop public education campaigns that focus on the benefits of a more plant-based diet and on the health and planetary benefits of reduced meat consumption. The 2020 *Dietary Guidelines for Americans* will provide an opportunity to revisit this issue.

Metrics and Monitoring

An important gap in many settings is the capacity to identify and disseminate model programs and to monitor the national uptake of these programs.

Agencies within HHS, most notably CDC, are ideally suited for that function. For example, because ECE settings have such a profound effect on young children, CDC should establish a national monitoring system to assess progress and policies that improve nutrition and physical activity in ECE settings. Although many workplaces have successful initiatives, the recognition and spread of successful programs remain low. Additional funds would enable CDC to conduct applied research in real-world settings, to evaluate the effects of established and long-standing workplace programs, and to monitor uptake of worksite wellness practices throughout the United States. A portion of research funding should be directed at evaluating innovative programs aimed at improving the health and well-being of federal workers and members of the armed services. Active transportation, such as walking or biking, increases physical activity and reduces car use and thereby reduces the generation of greenhouse gases. CDC and the Department of Transportation have a joint interest in expanding the use and monitoring of policy and environmental approaches that increase walking, biking, or use of public transportation, all of which increase physical activity.

VITAL DIRECTIONS

The following vital directions were based on the authors' consensus that these strategies were the most feasible and of those considered were likely to have the greatest effect.

Strengthen Federal Efforts to Reduce Use by Youth of All Nicotine-Containing Products, Through Excise Tax Increases and the Regulatory Process

Despite recent progress in reducing smoking rates, tobacco use remains the leading cause of preventable deaths in the United States. Abundant research demonstrates that later initiation of tobacco use is associated with lower rates of addiction. Three strategies should be used to reduce the initiation of tobacco use. The policy likely to have the greatest population-based effect is raising the minimum age of tobacco purchase to 21 years (IOM, 2015b) and applying this minimum to all products that contain nicotine. The recent report that 24 percent of adolescents are using e-cigarettes compared with the 11 percent of adolescents who are smoking traditional cigarettes emphasizes the urgency of this step (Kann et al., 2016). Increased taxes on tobacco clearly reduce the initiation of smoking, and may also reduce smoking by people who are already addicted.

Fully Apply the Standards in the Healthy Hunger-Free Kids Act (HHFKA) to the National School Lunch Program, the School Breakfast Program, and to the Foods and Beverages Sold in Schools

The changes mandated by the HHFKA must be sustained. The HHFKA transformed the healthfulness of school meals, set limits on portion sizes, and set the first national nutrition standards for all foods and beverages sold in schools (Smart Snacks). Those changes resulted in an increase in the consumption of healthier foods, such as fruits and vegetables, without an increase in plate waste (Cohen et al., 2014). An evidence review and modeling of cost effectiveness of childhood nutrition interventions found that these improvements make the HHFKA "one of the most important national obesity-prevention policy achievements in recent decades" (Gortmaker et al., 2015). Of nine dietary interventions evaluated, improvements in school meals due to HHFKA were projected to have the largest effect on childhood obesity. For example, implementation of Smart Snacks was projected to prevent 345,000 cases of childhood obesity in 2025 and save more in reduced health costs over the next decade than the intervention would cost to implement. The net savings to society for each dollar spent was projected to be $4.56 (Gortmaker et al., 2015).

Provide Incentives for States and Local School Districts to Adopt the Comprehensive School Physical Activity Program Model (CSPAP)

States and local school districts should adopt the CS-PAP model (CDC, 2013), including provision of high-quality physical education, in K–12 schools. Although the HHFKA has transformed school meals, comparable progress has not been achieved in physical activity. Comprehensive programs for physical activity in schools include high-quality physical education; physical activity before, during, and after school; staff involvement; and family and community engagement. The recent NPAP, the *National Physical Activity Guidelines for Americans*, and the Institute of Medicine report *Accelerating Progress in Obesity Prevention and Educating the Student Body* point to the importance of physical activity in improving learning and behavior, preventing obesity, and reducing the risks of other chronic diseases and support the need for high-quality physical education programs. Such programs may have the added benefit of increasing the number of recruits eligible for military service.

SUMMARY RECOMMENDATIONS FOR VITAL DIRECTIONS

1. Strengthen federal efforts to reduce use by youth of all nicotine-containing products, through excise tax increases and the regulatory process.
2. Fully apply the standards in the Healthy Hunger-Free Kids Act to the National School Lunch Program, the School Breakfast Program, and to the foods and beverages sold in schools.
3. Provide incentives for states and local school districts to adopt the Comprehensive School Physical Activity Program model.

REFERENCES

Baicker, K., D. Cutler, and Z. Song. 2010. Workplace wellness programs can generate savings. *Health Affairs (Millwood)* 29(2):304–311.

CDC (Centers for Disease Control and Prevention). 2007. *Best practices for comprehensive tobacco control programs.* Atlanta, GA: CDC, U.S. Department of Health and Human Services.

CDC. 2010. *The association between school-based physical activity, including physical education, and academic performance.* Atlanta, GA: CDC.

CDC. 2013. *Comprehensive school physical activity programs: A guide for schools.* Atlanta, GA: CDC.

CDC. 2016. Economic facts about U.S. tobacco production and use. Available at http://www.cdc.gov/tobacco/data_statistics/fact_sheets/economics/econ_facts/ (accessed August 18, 2016).

Cohen, J. F., S. Richardson, E. Parker, P. J. Catalano, and E. B. Rimm. 2014. Impact of the new U.S. Department of Agriculture school meal standards on food selection, consumption, and waste. *American Journal of Preventive Medicine* 46(4): 388–394.

Committee on Prevention of Obesity in Children and Youth. 2005. *Preventing childhood obesity: Health in the balance.* Washington, DC: The National Academies Press.

Dietary Guidelines Advisory Committee. 2015. *Scientific report of the 2015 Dietary Guidelines Advisory Committee.* Washington, DC: US Department of Health and Human Services and US Department of Agriculture.

Dietz, W. H., L. S. Solomon, N. Pronk, S. K. Ziegenhorn, M. Standish, M. M. Longjohn, D. D. Fukuzawa, I. U. Eneli, L. Loy, N. D. Muth, E. J. Sanchez, J. Bogard, and D. W. Bradley. 2015. An integrated framework for the prevention and treatment of obesity and its related chronic diseases. *Health Affairs (Millwood)* 34(9):1456–1463.

Double Up Food Bucks: A win for families, farmers, and communities. 2016. Available at http://www.double-upfoodbucks.org/about/ (accessed April 10, 2016).

Dubowitz, T., M. Ghosh-Dastidar, D. A. Cohen, R. Beckman, E. D. Steiner, G. P. Hunter, K. R. Flórez, C. Huang, C. A. Vaughan, J. C. Sloan, S. N. Zenk, S. Cummins, and R. L. Collins. 2015. Diet and perceptions change with supermarket introduction in a food desert, but not because of supermarket use. *Health Affairs (Millwood)* 34(11):1858–1868.

Erickson, D., and N. Andrews. 2011. Partnerships among community development, public health, and health care could improve the well-being of low-income people. *Health Affairs (Millwood)* 30(11):2056–2063.

Evaluating Obesity Prevention Efforts: What have we learned? 2015. Available at https://publichealth.gwu.edu/sites/default/files/downloads/Redstone-Center/Evaluating%20Obesity%20Prevention%20Efforts%20What%20Have%20We%20Learned.pdf (accessed July 31, 2016).

Finkelstein, E. A., J. G. Trogdon, J. W. Cohen, and W. Dietz. 2009. Annual medical spending attributable to obesity: Payer- and service-specific estimates. *Health Affairs (Millwood)* 28(5):w822–w831.

Gortmaker, S. L., Y. C. Wang, M. W. Long, C. M. Giles, Z. J. Ward, J. L. Barrett, E. L. Kenney, K. R. Sonneville, A. Sadaf Afzal, S. C. Resch, and A. L. Cradock. 2015. Three interventions that reduce childhood obesity are projected to save more than they cost to implement. *Health Affairs (Millwood)* 34(11):1932–1939.

Han, E., and L. M. Powell. 2013. Consumption patterns of sugar-sweetened beverages in the United States. *Journal of the Academy of Nutrition and Dietetics* 113(1):43–53.

IOM (Institute of Medicine). 2007. *Nutrition standards for foods in schools: Leading the way toward healthier youth.* Washington, DC: The National Academies Press.

IOM. 2009. *School meals: Building blocks for healthy children.* Washington, DC: The National Academies Press.

IOM. 2011. *Child and adult care food program: Aligning dietary guidance for all.* Washington, DC: The National Academies Press.

IOM. 2013a. *Educating the student body: Taking physical activity and physical education to school.* Washington, DC: The National Academies Press.

IOM. 2013b. *Evaluating obesity prevention efforts: A plan for measuring progress.* Washington, DC: The National Academies Press.

IOM. 2013c. *Workshop on mapping the food system and its effects.* Washington, DC: The National Academies Press.

IOM. 2015a. *A framework for assessing effects of the food system.* Washington, DC: The National Academies Press.

IOM. 2015b. *Public health implications of raising the minimum age of legal access to tobacco products.* Washington, DC: The National Academies Press.

Kann, L., T. McManus, W. A. Harris, S. L. Shanklin, K. H. Flint, J. Hawkins, B. Queen, R. Lowry, E. O'Malley Olsen, D. Chyen, L. Whittle, J. Thornton, C. Lim, Y. Yamakawa, N. Brener, and S. Zaza. 2016. Youth Risk Behavior Surveillance—United States, 2015. *MMWR Surveillance Summaries* 65(6): 1–174.

Kant, A. K., B. I. Graubard, and S. K. Kumanyika. 2007. Trends in black-white differentials in dietary intakes of U.S. adults, 1971–2002. *American Journal of Preventive Medicine* 32(4):264–272.

Kit, B.K., T. H. Fakhouri, S. Park, S. J. Nielsen, and C. L. Ogden. 2013. Trends in sugar-sweetened beverage consumption among youth and adults in the United States: 1999–2010. *American Journal of Clinical Nutrition* 98(1):180–188.

Knowler, W. C., E. Barrett-Connor, S. E. Fowler, R. F. Hamman, J. M. Lachin, E. A. Walker, and D. M. Nathan. 2002. Reduction in the incidence of type 2 diabetes with lifestyle intervention or metformin. *New England Journal of Medicine* 346(6):393–403.

Moon, J. 2016. Investing to Reduce Economic and Racial Disparities. Available at http://www.frbsf.org/community-development/blog/investing-to-reduce-economic-racial-disparities/ (accessed August 1, 2016).

National Physical Activity Plan. 2016. Available at http://www.physicalactivityplan.org/theplan.ph (accessed April 1, 2016).

National Physical Activity Plan Alliance. 2016. The National Physical Activity Plan. Available at http://www. physicalactivityplan.org/index.php (accessed March 23, 2016).

NCI (National Cancer Institute). 2015. *Usual Dietary Intakes: Food Intakes, U.S. Population, 2007–10.* Epidemiology Research Program Updated May 20, 2015. Available at http://epi.grants.cancer.gov/diet/usual-intakes/pop/2007–10/ (accessed March 23, 2016).

Office of Personnel Management (OPM). 2016. *Tribal Employers—General Information.* https://www.opm.gov/healthcare-insurance/tribal-employers/general-information/ (accessed December 5, 2016)

Ogden, C. L., M. D. Carroll, C. D. Fryar, and K. M. Flegal. 2015. *Prevalence of obesity among adults and youth: United States, 2011–2014.* Hyattsville, MD: National Center for Health Statistics Data Brief.

Ogden, C. L., M. D. Carroll, H. G. Lawman, C. D. Fryar, D. Kruszon-Moran, and K. M. Flegal. 2016. Trends in obesity prevalence among children and adolescents in the United States, 1988–1994 through 2013–2014. *Journal of the American Medical Association* 315(21):2292–2299.

Physical Activity Guidelines Advisory Committee. 2013. PAG Midcourse Report: Strategies to Increase Physical Activity Among Youth. Washington, DC: US Department of Health and Human Services.

Powell, L. M., B. T. Nguyen, and E. Han. 2012. Energy intake from restaurants: Demographics and socio-economics, 2003–2008. *American Journal of Preventive Medicine* 43(5):498–504.

Soler, R. E., K. D. Leeks, S. Razi, D. P. Hopkins, M. Griffith, A. Aten, S. K. Chattopadhyay, S. C. Smith, N. Habarta, R. Z. Goetzel, N. P. Pronk, D. E. Richling, D. R. Bauer, L. R. Buchanan, C. S. Florence, L. Koonin, D. MacLean, A. Rosenthal, D. Matson Koffman, J. V. Grizzell, and A. M. Walker. 2010. A systematic review of selected interventions for worksite health promotion. The assessment of health risks with feedback. *American Journal of Preventive Medicine* 38(2 Suppl):S237-S262.

Steele, E. M., L. G. Baraldi, M. L. da Costa Louzada, J. C. Moubarac, D. Mozaffarian, and C. A. Monteiro. 2016. Ultra-processed foods and added sugars in the US diet: Evidence from a nationally representative cross-sectional study. *BMJ* 6(3): e009892.

Task Force on Community Preventive Services. 2016. *The guide to community preventive services: What works to promote health?* Atlanta, GA: CDC.

US Public Health Service. 1964. *Smoking and health: A report of the Advisory Committee to the Surgeon General of the Public Health Service.* Washington, DC: US Public Health Service.

USDA (US Department of Agriculture). No date. What we eat in america, NHANES 2011–2012, individuals 2 years and over (excluding breast-fed children), day 1. Available at http://www.ars.usda.gov/nea/bhnrc/fsrg (accessed April 6, 2016).

AUTHOR INFORMATION

William H. Dietz, MD, PhD, is Chair, Redstone Global Center for Prevention and Wellness, The George Washington University. **Ross C. Brownson, PhD,** is Director, Prevention Research Center and Bernard Becker Professor,

Brown School and School of Medicine, Washington University. **Clifford E. Douglas, JD,** is Vice President, Tobacco Control, American Cancer Society and Director, American Cancer Society's Center for Tobacco Control. **John J. Dreyzehner, MD, MPH, FACO-EM,** is Health Commissioner, State of Tennessee Department of Health. **Ron Z. Goetzel, PhD,** is Senior Scientist, Johns Hopkins Bloomberg School of Public Health and Vice President, Truven Health Analytics. **Steven L. Gortmaker, PhD,** is Professor of the Practice of Health Sociology, Department of Social and Behavioral Sciences, Harvard T.H. Chan School of Public Health. **James S. Marks, MD, MPH,** is Executive Vice President, Robert Wood Johnson Foundation. **Kathleen A. Merrigan, PhD,** is Executive Director of Sustainability, The George Washington University. **Russell R. Pate, PhD,** is Principal Investigator, Arnold School of Public Health, Univeristy of South Carolina. **Lisa M. Powell, PhD,** is Professor and Director of Health Policy and Administration, University of Illinois at Chicago. **Mary Story, PhD, RD,** is Professor, Duke University.

6

IMPROVING ACCESS TO EFFECTIVE CARE FOR PEOPLE WHO HAVE MENTAL HEALTH AND SUBSTANCE USE DISORDERS

James Knickman, PhD, K. Ranga Rama Krishnan, MB, ChB, Harold A. Pincus, MD, Carlos Blanco, MD, PhD, Dan. G. Blazer, MD, PhD, MPH, Molly J. Coye, MD, MPH, John H. Krystal, MD, Scott L. Rauch, MD, Gregory E. Simon, MD, MPH, and Benedetto Vitiello, MD

Mental health and substance use disorders affect people of all ages and demographics and are extremely burdensome to society. At least 18.1 percent of American adults experience some form of mental disorder, 8.4 percent have a substance use disorder, and about 3 percent experience co-occurring mental health and substance use disorders (SAMHSA, 2016). In 2013, health-related spending on mental health disorders in the United States was about $201 billion (Roehrig, 2016). Moreover, 4 of the top 5 sources of disability in people 18–44 years old are behavioral health conditions (WHO, 2001). While knowledge regarding recognition and treatment has steadily advanced, the public health effects of that knowledge have lagged. More effective and specific treatments exist now than in the past, and increased numbers of people who have these conditions can now lead productive, useful lives if they are treated properly.

Behavioral health is an essential component of overall health. People seen in primary care settings with chronic medical conditions—such as diabetes, asthma, and cardiovascular disorders—have a higher probability of having a substance use disorder or more common mental health disorders, such as depression and anxiety disorders. Coexistence of mental health or substance use disorders with general medical conditions complicates the management of both.

People who have more severe behavioral health conditions—such as psychotic disorders, complex bipolar disorders, treatment-resistant depression, severe obsessive–compulsive disorder, and substance use disorders—commonly have or develop medical problems such as diabetes or heart disease and often die early, as much as two decades earlier than the general population.

Although behavioral health and overall health are fundamentally linked, systems of care for general medical, mental health, and substance use disorders are splintered. For historical, cultural, financial, and regulatory reasons, the three care systems operate separately from one another.

People who have co-occurring behavioral health and general medical conditions make up a high fraction of the so-called super user group. The extra health care costs due to the co-occurrence of medical, mental health, and substance use disorders were estimated to be $293 billion in 2012 for all beneficiaries in the United States. Most of the increased cost for those who have comorbid mental health and substance use disorders is due to medical services, so there is a potential for substantial savings through integration of behavioral and medical services (Melek et al., 2014).

We have an "execution" problem and a "know-how" problem in the fields of mental health and substance use. Although for many conditions there is still a need to develop better and more effective personalized treatments, we do have effective treatments; but we have not been successful in getting these treatments to many of the people who can benefit from them. We often fail to identify, engage, and effectively treat people in primary care settings who are suffering from behavioral health conditions. People who have severe mental health and substance use disorders have difficulty in accessing effective primary and preventive care for chronic medical conditions. Yet, there are well-tested models for providing care for people who have common behavioral health conditions in primary care settings with support from behavioral health providers. And, there are effective care models that provide integrated care for people who have complex behavioral health conditions in behavioral health settings with support from other medical care providers. In both cases, establishing a team approach fostered by an integrated care system and supported by effective use of technology needs to have high priority. We are not routinely applying accountability strategies that offer incentives to use these models. Execution is hampered by shortages and maldistribution of psychiatrists, psychologists, social workers, counselors, and other providers that care for these populations. The stigma attached to these conditions, as is often perpetuated in the mass media, still presents a challenge to getting people the care that they need. And we have substantial knowledge gaps. Currently, available treatment approaches are not always effective, and many patients are not able to achieve optimal response. We need to develop more effective treatments and learn much more about tailoring treatments to individuals. We also need to develop better strategies for implementing effective programs across large and diverse health systems.

BARRIERS TO SERVICE DELIVERY
AND COORDINATION

Three key barriers to improving well-being and health outcomes for people who have behavorial health conditions and general medical conditions need to be addressed.

A Fragmented Care System

Most Americans who have both medical and behavioral health conditions must interact with separate, siloed systems: a medical care system, a mental health care system, and a substance use service system. Each system has its own culture, regulations, financial incentives, and priorities. Each focuses on delivering a specific set of services and overlooks key questions, such as, "How can I help this person to lead a productive, satisfying life?"; "What is the full array of needs that must be addressed to make this person healthier and put him or her on a path to well-being?" Many small frontline agencies, offices, and organizations in primary care, mental health, and addiction are poorly run, poorly capitalized, and poorly staffed. They are struggling to adopt more modern approaches to patient care.

Amplifying the fragmentation is the failure to ensure that behavioral health is fully integrated into the mainstream of health information technology (HIT). Strong HIT is a cornerstone of effective coordinated and integrated care; it has the potential to enable the automated provision of outcome assessments to patients and to summarize data in practical formats to facilitate provider decision making, quality measurement, and improvement. However, behavioral health providers face key barriers of cost, sustainability, concern about privacy and information sharing in the context of behavioral health conditions, and regulation in implementing electronic health record (EHR) systems. Notably, the 2009 Health Information Technology for Economic and Clinical Health (HITECH) Act—which promotes the adoption of EHRs in medical settings, authorizes financial incentives for HIT uptake, and defines minimum acceptable standards for EHR systems—excludes behavioral health organizations and nonphysician providers from eligibility for the HIT incentive payments and thus renders EHR implementation and sustainability prohibitively expensive for many of these providers.

Until our nation establishes shared accountability in culture and in practice and integrates the various elements of its care systems, good outcomes and value-based efficient service strategies are unlikely to be achieved.

An Undersized, Poorly Distributed, and Underprepared
Behavioral Health Workforce

The diversity of health care workers required to deliver effective care of Americans who have behavioral health and complex medical conditions includes professionals with a wide array of backgrounds and skills, including physicians, psychologists, nurses, mental health and substance use counselors, care managers and coordinators, and social workers. Our current workforce is undersized and inadequately resourced, and available providers often lack the specific skills and experience to offer effective, evidence-based and integrated care. Racial, ethnic, and geographic diversity of the workforce is lacking, and there is extreme maldistribution of behavioral health professionals; people in rural and impoverished areas have limited access.

Psychiatry is the only medical specialty other than primary care in which the Association of American Medical Colleges has identified a physician shortfall, a deficit that will get progressively worse by 2025 if not addressed (IHS, 2015). According to the federal government, in 2013, the nation needed 2,800 more psychiatrists to address the gap (IHS, 2015). But the psychiatry deficit is growing. For example, the number of psychiatrists per 10,000 of population decreased from 1.28 in 2008 to 1.18 in 2013 (Bishop et al., 2016). It is difficult to see how the current national infrastructure for psychiatry training would address the gap, inasmuch as only 1,373 medical school graduates matched to psychiatry in 2016 (NRMP, 2016). The number of PhD psychologists was virtually unchanged over the same period (Olfson, 2016). Similar trends persist for social workers and substance use counselors. The constant size of the mental health and substance use provider workforce is one factor that has made it so difficult for many people who have behavioral health needs to get access to services. One recent study found that two-thirds of primary care physicians report that they cannot obtain referrals to psychiatrists for their patients in need (Roll et al., 2013). Workforce shortages exist in most areas of the country, but some locales have rather small numbers of trained professionals who are delivering behavioral health services.

Providers in different parts of our care system are not sufficiently incentivized to work efficiently as a coordinated team to identify, engage, and manage care effectively for people who have both medical and behavioral health conditions. Primary care doctors need to be effective in identifying mental health and substance use problems and in engaging patients to get the care that they need on a continuing basis. Similarly, behavioral health providers need to be prepared to identify medical problems faced by patients and either manage patients or link them to required medical care. Mental health and substance use providers often lack up-to-date training in delivery of empirically supported treatments. In addition to shortcomings in specific clinical skills, behavioral health providers often work in solo or small independent practices, and our training system has not prepared them to work effectively in teams or collaborative settings. Nor has our payment system offered incentives to encourage providers to work in these settings. Working in isolated practice settings also limits the adoption and implementation of integrated delivery approaches. In addition, reductions in public-sector programs, low percentage of commercial insurance premium attributable to behavioral health, and low market rates for these services help to keep the numbers of people entering these professions low and thereby limit access to care and the ability of providers to embrace and implement new technologies.

There are important needs and barriers regarding care for behavioral health conditions in children and youth—in whom these conditions typically emerge. There are clear benefits to early intervention, but effective treatments are often not implemented. The relative shortage of child psychiatrists serves as a major barrier to developing effective integrated care models for this population. And, there are profound challenges at the other end of the age spectrum as a consequence of the growing number of older Americans and the high prevalence of chronic conditions in this population (IOM, 2012).

Finally, our health system has not made full use of new communication technologies, such as telehealth and mobile health, to leverage the capacity of the existing behavioral health workforce. New technologies are simplifying communication with patients and offering opportunities for real-time health monitoring of patients. A major barrier has been tensions regarding information sharing and confidentiality that are specific to clinical substance use and mental health data. Emerging technologies have the capacity to overcome those barriers and improve the productivity and effectiveness of the workforce, but it is crucial to integrate new technologies with other treatment approaches so that they do not constitute an extra burden but rather become a seamless part of practice that enhances outcomes.

Payment Models That Reinforce Care Silos and Fragmentation of Care

The dominant approach to medical care and behavioral health care reimbursement is to use a fee-for-service (FFS) system. Essential elements of integrated care (outreach, provider-to-provider consultation, and population management) are often not reimbursed. FFS payment does not provide the flexibility to implement needed coordinated care effectively. Moreover, the current FFS system does not sufficiently value payment for behavioral health services (which are generally cognitive and time based, as opposed to procedure based).

In theory, bundled or capitated approaches can allow more flexibility in how resources are used by a provider and allow a broader team of professionals to coordinate the care of patients. However, the methods for implementing and pricing capitated payment arrangements are less than ideal for patients who have behavioral health conditions.

One barrier is that the wrong provider may be capitated. For example, if a physician group receives a fixed payment for managing the nonhospital care of patients, the effects of better treatment approaches on hospital use will not accrue to the provider. In the case of Medicaid, the capitated payment by a state government to a managed care organization might be distributed to individual providers by using FFS payment approaches; the actual provider has little flexibility to use the capitated payment to improve outcomes and efficiency.

One other substantial challenge in using reimbursement schemes to provide incentives to make care more effective is that the needs of patients who have behavioral health conditions can vary from one patient to another. Thus, capitated or bundled payments for patients who have behavioral health conditions need to be appropriately risk adjusted to account for differences in the expected costs of care for different patterns of problems. McGuire shows that current risk-adjustment approaches are not sophisticated enough to pay providers the fair amount for high-need patients (McGuire, 2016). That failure can lead providers and payers who use capitated payment systems to discourage the enrollment of high-need patients in a practice or plan. More work is needed to ensure that risk adjustment creates proper incentives for enrolling and effectively treating patients who have behavioral health conditions. In addition, for these payment models to work, they must properly account for the real costs of caring for people who have behavioral health conditions. As noted earlier, behavioral health conditions are the most expensive at a societal level. But the proportion of direct health care costs for these conditions has dropped substantially over the last several decades and now only makes up about 3.5 percent of the costs of commercial plans and 7 percent of public payments (Frank et al., 2009; Mark et al., 2014, 2016).

Parity laws now require insurance coverage to have the same policies to guide payments for medical care as for behavioral health care, but there are tactics that payers can use to avoid having to care for the latter. For example, the presence of inadequate networks of behavioral health providers can push patients with behavioral health conditions away from a specific managed care organization. Moreover, many people in need of behavioral health care face additional barriers when they find that a large proportion of psychiatrists have opted out of accepting public and private insurance plans (Bishop et al., 2014; Boccuti et al., 2013). Of all physician specialists, psychiatrists are least likely to accept new Medicare patients. Only 64 percent of psychiatrists report that they accept new Medicare patients in their practices, whereas 53 percent report taking new patients who have private noncapitated insurance, and 44 percent take new Medicaid patients (Bishop et al., 2014). Thus, a large number of psychiatrists accept only new patients who have the capacity to pay higher fees out of pocket (Bishop et al., 2014; Boccuti et al., 2013).

FACILITATORS OF POTENTIAL IMPROVEMENTS IN CARE

There are opportunities to overcome the barriers to effective care to improve the well-being of people who are coping with mental health disorders, substance use disorders, and medical care conditions. A new administration can take advantage of the opportunities both to improve outcomes for people who have those problems and to reduce the financial burden of the services that they need. Several key facilitators are described below.

Know-How

Effective Treatments

Abundant evidence demonstrates the acceptable efficacy of several pharmacologic, psychotherapeutic, and behavioral treatments for management of most mental health disorders. In addition, there is a substantial evidence base supporting the efficacy of psychotherapies and pharmacotherapies for treatment for substance use disorders. Recent progress led to Food and Drug Administration (FDA) approval of medications for treatment for smoking, alcohol use disorders, and opioid dependence. There are not yet FDA-approved pharmacotherapies for treatment for cannabis use disorder, stimulant use disorders (involving cocaine, amphetamine, or MDMA), or hallucinogen abuse disorders (involving ketamine, PCP, LSD, or psilocybin). With the possible exception of disulfiram (Antabuse) treatment for alcohol use disorders, which generates high rates of abstinence among fully adherent patients (the minority of treated patients), medications for addiction are more successful in reducing the intensity of use of the abused substance than in producing and sustaining abstinence. That finding has led to a growing focus on reducing the harm associated with substance use as a treatment objective that may complement that of attaining total abstinence. In addition, there are various group and individual therapeutic approaches and counseling strategies that have favorable effects on the lives of people who use such services. The growing recognition of the link between early life trauma, mental health, addiction, and poor health outcomes has led to increased interest in trauma-informed care. With the increasing evidence base, there is a need to develop, train in, and implement these approaches.

Effective Models of Care

Substantial investment in research and demonstrations has improved our understanding of what effective care is. Examples of models of care that have been demonstrated to be effective and scalable are collaborative-care models in primary care, integrated-care models in mental health clinics, team-based, assertive, community treatment programs for people who have severe mental health disorders, and early-intervention programs for first-episode psychosis.

The Current Imperative for Integration

Health care providers around the country have entered an era of business integration. Hospitals are merging, hospitals and physician practices are merging, and traditional medical care practices are affiliating more closely with mental health, substance use, long-term care, oral health, and social service providers. In part, the imperative for integration is driven by market forces that seem to encourage scale and scope in service offerings. But the integration imperative also has been encouraged by federal policy initiatives that have created financial incentives for providers to integrate, especially with a focus on services supported by Medicare and Medicaid.

Changing Approaches to Paying for Care

The first and foremost principle that has to be adopted is that payment by payers and provider agencies should be reasonable and adequate for evidence-based practices. If that simple principle is not observed, all other issues will remain difficult to solve.

In addition to integration, our national health system has been exploring a broad array of value-based payment systems that reward providers for good outcomes rather than for the volume of services provided. Experiments in changing incentives in payment systems are occurring among the three key types of payers: Medicare, Medicaid, and private insurers.

Value-based approaches and bundled payment models not only create better incentives to improve outcomes but also allow flexibility to support nontraditional services or nontraditional providers that are central to integrated care. For example, Colorado-based Rocky Mountain Health Plans is testing whether a global payment model can support the provision of behavioral services in local primary care practices. Under the Sustaining Healthcare Across Integrated Primary Care Efforts pilot, which was launched in 2012, three practices in western Colorado that have already integrated behavioral health care are receiving global payments to pay for team-based care; three integrated practices that earn FFS payments are serving as controls.

Insurance Expansion and Mental Health Parity Laws

The large increase in the number of Americans now covered by health insurance because of the Patient Protection and Affordable Care Act (ACA) facilitates improvements in the care of people who have complex conditions. And, insurance policies offered in the ACA marketplaces are required to cover behavioral health services. Furthermore, recent health parity laws prevent insurers from placing greater financial requirements (such as copayments or treatment limits) on mental health services than are placed on medical care services in any insurance policy offered. Those laws will substantially expand financial access to a full array of behavioral health services.

Technology

Advances in technology have the potential to enhance access to and quality and cost efficiency of behavioral health and mental health care.

Electronic Health Records

Quality and cost efficiency of care rely on effective and efficient communication among providers and on the smooth flow of information into and among medical records. Similar benefits could derive from EHR use in behavioral and mental health, but their adoption has been notably slow. In fact, in comparison with the rapid rise in EHR use in general medical and primary care settings, less than 20 percent of behavioral health facilities have adopted EHRs (Walker et al., 2016). Reasons for slow adoption include concerns about information sharing and confidentiality that are specific to clinical substance use and mental health data and to the cost and affordability of HIT, particularly in small and widely disseminated practice settings, which have substantial financial barriers to adoption. To realize the benefits of HIT, innovative solutions are needed to address confidentiality issues and provide incentives for behavioral health providers to purchase and use the technology in ways that are integrated into general medical systems. Innovative solutions are also needed to make the EHR more efficient, more informative, and easier for providers to use.

Technology-Enabled Therapy for Behavioral and Mental Health

Technology-based therapies that patients can access with greater ease and at lower cost than face-to-face conventional psychotherapy have been developed, such as Mood Gym (Australia National University, 2016), Beating the Blues (2015), and ThisWayUp (2016) (Richards and Richardson, 2012). Although much work remains to optimize the application of the therapies in clinical settings, evidence suggests that, with proper patient selection and appropriate strategies for successful engagement, patients who have less complicated psychiatric needs (such as for mild to moderate depression or anxiety) can derive clinical benefit at lower cost while overcoming the logistical hurdles to access, including basic availability of clinicians in a locale. Such online resources are rapidly expanding to cover a broad continuum from educational and self-help materials to modular offerings that emulate manualized, evidence-based, cognitive behavioral therapies.

Virtual visits provided by clinicians over the Internet improve access and outcomes principally by enhancing patient convenience. Compelling examples include geriatric patients who have mobility challenges and young patients who have autism and for whom transport to a doctor's office can be difficult or even prohibitive. In such instances, the ability to hold a session by video conference can reduce cancellations and "no shows" and give clinicians a better window into behavior in the actual home context.

VITAL DIRECTIONS

To improve the lives of people who have behavioral health and medical conditions, it is essential that public policy play important roles in changing the approach to delivering services to this population. The following three vital directions are critical for improving outcomes by increasing access to effective services:

- New payment approaches that recognize the costs of managing the care of patients who have complex conditions and that encourage the use of teams and technology to identify, engage, and manage the care of such patients.
- Investment in strategies and programs to expand, improve, diversify, and leverage—through technology and more efficient team-based approaches—the clinical workforce and to develop incentives to improve service in underserved areas.
- Development and implementation of clearly measurable standards to encourage dissemination of tested organizational models and to establish a culture of shared accountability to integrate the delivery of services.

Implement Payment Models That Support Service Integration

The current approach to paying for behavioral health care and general medical care will never lead providers to meet the needs of people for these types of care adequately. The emphasis is on payment for the volume of service provided, and incentives to push providers to focus on patients' outcomes are not in place.

A first public policy goal should be greater use of payment approaches that offer incentives to providers to improve outcomes by paying adequately for evidence-based services. Current trends toward more integration of service capacity among health care providers will make it more likely that the provider system will develop care approaches that meet the varied needs of people who are facing behavioral health challenges.

To design a payment system that works, we need a blend of policy strategies that create incentives for good care for the full array of patients who have behavioral health conditions:

- Payment models should encourage quality and value, as well as allow flexibility, so that providers can choose management strategies that will lead to the best possible outcomes. Through Medicare and Medicaid, the federal government can lead the way in the transition to value-based payment.
- People who have complex behavioral health and medical conditions should be specifically encouraged to enroll in Medicaid programs and exchange policies offered through the ACA.
- Payments should be risk adjusted with sophisticated methods so that providers are paid appropriately to ensure that adequate resources flow to providers who care for the neediest in our population.
- Regulations to complement new reimbursement approaches should be implemented so that there is a level playing field for providers and so that delivery of adequate care will be guaranteed.

Such strategies should have high priority in the coming years and could lead to better outcomes and more efficient use of our medical care investment.

Train a Workforce Skilled in Managing Behavioral Health Conditions

The workforce needs to grow and diversify to meet the demand to engage and serve people who have mental health and substance use disorders more effectively. Access to insurance is growing, but insurance is not valuable if there are no providers to deliver needed services. The development of innovative organizational models for managing behavioral health conditions is laudable, but they will not be sufficiently implemented if there is not a workforce that understands and is trained to deliver services with the new models of care that have been tested in careful studies.

A new administration should give high policy priority to ensuring that our health system workforce can deliver the services required to improve outcomes for people who have behavioral health conditions. Three policy approaches could contribute:

- *Fund well-tested programs that could encourage new entry into the behavioral health services field.* A wide array of federal programs supports the training of physicians and other traditional medical care providers, such as nurses and dentists. For example, the federal Bureau of Health Workforce oversees loan repayment programs for physicians and dentists, and scholarship programs are aimed at increasing the numbers of primary care physicians, dentists, and nurses. Those programs should be expanded and should focus on increasing the numbers of professionals who care for people who have mental health and substance use disorders.
- *Provide opportunities for providers to learn principles of care coordination and of teamwork.* Building an effective workforce to improve outcomes of people who have mental health and substance use disorders requires more than scaling up of the workforce. Public policies should also focus on new skills for members of the workforce. Educational programs directed at the skills needed to work in teams and the skills needed for effective care coordination are needed around the country. Similarly, primary care physicians need additional training to be comfortable in working collaboratively with providers of care for mental health and substance use disorders because they must often manage patients who have these conditions, especially patients whose disorders are mild to moderate.
- *Spread use of new technologies that leverage the workforce.* New technologies that can help leverage the skills of providers in this field are being developed each year. For example, telehealth technologies can link psychiatrists to primary care providers in rural areas who require help in diagnosing problems and developing treatment plans. Public policy should correct the failure to provide the needed incentives for behavioral health organizations and providers to invest in and use tools and information systems to "defragment" care and accelerate the development of new technologies that assist in managing behavioral health care. Federal policies should fund training to help the existing workforce to learn how to use technology more effectively to leverage the ability to treat as many patients as possible and as effectively as possible.

Develop Incentives to Disseminate Tested Organizational Models

A third vital direction for public policy in behavioral health is to fund improvements in know-how for building better care models, in organizational strategies, and in accountability to attain better outcomes.

Expand Investment to Develop, Evaluate, and Implement Behavioral Health Quality Measures

Better care models can be identified only when there are clear, routinely collected quality measures for tracking the effectiveness of health care integration. Several strategies could support development of measures at the interfaces between behavioral health care and general medical care:

- Expanding expectations for health systems to establish structural mechanisms for integration of mental health care, substance abuse care, and general health care. This could include expanding requirements for accreditation or recognition programs, such as the Patient-Centered Medical Home, that focus on the population of people who have mild to moderate behavioral health conditions and are being seen in general medical settings.
- Expanding measures that focus on access to effective behavioral health care and behavioral health outcomes for patients in general medical care settings.
- Developing measures to assess access to preventive health services, primary care, and chronic disease care for people in behavioral health care settings and to assess their associated outcomes.

Beyond specifically developing measurement strategies for integrated care, a lead agency should be identified that has responsibility, expertise, and resources for stewarding the field of behavioral health quality measurement to be held accountable for their development. In collaboration with other public and private stakeholders among the "six Ps"—patients, providers, practice organizations, payers, purchasers, and policymakers—that agency should develop a coordinated plan to implement this and the next two recommendations (Pincus et al., 2003).

Take Action to Overcome Barriers to Improve and Link Data Sources

Effective integration of behavioral health and general medical care must incorporate strategies to develop, implement, use, and coordinate HIT to meet the needs of consumers who have behavioral health conditions and of their health care providers and systems.

Gaps in standardizing and capturing behavioral health information must be addressed. For example, under the HITECH Act, SNOMED-CT and LOINC are mandated medical terminologies for the exchange of clinical information, but if these terminologies do not accommodate behavioral health needs, the goals of the act cannot be achieved. A recent Institute of Medicine report recommended incorporating evidence-based behavioral health psychosocial intervention in classification systems, such as Current Procedural Terminology

(IOM, 2015). Policies and regulations should include specifications for standardizing behavioral HIT among different general medical, mental health, and substance use treatment settings to ensure data sharing and data transportability. More sophisticated information exchange protocols are needed to address behavioral health privacy and security concerns. Vendors should be expected to develop EHRs that enable tagging of specific data elements with different privacy levels; this would be important for accommodating the use of consumer-driven technologies, such as mobile applications. Finally, behavioral health clinical organizations and nonphysician behavioral health providers will need funding (possibly as part of bundled payments) to assist in deploying and using HIT that meets specifications that the HITECH Act provided for hospitals and physicians.

Conduct Research to Develop the Evidence Necessary to Expand Our Treatment Armamentarium and Support a More Robust and Comprehensive Set of Standards and Measures

Standards and measures should be developed to:

- document the mechanisms underlying mental health and substance use conditions better;
- develop and test new, more effective, safer treatments;
- determine which treatments achieve the best outcomes for different types of patients, especially in the context of different comorbidities; and
- implement evidence-based treatments.

Collaboration among funding agencies and health care organizations should inform the development of a research agenda that could marry the goals of intervention development and testing with the needs of quality measurement and improvement at clinical, organizational, and policy levels.

CONCLUSIONS AND SUMMARY

We face substantial and enduring challenges to improve the lives of many Americans who cope with mental health and substance use disorders. Those disorders are often chronic, and recovery can be a lifelong process, but better outcomes and the potential for better life courses are within easy reach for our society. There are barriers to progress, but our nation is at a moment when there also are many facilitators that can help us to make striking progress in improving people's lives. We have much of the know-how that is needed, and now we need to put the know-how into action.

It will take the energy and commitment of many parts of our society to improve outcomes for people who have mental health and substance use disorders, especially in the presence of other medical problems that these people commonly face. We need supportive and supported families, supportive workplaces, supportive health providers, and supportive communities. But public policy at the federal level can also play a role in leading progress in this social challenge.

Three vital directions are offered to guide efforts to improve behavioral health care across our nation:

- **New payment approaches:** Develop and apply new payment approaches that provide fair payments that recognize the costs of managing the care of patients who have interacting medical and behavioral health conditions and encourage the use of teams and technology to implement evidence-based strategies to identify, engage, and manage the care of such people effectively.
- **Workforce development:** Invest in strategies and programs to expand, improve, diversify, and leverage—through technology and more efficient team-based approaches—the clinical workforce and to develop incentives to improve service in underserved areas.
- **Standards and incentives to disseminate tested organizational models:** Encourage and invest in improvements in know-how for building better care models, clinical and organizational strategies, and accountability mechanisms to attain better outcomes. Measurable standards must be created to implement incentives to diffuse tested organizational models and establish a culture of shared accountability to integrate the delivery of services.

There are barriers that make progress difficult, but there are also clinical and policy strategies that hold potential for enabling striking progress in improving the lives of people who face these challenges. We have much of the know-how that is needed, but we need to put it into action.

SUMMARY RECOMMENDATIONS FOR VITAL DIRECTIONS

1. Implement payment models that support service integration.
2. Train a workforce skilled in managing mental health and substance abuse in the context of integrated care.
3. Develop incentives to disseminate tested organizational models and create new approaches.

REFERENCES

Australia National University. 2016. MoodGYM Training Program. Available at https://moodgym.anu.edu.au/welcome (accessed June 29, 2016).

Beating the Blues. 2015. Available at http://www.beatingtheblues.co.uk/ (accessed June 29, 2016).

Bishop, T. F., M. J. Press, S. K. Keyhani, and H. A. Pincus. 2014. Acceptance of insurance by psychiatrists and the implications for access to mental health care. *JAMA Psychiatry* 71(2):176–181. doi: 10.1001/jamapsychiatry.2013.2862.

Bishop, T. F., J. K. Seirup, H. A. Pincus, and J. S. Ross. 2016. Population of US practicing psychiatrists declined, 2003–13, which may help explain poor access to mental health care. *Health Affairs* 25(7):1271–1277. doi: 10.1377/hlthaff.2015.1643.

Boccuti, C., C. Swoope, A. Damico, and T. Neuman. 2013. Medicare Patients' Access to Physicians: A Synthesis of the Evidence (The Henry J. Kaiser Family Foundation, December 13, 2013). Available at http://kff.org/medicare/issue-brief/medicare-patients-access-to-physicians-a-synthesis-of-the-evidence/ (accessed August 24, 2016).

Frank, R. G., H. H. Goldman, and T. G. McGuire. 2009. Trends in mental health cost growth: An expanded role for management? *Health Affairs* 28(3):649–659. doi: 10.1377/hlthaff.28.3.649.

IHS Inc. 2015. The Complexities of Physician Supply and Demand: Projections from 2013 to 2025. Prepared for the Association of American Medical Colleges. Washington, DC: Association of American Medical Colleges.

IOM. 2012. *The mental health and substance use workforce for older adults: In whose hands?* Washington, DC: The National Academies Press. doi: 10.17226/13400.

IOM. 2015. *Psychosocial interventions for mental and substance use disorders: A framework for establishing evidence-based standards.* Washington, DC: The National Academies Press. doi: 10.17226/1901.

Mark, T.L., K.R. Levit, T. Yee, and C.M. Chow. 2014. Spending on mental and substance use disorders projected to grow more slowly than all health spending through 2020. *Health Affairs.* 33(8):1407–1415. doi:10.1377/hlthaff.2014.0163.

Mark, T. L., T. Yee, K. R. Levit, J. Camacho-Cook, E. Cutler, and C. D. Carroll. 2016. Insurance financing increased for mental health conditions but not for substance use disorders, 1986–2014. *Health Affairs* 35(6):958–965. doi: 10.1377/hlthaff.2016.0002.

McGuire, T. G. 2016. Achieving mental health care parity might require changes in payments and competition. *Health Affairs* 35(6):1029–1035. doi: 10.1377/hlthaff.2016.0012.

Melek, S. P., D. T. Norris, and J. Paulus. 2014. *Economic impact of integrated medical-behavioral healthcare: Implications for psychiatry.* Denver, CO: Milliman Inc.

NRMP (National Resident Matching Program). 2016. *Results and data: 2016 Main Residency Match®.* Washington, DC: NRMP.

Olfson, M. 2016. Building the mental health workforce capacity needed to treat adults with serious mental illnesses. *Health Affairs* 35(6):983–990. doi: 10.1377/hlthaff.2015.1619.

Pincus, H. A., L. Hough , J. K. Houtsinger, B. L. Rollman, and R. G. Frank. 2003. Emerging models of depression care: Multilevel ('6 P') strategies. *International Journal of Methods in Psychiatric Research* 12(1):54–63. doi: 10.1002/mpr.142.

Richards, D., and T. Richardson. 2012. Computer-based psychological treatments for depression: A systematic review and metaanalysis. *Clinical Psychology Review* 32(4):329–342. doi: 10.1016/j.cpr.2012.02.004.

Roehrig, C. 2016. Mental disorders top the list of the most costly conditions in the United States: $201 billion. *Health Affairs* 35(6):1130–1135. doi: 10.1377/hlthaff.2015.1659.

Roll, J. M., J. K. Kennedy, M. Tran, and D. Howell. 2013. Disparities in unmet need for mental health services in the United States, 1997–2010. *Psychiatric Services* 64(1):80–82.

SAMHSA (Substance Abuse and Mental Health Services Administration). 2016. Mental and Substance Use Disorders. Available at http://www.samhsa.gov/disorders (accessed June 29, 2016).

This Way Up. 2016. Available at https://thiswayup.org.au (accessed June 29, 2016).

Walker, D., A. Mora, M. M. Demosthenidy, N. Menachemi, and M. L. Diana. 2016. Meaningful use of EHRs among hospitals ineligible for incentives lags behind that of other hospitals, 2009–2013. *Health Affairs* 35(3):495–501.

World Health Organization (WHO). 2001. Chapter 2: Burden of Mental and Behavioural Disorders. In *The World Health Report 2001.* Geneva, Switzerland: World Health Organization.

AUTHOR INFORMATION

James Knickman, PhD, is Derzon Clinical Professor, Robert F. Wagner Graduate School of Public Service, New York University. **K. Ranga Rama Krishnan, MB, ChB,** is Henry P. Russe Dean of Rush Medical College and is Senior Vice President for Medical Affairs, Rush University Medical Center.

Harold A. Pincus, MD, is Professor and Vice Chair, Department of Psychiatry, College of Physicians and Surgeons, and is Co-Director, Irving Institute for Clinical and Translational Research, Columbia University and is Director of Quality and Outcomes Research, New York Presbyterian Hospital. **Carlos Blanco, MD, PhD,** is Division Director, Division of Epidemiology, Services, and Prevention Research, National Institute on Drug Abuse, National Institutes of Health. **Dan. G. Blazer, MD, PhD, MPH,** is J.P. Gibbons Professor of Psychiatry Emeritus, Duke University Medical Center. **Molly J. Coye, MD, MPH,** is Executive in Residence, AVIA. **John H. Krystal, MD,** is Robert L. McNeil Jr. Professor of Translational Research, and Chair, Department of Psychiatry, Yale University School of Medicine. **Scott L. Rauch, MD,** is President, Psychiatrist in Chief, and Chair, Partners Psychiatry and Mental Health, McLean Hospital. **Gregory E. Simon, MD, MPH,** is Senior Investigator and Psychiatrist, Group Health Research Institute. **Benedetto Vitiello, MD,** is Chief, Treatment and Preventive Interventions Research Branch, National Institute of Mental Health, National Institutes of Health.

7

ADVANCING THE HEALTH OF COMMUNITIES AND POPULATIONS

Lynn R. Goldman, MD, MPH, Georges C. Benjamin, MD, Sandra R. Hernández, MD, David A. Kindig, MD, PhD, Shiriki K. Kumanyika, PhD, MPH, Carmen R. Nevarez, MD, MPH, Nirav R. Shah, MD, MPH, and Winston F. Wong, MD

We have a long way to go to strengthen the public health system to provide adequate protection for communities. Dollar for dollar, our health care expenditures fail to provide us with good health at the most basic level as measured by life expectancy and infant mortality. The United States spends 18 percent of its gross domestic product—more than $10,000 per person per year—on the provision of medical care and hospital services. That is 2.5 times the average of industrialized nations in the Organisation for Economic Co-operation and Development (OECD), but by any measure our population is less healthy; US life expectancy at birth is well below the OECD average, and our infant mortality is higher than that of all 26 other industrialized nations. In fact, Americans are at a disadvantage at every stage of the life cycle relative to counterparts in peer countries (NRC and IOM, 2013).

Recent events like lead contamination in drinking water in Flint, Michigan, and other cities across our country; the epidemic of obesity and related chronic diseases in the United States; outbreaks of new microorganisms in drinking water like naegleria and legionella; spread of *Aedes* mosquitos that carry tropical diseases like Zika, dengue, and chikungunya; the serious impacts of catastrophic storms like Hurricanes Katrina and Sandy; and the epidemics of opiate addiction and HIV that are reappearing across the United States are ringing alarm bells about our weak public health system.

The World Health Organization has defined health as "the state of complete physical, mental, and social well-being and not merely the absence of disease or infirmity" (WHO, 1948). Health of nations and other population groups can be compared via use of health outcome metrics that reflect both positive and negative states of health. Such metrics include "1) life expectancy from birth, or age-adjusted mortality rate; condition-specific changes in life expectancy, or condition-specific or age-specific mortality rates; and self-reported level of health, functional status, and experiential status" (Parrish, 2010).

The United States should be capable of meeting or exceeding levels of good health enjoyed by people in other countries. Most factors that influence health are embedded in daily life circumstances apart from interactions with the health care system. These factors have to do with social, environmental, and behavioral inflluences on health that affect everyone in the population. We need to address environmental factors that range from exposure to pathogens, harmful substances, and pollutants to the widely available and aggressively promoted sugary drinks; foods high in salt, fat, and sugar; tobacco; and alcohol products. Behavioral factors can be addressed, as in successful efforts to reduce smoking, but even in the case of smoking, efforts need to be intensified and directed more precisely to populations at greatest risk of tobacco-related chronic diseases. Addressing social, behavioral, and environmental factors that discourage healthy eating patterns or promote unhealthy exposures like smoking—public health—ensures conditions in which people can be healthy.

In the face of our elaborate and expensive health care system, there is direct and undeniable evidence that there are major opportunities to improve population health that lie outside this system or require fundamental changes in how the system operates. There is strong evidence that investments in prevention at the population level, via public health expenditures, are very effective in promoting health and wellness and reducing costs of medical care (McCullough et al., 2012). People who have social and economic advantages have a greater chance of achieving and maintaining good health in spite of adverse environmental exposures compared to people who are disadvantaged by such factors as chronic poverty, lack of education, racial or ethnic discrimination, and geographic isolation. In part, the poor US performance on key health measures reflects the apparent greater effect of such disadvantages in the United States than in peer countries. Peer countries may mitigate social disadvantages better through institutionalized universal and targeted social and economic programs (McLeod, et al., 2012). Health economists are beginning to demonstrate that investments in social services (along with public health) also generate positive health impacts as assessed by a number of measures including obesity, asthma, mental health status, lung cancer, heart attacks, and type 2 diabetes (Bradley et al., 2016).

As defined by Kindig and Stoddart, *population health* refers to "the health outcomes of a group of individuals, including the distribution of such outcomes within the group" (Kindig and Stoddart, 2003). Historically in the United

States (Jacobson and Teutsch, 2012), health care evolved in two, mostly separate, systems—one that provides clinical care, is largely private, and provides individual prevention and treatment to patients, and a second public health system that is mostly governmental and provides population-based health promotion and disease prevention strategies to people who reside in entire geopolitical jurisdictions. Jacobson and Teutsch have proposed that it might be clearer to use the term "total population health" when referencing actions to improve health in entire geographic regions, to distinguish this concept from the growing use of the term "population health" to reference actions to improve health among groups of people served by various health providers, health insurance systems, and/or specific governmental programs (Jacobson and Teutsch, 2012). In this paper, the term *population health* should be viewed as synonymous with the concept of *total population health*. In this context, population health is concerned not only with delivering preventive services to individuals, or groups, but also with addressing broader social and environmental determinants of health in entire regions. (Some might refer to this same concept as *community health*.)

Traditionally, the "public health" side of the US two-part health system has had the responsibility for populations in organizational and financial arrangements that are largely separated from the treatment side. Recognition of the need to bring these subsystems together has increased over time. The shift in thinking toward a more comprehensive approach to achieving population health and wellness was prominent in the advice of the Secretary for Health's Task Force on Health Promotion and Disease Prevention Objectives for 2020 and in the character of the subsequent federal health objectives for this decade (Fielding et al., 2014).

As noted below, the Patient Protection and Affordable Care Act (ACA) included a number of provisions that support total population health approaches within the health care system, including both traditional public health efforts as well as efforts to better integrate total population health and health care.

OPPORTUNITIES FOR PROGRESS AND POLICY IMPLICATIONS: A CALL FOR CHANGE

The many excellent efforts under way to revitalize, expand, and innovate in advancing the health of populations and communities indicate that the United States is at a critical inflection point for taking more deliberate and effective actions to improve public health and prevention capacity. Such efforts are both expanding access to health care and are extending outside the health sector and, if supported and expanded, create major opportunities for improving the health of populations and communities. These efforts include the establishment of the

Prevention and Public Health Fund under the ACA, community needs assessments under the ACA, the establishment of minimum standards for state and local public health programs, support of community-based programs and coalitions, a new Office of Disease Prevention in the National Institutes of Health, and health and wellness programs in corporations. These recent developments have set the stage for making major improvements in population health in the United States.

In addition, many far-reaching recommendations relevant to improving population health outcomes have emerged from the National Academies of Sciences, Engineering, and Medicine in recent years. While supporting those longer-term recommendations, this paper identifies potentially transformative initiatives that can be implemented quickly with relatively little incremental expense. These initiatives are predicated on a vision of a healthy community as a "strong, healthful and productive society, which cultivates human capital and equal opportunity. This vision rests on the recognition that outcomes such as improved life expectancy, quality of life, and health for all are shaped by interdependent social, economic, environmental, genetic, behavioral, and health care factors, and will require robust national and community-based policies and dependable resources to achieve it" (National Prevention Council, 2011).

These recent developments set the stage for a number of specific opportunities to set the nation's prevention and public health efforts on a new path *(Figure 7-1)*.

GOAL 1: SUPPORT STRONG NATIONAL PUBLIC HEALTH OBJECTIVES WITH LEADERSHIP AND INVESTMENTS

The achievement of health goals for communities—total populations—is quite challenging in that many of the factors that influence health are not, and never will be, controlled or directed by the health sector. Public health leaders exert influence in many ways, for example, with information and recommendations (e.g., successive Surgeon General's reports), through influencing (e.g., First Lady Michelle Obama's campaign to promote healthy eating and physical activity), and through work in local communities.

The US Department of Health and Human Services' (HHS's) Healthy People 2020 initiative, with input from thousands of members of the public and organized public health and health groups, culminated in more than 1,200 objectives, from which HHS leadership identified a set of 26 Leading Health Indicators that are tracked at various government levels (Koh et al., 2014). That approach can support implementation of a recommendation of a recent consensus study of the National Academies that "the Secretary of the

Department of Health and Human Services should adopt an interim explicit life expectancy target, establish data systems for a permanent, health-adjusted, life expectancy target, and establish a specific per capita health expenditure target to be achieved by 2030. Reaching these targets should engage all health system stakeholders in actions intended to achieve parity with averages among comparable nations on healthy life expectancy and per capita health expenditures" (NRC and IOM, 2013).

Building on this, a White House–led effort could bring to bear political leadership—across the entire federal government—to invoke more integrated action across sectors and investments in communities to achieve health via application of a Health in All Policies (HiAP) approach. Developed in Finland, HiAP has been adopted by the European Union and has been credited with resulting in an increased focus on population health in a number of areas, including social services, diet, nutrition and physical activity, alcohol policies, environmental and health consequences of transport, and mental health impact assessment of public policies (Puska and Ståhl, 2010).

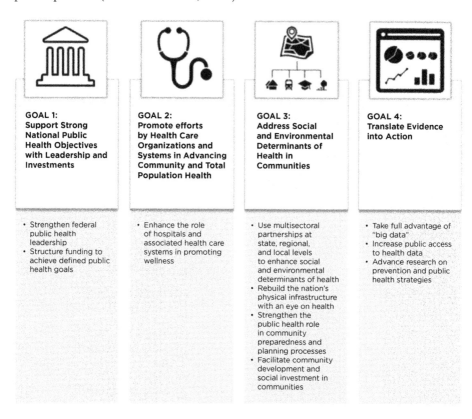

GOAL 1:
Support Strong National Public Health Objectives with Leadership and Investments

- Strengthen federal public health leadership
- Structure funding to achieve defined public health goals

GOAL 2:
Promote efforts by Health Care Organizations and Systems in Advancing Community and Total Population Health

- Enhance the role of hospitals and associated health care systems in promoting wellness

GOAL 3:
Address Social and Environmental Determinants of Health in Communities

- Use multisectoral partnerships at state, regional, and local levels to enhance social and environmental determinants of health
- Rebuild the nation's physical infrastructure with an eye on health
- Strengthen the public health role in community preparedness and planning processes
- Facilitate community development and social investment in communities

GOAL 4:
Translate Evidence into Action

- Take full advantage of "big data"
- Increase public access to health data
- Advance research on prevention and public health strategies

FIGURE 7-1 Opportunities for progress and policy implications.

Opportunity: Strengthen Federal Public Health Leadership

Within the United States the National Prevention Council (NPC) is an example of a HiAP-oriented initiative at the federal level. This Council, which is chaired by the Surgeon General, brings together representatives from 20 federal departments, agencies, and offices, including sectors such as housing, transportation, education, environment, and defense. The National Prevention Strategy (National Prevention Council, 2011), developed by the NPC with broad input from diverse stakeholders, needs to be raised to a much higher level of priority in the administration. This includes creating a stronger focus in the White House with adequate funding and decision authority to coordinate multisectoral population health and prevention efforts throughout the government and by vesting stronger authority at the highest levels in the HHS to align all HHS activities with population health and prevention goals. Such leadership in the White House could be achieved via strengthening the role of the Domestic Policy Council (DPC) in population health promotion, or via establishment of a new office. The role of the Secretary of HHS and other leaders could be elevated. Of note, both the DPC and the Secretary of HHS have congressional authority to undertake such an initiative already. Such efforts can build upon the NPC's National Prevention Strategy. Finally, the administration needs to be a clear champion of the concept that investing in prevention has high priority and has a greater proven return than does other health care investment (McCullough et al., 2012).

The HiAP approach has been supported by a tool called the Health Impact Assessment (HIA), which can be applied when a more formal assessment is required (Wernham and Teutsch, 2015). Many have suggested formal adoption of an HIA approach in the United States, and there is an emerging body of evidence for its applicability (IOM, 2014). By Executive Order, the White House could require explicit consideration of health impacts (or benefits) for major federal expenditures.

Specific White House coordination could help support activities to promote health in communities. Such an effort could build on the last administration's "Sustainable Communities" initiative (which included housing, environment, and transportation but not health.) It could benefit from a number of initiatives that have been carried out by the private sector to address housing and economic opportunity, environmental health, and access to health services in communities to improve health (Acosta et al., 2016).

Less obvious but perhaps of equal importance is tax policy. For example, there are corporate tax credits for affordable housing ($7.8 billion for 2016), wind power ($2.9 billion in 2016), and orphan-drug research ($900 million). There are exclusions and deductions for "research and experimentation" ($5.8 billion), domestic production ($13.2 billion), and charitable contributions to health organizations ($1.9 billion) (US Treasury, 2016). There are numerous opportunities in existing tax policies for the White House to enhance the health benefits for communities and promote a full-scale, population health improvement strategy.

The White House could also consider the development of an Opportunity Development Bank, a public–private partnership that is dedicated to infrastructure development and invests tax revenues at high rates of economic and social return. The investments could include early childhood interventions, preschool enhancements, juvenile justice diversion programs, high school counseling programs, adult job training programs, adult criminal rehabilitation, substance use prevention programs, housing support, and library expansions. Returns on such investment potentially can be extremely high (Washington State Institute for Public Policy, 2016). Some programs have a rate of return as high as 100 percent; the social returns can be even higher, perhaps $15 or $20 for every dollar invested.

Opportunity: Structure Funding to Achieve Defined Public Health Goals

According to the National Academies, a minimum set of public health services is needed in every community (IOM, 2012). In 2012, it recommended that Congress "authorize a dedicated, stable, and long-term financing structure to generate the enhanced federal revenue required to deliver the minimum package of public health services in every community." It also stated that "such a financing structure should be established by enacting a national tax on all medical care transactions to close the gap between currently available and needed federal funds" (IOM, 2012).

Congress and the administration can work together to define the public health services that could be supported by the federal government and others and to enact legislation that would authorize and appropriate resources, including funding, for these purposes.

GOAL 2: PROMOTE EFFORTS BY HEALTH CARE ORGANIZATIONS AND SYSTEMS IN ADVANCING COMMUNITY AND TOTAL POPULATION HEALTH

Health care organizations and systems, both public and private, need support in expanding their missions and activities to include a focus on the maintenance of good health and well-being in the people and communities that they serve. The traditional focus on disease screening and treatment reinforces a focus on health problems at a relatively late stage in the process and is not cost effective (McCullough et al., 2012). It discourages accountability for overall community and population health and engagement in the large-scale, community-based health promotion and disease prevention activities of which medical encounters are only one aspect.

For many years the public health system has been engaged in providing access to medical care for underserved populations as well as promotion of clinical preventive services like immunizations, blood pressure screening, and cancer screening. Developments of the last few years are shifting many of these clinical preventive activities into the clinical care system; at the same time, until all Americans have access to health care, the public health system will continue to be responsible for safety net function. More recently, the clinical care system is seeking the achievement of the "Triple Aim" that was proposed by the Institute for Healthcare Improvement (IHI, 2016), and seeks to simultaneously lower the costs of health care, improve the quality of health care delivery, and improve health outcomes among the populations that are served. The Centers for Medicare & Medicaid Services (CMS) has embraced the concept of population health promotion under the triple aim and there is evidence of progress in several areas. Under the ACA, federal funds can be used for US Preventive Services Task Force—approved preventive services without copay. The ACA has also permitted the use of federal health care funds for community-based prevention for the first time (the PH Trust Fund). Additionally, the movement toward Medicaid and Medicare managed care and increasing incentives for managed Medicare and Medical Homes are examples of financial incentives that are beginning to reward prevention activities in the context of individual patient care. All of these activities are laying the groundwork for more engagement of health care organizations and systems in advancing community and total population health.

Opportunity: Enhance the Role of Hospitals and Associated Health Care Systems in Promoting Wellness

Community benefits requirements for nonprofiit hospitals under Internal Revenue Service (IRS) 501(c)(3) regulations have foreseen the benefiits of changes in progressive hospital and community systems (Rosenbaum, 2016). We would favor refining community benefiits requirements to provide incentives to regional efforts and to ensure the inclusion of local health departments and public health schools and programs in analysis and planning efforts. Those efforts are accountable to hospitals' community benefits obligation, except where community benefits funds are already subsidizing Medicaid or uncompensated care, and generate a large amount of revenue, more than $24 billion in 2011 (Rosenbaum et al., 2015). Such activities include generation of community demographic and health data and community engagement and participation functions. Specific policies could include erasing the distinction between community health improvement and community building, creating a new IRS category for priorities identified in total population health needs assessments, offering incentives for multiinstitutional pooling, and encouraging hospitals to move toward allocating the full value of their tax benefit to community health improvement and charity care.

Accountable care organizations (ACOs) emerged as a component of the ACA as a means of encouraging health care providers to coordinate care throughout the spectrum of wellness, prevention, and treatment, with shared accountability and risk. Hundreds of ACOs have been formed, and some have led to better outcomes, lower total costs; and improved patient care and experiences (Kassler et al., 2015). Even so, ACOs as currently constructed entail only traditional components of medical care and have yet to develop comprehensive wellness models that incorporate other elements of prevention and wellness. For example, oral health services continue to be marginalized rather than embraced as a vital feature of population health, particularly in low-income and otherwise vulnerable populations, despite recognition by CMS in 2011 that "oral health [should be] included in . . . the Accountable Care Organization demonstration" and that the Center for Medicare and Medicaid Innovation should "develop innovative scalable models for the delivery of oral health care" (CMS, 2011). Drawing from the initial success of many ACOs, the model needs to be more expansive in this and other fields, such as mental health.

The principal role of Medicaid is to be the provider of health insurance for the poor. However, it also has a tradition of promoting health and wellness. As Medicaid continues to expand and evolve, state waivers are increasingly extending its reach to promote better health for the underserved. That affords an opportunity to test new models and partnerships between health care providers and community-based programs that have been shown to improve social conditions that promote well-being. CMS could be given more authority to waive Medicaid rules and work with states to accelerate the incorporation of prevention and population health into state Medicaid programs. Outcomes related to improved total population health and reduction in health disparities should be included as valid outcomes of Medicaid.

GOAL 3: ADDRESS SOCIAL AND ENVIRONMENTAL DETERMINANTS OF HEALTH IN COMMUNITIES

Because no two communities are exactly alike, strong community engagement not only by local public health agencies and health care providers but also by housing, environmental, financial, transportation, and other sectors is needed to address social and environmental determinants of health. How we build and maintain our homes, buildings, and cities and the infrastructure for transportation, physical activity, drinking water, and sanitation has a critical effect on our health. Moreover, communities will not be healthy unless all are served equitably. Current fragmented approaches exacerbate health inequities, but multisectoral approaches improve equity. In many ways such efforts reflect application of the HiAP approach at a local level.

Opportunity: Use Multisectoral Partnerships at State, Regional, and Local Levels to Enhance Social and Environmental Determinants of Health

To carry out the population health improvement planning and resource mobilization that we call for, the administration could stimulate and assist in funding of broad multisectoral partnerships that promote total population health. Many communities across the country already are creating community health agendas, leveraging assets, making health a locally defiined issue in which everyone has a stake, and moving policy change at the local and regional levels. But, too few health departments have the resources needed to lead such community efforts. A federal effort to support community multisectoral partnerships could be launched in 100 communities across the country in a 3-year program to establish national models. Effects measured should include educational, public safety, and economic indicators and health indicators already defiined in Healthy People 2020.

Opportunity: Rebuild the Nation's Physical Infrastructure with an Eye on Health

The brown water flowing from spigots in Flint, Michigan, is just the tip of the iceberg for the gradual breakdown in many of our drinking water systems, as well as our neglected transportation systems, sewer systems, and energy distribution systems. Large adverse health and economic consequences are already being felt directly in many communities (ASCE, 2013). We propose a multisectoral approach targeted to jurisdictions with older physical infrastructures that will engage them in an assessment of infrastructure weak spots so that they can plan for and fund community structural improvements—leveraging not only health assets but the Department of Labor, Department of Housing and Urban Development, and other relevant department efforts in a coordinated and collaborative manner. A multisectoral approach is important because much of the work could be funded by the private sector (gas, electric power, water, and sanitation utilities). In New York City, Mayor de Blasio's Underground Infrastructure Working Group is an example of an effort to bring sectors together to coordinate infrastructure repair work so that it can be done more quickly and efficiently. Congress and the executive branch could pair the effort with existing job training efforts to prepare people in low-income communities for work in the many sectors that are involved with maintenance and improvement of the physical infrastructure. Public health should inform these efforts so that infrastructure improvements address environmental health and safety issues that are critical for the health of communities.

Opportunity: Strengthen the Public Health Role in Community Preparedness and Planning Processes

Rather than respond to the "disaster of the month" (Zika virus, Ebola, hurricanes, earthquakes, floods, and the like), we need efforts to enable communities to withstand and recover from myriad disastrous events. Such efforts need to anticipate threats, minimize adverse effects on health, and rapidly restore function after a crisis. Community preparedness planning is multisectoral, but public health has an important role to play in ensuring that those who are most vulnerable (such as residents of assisted-living facilities) are protected from health consequences; in strengthening community health systems and integrating them with community resources, including the private sector; and in integrating community preparedness effort with day-to-day planning to combat the health threats posed by daily living and the epidemic of chronic diseases and prevalence of untreated mental illnesses that are the causes of premature death, disability, and diminished quality of life. Collaboration between the private and public sectors could improve the ability of communities to plan, prepare, respond, and recover. It has been shown to work during the recent H1N1 influenza outbreak in which federal, state, and local partnerships addressed a serious epidemic. Public health preparedness systems need to be adequately resourced and sustained if they are to be able to identify the emergence of new health threats and respond to them effectively.

Opportunity: Facilitate Community Development and Social Investment in Communities

Under White House leadership, broadening investment in human capital through new financial vehicles can be encouraged. We bring several ideas to the table to identify new ways to mobilize resources for total population health. Some of these could be led by the White House via consideration of tax and investment policies as described above. Others could emanate from local efforts.

The partnership of the Federal Reserve Bank, the Robert Wood Johnson Foundation, and the Kresge Foundation has played a key role in connecting financial investment in commercial development and housing to improved health in communities. In several communities, it has facilitated loans in conjunction with philanthropic investment that addresses housing and economic opportunity, environmental health, and access to health services.

Corporations can be involved in ways that go well beyond workplace wellness programs. Direct linkages between local public health agencies, business leaders, community groups, not-for-profit organizations, and the health care community can forge a common language and understanding of employee and community health problems and broaden participation in setting total population health goals and strategies. Corporations can work with government to gather, interpret, and exchange mutually useful data. They can use their knowledge of marketing and social marketing techniques to promote individual behavior and community change (IOM, 2015).

Health care systems and organizations have a key opportunity to create environments for improved population health. If they leverage the entirety of their assets—for example, as employers, purchasers, consumers, and potential energy conservers—the effect of intentional business practices can potentially improve the health of a population more than actual delivery of services. Moreover, studies suggest that a large moderate-income workforce can have a greater role in generating income in a community than a smaller high-income workforce. When income disparities narrow in a community, population health improves.

GOAL 4: TRANSLATE EVIDENCE INTO ACTION

Advancing community and population health requires acting immediately on what we know even while we are setting research priorities and funding mechanisms to strengthen the evidence base of new population health interventions. The HHS Advisory Committee on Health Promotion and Disease Prevention Objectives for 2020 identified where taking action on the basis of what we already know about interventions can improve community and population health. This includes evidence on what works and what does not work. The marked increases in the availability of health data to facilitate evidence translation and generation increase the practicability of use for prevention.

Opportunity: Take Full Advantage of "Big Data"

The use of "Big Data" is an emerging field that may be key to the promotion of population health. The term "Big Data" refers to very large datasets obtained from a variety of sources that, if appropriately managed and analyzed, can yield a wealth of detailed information to support achievement of various population health objectives. All efforts related to assessments, planning, preparedness, and development of a common understanding of facts at very granular levels geographically can help to identify social and environmental determinants of health, and give a clearer picture of health status and trends in a number of dimensions (NASEM, 2016). Efforts like the County Health Rankings project, which ranks the more than 3,000 counties in the United States based on a model that combines health outcomes with health factors, provide a basis for identifying communities that most need health improvement efforts, and for rallying support for those efforts across sectors (Remington et al., 2015).

Nationally, billions of dollars have been invested in efforts led by the Office of the National Coordinator for Health Information Technology to individual access to electronic health information as well as connectivity among systems so that information can be shared across systems while protecting data security and privacy (DeSalvo et al., 2015). No such strong national efforts have been undertaken to understand the data needs to support population health efforts. Such efforts should build on clinical data collection to support the broader advancement of population health by standardizing reporting of population health measures (for example, patient-reported measures of wellness and reported health conditions). They should also include geographic and, where possible, individual data relevant to environmental and social determinants of health. A later step would be to aggregate and release this information in a way that complies with the Health Insurance Portability and Accountability Act to allow policymakers to address issues comprehensively among sectors that currently remain siloed (i.e., to integrate across data with regard to underlying physical and social environments, with data on health and wellness, to assist with community-wide prevention efforts).

Opportunity: Increase Public Access to Health Data

HHS should expand early success in supporting public availability of health datasets and the development of informatics tools to facilitate aggregation and linkages with related datasets. Data.gov and similar efforts already have helped researchers to understand and policymakers to solve persistent problems related to health effects in association with physical and social environments, factors related to timing and identification of risk factors, and triggers of predictable events. It is of critical importance that public health researchers and policymakers work closely with the health care industry to improve its data so that it can maximize their use for population health. There are substantial opportunities for sharing and co-mingling of public and private datasets, which would advance the open-data movement to the next level.

Opportunity: Advance Research on Prevention and Public Health Strategies

Community prevention activities are too often undertaken with a weak evidentiary base, largely because the support for such research is meager. Unlike clinical practice, the practice of public health has few opportunities for product development and promotion. The onus is on government to fund public health research.

A report of the National Research Council and Institute of Medicine (IOM), *U.S. Health in International Perspective: Shorter Lives, Poorer Health,* stated that "the National Institutes of Health and other research-funding agencies should commit to a coordinated portfolio of investigator-initiated and invited research devoted to understanding the factors responsible for the US health disadvantage and potential solutions, including lessons that can be learned from other countries" (NRC and IOM, 2013). In addition, the report also recommended that the federal government increase the portion of its budget allocated to population and community-based prevention research that:

- addresses population-level health problems;
- involves a definable population and operates at the level of the whole person;
- evaluates the application of discoveries and their effects on the health of the population; and
- focuses on behavioral and environmental (social, economic, cultural, and physical) factors associated with primary and secondary prevention of disease and disability in populations.

CMS has recently funded a number of Health Care Innovation Awards, some of which support linkage between health services and community social services to support the broader needs of individual patients. They have announced an intention of expanding this approach via a recently announced 5-year, $157 million program to test a model called Accountable Health Communities. The CMS Innovation Center will use these grants to "test whether systematically identifying and addressing health-related social needs can reduce health care costs and utilization among community-dwelling Medicare and Medicaid beneficiaries" (Alley et al., 2016). Such prevention research explicitly seeks to fund itself through health care savings. However, prevention research funded by other agencies also is an excellent investment even though the costs and savings are not directly linked within their budgets.

A number of efforts have been made to encourage the National Institutes of Health (NIH) to fund more prevention research and these need to be intensified.

There are other agencies whose research programs should be strengthened: Centers for Disease Control and Prevention (CDC) and Environmental Protection Agency. Federal health research agencies need to focus not only on genetic but also social and environmental determinants of health, both discovery-oriented research about how these determinants cause ill health (or promote wellness) and translational research on how to apply this knowledge to improve health in communities. Such research needs to focus on the most vulnerable, (e.g., pregnant women, infants, children, the elderly, and those who are genetically vulnerable or immunocompromised).

In the long run, health care expenditures need to help to support a Prevention Research Trust Fund to support community-centered outcomes research just as we now have support for the Patient-Centered Outcomes Research Institute (PCORI) via the ACA. Such research could be housed in NIH or CDC as a freestanding institute on the model of or within PCORI. It should involve not only academic research but also community participatory models that are directed especially to underserved communities and social and environmental determinants of health and that empower communities to manage interventions (Selby et al., 2015). The effort would generate the evidence needed for tackling the most serious public health problems at the community level via research that is difficult to fund through existing avenues in NIH and elsewhere. Priorities for the effort should be drawn from existing expert bodies, such as the Community Preventive Services Task Force recommendations, public health professional and government organizations, and National Academies report recommendations. The research should explicitly address both costs and benefits of prevention strategies.

CONCLUSION

We have made a number of proposals, of which the most important are related to the establishment of clear points of accountability and leadership for total population health in the United States, both in the White House and in HHS. The United States can have the best community and population health in the world, but that cannot happen unless such strong public health objectives are articulated and widely shared.

We suggest that not only the public health system, but also many other entities will need to play a role if we are to be successful. Health care organizations, both public and private, need to be held accountable for promotion of good health and disease prevention, not just for treatment of the illnesses. Communities need to be accountable for bringing public health agencies together with other sectors in a number of contexts to develop a shared sense of what can be done collaboratively to promote health and to address shortcomings in our physical infrastructure and community preparedness efforts that are increasing risks. The government and the finance communities need to be brought together to pursue new financing strategies for infrastructure investment and community development, including efforts that directly address the social determinants of poor health in communities.

"Big data" needs to be harnessed to support public health and disease prevention efforts. Public health translational research is needed to move discoveries from fundamental bench science and social science to the development and testing of community and population-level interventions. Such research is unlikely to be funded unless a trust fund is created and a government entity is made accountable for ensuring that it is done.

This paper has focused on opportunities to advance the health of the nation through a lens that considers whole communities and focuses on public health or population health approaches to creating or enhancing physical and economic environments for promoting health and preventing diseases. The approaches and opportunities discussed here complement those identified in other *Vital Directions* discussion papers. In particular, public health approaches can engender transformative changes in the systems and entrenched institutional policies and practices that lower our overall standard of living and perpetuate systemic social disadvantages for some demographic groups; and they can address the "social determinants" of health and achieve health equity (Adler et al., 2016); improve options for healthy eating and physical activity (Dietz et al., 2016); and foster good physical and mental health and well-being throughout the life course. It is essential to recognize the connections among these papers to find strategies that are compatible and mutually reinforcing. For example, many communities that have poor access to services have the highest burden of mental health and substance-abuse problems (Knickman et al., 2016).

The United States has great opportunities to advance the health and well-being of communities and populations at large and to make progress both in saving lives and in reducing the cost of health care. We have identified a number of approaches for moving forward; at the core of all of them is the need to marshal and align forces across sectors and communities toward disease prevention. Achieving the highest possible level of health in communities and populations requires a rebalancing of our overall investment in ways that enhance disease prevention and wellness strategies throughout the lifespan and builds the strength and resilience of communities.

SUMMARY RECOMMENDATIONS FOR
VITAL DIRECTIONS

1. Support strong national public health objectives with leadership and investments.
2. Promote efforts by health care organizations and systems in advancing community and total population health.
3. Address social and environmental determinants of health in communities.
4. Translate evidence to action.

REFERENCES

Acosta, J., M. D. Whitley, L. W. May, T. Dubowitz, M. Williams, and A. Chandra. 2016. *Stakeholder perspectives on a culture of health: Key findings.* Santa Monica, CA: RAND Corporation.

Adler, N.E., D.M. Cutler, J.E. Jonathan, S. Galea, M. Glymour, H.K. Koh, and D. Satcher. 2016. *Addressing Social Determinants of Health and Health Disparities.* Discussion Paper, Vital Directions for Health and Health Care Series. National Academy of Medicine, Washington, DC. https://nam.edu/wp-content/uploads/2016/09/addressing-social-determinants-of-health-and-health-disparities. pdf.

Alley, D. E., C. N. Asomugha, P. H. Conway, and D. M. Sanghavi. 2016. Accountable health communities—addressing social needs through Medicare and Medicaid. New England Journal of Medicine 374:8–11.

ASCE (American Society for Civil Engineers). 2013. *2013 report card for America's infrastructure.* Reston, VA: ASCE.

Bradley, E. H., M. Canavan, E. Rogan, K. Talbert-Slagle, C. Ndumele, L. Taylor, and L.A. Curry. 2016. Variation in health outcomes: The role of spending on social services, public health, and health care, 2000–09. *Health Affairs (Millwood)* 35:760–768.

CMS (Centers for Medicare & Medicaid Services). 2011. Improving access to and utilization of oral health services for children in Medicaid and CHIP programs: CMS oral health strategy. Washington, DC: US Department of Health and Human Services.

DeSalvo, K. B., A. N. Dinkler, and L. Stevens. 2015. The US Office of the National Coordinator for Health Information Technology: Progress and promise for the future at the 10-year mark. *Annals of Emergency Medicine* 66:507–510.

Dietz, W.H., R.C. Brownson, C.E. Douglas, J.J. Dreyzehner, R.Z. Goetzel, S.L. Gortmaker, J.S. Marks, K.A. Merrigan, Pate, L.M. Powell, and M. Story. 2016. *Improving Physical Activity and Nutrition and Reducing Tobacco Use and Obesity to Prevent Chronic Disease.* Discussion Paper, Vital Directions for Health and Health Care Series. National Academy of Medicine, Washington, DC. https://nam.edu/wp-content/uploads/2016/09/chronic-disease-prevention-tobacco-physical-activity-and-nutrition-for-a-healthy-start.pdf.

Fielding, J., S. Kumanyika, and R. Manderscheid. 2014. Healthy People 2020—a strategy for improving population health in the United States. *Public Health Reviews* 35:1–24.

IHI (Institute for Healthcare Improvement). 2016. IHI Triple Aim Initiative. Cambridge, MA: IHI.

IOM (Institute of Medicine). 2012. *For the public's health: Investing in a healthier future.* Washington, DC: The National Academies Press.

IOM. 2014. *Applying a health lens to decision making in non-health sectors: Workshop summary.* Washington, DC: The National Academies Press.

IOM. 2015. *Business engagement in building healthy communities: Workshop summary.* Washington, DC: The National Academies Press.

Jacobson, D. M., and S. M. Teutsch. 2012. *An environmental scan of integrated approaches for defining and measuring total population health by the clinical care system, the government public health system, and stakeholder organizations.* Washington, DC: National Quality Forum.

Kassler, W. J., N. Tomoyasu, and P. H. Conway. 2015. Beyond a traditional payer—CMS's role in improving population health. *New England Journal of Medicine* 372:109–111.

Kindig, D., and G. Stoddart. 2003. What is population health? *American Journal of Public Health* 93:380–383.

Knickman, J., K.R.R. Krishnan, H.A. Pincus, C. Blanco, D.G. Blazer, M.J. Coye, J.H. Krystal, S .L. Rauch, G .E. Simon, and B. Vitiello. 2016. *Improving Access to Effective Care for People Who Have Mental Health and Substance Use Disorders.* Discussion Paper, Vital Directions for Health and Health Care Series. National Academy of Medicine, Washington, DC. https://nam.edu/wp-content/uploads/2016/09/improving-access-to-effective-care-for-people-who-have-mental-health-and-substance-use-disorders.pdf.

Koh, H. K., C. R. Blakey, and A. Y. Roper. 2014. Healthy People 2020: A report card on the health of the nation. *Journal of the American Medical Association* 311:2475–2476.

McCullough, J. C., F. J. Zimmerman, J. E. Fielding, and S. M. Teutsch. 2012. A health dividend for America: The opportunity cost of excess medical expenditures. *American Journal of Preventive Medicine* 43:650–654.

McLeod, C. B., P. A. Hall, A. Siddiqi, and C. Hertzman. 2012. How society shapes the health gradient: Work-related health inequalities in a comparative perspective. *Annual Review of Public Health* 33:59–73.

NASEM (National Academies of Sciences, Engineering, and Medicine). 2016. *Metrics that matter for population health action: Workshop summary.* Washington, DC: The National Academies Press.

National Prevention Council. 2011. *National Prevention Strategy.* Washington, DC: US Department of Health and Human Services, Office of the Surgeon General.

NRC (National Research Council) and IOM. 2013. *U.S. health in international perspective: Shorter lives, poorer health.* Washington, DC: The National Academies Press.

Parrish, R. 2010. Measuring population health outcomes. *Preventing Chronic Disease* 7(4):A71. Available at http://www.cdc.gov/pcd/issues/2010/jul/10_0005. htm (accessed September 11, 2016).

Puska, P., and T. Ståhl. 2010. Health in all policies—the Finnish initiative: Background, principles, and current issues. *Annual Review of Public Health* 31:315–328.

Remington, P. L., B. B. Catlin, and K. P. Gennuso. 2015. The county health rankings: Rationale and methods. *Population Health Metrics* 13:11.

Rosenbaum, S. 2016. Hospital community benefit spending: Leaning in on the social determinants of health. *Milbank Quarterly* 94:251–254.

Rosenbaum, S., D. Kindig, J. Bao, M. Byrnes, and C. O'Laughlin. 2015. The value of the nonprofit hospital tax exemption was $24.6 billion In 2011. *Health Affairs (Millwood)* 34:1225–1233.

Selby, J. V., L. Forsythe, and H. C. Sox. 2015. Stakeholder-driven comparative effectiveness research: An update from PCORI. *Journal of the American Medical Association* 314:2235–2236.

US Treasury. 2016. 2016 Tax Expeditures. US Treasury. Washington State Institute for Public Policy. 2016. *Benefit-cost results: Public health.* Olympia, WA: Washington State Institute for Public Policy.

Wernham, A., and S. M. Teutsch. 2015. Health in all policies for big cities. *Journal of Public Health Management and Practice* 21:S56–S65.

WHO (World Health Organization). 1948. Preamble: Constitution. Geneva: WHO.

AUTHOR INFORMATION

Lynn R. Goldman, MD, MPH, is Michael and Lori Milken Dean, Milken Institute, School of Public Health, George Washington University. **Georges C. Benjamin, MD,** is Executive Director, American Public Health Association. **Sandra R. Hernández, MD,** is President and CEO, California HealthCare Foundation. **David A. Kindig, MD, PhD,** is Emeritus Professor of Population Health Sciences, Emeritus Vice Chancellor for Health Sciences, University of Wisconsin-Madison School of Medicine. **Shiriki K. Kumanyika, PhD, MPH,** is Emeritus Professor of Biostatistics and Epidemiology, Center for Clinical Epidemiology and Biostatistics, Perelman School of Medicine, University of Pennsylvania. **Carmen R. Nevarez, MD, MPH,** is Vice President, External Relations, and Preventative Medicine Advisor, Public Health Institute. **Nirav R. Shah, MD, MPH,** is Senior Vice President and Chief Operating officer for Clinical Operations, Kaiser Permanente, Southern California. **Winston F. Wong, MD,** is Medical Director, National Program Office, Kaiser Permanente.

PART II

HIGH-VALUE HEALTH CARE

8

BENEFIT DESIGN TO PROMOTE EFFECTIVE, EFFICIENT, AND AFFORDABLE CARE

Michael E. Chernew, PhD, A. Mark Fendrick, MD, Sherry Glied, PhD, Karen Ignagni, MBA, Stephen Parente, PhD, Jamie Robinson, PhD, MPH, and Gail R. Wilensky, PhD

As health care spending has risen, employers have tried to alleviate the pressure on premiums and wages by increasing patients' cost sharing at the point of service. Since 2010, deductibles have increased by 67 percent and premiums by 24 percent compared with only a 10 percent increase in earnings (Long et al., 2016). Moreover, the Medicare benefit package is incomplete. Most Medicare beneficiaries purchase supplemental coverage, but rising health care premiums and policy changes, such as lower payment to Medicare Advantage plans, may create financial barriers for Medicare beneficiaries. The growth in cost sharing has led to concerns about an increase in underinsurance (when insured people must pay a large share of their income at the point of service to access care). In 2014, 23 percent of adults were underinsured compared with 13 percent in 2005 (Collins et al., 2015).

The projected increase in health care spending and associated increases in premium contributions and cost sharing create concerns about the ability of households to afford coverage or care. The form of higher spending at the household level also matters. Higher premiums make it harder for people to afford coverage, but benefit design strategies to reduce premiums (such as higher deductibles, coinsurance, and copays) increase risk, causing some unlucky households to face very high out-of-pocket spending.

Publicly financed efforts to mitigate households' financial burden of premiums and out-of-pocket spending must be weighed against the efficiency losses associated with increased taxes. It is crucial to ask how much health care we can afford to finance with tax revenue, whether directly or through tax exclusions (Glied, 1997). Ultimately, addressing concerns about affordability requires addressing the underlying issue of health care spending growth. Doing that requires some combination of supply-side interventions (such as payment reform) and demand-side interventions (including policies that affect premium contributions or cost sharing at the point of service).

This chapter discusses the theory and evidence related to demand-side strategies. It focuses on innovative private and public cost-sharing strategies, barriers to progress, and policy options.

CONCEPTUAL ISSUES

Health insurance, which mitigates risk by lowering prices at the point of service, can distort incentives for efficient consumption of care, creating what is commonly known as moral hazard. The inefficiency may take the form of overuse (for example, use of services that receive a D rating from the US Preventive Services Task Force—"there is moderate or high certainty that the service has no net benefit or that the harms outweigh the benefits") or poor shopping (failure to purchase care from low-price, high-quality providers). The lack of effective shopping probably contributes to provider prices well above marginal cost (optimal prices in most economic models are equal to marginal cost) or even inefficient investment in innovation because high prices may direct investment toward excessively priced services. Cost sharing at the point of service can mitigate those distortions.

However, cost sharing at the point of service also often induces poor decision making. For example, in a high-deductible health plan, in which there is an incentive to shop, most beneficiaries do not shop well (Brot-Goldberg et al., 2015; Sinaiko et al., 2016). Moreover, the RAND Health Insurance Experiment found that, although higher cost sharing was associated with lower spending, patients reduced use of appropriate and inappropriate services in about the same proportions (Siu et al., 1986). Other evidence suggests that higher cost sharing reduces use of high-value preventive services for chronic disease (Goldman et al., 2007). To the extent that higher cost sharing reduces use of high-value preventive or chronic care services, whatever savings result may be fully or partially offset by increased use of services related to disease exacerbations (Chandra et al., 2010; Goldman et al., 2007). High cost sharing may not have large deleterious effects on health on the average in the general population, but low-income and very sick populations are probably particularly vulnerable.

Higher out-of-pocket costs at the point of service also increase the risk faced by households (Jacobs and Claxton, 2008). With high cost sharing, households that include sicker members will face higher total costs. Many households, particularly low-income households, may not have the savings available to pay the bills; higher cost-sharing can exacerbate problems with bad debt (Daly, 2013) and even lead to bankruptcy. Pooling risk (through premiums or taxes) can help to reduce spending by those who have expensive chronic conditions or who suffer unexpected expensive health events.

Although this chapter focuses on cost sharing at the point of service, evidence also suggests that consumers do not make optimal choices among plans. For example, Abaluck and Gruber (2011) suggest that if seniors had made better choices in Medicare Part D, their welfare may have risen by 27 percent. A recent study showed that when an employer changed plan offerings in such a way that one plan was clearly inferior to one of the others, almost one-third of employees nonetheless enrolled in the inferior plan, many of them for the first time (as active enrollees) (Sinaiko and Hirth, 2011). Similarly, some patients on the exchange may unnecessarily pay higher premiums for gold or platinum when cost-sharing reductions would probably render the lower-premium silver plan just as generous (Sprung, 2015). Thus, although having consumers face the full incremental premium (the amount of the premium above the least expensive alternative) will encourage shopping for lower-premium plans and thus create competition among insurers to provide affordable, high-quality benefit packages, marketplace design must also recognize imperfection in choices.

Despite flaws in decision making (which occur in all markets), reliance on out-of-pocket payments in allocating resources is probably needed to maintain a consumer-centric system. Therefore, it is important to assess the consequences of greater risk and poor decision making and to determine how to improve choice (which will never be perfect).

Even if premiums and cost sharing are set at the economically efficient level (equal to marginal or incremental cost), they will generate socioeconomic disparities. Willingness to pay, the key determinant of consumer decisions, reflects ability to pay. Free markets lead to income-related disparities in access. Because health care market participants of high and low socioeconomic status are connected through shared-risk pools and provider networks, income-related disparities may have consequences that extend beyond the disadvantaged population.

EXISTING OPPORTUNITIES FOR PROGRESS

Efforts have been under way to develop more sophisticated tools and benefit designs that can replace the traditional blunt cost-sharing structures. Specifically, value-based insurance design (VBID) focuses on encouraging efficient use of services (with less emphasis on the provider or product chosen). Reference pricing and tiered-network products focus on encouraging more efficient choice of provider (with less emphasis on the value of the service).

Value-Based Insurance Design

In traditional benefit packages, out-of-pocket costs do not reflect the expected clinical benefit or value of care. VBID plans attempt to promote efficiency by aligning patients' out-of-pocket costs with the value of services. Specifically, VBID calls for higher cost sharing for low-value services and lower cost sharing for high-value services. VBID plans are designed with "clinical nuance" in mind, in recognition that clinical services differ in associated clinical benefit and that the clinical benefit of a specific service depends on who receives it (and where and when).

Implementation of clinically nuanced cost sharing has been driven by private payers and was included in Section 2713 of the Patient Protection and Affordable Care Act (ACA), which eliminates patient cost sharing for primary preventive services (for specified populations) as selected by the US Preventive Services Task Force, the Centers for Disease Control and Prevention, and other agencies.

Early adopters of VBID reduced cost sharing primarily for medications considered important for controlling chronic conditions. One plan that lowered cost sharing reduced nonadherence to medication by about 10 percentage points over a year (Chernew et al., 2008). The available evidence suggests that reductions in cost sharing moderately increase the use of targeted high-value services. However, achieving greater cost savings may require raising copays more aggressively for low-value services. A benefit change in the Mayo Clinic health plan that increased cost sharing for targeted overused or "preference-sensitive" services—such as diagnostic imaging, outpatient procedures, and laboratory tests—reduced their use (Shah et al., 2011).

Reference Pricing

Health insurance with low cost-sharing and wide provider networks dampens patients' interest in shopping for lower-priced, high-quality providers and thus reduces providers' incentive to compete for patients by reducing prices. That dynamic may explain the wide differences (often a factor of 10) in the prices paid for services by private insurers within and among geographic markets (Cooper et al., 2015). Reference pricing (sometimes known as reference-based benefits or reference-based payment) targets that variation in pricing, as distinct from variation in use. A sponsor (employer or insurer) identifies a point along the distribution of prices within the relevant market and limits its payment to that amount, the reference price. The insurer payment limit typically is set at the 60th or 80th percentile in the distribution; this ensures that enough providers charge below the limit. Patients often can compare prices among providers by using online transparency tools. Patients who live in remote geographic areas without access to low-priced providers are often exempted, as are patients whose physicians identify a clinical need to use a high-priced provider or product.

A patient that selects a provider that charges less than or the same amount as the reference amount obtains full insurance coverage. However, a patient that selects a provider that charges more than the reference amount pays the difference. Commonly, the additional payment does not count toward the patient's deductible or annual out-of-pocket maximum, because it is considered a network exclusion rather than a cost share. For that reason, reference-price payments are not constrained by the limits on annual out-of-pocket payments legislated as part of the ACA.

Research shows strong and consistent consumer responses to reference pricing. In one example, in the 2 years after implementation of the design, consumers increased their use of low-priced providers by 9 percent for cataract removal, 21 percent for joint replacement, 14 percent for arthroscopy, 21 percent for colonoscopy, and 25 percent for in vitro laboratory tests compared with matched control groups (Robinson and Brown, 2013; Robinson et al., 2015a,b,c, 2016). No observed effects on quality have been observed.

The savings generated by reference pricing stem mostly from changes in market shares rather than from price reductions by high-priced providers (price competition). One exception is the observed reductions in prices charged for orthopedic surgery by some initially high-priced hospitals that faced reference pricing in the California public employees' health program, which accounts for a large share of privately insured patients in some geographic markets. In other cases, the share of any one provider's patients subject to reference pricing has been far too small to induce competitive pricing strategies; this might change if the design is adopted by a larger number of payers.

Tiered and Narrow Networks

Tiered-network plans are plans that place in-network providers into multiple categories (tiers), such as preferred and nonpreferred providers. They require patients to pay more out of pocket if they receive care from nonpreferred providers. They are similar to narrow-network plans, which may not tier in-network providers but drive patients to preferred providers by dropping nonpreferred providers from the network completely.

Tiered- and narrow-network plans are similar to reference-pricing models in that they are designed to encourage patients to seek care from high-value providers, although value often reflects variation in cost more than in quality. However, whereas reference-pricing programs focus on a small number of services, tiered-network plans often address all (or nearly all) services of a given type. For example, tiered physician networks generally focus on all physician visits, and tiered hospital networks focus on all admissions (with a few exceptions, such as admissions from the emergency room). Unlike a limited or narrow network, which provides no coverage when an out-of-network provider is used, a tiered network provides coverage at nonpreferred in-network providers subject to higher cost sharing (but still well below the price of the service).

Evaluations of tiered networks generally find that they influence patient choices, but the evidence is mixed, and effect sizes are modest. For example, one study of incentives to direct care to hospitals that performed well on safety criteria found effects in only one of two groups studied, and then only for medical, not surgical, admissions (Scanlon et al., 2008). Another study of hospital tiering found that the likelihood of admission to the preferred hospitals rose by about 7 percent and admission to nonpreferred hospitals fell by a comparable percentage (Frank et al., 2015). A study of physician tiering found that it did not cause patients to switch physicians but that new patients were less likely to choose physicians in the lower tier (Sinaiko and Rosenthal, 2014).

Tiered networks raise a number of concerns (beyond the standard concerns related to cost sharing). They include patient reluctance to switch primary care providers (for tiered physician programs), a patient's physician's lack of admitting privileges at a preferred hospital, lack of patient (or referring physician) information about the tiers and thus failure to shop, challenges in measuring quality at a provider-specific level (particularly for individual physicians), and the possibility that tiering will not recognize that quality varies with service. Given those concerns, tiered-network and narrow-network plans are a work in progress. Designers are striving to balance the benefits of better choices (and lower spending) with added risk. Other plan features may enable better versions of the products to be created. For example, if providers in a narrow network work better together, the limitations on choice pose less concern.

BARRIERS TO PROGRESS

There are several barriers to more effective use of cost sharing.

Quality Measurement

Effective markets require reasonable measures of plan or provider quality. Efforts to measure quality are extensive and continuing, but they are impeded by an inability to get comprehensive data on providers (because data often are controlled by individual payers), by incomplete and imperfect measures, and by challenges in conveying the information to consumers or patients. For example, the Institute of Medicine convened a work group to identify core quality measures with the intent of providing guidance on how to reduce the number of quality measures. Boiling quality measures down to a relatively small set inevitably leaves gaps in measurement, but expanding the set of measures creates administrative burdens and communication challenges.

The details of what is being measured depend on the intent of measurement. Measuring to support patient choice of provider requires provider-specific measurement at a detailed level. For example, a quality measure of cancer care would probably need to reflect cancer type reported at a physician or practice level and adjusted for risk. That creates statistical challenges. Measures and measurement approaches used for payment (in which case aggregation of data on different conditions may be fine) may differ from those used to support clinical improvement. Much of the current attention to quality measurement has not recognized that measurement strategy must reflect intended use and that multiple measurement strategies may therefore be needed. Current quality-measurement efforts often search for a single measure set; too little attention is paid to the intent of measurement or the system of data aggregation and reporting. Existing approaches certainly help patients, but they are a long way from supporting patients' ability to shop on the basis of price and quality.

Transparency

The effectiveness of the aforementioned benefit-design tools in promoting efficiency and affordability (at least for high-value services and providers) depends on readily accessible and usable information for comparing the cost and quality of health plans, providers, and services. Many services are shoppable, but most patients do not shop (Newman et al., 2016).

To support transparency initiatives, private and public insurers recently have developed and distributed tools to inform consumers about health care quality and cost. For example, the Centers for Medicare & Medicaid Services (CMS) continues to disseminate quality information, and most large insurers and many private firms have created transparency tools to support choices of health plans and providers. There is some encouraging evidence, but it is based on a small number of clinical areas and for the very small number of patients (about 10 percent) that use the tools (Whaley et al., 2014). Broader evidence suggests a minimal effect of transparency tools on spending, in part because so few patients use them (Desai et al., 2016).

One factor limiting diffusion of transparency tools is the proprietary nature of prices (in the private sector); another is the fact that complex benefit designs result in the dependence of price to the patient on prior claims (for example, whether patients have met their deductible). In fact, CMS lacks enough information on supplemental coverage to support price-transparency efforts tailored to beneficiaries at the point of service. Moreover, cognitive problems (particularly for Medicare beneficiaries), time sensitivity, and the complex and stressful nature of medical care may limit the effectiveness of transparency tools in health care markets, but certainly some shopping is feasible and may improve (Ketcham et al., 2012).

Regulatory Barriers

A number of important regulations limit the ability of sophisticated designs to promote efficiency and affordability. These include nondiscrimination rules, which are vital in ensuring equality and access for all but limit the ability to tie cost sharing to clinical conditions even though the value of services varies by condition. For example, annual eye examinations are a quality-of-care measure for people who have diabetes mellitus but are not recommended on clinical grounds for those who do not have the condition. Network rules can limit the ability of insurers to create high-value networks and to shop aggressively on behalf of consumers. Consumer and patient protections are vital, but greater targeted flexibility, perhaps for organizations that meet quality benchmarks, could be useful.

Attitudes and Evidence

The benefit designs discussed here are offered by few large, self-insured employers. Most employers focus on traditional aspects of benefit design (such as the deductible) to increase consumer cost consciousness. It remains to be seen whether the disadvantages of high deductibles and narrow networks will be widely recognized and lead purchasers to pursue the admittedly more complex alternatives discussed above.

When given a choice, most employers (when selecting insurance on behalf of their employees) and individuals (when choosing within the ACA exchanges) prefer designs that have lower premiums and higher cost sharing over designs that have higher premiums and lower cost sharing. That may reflect familiarity with the term premium (in contrast with deductible, for example, which may be poorly understood), shortsightedness on the part of purchasers, misestimation of risk, or other information imperfections. Or, it may simply reflect a preference to bear the risks of higher cost sharing when the alternative is higher premium contributions.

POLICY IMPLICATIONS

Cadillac Tax

Under the current tax code, workers commonly do not pay income or Social Security taxes on health-insurance premiums; in contrast, wages are subject to both. That favorable treatment encourages the purchase of more comprehensive insurance, which shields people from the costs of health care at the point of service. The benefit is the largest for high-income workers inasmuch as they face the highest marginal income-tax rates. The combined effect makes the current tax treatment both inefficient and inequitable.

The ACA includes a "Cadillac tax," which limits such favorable tax treatment by placing a 40 percent excise tax, to be paid by the employer or other sponsor, on high-cost employer-provided insurance. The tax was scheduled to begin in 2018, but the start date has been delayed by 2 years. Many economists would prefer that the Cadillac tax take a different form in which any excess employer contribution would become ordinary taxable income of the employee. The "tax cap," although disproportionately affecting those in areas that have high health care costs, would make the limit clearer and shift responsibility from employers to employees, who would be encouraged to choose plans that do not exceed the limit. The plans would probably have higher cost sharing. The concerns associated with imperfections in markets discussed above, as well as equity and affordability concerns associated with higher cost sharing, may be mitigated by more sophisticated benefit design. Moreover, such a tax cap would also be more progressive than the Cadillac tax in that the marginal tax rate rises as income rises.

High-Deductible Health Plans with Health Savings Accounts

High-deductible health plans (HDHPs) coupled with health savings accounts (HSAs) are among the fastest-growing plan types. People who have HSA-eligible HDHPs are required to pay the full cost of most care until deductibles are met. Current regulations permit a "safe harbor" that allows first-dollar coverage of primary preventive services before satisfaction of the deductible. Services meant to treat "an existing illness, injury, or condition" are excluded from predeductible coverage in HSA-eligible HDHPs. Evidence shows that consumers who switch to an HDHP reduce use of all services, including potentially valuable care and wasteful services (Brot-Goldberg et al., 2015).

Theoretically, HDHPs could adopt a more flexible benefit design that offers more protection for high-value services through a value-based plan structure. A strategy that explores allowing predeductible coverage for some high-value, clinically indicated health services on the basis of actuarial value to limit the cost of such additions could produce more effective high-value health–plan designs without fundamentally altering the original intent and spirit of the plans. That could be particularly important for treatments for chronic diseases, which account for 75 percent of total US health spending.

Clinically nuanced, or "smarter," deductibles might be a natural evolution of HDHPs in that cost sharing might be reduced for high-value services and providers and increased for low-value services and providers. That would require greater efforts to measure high-value and low-value services that depend on clinical condition, but as the market for HSA-eligible HDHPs grows, it is important that they avoid creating barriers to access the services that prevent deleterious consequences of chronic disease—services that are among the most important for high-cost patients.

Medicare Benefit Design

The Medicare benefit package has many gaps, including gaps in coverage for long-term care services, dental care, eyeglasses, and hearing aids (Henry J. Kaiser Family Foundation, 2014). Unlike most private insurance plans, Medicare does not have a limit on out-of-pocket costs. Thus, beneficiaries face potentially catastrophic out-of-pocket costs (Cubanski et al., 2014). To avoid such costs, many enroll in supplemental insurance plans that have additional premiums, but these plans, sold separately, increase Medicare spending because Medicare pays a share of the cost of induced use.

One solution would be to restructure the currently fragmented Medicare benefit package (Parts A, B, and D) to provide comprehensive benefits to beneficiaries with lower deductibles and a limit on out-of-pocket costs. Several variants have been proposed, some including Medicare provision of supplemental coverage for an added premium (Aaron and Reischauer, 2015; Davis et al., 2013; Ginsberg and Rivlin, 2015). Because this is premium-financed, it would not have an adverse budgetary effect. Estimates related to one such proposal predict that beneficiaries would spend 17 percent less than what they are spending if they have traditional Medicare with Part D and a Medigap supplemental plan (Davis et al., 2013).

VITAL DIRECTIONS

Rising health care spending has created serious challenges for purchasers in the American health care system. Solutions will require both supply-side and demand-side interventions if they are to improve the effectiveness and efficiency of care to maintain affordability. The different types of strategies are not mutually exclusive but should be harmonized in recognition that neither is perfect.

Demand-side strategies, for example, impose risk and may exacerbate socio-economic disparities. Nevertheless, beneficiary cost sharing will probably be an important feature of the health care system, and we should strive to ensure that benefit designs do not create barriers to but instead encourage access to high-value services from high-value providers.

In that spirit, we offer four vital directions:

1. **Modify safe-harbor regulations for HSA-HDHP plans to permit first-dollar coverage of high-value services.** Effective management of chronic disease is important for creating value in the health care system. Existing rules force HSA-eligible HDHPs to create financial barriers to chronic-disease management, which both discourages takeup of these plans and may lead to deleterious outcomes for enrollees. Redesign of the rules to allow more flexibility in the context of an HDHP could help promote efficient use of care without substantially altering the average plan generosity.

2. **Standardize plans offered on the exchange to incorporate principles of value-based insurance design.** Given the relatively low actuarial values of plans on the exchange, optimizing the designs to support value-based insurance and shopping (without raising actuarial values) could be important. Standardization is important to support plan choice, but the standardized plans should promote value. Covered California has moved in that direction by lowering copays and removing deductibles for primary care services for most enrollees, but more progress could be made.

3. **Redesign the Medicare benefit package.** The Medicare benefit package has many gaps and does not have a limit on out-of-pocket costs. Over time, supplemental coverage may become less generous and more expensive. Redesigning the benefit package to provide comprehensive benefits with lower deductibles and a limit on out-of-pocket costs and with financing by added premiums could help to provide more effective risk protection without a substantial federal budgetary effect. Beneficiaries may pay less because they would not need to buy supplemental coverage.

4. **Limit the favorable tax treatment of insurance.** Favorable tax treatment of insurance is regressive and discourages efficient benefit design. Limiting the tax deductibility of coverage by implementing the Cadillac tax or, preferably, imposing a similar alternative, such as a tax cap, would support efforts to design efficient benefit packages. However, it must be done in a way that uses some of the added revenue to mitigate the adverse consequences, particularly the burden on lower-income taxpayers.

Tradeoffs are inevitable. No policies are perfect. The ultimate test of any health-reform proposal will be whether it improves health and addresses rising costs. Flexibility in benefit design that allows better alignment with value is one leg of the stool and can transform a system driven by incentives to increase volume into a system that encourages better outcomes at an affordable cost.

SUMMARY RECOMMENDATIONS FOR VITAL DIRECTIONS

1. Modify safe-harbor regulations for health savings account-eligible high-deductible health plans (HSA-HDHP) to permit first-dollar coverage of high-value services.
2. Standardize plans offered on the exchange to incorporate principles of value-based insurance design.
3. Redesign the Medicare benefit package.
4. Limit the favorable tax treatment of insurance.

REFERENCES

Aaron, H., and R. Reischauer. 2015. The transformation of Medicare, 2015 to 2030. *Forum for Health Economics and Policy* 18(2):119–136.

Abaluck, J., and J. Gruber. 2011. Choice inconsistencies among the elderly: Evidence from plan choice in the Medicare Part D program. *American Economic Review* 101:1180–1210.

Brot-Goldberg, Z., A. Chandra, B. Handel, and J. Kolstad. 2015. What Does a Deductible Do? The Impact of Cost-Sharing on Health Care Prices, Quantities, and Spending Dynamics. National Bureau of Economic Research Working Paper 21632.

Chandra, A., J. Gruber, and R. McKnight. 2010. Patient cost-sharing and hospitalization offsets in the elderly. *American Economic Review* 100(1):193–213.

Chernew, M., M. Shah, A. Wegh, S. Rosenberg, I. Juster, A. Rosen, M. Sokol, K. Yu-Isenberg, and A.M. Fendrick. 2008. Impact of decreasing copayments on medication adherence within a disease management environment. *Health Affairs* 27(1):103–112.

Collins, S., P. Rasmussen, S. Beutel, and M. Doty. 2015. *The problem of under-insurance and how rising deductibles will make it worse.* The Commonwealth

Fund. Available at http://www.commonwealthfund.org/publications/issue-briefs/2015/may/problem-of-underinsurance (accessed June 7, 2016).

Cooper, Z., S. Craig, M. Gaynor, and J. Van Reenen. 2015. The Price Ain't Right? Hospital Prices and Health Spending on the Privately Insured. National Bureau of Economic Research Working Paper 21815.

Cubanski, J., C. Swoope, A. Damico, and T. Neuman. 2014. *How much is enough? Out-of-pocket spending among Medicare beneficiaries: A chartbook.* The Henry J. Kaiser Family Foundation. Available at http://kff.org/medicare/report/how-much-is-enough-out-of-pocket-spending-among-medicare-beneficiaries-a-chartbook/ (accessed June 15, 2016).

Daly, R. 2013. Shifting burdens: Hospitals increasingly concerned over effects of cost-sharing provisions in health plans to be offered through insurance exchanges. *Modern Healthcare.* Available at http://www.modernhealthcare.com/article/20130615/MAGAZINE/306159953 (accessed May 25, 2016).

Davis, K., C. Schoen, and S. Guterman. 2013. *Medicare essential: An option to promote better care and curb spending growth.* The Commonwealth Fund. Available at http://www.commonwealthfund.org/~/media/files/publications/in-the-literature/2013/may/1689_davis_medicare_essential_ha_05_2013_itl.pdf (accessed May 29, 2016).

Desai, S., L. Hatfield, A. Hicks, M. Chernew, and A. Mehrotra. 2016. Association between availability of a price transparency tool and outpatient spending. *Journal of the American Medical Association* 315(17):1874–1881.

Frank, M. B., J. Hsu, M. B. Landrum, and M. E. Chernew. 2015. The impact of a tiered network on hospital choice. *Health Services Research* 50(5):1628–1648.

Ginsberg, P., and A. Rivlin. 2015. Challenges for Medicare at 50. *New England Journal of Medicine* 373:1993–1995.

Glied, S. 1997. *Chronic condition: Why health reform fails.* Cambridge, MA: Harvard University Press.

Goldman, D., G. Joyce, and Y. Zheng. 2007. Prescription drug cost sharing: Associations with medication and medical utilization and spending and health. *Journal of the American Medical Association* 298(1):61–69.

The Henry J. Kaiser Family Foundation. 2014. Medicare at a Glance. Available at http://kff.org/medicare/fact-sheet/medicare-at-a-glance-fact-sheet/ (accessed June 18, 2016).

Jacobs, P., and G. Claxton. 2008. Comparing the assets of uninsured households to cost sharing under high-deductible health plans. *Health Affairs* 27(3).

Ketcham, J., C. Lucarelli, E. Miravete, and M. C. Roebuck. 2012. Sinking, swimming, or learning to swim in Medicare Part D. *American Economic Review* 102(6):2639–2673.

Long, M., M. Rae, G. Claxton, A. Jankiewicz, and D. Rousseau. 2016. Recent trends in employer-sponsored health insurance premiums. *Journal of the American Medical Association* 315(1):18.

Newman, D., E. Barrette, S. Parente, and K. Kennedy. 2016. An examination of commercially insured health care service prices in the U.S. *Health Affairs* 35(5):923–927.

Robinson, J., and T. Brown. 2013. Increases in consumer cost sharing redirect patient volume and reduce hospital prices for orthopedic surgery. *Health Affairs* 32(8):1392–1397.

Robinson, J., T. Brown, and C. Whaley. 2015a. Reference-based benefit design changes consumers' choices and employers' payments for ambulatory surgery. *Health Affairs* 34(3):415–422.

Robinson, J., T. Brown, C. Whaley, and K. Bozic. 2015b. Consumer choice between hospital-based and freestanding facilities for arthroscopy. *Journal of Bone and Joint Surgery* 97:1473–1481.

Robinson, J., T. Brown, C. Whaley, and E. Finlayson. 2015c. Association of reference payment for colonoscopy with consumer choices, insurer spending, and procedural complications. *JAMA Internal Medicine* 175(11):1783–1791.

Robinson, J., C. Whaley, and T. Brown. 2016. Impact of reference pricing on consumer choices, laboratory prices, and total spending for diagnostic tests. *JAMA Internal Medicine* 176(9):1353–1359.

Scanlon, D., R. Lindrooth, and J. Christianson. 2008. Steering patients to safer hospitals? The effect of a tiered hospital network on hospital admissions. *Health Services Research* 43(5):1849–1868.

Shah, N., J. Naessens, D. Wood, R. Stroebel, W. Litchy, A. Wagie, J. Fan, and R. Nesse. 2011. Mayo Clinic employees responded to new requirements for cost sharing by reducing possibly unneeded health services use. *Health Affairs* 30(11):2134–2141.

Sinaiko, A., and R. Hirth. 2011. Consumers, health insurance, and dominated choices. *Journal of Health Economics* 30(2):450–457.

Sinaiko, A., and M. Rosenthal. 2014. The impact of tiered physician networks on patient choices. *Health Services Research* 49(4):1348–1363.

Sinaiko, A., A. Mehrotra, and N. Sood. 2016. Cost-sharing obligations, high-deductible health plan growth, and shopping for health care: Enrollees with skin in the game. *JAMA Internal Medicine* 176(3):395–397.

Siu, A., F. Sonnenberg, W. Manning, G. Goldberg, E. Bloomfield, J. Newhouse, and R. Brook. 1986. Inappropriate use of hospitals in a randomized trial of health insurance plans. *New England Journal of Medicine* 315:1259–1266.

Sprung, A. 2015. When Silver is worth more than Gold or Platinum: Media coverage of high out-of-pocket costs neglects to note that ACA's Silver plans are often worth more than their weight in gold. Available at https://www.healthinsurance.org/blog/2015/06/12/when-silver-is-worth-more-than-gold-or-platinum/ (accessed August 1, 2016).

Whaley, C., J. Chafen, S. Pinkard, G. Kellerman, D. Bravata, R. Kocher, and N. Sood. 2014. Association between availability of health service prices and payments for these services. *Journal of the American Medical Association* 312(16):1670–1676.

AUTHOR INFORMATION

Michael E. Chernew, PhD, is the Leonard D. Schaeffer Professor, Director, Healthcare Markets and Regulation, Harvard Medical School. **A. Mark Fendrick, MD,** is Professor, Department of Internal Medicine and Department of Health Management and Policy, University of Michigan. **Sherry Glied, PhD,** is Dean, Robert F. Wagner Graduate School of Public Service, New York University. **Karen Ignagni, MBA,** is President and CEO, EmblemHealth. **Stephen Parente, PhD,** is Professor and Director, Medical Industry Leadership Institute, Carlson School of Management, University of Minnesota. **Jamie Robinson, PhD, MPH,** is Leonard D. Schaeffer Professor of Health Economics and Director, Berkley Center for Health Technology and is Head, Division of Health Policy and Management, School of Public Health, University of California, Berkley. **Gail R. Wilensky, PhD,** is Senior Fellow, Project HOPE.

9

PAYMENT REFORM FOR BETTER VALUE AND MEDICAL INNOVATION

Mark B. McClellan, MD, PhD, David T. Feinberg, MD, MBA, Peter B. Bach, MD, Paul Chew, MD, Patrick Conway, MD, Nick Leschly, MBA, Greg Marchand, Michael A. Mussallem, and Dorothy Teeter, MHA

Over the past 50–60 years, biomedical science and technology in the United States have advanced at a remarkable pace, allowing Americans to live longer, healthier lives. And, while we have gained tremendous benefit from continuous medical innovation, health care delivery has simultaneously become more complex, expensive, and, in some ways, less patient-centric (IOM, 2001). In 2015, US health care spending grew 5.8 percent, totaling $3.2 trillion or close to 18 percent of GDP (CMS, 2016a), and it has been estimated that upward of 30 percent of health expenditures may not contribute to health improvement (IOM, 2013). In tandem, health indicators and outcomes in the US are lagging, including measures of access, efficiency, equity, and quality (IOM and NRC, 2013). And, while these trends could be attributed to myriad factors, ultimately, how we pay for care strongly influences how care is delivered (IOM, 2013). With fee-for-service (FFS)—the longstanding, traditional payment model used in the US—health care services are paid for individually and aggregate payment is driven by the volume of services rendered. In an effort to rein in health care costs, increase clinical efficiency, encourage greater coordination among providers to better meet the needs of patients, and provide value for true engagement of patients' and family members' care decisions, payment reform efforts are focusing on value-based models of care delivery. These models aim to incentivize providers to keep their patients healthy, and to treat those with acute or chronic conditions with cost-effective, evidence-based treatments.

Value-based payment strives to promote the best care at the lowest cost, allowing patients to receive higher-value, higher quality care. Payment reform, with the goals of shifting provider payments and incentives from volume to value, is a health policy issue that has bipartisan support. Consistent with these goals and building on early, successful payment reform models carried out in the public and private sectors (Abrams et al., 2015), provisions contained in the Patient Protection and Affordable Care Act of 2010 (ACA) set in motion several initiatives that seek to reform how health care is paid for and delivered more broadly. Through these provisions, the law uses a multipronged approach to instituting reforms, focusing on: testing new payment and care delivery models that aim to increase care coordination, quality, and efficiency (e.g., patient-centered medical homes and accountable care organizations); shifting the provider reimbursement system orientation to outcomes rather than services; and investing in methods to improve health system efficiency, such as issuing grants to establish community health teams to support a medical home model (Abrams et al., 2015; Davis et al., 2010).

Payment and delivery reform, alongside related legislative and regulatory changes, has the potential to make transformative models of health care delivery more sustainable, with the promise of better outcomes, lower costs, and more support for investment in new treatments that are truly valuable. Simultaneously, the potential for medical innovations to improve the patient care experience, produce better health outcomes, and reduce health cost seems greater than ever. This includes new treatments for unmet needs, new cures, innovations in digital health, much larger data analytics, and team-based care that is much more prevention-oriented, convenient, and personalized. As with most transformative change, transitioning to value-based models of care delivery and payment has been met with some challenges. While payment reforms have shown some promising results, overall impacts on spending trends have been modest and critical obstacles remain to successful implementation, including inadequate performance measures, regulatory barriers, insufficient evidence on successful models, and limited knowledge of the competencies required for providers to succeed within this new paradigm. Policymakers will need to address and mitigate these and other challenges as they chart the next steps of payment reform. This discussion paper seeks to highlight payment reform initiatives underway, underscore pressing challenges in need of attention, and provide recommended vital directions to advance reform and better ensure its success.

PAYMENT REFORM INITIATIVES
AND STAKEHOLDER CONTRIBUTIONS

The Center for Medicare and Medicaid Innovation's Pilot Initiatives

Among the most significant of the payment reform provisions contained in the ACA is the creation of the Center for Medicare and Medicaid Innovation (CMMI or "Innovation Center") within the Centers for Medicare and Medicaid

Services (CMS), which went into effect in 2011. The Innovation Center was established to identify, develop, assess, support, and spread new payment and delivery models that hold significant promise for lowering expenditures under Medicare, Medicaid, and the Children's Health Insurance Program (CHIP), while simultaneously improving or maintaining quality of care delivered (Berenson and Cafarella, 2012; Abrams et al., 2015). The law authorizes the Secretary of Health and Human Services (HHS) to spread successful CMMI-supported payment innovations, if sufficient evidence exists demonstrating reduced costs and improved outcomes (Guterman et al., 2010). The law appropriates $10 billion to the Innovation Center every 10 years; CMMI received the first $10 billion for 2011–2019 to execute pilot programs initiated during this time. The law identified several priorities and existing models that CMMI ought to consider in constructing its pilots, emphasizing reforms to promote care coordination, encourage efficient and high-quality care, and improve patient safety. The Innovation Center organizes its innovation models into seven categories (*Table 9-1*). Currently, CMMI has 33 ongoing pilot initiatives across these categories, and another 25 initiatives under development, announced, or just getting started (CMS, 2016b).

Patient-centered medical homes (medical homes), accountable care organizations (ACOs), and bundled payments are among the most commonly cited and discussed alternative payment models. A *medical home* is a model that provides care that is comprehensive, patient-centered, coordinated and team-based, accessible, high-quality, and safe (AHRQ, 2016). Medical home models rely heavily on a primary care practice to deliver and coordinate the majority of care for the beneficiary. An *accountable care organization* is a group of health care providers, such as doctors, hospitals, health plans, who voluntarily come together to provide coordinated, high-quality care to populations of patients, and agree to assume responsibility for the quality and costs of care provided. To encourage the formation of ACOs, the ACA established the Medicare Shared Savings Program, whereby participating ACOs could keep half of the resulting savings if they met the quality benchmarks established and kept costs below budget. ACOs could also enter into a "two-sided risk" model—with potential shared savings of up to 60 percent, if total savings exceed the minimum savings rate—which would require the ACO to pay for a portion of the losses if spending were to go beyond the established budget. While participation in the Shared Savings Program exceeded expectations, overall performance results have been mixed (Abrams et al., 2015). Finally, a *bundled payment* reimburses the provider(s) in a single payment for all the services required to treat a specific condition or provide a specific treatment over a defined period of time. Bundled payments incentivize providers to come in below budget for a given care episode.

TABLE 9-1 | CMMI Innovation Initiative Categories

INITIATIVE	DESCRIPTION	EXAMPLE PROGRAMS
Accountable Care	Accountable Care Organizations and similar care models are designed to incentivize health care providers to become accountable for a patient population and to invest in infrastructure and redesigned care processes that provide for coordinated care, high quality and efficient service delivery.	• Pioneer ACOs • Medicare Health Care Quality Demonstration • Comprehensive ERSD Care Model • Rural Community Hospital Demonstration
Episode-Based Payment	Under these models, health care providers are held accountable for the cost and quality of care beneficiaries receive during an episode of care, which usually begins with a triggering health care event (such as a hospitalization or chemotherapy administration) and extends for a limited period of time thereafter.	• Bundled Payments for Care Improvement Models
Primary Care Transformation	Primary care providers are a key point of contact for patients' health care needs. Strengthening and increasing access to primary care is critical to promoting health and reducing overall health care costs. Advanced primary care practices—also called "medical homes"—utilize a team-based approach, while emphasizing prevention, health information technology, care coordination, and shared decision making among patients and their providers.	• Advanced Primary Care Practice (medical home) • Comprehensive Primary Care Initiative • Independence at Home Demonstration • Multi-Payer Advanced Primary Care Practice Demonstration
Medicaid and CHIP	Medicaid and the Children's Health Insurance Program (CHIP) are administered by the states but are jointly funded by the federal government and states. Initiatives in this category are administered by the participating states.	• Medicaid Innovation Accelerator Program • Medicaid Incentives for Prevention of Chronic Diseases • Strong Start for Mothers and Newborns
Dual-Eligibles (Medicare-Medicaid)	The Medicare and Medicaid programs were designed with distinct purposes. Individuals enrolled in both Medicare and Medicaid (the "dual eligibles") account for a disproportionate share of the programs' expenditures. A fully integrated, person-centered system of care that ensures that all their needs are met could better serve this population in a high quality, cost effective manner.	• Financial Alignment Initiative • Initiative to Reduce Avoidable Hospitalization Among Nursing Facility Residents
New Payment, Service Delivery, and Accountability Models	Many innovations necessary to improve the health care system will come from local communities and health care leaders from across the entire country. By partnering with these local and regional stakeholders, CMS can help accelerate the testing of models today that may be the next breakthrough tomorrow.	• Accountable Health Communities Model • Health Care Innovation Awards • Health Plan Innovation Initiatives • State Innovation Models
Best Practices Adoption	The Innovation Center is partnering with a broad range of health care providers, federal agencies professional societies and other experts and stakeholders to test new models for disseminating evidence-based best practices and significantly increasing the speed of adoption.	• Community-based Care Transitions Program • Health Care Payment Learning and Action Network • Partnership for Patients

SOURCE: CMS, 2016.

HHS's Historic Shift to Alternative Payment Models

In January 2015, the Department of Health and Human Services (HHS) made a historic announcement, setting a timeline with specific, measurable goals to shift Medicare and the greater health care system toward reimbursing providers through alternative payment models (APMs) (HHS, 2015). In setting its goals, HHS adopted a framework categorizing health care payment models based on how providers receive payment for the care they provide (CMS, 2015):

- Category 1: Fee-for-service with no link of payment to quality
- Category 2: Fee-for-service with a link of payment to quality
- Category 3: Alternative payment models built on fee-for-service architecture
- Category 4: Population-based payment

Value-based payments are considered those falling within categories 2–4. Based on the framework, moving from category 1 to category 4 would necessitate both increased accountability for quality and total cost of care, and shifting focus toward population health management.

In 2015, HHS set the goal of tying 30 percent of traditional (fee-for-service) Medicare payments to APMs (categories 3 and 4) by the end of 2016, and tying 50 percent of payments to APMs by the end of 2018 (CMS, 2015). HHS also set goals of tying 85 percent of all traditional Medicare payments to quality or value (categories 2–4) by 2016 and 90 percent by 2018 through programs such as the Hospital Value Based Purchasing and Hospital Readmissions Reduction Programs (*Figure 9-1*). In 2011, while over half of Medicare payments were linked to quality, practically none were in alternative payment models. By March 2016, almost a year ahead of schedule, the 2016 goals were met with 30 percent of Medicare payments tied to alternative payment models and 85 percent tied to quality. CMS continues to move toward meeting its 2018 goals.

To facilitate the scale and spread of these goals beyond Medicare, HHS created the Health Care Payment Learning and Action Network (LAN) to align stakeholders across sectors and accelerate the transition to value-based payment. Through the LAN, HHS works with private payers, employers, consumers, providers, states and state Medicaid programs, and other partners to adopt and expand APMs into their programs. Consistent with the goals set for Medicare, the LAN seeks to facilitate tying 30 percent of payments to APMs by 2016 and 50 percent by 2018 across the health care system. As part of their efforts, the LAN convened a work group to build on HHS' framework for categorizing and measuring APMs. The framework developed (*Figure 9-2*) expands upon that originally developed

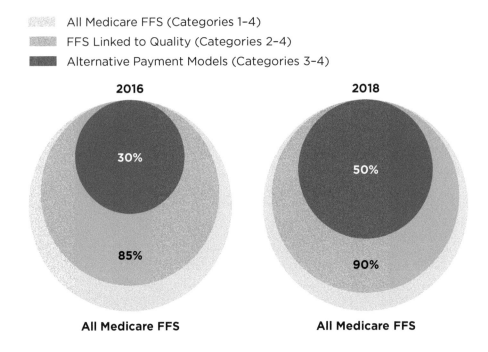

■ All Medicare FFS (Categories 1-4)
■ FFS Linked to Quality (Categories 2-4)
■ Alternative Payment Models (Categories 3-4)

FIGURE 9-1 | HHS value-based payment targets for Medicare in 2016 and 2018.
SOURCE: CMS, 2015.

by HHS (*Figure 9-3*) and includes 4 primary categories and 8 subcategories. The framework rests on 7 principles identified by the workgroup (HCPLAN, 2016):

1. Patients must be empowered as partners in health care transformation; changing providers' financial incentives is not sufficient to achieve person-centered care.
2. Health care spending must shift significantly toward population-based, more person-focused payments.
3. Value-based incentives should ideally reach the providers that deliver care.
4. Payment models that do not take quality into account are not considered APMs in the APM Framework, and do not count as progress toward payment reform.
5. Value-based incentives should be intense enough to motivate providers to invest in and adopt new approaches to care delivery.
6. APMs will be classified according to the dominant form of payment when more than one type of payment is used.

7. Centers of excellence, accountable care organizations, and patient-centered medical homes are examples of delivery systems, rather than categories, in the APM Framework.

Alongside the efforts of the LAN, many private organizations and industry consortia have set specific goals to transition to new payment models. The Health Care Transformation Task Force is an example of an industry consortium seeking to align and convene stakeholders across the private and public sectors to accelerate the adoption of value-based care. The Task Force brings together patient, payer, provider, and purchaser groups to collaborate and work together to make system transformation possible. Payer and provider members in the Task Force commit to have 75 percent of their businesses utilizing value-based payment arrangements by January 2020. Purchaser and patient members commit to building and maintaining the necessary demand, support, and education of their communities to achieve this target (HCTTF, 2016).

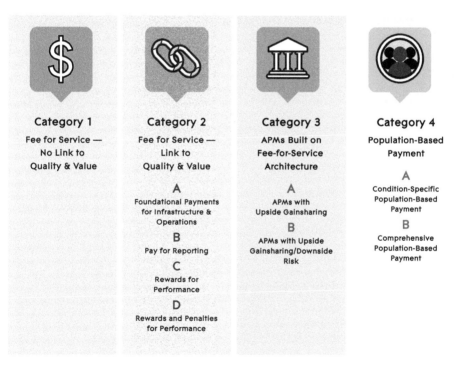

FIGURE 9-2 | Framework for Alternative Payment Models.
SOURCE: Health Care Payment Learning and Action Network, 2016.

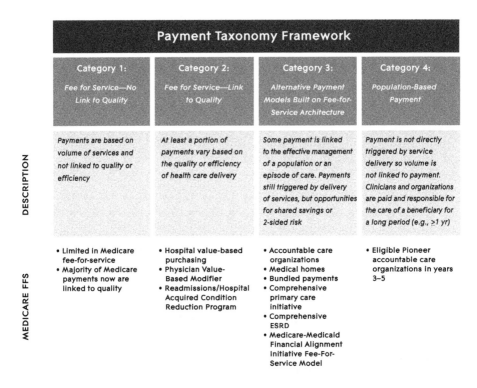

FIGURE 9-3 | HHS Payment Taxonomy Framework.
SOURCE: HHS, 2015.

Employer-Led Initiatives and Innovations

Nearly half of people with health insurance in the US receive their coverage through an employer (KFF, 2015). As the costs of health care have risen, so, too, have the financial burdens on the employers providing coverage. While some employers have responded by reducing or eliminating coverage, others have increased their involvement in efforts and initiatives that seek to curb costs and improve care quality (Schilling, 2011). Although employers have long been involved in efforts and initiatives to improve health care quality, overall, most payment reform efforts have not been spearheaded by employers (AcademyHealth et al., 2013). Many small to midsize organizations often lack the needed number of employees and/or critical competencies to drive these initiatives. Larger employers, however, with the sophistication and resources to influence change, have been capable of driving advancement in this space, often in partnership with providers. The payment reform experience of Boeing illustrates these trends (*Box 9-1*). Boeing has worked closely with health care organizations to test and

BOX 9–1

Employers Transitioning to Value-Based Care: Boeing as an Example

Boeing spends over $2.6 billion annually on health care coverage for more than 500,000 employees, retirees, and dependents in 48 states. Operating with the belief that employers must proactively improve the health and wellbeing of the workforce, Boeing has worked closely with health care organizations in the supply chain to test and expand appropriate ways to reengineer care, with payment reform as a central focus.

In a move to increase efficiency and ensure that patients get the right care at the right place, the company has initiated programs incentivizing employees to seek care from providers that have clear evidence of significantly better outcomes. For example, Boeing has entered into a "Centers of Excellence" arrangement, whereby eligible employees requiring specialized care can receive an "enhanced benefit," covering the cost of the procedure(s) and travel, if they visit a designated care center. Boeing selects these centers based on high ratings in performance, quality, safety, and reputation for excellence in care delivery. Employees also have access to the Best Doctors database as a second opinion service. Of those who engaged these programs, 33 percent had a change in diagnosis and 70 percent experienced a change in treatment.

In 2007, the company rolled out a medical home pilot—the Intensive Outpatient Care Program—structured to identify medically complex, high-risk patients who could benefit from high-touch, well-coordinated care. The pilot's results demonstrated a 20 percent annual decrease in medical spending per member, thanks primarily to reduced emergency room visits and hospital admissions. That model is evolving into a broader Accountable Care Organization initiative, which involves direct contracting and aligning incentives with large, integrated health systems. The goals and contract requirements are organized to achieve the Triple Aim—improving quality, enhancing the member experience, and lowering costs. Industry standard quality and member satisfaction metrics will be measured for continual improvement, and if quality and financial goals are met the program savings will be shared with the health system. By incentivizing employees to stay within a particular hospital system's network, the hospital can ensure high quality standards and continuity of care, subsequently removing wasteful spending. Boeing initiated this model at the beginning of 2015 in the Puget Sound area, in the St. Louis and Charleston areas at the beginning of 2016, and is actively exploring expansion to other markets.

expand appropriate ways to reengineer care, with payment reform as a central focus. To increase efficiency and ensure that patients get the right care at the right place, the company has initiated programs incentivizing employees to seek care from providers that have clear evidence of significantly better outcomes, and has aligned with providers committed to improving quality, enhancing the member experience, and lowering costs.

Traditionally, by participating in self-funded plans, large employers have assumed most of the insurance risk and thus cost of care for how the system performs, but have had very little control over how health care is delivered. In recent years, however, employers have been "doubling down on opportunities to impact health care quality and costs at the source—by working more closely with high performing providers through select networks and providing better information to help employees make higher-value health care choices" (Hoo and Lansky, 2016). In a 2014 Aon Hewitt Health Care survey of over 1,200 medium to large employers, 65 percent of companies identified moving toward provider payment models that strive for "cost-effective, high-quality" outcomes as a key strategic direction going forward (Aon Hewitt, 2014). Employers are hopeful that, as financial risk becomes shifted to providers, increased innovation and competition will ultimately lead to overall reduced costs and better health outcomes for beneficiaries. And, when risk is shared jointly among groups of providers, providers will be more likely to deliver coordinated, integrated care.

As the system transitions, employers are increasingly participating in and/or developing innovative, value-based approaches to delivering patient-centered, lower-cost, quality health care. In fact, more and more, employers are partnering with providers to build high-performance networks of their own through ACOs, medical homes, and centers of excellence (*Table 9-2*) (Hoo and Lansky, 2016).

Insurer-Led Initiatives and Innovations

As the health care system transitions from a fee-for-service to value-based approach, insurers are playing an important role in advancing innovative alternative payment models and approaches. For example, Blue Cross Blue Shield of Massachusetts' (BCBSMA) payment reform initiative, the Alternative Quality Contract (AQC) has been recognized for developing new and effective partnerships with its members and providers. The AQC seeks to reduce costs while improving quality and health outcomes by using both payment incentives as well as provider support tools. The model rests on a few core elements: a global budget structure; a significant performance incentive system; long-term contract assurance (3–5 years) between BCBSMA and providers with fixed spending and quality targets; and clinical and information support, including group-specific

TABLE 9–2 | Select Employer-Initiated Models of Value-Based Care

EMPLOYER-INITIATED MODELS	DESCRIPTION
Boeing's Preferred Partnership ACO	Boeing direct-contracts with leading health care providers offering value-based health plan options to improve care quality and afford-ability, and ensure a better patient experience. Currently available to employees in Charleston, Puget Sound, Southern California, and St. Louis (Boeing, 2016).
Intel Corporation's Connected Care program	Intel has partnered with Presbyterian Healthcare Services to cre-ate a health care model centered around a team-based approach to health care delivery. Performance measures correspond to 5 primary goals: 1) Right care: use of evidence-based medicine to improve population health; 2) Right time: timely access to care; 3) Best outcome: patient satisfaction 100 percent of the time; 4) Right price: material decrease in the cost of care; and 5) Best life: rapid return to productivity (Devore and Cates).
Employers Centers of Excellence	Companies including Lowe's, Walmart, McKesson, JetBlue, and Boeing use the Employers Centers of Excellence program with bundled payments.
Primary Care Medical Home (PCMH)	IBM and GE are among several companies to take on the PCMH model. The PCMH is a team-based model emphasizing care coordina-tion and communication to ensure patient-centered care.

reporting and analysis on spending and quality performance, as well as educational and best-practice sharing forums (Seidman et al., 2015). The AQC has a qual-ity measurement system that includes 64 measures (such as clinical performance and outcomes, patient experience), each of which has a range of "performance gates" to score and reward quality care. This performance score is not only tied to provider payment, but also to the provider's share of budget surplus and/or deficit. For example, with a higher quality score, a provider will get to keep more of the budget surplus and have to pay less of the deficit owed. Overall, the AQC model has been shown to be effective at improving health outcomes and quality, while reducing costs (Seidman et al., 2015; McKesson, 2016). AQC's success has been attributed to a combination of its robust incentives structure, as well as commitment to transparent sharing of data and best practices with its providers.

BCBSMA's AQC is a good case example of the ways in which payers are advancing payment reform models and initiatives. It offers several best prac-tices for insurers to drive and/or promote successful transformation. In 2015, Avalere examined BCBSMA's experience with the AQC and identified a series of observations related to the important role payers play in advancing alternative payment models and approaches (Seidman et al., 2015):

- *Payment reform programs can significantly change provider behavior*: if designed well, models can reduce costs and enable better quality care across providers.

- *Changing behavior requires providers to have "skin in the game," but payers need to meet providers where they are today*: effective and meaningful incentive schemes need to be in place to realize the desired behavior.
- *New payment models should hold providers accountable for the full range of patient care costs*: full accountability promotes care coordination, efficiency, and controlled spending.
- *Providers can implement meaningful change, but need time, consistent goals, and a similar commitment from payers to do so:* provider transformation requires time, support, and commitment from payers.
- *Providers need detailed spending and quality information and clinical support to take on risk:* transparency and access to data and care redesign support from payers are critical as providers assume more financial risk.
- *Payers with significant local presence are best positioned to implement innovative payment models:* payers with greater market share are more apt to have the resources and ability to achieve provider buy-in.

Much like the observations identified by Avalere, the Alliance of Community Health Plans (ACHP) has identified a series of strategies, best practices, and related case examples for ensuring the success of innovative payment and delivery models (ACHP, 2016) (*Table 9-3*). A few of the case examples noted are provider-sponsored plans, which have been growing in number as physician groups, health systems, and hospitals seek to reduce costs, improve care quality, and better meet the needs of the communities they serve.

Engaging Patients in Delivery and Payment Reform Initiatives

Methods to most effectively engage consumers in payment reform discussions are still evolving—partially due to the fact that the intricacies of payment reform can be largely foreign to the average health care consumer. Notably, the direct effect of alternative payment models on patients can be said to be variable (Delbanco, 2015). In the context of pay for performance, patients may not notice any discernable difference in their care. In ACO or medical home settings, however, there may, in fact, be a noticeable difference in the patient's care experience (Delbanco, 2015). In fact, research has been conducted indicating that, in these settings, patients recognized improvements in their care coordination and were overall more satisfied with their care (Miller, 2014). In focus group research conducted by the Robert Wood Johnson Foundation, focus group participants indicated that consumers (generally speaking) were not that interested in learning about the provider reimbursement process, and were uncomfortable with the idea that payment is linked to their health and health care (AF4Q, 2011). Participants

TABLE 9-3 | ACHP-Identified Strategies and Case Examples for Successful Transition

ACHP-IDENTIFIED STRATEGY	ACHP CASE EXAMPLES
Risk. Introduce increasing levels of risk gradually, regularly assessing for provider and practice readiness and investing in care management capabilities.	**Tufts Health Plan (Watertown, MA)** introduces risk along a spectrum and individually evaluates provider groups at each step to assess their readiness to assume more risk. The plan does not have a uniform timeline for progression, instead tailoring a path for each provider group depending on its abilities, needs and culture.
Value-focused measures. Tailor measures to the performance improvement goals of physician practices.	**Security Health Plan (Marshfield, WI)** has many payers in its market and as such uses the same measure set as the federal government which enables providers to more easily accept alternative payments from a variety of plans in the region, without placing an undue administrative burden on the practice
	UPMC Health Plan (Pittsburgh, PA) only has two major payers and has an affiliated delivery system where many of its enrollees receive care. As such, UPMC Health Plan leaders collaborated directly with providers to create measures that reflect the needs of the payers, providers, and patients, while driving value-based payment.
Improvement-focused measures. Develop actionable performance data, to include patient satisfaction and clinical outcomes measures, and initiate frequent payer-provider engagement to drive improvement and share best practices.	**HealthPartners (Minneapolis, MN)** produces quarterly reports customized to each provider practice and allowing clinicians to easily locate areas in need of improvement.
	Capital District Physicians' Health Plan (CDPHP) (Albany, NY) has made infrastructure investments for transformation including creating a performance management department and other analytic tools to support practices.
	UPMC Health Plan uses the expertise of its entire physician network (through monthly reports with financial and quality data to quarterly meetings with physician group leaders) to ensure that best practices are shared quickly
Incentives. Provide cost and quality information at the individual clinician level and, when possible, ensure that payment incentives go to both practices and individuals.	**Security Health Plan** is working with physician practices to ensure rewards reach individuals who demonstrate improvement in care delivery.

SOURCE: ACHP, 2016.

indicated that consumers do want enhanced quality from the health care system, including better primary care and coordination. Depending on the payment reform model, patients may desire and have use for varying levels of information.

Engaging consumers and consumer advocates in advancing payment reform innovations is important to driving progress. Involving consumers, caregivers, and their advocates in the process better assures that new models or approaches will actually have the intended effects of bettering the patient experience, improving outcomes, safety and quality, and controlling costs. Several hospitals and health systems, including the MCG Health System in Georgia and the Dana-Farber Cancer Institute in Massachusetts, have made deliberate efforts to deliver care in this way since the mid-1990s (AHA, 2005).

Today, continued efforts are underway to better engage consumers and their advocates in the design and delivery of care to best meet their needs. The activities of several organizations are developing efforts to help consumer advocates address health care and cost issues, such as the Healthcare Value Hub, created by Consumers Union. And, in an effort to engage patients and their families directly, Patient and Family Advisory Councils offer a model of engagement that has been used in delivery and payment reform discussions. These councils serve as an advisory resource, bringing together patients, their families, and members of the health care team to improve the experience of the patient and their family. The role of the council is to promote improved relationships, provide a venue for information sharing, and facilitate communication and coordination between patients, families, and the care team, all of which serves to actively involve patients and their families in the care design and delivery process (IPFCC, 2002). RWJF Aligning Forces for Quality communities in Humboldt County, California; Maine; and Oregon employed and had successes with these advisory councils during payment reform discussions (AF4Q, 2014).

CHALLENGES AND BARRIERS TO PAYMENT REFORM

While clear progress has been made in promoting payment innovation, by the federal and state governments, as well as stakeholder-led initiatives and innovations, there remain critical challenges to successful implementation. Among these challenges include: aligning multiple, heterogeneous payer profiles; identifying the necessary provider competencies for success; developing robust performance measures; navigating regulatory and legal barriers; and accessing data and evidence on successful models.

Participation and Alignment of Multiple Payers

Broad payer participation and alignment are critical for providers to commit to the delivery of value-based care and for payment reform to be successful. Across the country, providers (physicians, hospitals, etc.) are reimbursed by multiple payers, ranging from the major public payers—Medicare and Medicaid—to numerous commercial insurance companies, and also self-pay individuals.

Individual payers use differing and sometimes multiple approaches to pay for health care. This variation, combined with the differing strategies among payers as they undertake transition from fee-for-service to value-based care, underlies the substantial complexity in the marketplace. In the presence of multiple payers, there exists an incentive for any given payer to refrain from adopting alternative payment models, while still recouping savings required of providers working under payment reform approaches implemented by other payers (Miller, 2014). Further, initial provider responses to payer constraints may not necessarily yield care delivered in a value-based way. For providers to truly transform the way they deliver care, critical financial incentives need to be in place, and will only be possible if a sufficient number of payers—beyond Medicare and Medicaid—support and implement payment reform (Rajkumar et al., 2014). For payment reform to be successful, all payers need to change their payment systems in similar ways (IOM, 2010), such that they have common incentives, measurement, and quality improvement goals (McGinnis and Newman, 2014).

Limited Experience and Knowledge About How to Succeed in New Payment Models

While alternative payment models have demonstrated some promising outcomes, early performance has been mixed overall; reductions in spending and improvements in quality have been modest, although still meaningful (McWilliams et al., 2016). While these early findings have highlighted an important need to improve model design, they have also underscored an important issue, which is that many providers (including physician practices and hospitals) do not know how to effectively engage and succeed in alternative payment models to improve care quality and outcomes, and reduce costs. The resource and skill challenges facing providers include: the lack of sufficient educational programs to train the case workers, community workers and others who will be needed in these new models; the need to resource new programs to effectively work in different environments; and the costs of the new technologies and infrastructure needed to support this work. Identifying and supporting competencies for providers to implement and thrive under value-based models will be critical for the success of payment reform, and is a topic of a companion discussion paper in the *Vital Directions* series, "Competencies and Tools to Shift Payments from Volume to Value" by Governor Mike Leavitt and colleagues (see Chapter 10).

Inadequate Performance Measures and the Burden of Excessive Measurement

New payment systems require robust measures of performance to better ensure that providers are delivering high-value, quality care to their patients, in addition to reducing the cost of care. While measures are important sources of accountability, measures themselves will not improve care quality (Dunlap et al., 2009; Pronovost et al., 2016). Unless carefully developed and applied, performance and quality measures can function as little more than a burden for providers, particularly when they target aspects of care they cannot easily, if at all, control. In such cases, measures can deter providers from participating in alternative payment models (Miller, 2014). For example, when the regulations for the Medicare Shared Savings Program were first proposed, they included 65 different quality measures, yet made no changes to the existing fee-for-service framework in place. Unsurprisingly, the regulations received a great deal of scrutiny, leading CMS to bring down the number of measures to 33 in the final regulations.

Further, even in the presence and use of large numbers of performance measures, there may be aspects of care quality and/or performance that are not being measured, such as those related to specialty care, where cost containment and reduction efforts are anticipated to focus (Miller, 2014). Related, there are many dimensions of "value" to patients that are difficult to measure and are not measured at all. Equally concerning, many of the measures used by payers are further processes of marginal relevance to outcomes, and sometimes with even perverse implications for value and costs.

Nonetheless, reliable and valid measurement is fundamental to the implementation of value-based payment models, and CMS has been working to shift its quality measurement from mostly process measures to mostly outcome measures, while reducing the total number of measures in its programs and models. Looking ahead, building more meaningful outcomes measures will require access to more robust and comparable patient-reported data and information. Building this capability will require a significant investment, but the anticipated return that would result from better outcome measures producing better, more efficient care would seemingly justify the initial investment (Miller, 2014). Further work must be done to ensure that collection and reporting of these measures can be integrated seamlessly into provider workflow, and not pose an excessive burden.

Regulatory and Legal Hurdles

Additional barriers to payment reform are imposed by certain existing regulations designed for a fee-for-service system (AHA, 2016), (e.g., regulations offering cash incentives under fee-for-service models). Further, a number of laws and regulations impair efforts to create the care coordination and collaboration that is being encouraged through federal payment reforms, including:

- **The Patient Referral Law,** more often called the Stark Law, which has grown beyond its original intent to prevent physicians from referring their patients to a medical facility in which they have an ownership interest, to limit practically any financial relationship between hospitals and physicians. The law's strict requirements mandate that compensation be set in advance and paid on the basis of hours worked. Consequently, health care providers are concerned that payments tied to quality and care improvement could violate this law.
- **The Civil Monetary Penalty Law (CMP)** is a vestige of concerns raised in the 1980s that Medicare patients might not receive the same level of services as other patients after the inpatient hospital prospective payment system bundled multiple services under a single Diagnosis Related Group (DRG). While health reform is about encouraging the use of best practices and clinical protocols, using incentives to reward physicians for following best practices and protocols can be penalized under the CMP law.
- **Antikickback laws,** which originally sought to protect patients and federal health programs from fraud and abuse by making it a felony to knowingly and willfully pay anything of value to influence the referral of federal health program business. Today's expanded interpretation includes any financial relationship between hospitals and doctors, which has the potential to discourage clinical integration.
- **Internal Revenue Service (IRS) Rules** prevent a tax-exempt institution's assets from being used to benefit any private individual, including physicians. This complicates clinical coordination arrangements between not-for-profit hospitals and private clinicians.

Certain Medicare regulations also may impose limitations on what provider organizations can do to streamline, integrate, and reform care delivery. For example:

- A small system consisting of three or four hospitals in reasonable proximity to each other is not allowed to centralize the oversight of the nursing staff, which would promote use of uniform protocols, the sharing of staffing to meet patient surges, or a unified approach to oversight and education of nurses.
- Conditions of Participation—conditions established by CMS that must be met by organizations to participate in Medicare and Medicaid programs—have been interpreted to mean that a hospital serving a rural community cannot rent clinical space to visiting specialists a few days a month so local patients can more conveniently and routinely see the specialist treating their particular condition. As a result, patients may have to travel great distances for their specialist visits. This restriction on specialty "rental" in hospitals is, in part, a

result of CMS concerns that such rentals will encourage specialists to reclassify themselves as outpatient providers and significantly increase their payment rates. Clarification and resolution of these issues is important.

- Medicare payment rules meant to limit patients sent to specific postacute care settings as a way of controlling Medicare costs under fee-for-service may prevent certain patients from obtaining services in the most appropriate and efficient settings.

CMS has relaxed some of these requirements in more advanced payment reform models, such as its "Next Generation" ACO model and its other programs that enable ACOs to accept "downside" risk. But the right balance is not yet clear between restrictions to limit volume and intensity in payment models that partially shift to value-based payments, but retain a fee-for-service infrastructure.

Finally, some state laws also impose barriers to integrated care arrangements, including laws that: prohibit the employment of physicians (corporate practice of medicine laws); govern the scope of practice of health professionals; govern the use of telemedicine and other distance services; and govern those deemed to be insurers based on the amount of risk they take on for patient services. Requirements for insurers to have adequate capitalization and to comply with insurance regulations while reflecting the need for financial protection for those covered by the entity may not be good fits for provider-based arrangements.

Limited Evidence on Successful Payment Models

Payment reform requires developing better evidence on the payment reforms themselves. The Centers for Medicare and Medicaid innovation, and many states, employers, and health plans, are testing a growing number of payment reform models; but, in many cases, evaluations are not performed at all and the evaluations that are performed could be done more effectively. Overall, the evidence is accumulating and diffusing slowly, given the volume of payment reform activity underway. In particular, there is still limited evidence on determinants of successes for Medicare ACOs and the Medicare Shared Savings Program (MSSP) (McClellan et al., 2015). Overall, the early financial performance of MSSP ACOs has been found to be highly variable (across ACOs and geographically)—with some ACOs generating major shared savings, and others more marginal shared savings. Early findings also indicate that large ACOs do not have an advantage over smaller ACOs in terms of financial performance, and that there appears to be no meaningful association between initial financial performance and overall quality (McClellan et al., 2015). In fact, a relatively small share of ACOs demonstrated both favorable cost and quality trends.

More data about ACO features, activities, and performance need to be developed and shared, so that best practices and determinants of success can be identified and implemented (Bodaken et al., 2016). Linking more detailed CMS data on ACO features and performance would facilitate the process of identifying what organizations can do to improve performance and better ensure success. Ultimately, getting more ACOs to commit to two-sided risk models and undertake more extensive payment reforms will require the identification of evidence-based determinants of success, as well as clear demonstrations and pathways to succeed under these models.

SAFEGUARDING AGAINST UNINTENDED CONSEQUENCES

Consolidation and Market Power

As payment reform and the adoption of value-based models of care delivery has proceeded, so has a trend toward provider integration and consolidation. Under emerging models, providers are more accountable for the cost and quality of care provided to predefined patient populations. This, combined with additional quality reporting requirements and penalties for hospital readmissions and hospital-acquired conditions, has contributed to provider integration, as they try to better manage care and mitigate costs across the continuum (AHA, 2014).

Provider integration can be clinical or financial, horizontal or vertical, and can exist at the level of nonbinding agreements on through to the level of complete mergers (AHA, 2014; Vaida and Wess, 2015). On the whole, integration aims to benefit and improve care quality, cost, and access. Integration can improve efficiency and quality through greater care coordination and increased communication and information-sharing among providers. In this way, integration can reduce unnecessary or duplicative tests and procedures, and other forms of wasteful spending, while ensuring patients receive the right treatment at the right time. To the same effect, integration can reduce the burden of administrative costs, make greater use of resources, such as specialists, and improve the breadth of care available. It can also improve the patient experience by providing more comprehensive care and streamlined access.

Alongside the benefits, there is some concern that provider consolidation can, in some circumstances, lead to higher prices and spending, since larger, consolidated organizations have greater market power, and thus more negotiating power, over prices with private insurance companies (McClellan et al., 2016). In addition to higher prices and outpatient spending, some studies indicate that increasing rates of hospital-provider integration have not always resulted in more efficient, quality care or better outcomes for patients (Gaynor and Town, 2012; Neprash et al., 2015).

With the recent Medicare Access and CHIP Reauthorization Act (MACRA), it is possible that providers may be more apt to integrate. Originally passed in April 2016, MACRA replaces the old, sustainable, growth-rate formula for physician payment with a new model to move providers away from fee-for-service toward value-based payment. MACRA presents two payment pathways for providers (collectively called "the Quality Payment Program"): the Merit-Based Incentive Payment System (MIPS), which adjusts fee-for-service payments according to a composite measure of quality and value, and advanced APMs, which transition from fee-for-service payment. MIPS is a consolidation of Medicare's existing quality reporting programs intended to reduce possible financial penalties incurred by providers and increase the likelihood that providers will attain bonus payments. Components of MIPS include quality activities, clinical improvement activities, advancing care information performance, and cost/resource use. MIPS has been described as MACRA's "base program," which all providers must participate in (or get an exemption from), or face a payment cut (Wynne, 2016). Those providers participating in Advanced APMs (the second pathway) are exempt from MIPS and are eligible for 5 percent bonus payments beginning in 2019. For APMs to be considered "advanced," they must bear more than a nominal financial risk for the costs of care provided (McClellan et al., 2016).

Few existing Medicare APMs meet the criteria for "advanced" status. As such, under MACRA as originally proposed, there was the potential that many small and midsize practices would be met with increased administrative burdens resulting from additional reporting requirements, and would be incapable of bearing the financial risk required to qualify for bonus payments. In such cases, smaller practices could be inclined to merge with larger practices or health systems. Acknowledging these concerns, in its final rule, CMS took steps to support smaller practices implementing alternative payment models. Notably, CMS increased the minimum threshold requirements for participation in MIPS ($30,000 in Medicare claims or at least 100 Medicare patients per year), and has allowed for the creation of "virtual groups," whereby up to 10 clinicians can band together to report as one group. CMS also agreed to provide $100 million in technical assistance to smaller practices participating in MIPS over the next 5 years, and instituted lower reporting thresholds than those originally proposed.

Stifling Valuable Health Care Innovation and Treatment

Some have expressed concern that value-based payment schemes and risk-based reimbursement models might stifle valuable health care innovation and treatment by putting increasing pressure on manufacturers to provide unrealistic evidentiary support demonstrating the cost-effectiveness of their products within constrained time-frames. As bundled payment approaches evolve, it will be important to ensure the payment environment does not discourage investments in new devices or medications that potentially have enormous benefit to patients and potentially reduce lifetime care costs. Innovative drugs and devices, and new, potentially curative treatments like regenerative medicine and gene therapies, may avert downstream costs of medical complications. But, those downstream cost savings may not be realized until years later. They may not fit into the usual proximal timeframe for payment models.

In the case of pharmaceuticals, discussions of value may take place at the time of the launch but typically do not account for the benefit of the drug over its lifecycle. For example, HIV drugs are estimated to have generated a societal benefit exceeding $750 billion (NBER, 2015). Similarly, from 1987 to 2008, consumers are estimated to have captured $947.4 billion (76 percent) of the total societal value of the survival gains from statins (Grabowski et al., 2015).

Biomedical innovations often represent valuable breakthroughs for patients in terms of longer and better lives. Their development often involves significant time, cost, and uncertainty. Estimates of the average present-value cost of bringing a new drug to market have increased from $1 billion in 2000 to, by some estimates, as much as $2.6 billion in 2015 (DiMasi et al., 2016). If there is no clear path for per-capita or per-episode payments to reflect the value of breakthrough technologies, then pharmaceutical companies and device manufacturers will be reluctant to make the necessary investments.

These issues are especially notable for the emerging "curative," one-time treatments. Despite recent progress in payment reforms for health care providers, current payment models for most drugs are based on payment for units (e.g., pills and vials) and do not consider that a patient could be cured after a single treatment. Payers are coming to recognize that the binary concept of experimental vs. medically necessary is based on a simplified view of evidence and uncertainty, and that more nuanced policy mechanisms are necessary to align with the continuous health technology assessment and reimbursement as a one-off snapshot, to seeing them as ongoing processes aiming at providing greater certainty about value for money as evidence accumulates (Henshall and Schuller, 2013).

The prospects for prevention-oriented, long-term interventions such as gene therapies underscore the fact that biomedical science appears to be advancing more rapidly than the payment and regulatory infrastructure required to deliver it. While some promising payment reforms are being piloted and implemented, the US health care system remains centered on the delivery of traditional chronic treatments whose payments are focused on units and whose value is realized in the near-term. Current coverage policies and payment mechanisms are not well designed to support early interventions that can blunt the onset of a chronic disease, and do not capture the potential benefits over an extended period of time. New analytic tools are needed to assess the benefits of potential one-time curative therapies whose value proposition, delivery, and payment do not align well with conventional payment models. The emerging possibility of gene therapy could serve as a valuable pilot project to aid in the design and implementation of new, managed, product innovation and use agreements that seek to align the interests of payers, providers, policymakers, and biopharmaceutical companies with those of patients who need access to transformative therapies. This is consistent with the coverage-with-evidence-development concept proposed a decade ago, but not yet widely implemented.

In addition, there is a need for the patient voice to be a larger part of the conversation on medical innovation and access to new therapies. While there are efforts to better involve patients in the regulatory process, more can and should be done to ensure patient input is utilized. For example, the FDA's recent guidance document (FDA, 2015) and work through the Medical Device Innovation Consortium (MDIC, 2015), which seeks to create a framework and catalog of patient preference measurement tools, ought to help regulators and medical terminology sponsors better incorporate patients' perspectives into the approval process.

VITAL DIRECTIONS

To enable payment reform to fulfill its promise of promoting high-value, patient-centric care, four vital directions are identified for policymakers' consideration.

1. **Align the implementation of payment reform to encourage provider efforts to improve quality and value.** The federal government should increase support for existing collaborations, such as the Health Care Payment Learning Action Network and the Core Quality Measures Consortium, which are helping to reduce burden on providers, who are trying to navigate many different benchmarks, measures, risk adjustment methods, reporting requirements, and even payment models. Assistance is also needed with identifying and implementing patient-reported measures, particularly for those patients with serious or complex illnesses. To improve performance, providers need timely access to claims data from payers, as well as key clinical information from other institutions—preferably in

standard ways that facilitate action. More robust data should be matched by more tools and resources to help clinicians share best practices and learn from successes and failures; care transformation will necessitate ongoing investment in analytics, new skill sets, personnel, and new models of care. Further, laws and regulations originally designed for a fee-for-service system (e.g., the Patient Referral (Stark) Law, Civil Monetary Penalty Laws, anti-kickback laws) need to be reformed. These regulations pose barriers to the advancement of payment reform approaches, patient engagement, as well as many care coordination and transformation efforts.

2. **Address and incorporate costly but potentially lifesaving technologies.** Neither traditional fee-for-service payments for costly technologies, nor alternative payment models that do not account for high-cost but high-value innovation, provide a clear path for high-value biomedical innovation. However, some payment models both within and outside the United States have begun to align drug and device payments directly with accountability for improved outcomes or reduced spending for a population of patients. Rather than viewing payment reforms for biomedical technologies and for health care providers as distinct, CMS and private payers could encourage developers of alternative payment models to engage on ways to maximize the value brought by new technologies. For example, this could include model frameworks and regulatory clarifications for sharing data related to the benefits and risks of new technologies for particular patients, or for incorporating drug and device shared accountability in ACOs and bundled payments.

3. **Ensure that payment reform does not exacerbate adverse consolidation and market power.** While some large organizations have achieved better outcomes and lower costs through integrated care, many organizations including small primary-care practices and specialty groups have improved care without consolidation (McWilliams et al., 2016). Reflecting the risks of market power, larger organizations that have consolidated with the stated goal of improving outcomes and lowering costs should report on whether they are achieving these results. Better and more comparable quality and cost measures are needed to help payers, purchasers, and patients recognize and support better care—measures that use not only claims data but also clinical and patient data to better reflect the results that matter for patients, particularly those with serious illnesses. Larger organizations in particular have the capacity to produce such measures. Advanced payment models with proportionally smaller financial risks should be developed for smaller provider organizations—like ACOs led by primary care physicians and specialty providers who focus on specialized types of episodes of care.

4. **Conduct more timely and efficient evaluations of what is working.**
   CMS evaluates Medicare payment reform pilots, and other evaluations have
   been reported (Mechanic, 2016). But, those evaluations often occur on a
   costly one-off basis, using data that have to be generated outside of care
   delivery, and hundreds of payment reforms are being implemented in public
   and private health care programs across the country without substantial
   evaluation. Common data models and research networks now develop data
   and use validated methods to evaluate medical technologies and medical
   practices more quickly. These approaches could provide models for lower-
   cost, faster learning about the right directions and steps in payment reform.

The era of payment reform has introduced transformative models of health
care delivery focused on producing better outcomes, lower costs, and greater
investment in new and innovative treatments that are truly valuable. Despite the
challenges that remain, by shifting payments to reward the value rather than the
volume of health care services, the US health care system is making important
strides toward making care more affordable, efficient, and person-centric. Of
course, successful execution of payment reform will require related, complementary reforms including: redesigning medical education to include a greater
focus on value and patient-focused team care; training more health workers to
support value-based, person-centric care; as well as changes in benefit design for
patients and consumers. Combined with these advances, through payment reform
and high-value innovation, the nation can achieve better care, smarter spending,
and healthier people.

SUMMARY RECOMMENDATIONS FOR
VITAL DIRECTIONS

1. Align the implementation of payment reform to encourage provider
   efforts to improve quality and value.
2. Address and incorporate costly but potentially lifesaving technologies.
3. Ensure that payment reform does not exacerbate adverse consolidation and market power.
4. Conduct more timely and efficient evaluations of what is working.

REFERENCES

Abrams, M, R. Nuzum, M. Zezza, J. Ryan, J. Kiszla, and S. Guterman. 2015. *The Affordable Care Act's Payment and Delivery System Reforms: A Progress Report at Five Years.* Commonwealth Fund pub. 1816, Vol. 12.

AcademyHealth and Bailit Health Purchasing, LLC. *Facilitators and Barriers to Payment Reform.* Robert Wood Johnson Foundation, September 2013.

Agency for Healthcare Research and Quality (AHRQ). 2016. *Defining the PMCH.* https://pcmh.ahrq.gov/page/defining-pcmh (accessed November 2, 2016)

Aligning Forces for Quality (AF4Q). 2011. *Talking about Health Care Payment Reform with U.S. Consumers: Key Communications Findings from Focus Groups.* http://www.rwjf.org/en/library/research/2011/04/talking-about-health-care-payment-reform-with-u-s--consumers.html (accessed November 2, 2016)

Aligning Forces for Quality (AF4Q). 2014. *Engaging Consumers in Payment Reform Efforts That Impact Care Delivery Practices.* http://forces4quality.org/af4q/download-document/7282/Resource-rwjf411721.pdf (accessed November 2, 2016)

Alliance of Community Health Plans (ACHP). 2016. *Rewarding High Quality: Practical Models for Value-Based Physician Payment.* http://www.achp.org/wp-content/uploads/ACHP-Report_Rewarding-High-Quality_4.20.16.pdf (accessed November 2, 2016)

American Hospital Association (AHA). 2005. *Strategies for Leadership: Advancing the Practice of Patient- and Family-Centered Care.* http://www.aha.org/content/2005/pdf/resourceguide.pdf (accessed January 3, 2017).

American Hospital Association (AHA). 2014. *The Value of Provider Integration.* http://www.aha.org/content/14/14mar-provintegration.pdf (accessed November 15, 2016)

American Hospital Association (AHA). 2016. *Legal (Fraud and Abuse) Barriers to Care Transformation and How to Address Them.* http:// www.aha.org/content/16/barrierstocare-full.pdf (accessed November 15, 2016)

Aon Hewitt. 2014. *Aon Hewitt 2014 Health Care Survey.* http://www.aon.com/attachments/human-capital-consulting/2014-Aon-Health-Care-Survey.pdf (accessed November 2, 2014)

Berenson, R. and N. Cafarella. 2012. *The Center for Medicare and Medicaid Innovation: Activity on Many Fronts.* Urban Institute.

Bodaken, B., R. Bankowitz, T. Ferris, J. Hansen, J. Hirshleifer, S. Kronlund, D. Labby, R. MacCornack, M. McClellan, and L. Sandy. 2016. *Sustainable Success in Accountable Care.* Discussion Paper. Washington, DC: National Academy of

Medicine. http://nam.edu/wp-content/uploads/2016/04/Sustainable-Success-in-Accountable-Care.pdf.

Boeing. 2016. *Preferred Partnership: An innovative approach to health care.* http://www.healthpartnershipoptions.com/SiteAssets/pub/index.html (accessed November 2, 2016)

CMS (Centers for Medicare & Medicaid Services). 2015. *Better Care. Smarter Spending. Healthier People: Paying Providers for Value, Not Volume.* https://www.cms.gov/Newsroom/MediaReleaseDatabase/Fact-sheets/2015-Fact-sheets-items/2015-01-26-3.html (accessed November 2, 2016)

CMS. 2016a. *National Health Expenditure Data—Historical.* https://www.cms.gov/research-statistics-data-and-systems/statistics-trends-and-reports/nationalhealthexpenddata/nationalhealthaccountshistorical.html (accessed November 2, 2016).

CMS. 2016b. *Innovation Models.* https://innovation.cms.gov/initiatives/index.html#views=models (accessed November 2, 2016)

Davis, K., S. Guterman, S. Collins, K. Stremikis, S. Rustgi, and R. Nuzum. 2010. *Starting on the path to a high performance health system: analysis of the payment and system reform provisions in the Patient Protection and Affordable Care Act of 2010.* Commonwealth Fund pub. 1442.

Delbanco, S. 2015. *The Payment Reform Landscape: Impact on Consumers.* http://healthaffairs.org/blog/2015/04/15/the-payment-reform-landscape-impact-on-consumers/ (accessed November 2, 2016)

Department of Health and Human Services (HHS). 2015. *Better, Smarter, Healthier: In historic announcement, HHS sets clear goals and timeline for shifting Medicare reimbursements from volume to value.* http://www.hhs.gov/about/news/2015/01/26/better-smarter-healthier-in-historic-announcement-hhs-sets-clear-goals-and-timeline-for-shifting-medicare-reimbursements-from-volume-to-value.html (accessed November 2, 2016)

Devore, B.L. and L. Cates. *Disruptive Innovation for Healthcare Delivery.* Presbyterian Healthcare Services and Intel. http://www.intel.com/content/dam/www/public/us/en/documents/white-papers/disruptive-innovation-healthcare-delivery-paper.pdf (accessed November 2, 2016)

DiMasi, J.A., H.G. Grabowski, and R.W. Hansen. 2016. Innovation in the Pharmaceutical Industry: New Estimates of R&D Costs. *Journal of Health Economics* doi:10.1016/j.jhealeco.2016.01.012.

Dunlap, M.E., P.J. Greco, B.L. Halliday, and D. Einstadter. 2009. Lack of correlation between HF performance measures and 30-day rehospitalization rates (abstr). *Journal of Cardiac Failure* 15:283.

Food and Drug Administration (FDA). 2015. *Patient Preference Information-Submission, Review in PMAs, HDE Applications, and De Novo Requests, and Inclusion in Device*

Labeling; Draft Guidance for Industry, Food and Drug Administration Staff, and Other Stakeholders. http://www.fda.gov/downloads/medicaldevices/deviceregulation-andguidance/guidancedocuments/ucm446680.pdf (accessed November 2, 2016).

Gaynor, M., and R. Town. 2012. *The Impact of Hospital Consolidation—Update.* Robert Wood Johnson Foundation Synthesis Report. http://www.rwjf.org/en/library/research/2012/06/the-impact-of-hospital-consolidation.html (accessed November 2, 2016)

Grabowski, D.C., D.N. Lakdawalla, D.P. Goldman, et al. 2012. The large social value resulting from use of Statins warrants steps to improve adherence and broaden treatment. *Health Affairs.* 31(10):2276–2285. doi:10.1377/hlthaff.2011.1120.

Guterman S, K. Davis, K. Stremikis, and H. Drake. 2010. Innovation in Medicare and Medicaid will be central to health reform's success. *Health Affairs* 29(6):1188–1193. doi:10.1377/hlthaff.2010.0442.

Health Care Payment Learning & Action Network. 2016. *Alternative Payment Model (APM) Framework Final White Paper.*

Health Care Transformation Task Force (HCTTF). 2016. *About Health Care Transformation Task Force.* http://hcttf.org/aboutus/ (accessed November 2, 2016)

Henshall, C. and T. Schuller. 2013. Health Technology Assessment, Value-Based Decision Making, and Innovation. *International Journal of Technological Assessment in Health Care* 29:353–359.

Hoo, E. and D. Lansky. 2016. *Medical Network and Payment Reform Strategies to Increase Health Care Value.* American Health Policy Institute and Pacific Business Group on Health.

Institute of Medicine (IOM). 2001. *Crossing the Quality Chasm: A New Health System for the 21st Century.* Washington, DC: The National Academies Press. doi:10.17226/10027.

Institute of Medicine (IOM). 2010. *The Healthcare Imperative: Lowering Costs and Improving Outcomes: Workshop Series Summary.* Washington, DC: The National Academies Press. doi:10.17226/12750.

Institute of Medicine (IOM). 2013. *Best Care at Lower Cost: The Path to Continuously Learning Health Care in America.* Washington, DC: The National Academies Press, 2013. doi:10.17226/13444.

Institute of Medicine (IOM) and National Research Council (NRC). 2013. *U.S. Health in International Perspective: Shorter Lives, Poorer Health.* Washington, DC: The National Academies Press. doi:10.17226/13497.

Institute for Patient-And Family-Centered Care (IPFCC). 2002. Creating patient and family advisory councils. http://www.ipfcc.org/advance/Advisory_Councils.pdf (accessed November 2, 2016)

McClellan, M., S.L. Kocot, and R. White. 2015. Early evidence on Medicare ACOs and next steps for the Medicare ACO program. *Health Affairs Blog.* http://healthaffairs.org/blog/2015/01/22/early-evidence-on-medicare-acos-and-next-steps-for-the-medicare-aco-program/ (accessed November 2, 2016)

McClellan, M., F. McStay, and R. Saunders. 2016. The Roadmap To Physician Payment Reform: What It Will Take for All Clinicians to Succeed under MACRA. *Health Affairs Blog.* http://healthaffairs.org/blog/2016/08/30/the-roadmap-to-physician-payment-reform-what-it-will-take-for-all-clinicians-to-succeed-under-macra/ (accessed November 2, 2016)

McGinnis, T. and J. Newman. 2014. *Advances in Multi-Payer Alignment: State Approaches to Aligning Performance Metrics across Public and Private Payers.* http://www.milbank.org/wp-content/files/documents/MultiPayerHealthCare_WhitePaper_071014.pdf (accessed November 2, 2016)

McKesson. 2016. *Consider the Alternative.* http://www.mckesson.com/blog/consider-the-alternative/ (accessed November 2, 2016)

McWilliams, J.M., L.A. Hatfield, M.E. Chernew, B.E. Landon, and A.L. Schwartz. 2016. Early performance of accountable care organizations in Medicare. *New England Journal of Medicine* doi:10.1056/nejmsa1600142.

Mechanic, R.E. 2016. When new medicare payment systems Collide. *New England Journal of Medicine.* 374(18):1706–1709. doi:10.1056/nejmp1601464.

Medical Device Innovation Consortium (MDIC). 2015. Medical Device Innovation Consortium (MDIC) *Patient Centered Benefit-Risk Project Report: A Framework for Incorporating Information on Patient Preferences Regarding Benefit and Risk into Regulatory Assessments of New Medical Technology.*

Miller, J. 2014. *ACA Medicare Reforms Improve Patient Experiences.* https://hms.harvard.edu/news/aca-medicare-reforms-improve-patient-experiences (accessed November 2, 2016)

National Bureau of Economic Research (NBER). 2005. The National Bureau of Economic Research Working Paper No. 11810. Who Benefits from New Medical Technologies? Estimates of Consumer and Producer Surpluses for HIV/AIDS Drugs, Tomas J. Philipson and Anupam B. Jena.

Neprash, H.T., M.E. Chernew, A.L. Hicks, T. Gibson, J.M. McWilliams. 2015. Association of Financial Integration Between Physicians and Hospitals With Commercial Health Care Prices. *JAMA Internal Medicine* 175(12):1932–1939. doi:10.1001/jamainternmed.2015.4610

Pronovost, P.J., Austin, J.M., Cassel, C.K., Delbanco, S.F., Jha, A.K., Kocher, B., McGlynn, E.A., Sandy, L.G., Santa, J. 2016. *Fostering Transparency in Outcomes, Quality, Safety, and Costs.* Vital Directions for Health and Health Care Series. Discussion Paper, National Academy of Medicine, Washington,

DC. https://nam. edu/wp-content/uploads/2016/09/fostering-transparency-in-outcomes-quality-safety-and-costs.pdf.

Rajkumar, R, P. H. Conway, and M. Tavenner . 2014. CMS—Engaging Multiple Payers in Payment Reform. *JAMA* 311(19):1967–1968. doi:10.1001/jama. 2014.3703

Schilling, B. 2011. *Advancing Quality Through Employer-Led Initiatives,* The Commonwealth Fund.

Seidman, J., C. Kelly, N. Ganesan, and A. Gray. 2015. *Payment Reform on the Ground: Lessons from the Blue Cross Blue Shield of Massachusetts Alternative Quality Contract.* Avalere Health LLC. http://www.bluecrossma.com/visitor/pdf/avalere-lessons-from-aqc.pdf (accessed November 2, 2016)

The Henry J. Kaiser Foundation (KFF). 2016. *Health Insurance Coverage of the Total Population, Timeframe: 2015.* http://kff.org/other/state-indicator/total-population/ (accessed November 2, 2016)

Vaida, B. and A. Wess. 2015. *Health Care Consolidation—An Alliance for Health Reform Toolkit.* http://www.allhealth.org/publications/Consolidation-Toolkit_169.pdf health care consolidation alliance (accessed November 15, 2016)

Wynne, B. 2016. MACRA Final Rule: CMS Strikes A Balance; Will Docs Hang On? *Health Affairs Blog.* http://healthaffairs.org/blog/2016/10/17/macra-final-rule-cms-strikes-a-balance-will-docs-hang-on/ (accessed November 2, 2016)

AUTHOR INFORMATION

Mark B. McClellan, MD, PhD, is Director, Duke-Robert J. Margolis Center for Health Policy and Robert J. Margolis Professor, Duke University and former Adminstrator for the Centers for Medicare and Medicaid Services. **David T. Feinberg, MD, MBA,** is President and CEO, Geisinger Health System. **Peter B. Bach, MD,** is Director, Center for Health Policy and Outcomes, Memorial Sloan Kettering Cancer Center. **Paul Chew, MD,** is Chief Medical Officer, Omada Health. **Patrick Conway, MD,** is Chief Medical Officer, Centers for Medicare & Medicaid Services. **Nick Leschly, MBA,** is Chief Bluebird, Bluebir Bio. **Greg Marchand,** is Director, Benefits Policy and Strategy, The Boeing Company. **Michael A. Mussallem,** is Chairman and CEO, Edwards Lifesciences. **Dorothy Teeter, MHA,** is Director, Washington State Health Care Authority.

10

COMPETENCIES AND TOOLS TO SHIFT PAYMENTS FROM VOLUME TO VALUE

The Honorable Michael O. Leavitt, Mark B. McClellan, MD, PhD, Susan D. Devore, MM, Elliott Fisher, MD, MPH, Richard J. Gilfillan, MD, H. Stephen Lieber, CAE, Richard Merkin, MD, Jeffrey Rideout, MD, and Kent J. Thiry, MBA

Health reform remains at the forefront of US policy debates because of continued growth in public and private health care spending alongside increasing capabilities of medical care—as well as persistent evidence of inefficiencies and substantial variance in use, cost, and quality (NASEM, 2016). Bipartisan support has emerged for moving away from fee-for-service (FFS) payment because of its failure to support many innovative approaches to care delivery and its administrative burdens on clinicians and patients.

Alternative payment models have proliferated in federal, state, and commercial initiatives, including the Medicare and CHIP Reauthorization Act (MACRA) of 2015 (US Congress, 2015), with the hope of aligning financial support with higher-value care. The Health Care Payment Learning and Action Network has described a variety of payment reforms (Health Care Payment Learning and Action Network, 2016) and accompanying delivery models that represent a shift away from FFS, such as accountable care organizations (ACOs), fixed bundled payments for episodes of care, and primary care medical homes with shared savings. It is a reflection of the expansion of such alternative payment models (APMs) that, as of January 2016, 847 ACOs collectively provide coverage to over 28.3 million Americans *(Figure 10-1)* (Muhlestein and McClellan, 2016). With similar models not only proliferating in traditional Medicare but in Medicare Advantage plans, Medicaid programs, and commercial and employer plans, most Americans probably will be affected by one or more of those payment models in the near or not too distant future.

Despite the promise and enthusiasm, early results have been mixed. Some ACOs have demonstrated notable improvements in care quality with financial success, but most participants in Medicare's major APMs have not yet realized large savings (Dale et al., 2016; McWilliams et al., 2016). Early APM results suggest that improving quality does not generally lead to better financial performance. Consequently, there has been enormous interest in improving the design of APMs and the data available to support health care organizations in APMs.

Value-based payment policies will continue to evolve as evidence on their effectiveness accumulates, but even with further policy refinements, the "how" of improving care, reducing costs, and thus succeeding under new financing models is not well understood. Some assume that if the payment model is "right," the proper and corresponding care models will emerge naturally. But, many organizations do not have a good understanding of where to start or how to proceed in the transformation process, and many of the tools and approaches are of uncertain value. Pressure is rising to delay MACRA and other payment reforms, especially for smaller health care organizations and those serving vulnerable populations, because providers are not ready. From the standpoint of achieving the goals of higher-value care, policies to support care-delivery transformation are as critical as effective payment reforms.

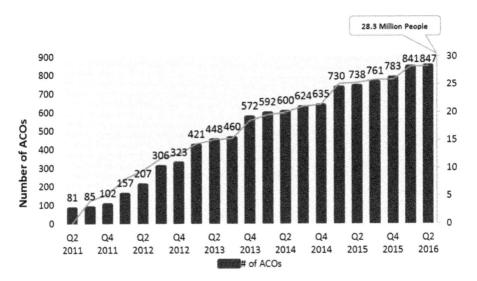

FIGURE 10-1 | ACO growth overall trajectory.
SOURCE: Halfon et al., 2014a.

CHALLENGES TO AND PROGRESS TOWARD DEFINING AND SUPPORTING COMPETENCIES FOR VALUE-BASED HEALTH CARE

US health care organizations have well-developed capabilities for FFS payment systems: scheduling, coding, billing, electronic data transmission, reporting, and other competencies to support the conduct and payment of covered services. In contrast, proficiencies in preventing disease and optimally managing the health of a population at the lowest possible cost have not yet been widely identified or applied, and most organizations are unsure about how and how much to invest in new capabilities.

TABLE 10-1 | Examples of Learning Collaboratives

COLLABORATIVE	DESCRIPTION
Learning and Action Network (LAN)	Department of Health and Human Services–supported program to support adoption of alternative payment models, with a focus on sharing information and evidence related to new payment models
Health Care Transformation Task Force (HCTTF)	Industry consortium aligning public and private sector toward care transformation with widespread adoption of new payment models and focus on identifying some key capabilities (such as management of high-risk patients) and making consensus recommendations on Centers for Medicare & Medicaid Services policies related to payment reform
National Academy of Medicine (NAM)	Expert-driven organization with a variety of activities related to reviewing and disseminating evidence, as well as expert opinion, on increasing value in health care through health care delivery and payment reform
Premier PACT Population Health Management Collaborative	Health care performance improvement alliance of Premier health systems to share data, experiences, and tools to support care transformation
California Association of Physician Groups (CAPG)	Group representing physician-led organizations practicing in capitated, coordinated care that has developed a variety of reports, tools, conferences, and other resources to help organizations to succeed under risk-based contracts
Toward Accountable Care Consortium (TAC)	Provider-based organization in North Carolina devoted to sharing lessons about ACO development
Network for Regional Healthcare Improvement (NRHI)	National organization of regional health-improvement collaboratives (RHICs) with a mission to transform health care delivery by supporting the implementation of new care models and information sharing supported by payment reform at the regional level
Accountable Care Learning Collaborative (ACLC)	Collaboration of health care stakeholders that seeks to advance accountable care by identifying needed competencies and linking organizations with resources to enable them to succeed in payment and delivery reform

Collaboratives, such as the Accountable Care Learning Collaborative (ACLC) and others illustrated in *Table 10-1*, focus on addressing those key issues, cost implications, and barriers to advancing accountable care. The collective goal for many groups is to help health care providers to develop needed competencies for care-delivery reform and to support providers in succeeding in value-based payment models. Many organizations are undertaking similar efforts on their own, but the unique benefit of collaboratives is the aggregation of both public and private evidence and expert opinion on how to improve care. Collaboratives can create a uniform set of best practices and strategies for success. For accountable care to progress, the collective knowledge concerning value-based care competencies needs to be aggregated, evaluated, and broadly disseminated.

Like many of the other groups in *Table 10-1*, the ACLC has drawn from the experiences of public and private collaborative efforts to develop a widely applicable framework describing the competencies that risk-bearing entities must develop to succeed in accountable care (ACLC Competencies, 2016). The ACLC's strategic goal is to help organizations to identify their current competency gaps and then to link them to relevant resources for developing those competencies.

The creation of the ACLC competency framework involved a process of preliminary identification of major competency areas, the commissioning of a set of collaborative workgroups to conduct an evidence and resource review in each area, an iterative consensus process in each workgroup to identify key capabilities and best practices, and a high-level review to refine the overall structure of the identified competencies. The competencies could form the basis of a capability-assessment tool for providers to use in determining their readiness to take on value-based payments and the basis of a resource set for linking providers to tools, resources, and supporting organizations that can help them to develop needed competencies.

The ACLC has identified seven primary competency domains, as shown in *Table 10-2*. Each competency domain can be expanded into a more complete set of capabilities, as illustrated in *Figure 10-2*. The framework illustrates the magnitude of the challenges facing health care organizations; it is not surprising that few have succeeded (Health Leaders Media, 2016). The framework provides a foundation for health care organizations to use in identifying the key tasks ahead of them and in taking some practical and feasible steps that are likely to succeed in enabling them to move forward.

TABLE 10-2 | ACLC Competency Domains and Scope of Competency

DOMAIN	SCOPE OF COMPETENCY
Governance and culture	Leadership and policy development; provider accountability; board representation for clinicians, community, and patients; decision-making processes aligned with value-based objectives
Financial readiness	Ability to assess longitudinal patient resource use; evidence-based mechanisms for management of financial and performance risk; established provider networks; mechanisms to distribute shared savings payments
Health information technology	Capacity to assess and implement products, platforms, and processes for accessing and using health care data; reliable and timely acquisition of key actionable data for longitudinal patient management; analytics to predict intervention impact
Patient risk assessment	Ability to assess patient needs for chronic-condition management and navigating the health system and to target strategies and specific resources to patients by using a validated risk- and impact-assessment tool
Care coordination	Longitudinal-care team with well-defined roles and responsibilities that foster continuity of care; mechanisms for access to well-targeted and community-based social services; reliable, straightforward sharing of encounters, test results, and other key information across care team
Quality	Capacity to assess and implement high-impact interventions to make care safer, more effective, patient-centered, timely, efficient, and equitable; provider and staff training; quality-improvement initiatives that are evidence-driven with impact measurement and adjustment
Patient-centeredness	Capacity to help people to maintain or return to health, supported by patient-driven, health-measurement capacity; incorporation of patient perspective into governance, care-system design, and individual interaction; capturing the individual patient's values, preferences, and expressed needs in care plans

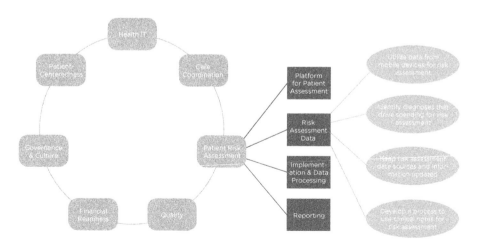

FIGURE 10-2 | Competency domains and their complete set of capabilities.

The goal of the competency framework is to help organizations to understand the totality of activities that they need to undertake and, more important, where to start and how to take initial steps that are needed to succeed. That point is illustrated by the following list of the five essential competencies enumerated within the integration strategies and partnerships category in the Quality domain:

1. Develop a process of effective collaboration with value-focused partners throughout the health care spectrum.
2. Ensure that patients, families, providers, and care-team members are involved in quality-improvement activities.
3. Capture and report data relevant to cost, processes of care and care delivery, medical and health outcomes, and service outcomes in an integrated and standard manner.
4. Build a team of operations experts and clinical, continuous, quality-improvement experts to guide the work of improvement teams from within the organization.
5. Participate in a formal quality collaborative with other health care organizations and strategic partners that necessitates sharing of data and knowledge.

For health care organizations seeking to move to value-based care, the specific competencies provide the genesis for leveraging partnerships and care integration to maximize the quality of care provided for a given population.

Figure 10-3 represents the competency journey map that provides context for how providers move from identifying gaps in their understanding of the competencies needed for value-based care through the stages of development that lead to mature capabilities.

Competency stages of development

FIGURE 10-3 | Competency provider journey map.

ACCELERATING THE DEVELOPMENT OF HEALTH CARE CAPABILITIES TO SUCCEED IN VALUE-BASED PAYMENT MODELS

Even with resources like those being developed in the ACLC and other collaboratives, delivery reform is challenging. Policy support is needed to refine this type of competency framework by improving the evidence underlying it and encouraging organizations to draw on the resources.

Given governments' role as major purchasers of health care, federal and state payment policies have been a primary policy focus, as evidenced by Department of Health and Human Services (HHS) Secretary Sylvia Burwell's 2015 announcement to shift 80 percent of care into value-based purchasing models by 2018 and related initiatives, such as the Health Care Payment Learning and Action Network. However, despite the need for payment reform, without organizations that are able to function well with new payment models, progress both in payment and in delivery of higher-value health care will be slow and cumbersome.

Public policy needs to put comparable effort into identifying what works and what does not work in delivering care in value-based payment models and into supporting health care providers and the organizations working with them to develop the capabilities that they need to succeed. Government does not have the capacity or expertise to dictate what works, but it can facilitate networks to find and spread solutions more quickly.

There is also a need for policymakers to support the development of a clearinghouse to link health care providers to resources that can help them to develop needed competencies. The collaborative efforts would have the goal of assisting federal and state policymakers to identify and adopt lessons learned from data and experience in the varied collaborations about how policies can support effective delivery reform better.

VITAL DIRECTIONS

Policymakers should match support for improving the design and evaluation of payment-reform models with commensurate support for health care providers to develop the competencies needed to succeed. We highlight four vital directions below.

1. **Support public–private "precompetitive" collaborations to accelerate the development of alternative payment model competencies, measures, and benchmarks.** We encourage federal and state governments to support and participate in privately led collaborations to accelerate delivery reform. Collaborations aiming to provide tools and resources to accelerate the development of APM competencies include such initiatives as Premier's Population Health Management Collaborative, the Health Care Transformation Task Force, the ACLC, and the National Academy of Medicine's Leadership Consortium on Value and Science-Driven Health.

The Centers for Medicare & Medicaid Services (CMS) and HHS should participate actively, and the federal government should provide financial support for using the initiatives to develop better publicly available resources for providers. For example, CMS "learning networks" for particular Medicare payment reforms should be conducted in closer collaboration with private-sector efforts in similar payment reforms with specific goals for improved resources for providers. High priority should be attached to better tools for different types of providers to assess gaps and to track and evaluate progress in APM capabilities through the development, refinement, and wider use of measures of key care-delivery competencies. Publicly supporting collaborations could help to facilitate the identification of competencies and value-based terminology, articulate ways to measure organizational performance, and direct the dissemination of the findings.

2. **Develop evidence on the effects of improved competencies on the performance of health care organizations.** Collaboration in competency assessment and development should be based on a stronger foundation of empirical evidence. Organizations that apply the same competency framework can more easily benchmark themselves against other, similarly situated organizations, and the framework can enable more valid analyses of whether proprietary tools and approaches are helping to improve capabilities. This work will also support research studies on how organizational capabilities translate into improvements in quality and cost, which will provide needed evidence to guide further payment reforms and competency-development work. The federal government should support research on the impact of improved competencies on organizational quality and cost performance. The improving evidence base will lead to a better understanding of which competencies are needed for success and the best ways to develop them.

3. **Align federal payments for health-profession education with value-based health care competencies.** Federal payments for health-profession education with value-based health care competencies will help more medical schools and other health care professional education programs to make needed changes to reflect the new kinds of skills that health professionals need to succeed in a system focused on value (Scheibal, 2016). Some have already begun to change. The University of Wisconsin School of Medicine and Public Health, for example, changed its name and curriculum in 2005 to emphasize the need to treat the whole patient rather than just a patient's physical condition (Jablow, 2015). New medical schools, including Dell Medical School of the University of Texas at Austin and the recently

announced Kaiser Medical School, are implementing fundamentally different approaches to clinical education that are much better aligned with accountability for population health. Continuing-medical-education activities are also increasingly focusing on new care competencies. Despite those efforts, however, federal educational support is only slightly aligned with the emerging national priorities in care delivery.

4. **Implement rewards for data-exchange capacities to support competency development and evaluation.** Health information technology (HIT) is the backbone of success in patient-centered delivery reforms that improve quality and lower cost. In building on the interoperability roadmap developed by the Office of the National Coordinator for Health Information Technology (DeSalvo, 2015), it is important for CMS to focus payment policies for HIT more directly on "use case"–demonstrated competencies in data exchange and to reduce administrative burdens and barriers to data exchange caused by some interpretations of current privacy rules.

CONCLUSION

American health care needs to be reformed to bend the cost curve and to deliver better, less expensive care to patients, which is increasingly possible. Sharing solutions and collaborating on effective methods for reform throughout the industry not only can reduce disruptions in patient care but also will encourage greater competition and collaboration on value in health care.

Federal and state leaders have an opportunity to support those changes by complementing payment reform with provider support in care-delivery transformation. Given the complex infrastructure needs and competencies necessary for successful delivery reform, without support many providers may fail to evolve successfully, and this would slow progress. Government can mitigate failures and increase successes by advocating for and participating in industry collaborations and by adopting the resulting knowledge in regard to value-based care competency measurement and benchmarking, shared competency evidence development, value-based health care education reform, and increasing access to data available through HIT.

The collective state of and spending on American health care has created a small window for the private and public sectors to coalesce around the adoption of value-based care. The transformation away from FFS payments will not be without its challenges, but by incorporating the above recommendations related to greater competency development by providers, policymakers can make important contributions to the sustainability of value-based payment reforms.

SUMMARY RECOMMENDATIONS FOR
VITAL DIRECTIONS

1. Support public–private "precompetitive" collaborations to develop alternative payment model (APM) competencies, measures, and benchmarks.
2. Develop evidence on the impact of improved competencies on the performance of health care organizations.
3. Align federal payments for health professional education with value-based health care competencies.
4. Implement rewards for data exchange capacities to support competency development and evaluation.

REFERENCES

ACLC Competencies. 2016. Available at http://www.accountablecarelc.org/aclc-competencies (accessed August 7, 2016).

Dale, S. B., A. Ghosh, D. N. Peikes, T. J. Day, F. B. Yoon, E. F. Taylor, K. Swankoski, A.S. O'Malley, P.H. Conway, R. Rajkumar, M.J. Press, L. Sessums, and R. Brown. 2016. Two-year costs and quality in the comprehensive primary care initiative. *New England Journal of Medicine* 374(24):2345–2356.

DeSalvo, K. 2015. Connecting health and care for the nation: A shared nationwide interoperability roadmap. Available at https://www.healthit.gov/sites/default/files/hie-interoperability/nationwide-interoperability-roadmap-final-version-1.0.pdf (accessed August 22, 2016).

Health Care Payment Learning and Action Network. 2016. Alternate Payment Model (APM) Framework: Final White Paper. Available at https://hcp-lan.org/groups/apm-fpt/apm-framework/ (accessed August 22, 2016).

HealthLeaders Media. 2016, July. Case B. Value-based readiness: Building momentum for tomorrow's healthcare. Available at http://www.healthleadersmedia.com/report/intelligence/value-based-readiness-building-momentum-tomorrow%E2%80%99s-healthcare (accessed August 22, 2016).

Jablow, M. 2015. The public health imperative: Revising the medical school curriculum. Available at www.aamc.org/newsroom/reporter/may2015/431962/public-health.html (accessed August 22, 2016).

McWilliams, J., L.A. Hatfield, M.E. Chernew, B.E. Landon, and A.L. Schwartz. 2016. Early performance of accountable care organizations in Medicare. *New England Journal of Medicine* 374:2357–2366. doi: 10.1056/NEJMsa1600142.

Muhlestein, D., and M. McClellan. 2016. Accountable care organizations in 2016: Private and public-sector growth and dispersion. *Health Affairs* blog, April 21. Available at http://healthaffairs.org/blog/2016/04/21/accountable-care-organizations-in-2016-private-and-public-sector-growth-and-dispersion/.

NASEM (National Academies of Sciences, Engineering, and Medicine). 2016. *The role of public-private partnerships in health systems strengthening: Workshop summary.* Washington, DC: The National Academies Press. doi: 10.17226/21861.

Scheibal, S. 2016. Leading health care transformer joining Dell Med. UT News, The University of Texas at Austin. Available at http://news.utexas.edu/2016/06/22/health-care-transformer-joining-dell-med (accessed August 23, 2016).

US Congress. 2015. Medicare Access and CHIP Reauthorization Act of 2015, P.L. 114–10. Available at https://www.congress.gov/bill/114th-congress/house-bill/2/text/pl (accessed August 22, 2016).

AUTHOR INFORMATION

Michael O. Leavitt is Founder and Chairman, Leavitt Partners and former Secretary of the Department of Health and Human Services. **Mark. B. McClellan, MD, PhD,** is Director, Duke-Robert J. Margolis Center for Health Policy and Robert J. Margolis Professor, Duke University and former Adminstrator for the Centers for Medicare and Medicaid Services. **Susan D. Devore, MM,** is President and CEO, Premier, Inc. **Elliott Fisher, MD, MPH,** is Director, Dartmouth Institute for Health Policy and Clinical Practice. **Richard J. Gilfillan, MD,** is President and CEO, Trinity Health. **H. Stephen Lieber, CAE,** is President and CEO, Healthcare Information and Management Systems Society. **Richard Merkin, MD,** is President and CEO, Heritage Provider Network, Inc. **Jeffrey Rideout, MD,** is President and CEO, Integrated Healthcare Association. **Kent J. Thiry, MBA,** is Chairman and CEO, DaVita Healthcare Partners, Inc.

11

TAILORING COMPLEX-CARE MANAGEMENT, COORDINATION, AND INTEGRATION FOR HIGH-NEED, HIGH-COST PATIENTS

David Blumenthal, MD, Gerard Anderson, PhD, Sheila P. Burke, MPA, RN, Terry Fulmer, PhD, RN, Ashish K. Jha, MD, MPH, and Peter Long, PhD

The increasingly complex health care needs of the US population require a new vision and a new paradigm for the organization, financing, and delivery of health care services. Some 5 percent of adults (12 million people) have three or more chronic conditions and a functional limitation that makes it hard for them to perform basic daily tasks, such as feeding themselves or talking on the phone (Hayes et al., 2016). This group, "high-need, high-cost" (HNHC) people, makes up our nation's sickest and most complex patient population. HNHC adults are a heterogeneous population that consists of adults who are under 65 years old and disabled, those who have advanced illnesses, the frail elderly, and people who have multiple chronic conditions.

Those complex patients account for about half the nation's health care spending (Cohen and Yu, 2012). HNHC patients are often people who, despite receiving substantial health care services, have critical health needs that are unmet. That population will often receive ineffective care, such as unnecessary hospitalizations. By giving high priority to the care of HNHC patients, we can target our resources where they are likely to yield the greatest value—better outcomes at lower cost.

We have an unprecedented opportunity to increase value of health care by rethinking our approaches to serving HNHC patients. The Patient Protection and Affordable Care Act (ACA) offers an array of incentives and tools for pilot-testing and refining alternative delivery and payment models, and many states and private payers have been experimenting with new approaches. Health systems have responded by developing new approaches to health care delivery and greater public health outreach. The shift toward value-based, population-oriented care encourages the multiple providers (in and outside the health care system) involved in a patient's care to collaborate to provide appropriate, high-quality care and achieve better patient outcomes. Now we need to disseminate information about successful programs, modify payment and financing systems, create a health care system that is conducive to the spread and scale of promising innovations, and eliminate remaining barriers that have impeded the adoption of effective approaches to caring for the nation's most clinically and socially disadvantaged patients.

This chapter explores key issues, spending implications, and existing barriers to meeting the needs of HNHC patients. We suggest policy options for a new federal administration to improve complex care management, care coordination, and integration of services for that population. Given that the number of patients living with multiple chronic illnesses is likely to grow, finding ways to improve outcomes for this population while avoiding unnecessary or even harmful use of health care services should have high priority for the new president and new administration.

OVERVIEW OF HIGH-NEED, HIGH-COST PATIENTS

HNHC patients are people who have clinically complex medical and social needs, often with functional limitations and behavioral-health conditions, and who incur high health care spending or are likely to in the near future. The people in that population have varied medical, behavioral-health, and social-service needs and service-use patterns. A recent analysis of the nationally representative 2009–2011 Medical Expenditure Panel Survey by Gerard Anderson, of Johns Hopkins University, showed that 94 percent of people whose annual total health care expenditures were in the top 10 percent of spending for all adults had three or more chronic conditions (Hayes et al., 2016). Some 34 percent of the total adult population, more than 79 million people, have 3 or more chronic conditions without any functional limitation, and their average annual health care spending ($7,526) is 55 percent higher than that of the total adult population ($4,845).

The additional burden of a functional impairment in the presence of multiple chronic conditions—that is, a long-term limitation in performing activities of daily living, such as bathing and eating, or instrumental activities of daily living, such as using the telephone or managing money without assistance—can substantially increase health care spending and use and the likelihood of receiving poor-quality care. Average annual health care expenditures are nearly three times as high for adults who have chronic conditions and functional impairments as for adults who have only chronic conditions ($21,021 vs $7,577) (Hayes et al., 2016) *(Figure 11-1)*. People who had multiple chronic conditions and functional limitations were more than twice as likely to visit the emergency department and three times as likely to experience an inpatient hospital stay as adults who had only multiple chronic conditions. They also were less able to remain in the workforce, so their annual incomes were much lower and they had greater difficulty in paying for medical services. They shouldered a greater cost burden with higher out-of-pocket costs ($1,169) than the US average ($702) (Hayes et al., 2016). Thus, functional impairments, both physical and cognitive, are important considerations when one is trying to identify and understand sick and frail patients whose health care is expensive.

The challenges facing HNHC patients extend beyond medical care into other related areas in which the relationship with their underlying illnesses can be complex. These patients often have substantial social needs and behavioral-health concerns. Serious illnesses can lead to job losses, substantial economic hardships, and difficulties in navigating the health care system, including being unable to get to appointments. Inadequate social services—such as a lack of stable housing, a reliable food source, or basic transportation—can exacerbate health outcomes and increase health spending (Taylor et al., 2015). Similarly, adults who have behavioral-health conditions frequently experience fragmented care with no single coordinating provider, and this can result in higher spending and poorer outcomes (Druss and Walker, 2011). And, people who are experiencing serious illness and approaching the end of life, primarily older people, often receive care that is unwanted, contrary to their preferences for care, and of highest cost (Brownlee and Berman, 2016). Addressing any one part of these complex relationships in isolation (e.g., just the medical issues, just the social factors, or just the mental health problems) is probably inadequate. It is critical to take a holistic approach in which programs are tailored to address the whole array of issues for HNHC patients. Health-system leaders, payers, and providers will need to look beyond the regular slate of medical services to coordinate, integrate, and effectively manage care for behavioral-health conditions and social-service needs for functional impairments to improve outcomes and lower spending.

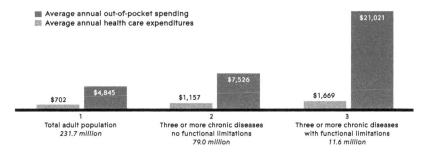

Note: Noninstitutionalized civilian population age 18 and older.
Data: 2009–2011 Medical Expenditure Panel Survey (MEPS). Analysis by C.A. Salzberg, Johns Hopkins University.

FIGURE 11-1 Adults with high needs have higher health care spending and out-of-pocket costs.
SOURCE: Hayes et al., 2016

POPULATION SEGMENTATION: A CRITICAL FIRST STEP TO MATCH INTERVENTIONS TO PATIENTS' NEEDS

HNHC patients make up a diverse population, including people who have major complex chronic conditions in multiple organ systems, the nonelderly disabled, frail elders, and children who have complex special health care needs. The heterogeneity of the population speaks to the implausibility of finding one delivery model or one program that meets the needs of all HNHC patients. Instead, payers and health systems may need to divide these patients into groups that have common needs so that specific, complex, care-management interventions can be targeted to the people who are most likely to benefit. Research by Ashish Jha, of the Harvard School of Public Health, is under way to derive a manageable number of groups among high-cost Medicare beneficiaries empirically on the basis of an analysis of multiple years of Medicare claims data.

Value-based delivery systems require a shift away from the disease-specific medical model, in which each clinician operates in his or her own specialty, to one that is more integrative and accepts multimorbidity and multidisciplinary care as the norm. In most health systems, care coordination occurs sequentially, and this may be adequate for uncomplicated cases. However, complex cases require seamless coordination with the spectrum of providers, patients, and caregivers reviewing and sharing information concurrently to inform and modify treatment plans simultaneously (Thompson, 2003). Many HNHC patients may move between groups and settings as their needs change, so flexibility and adaptability are essential for any intervention.

Denver Health, an integrated health system and the largest safety-net provider in Colorado, stratifies all patients according to risk by using a combination of risk-prediction software, medication data, functional status, and clinical indicators to identify patients who may need the help of nurse care managers, patient navigators, or clinical pharmacists (Hughes et al., 2004). The highest-risk patients are divided into nine segments, for example, people who have catastrophic conditions that include long-term dependence on medical technology (such as dialysis machines or respirators) and patients whose conditions require continuing care (such as AIDS or heart-transplantation patients). Low-risk patients may receive text messages with reminders about appointments, but higher-need patients receive comprehensive follow-up care after appointments and substantial social- and behavioral-health support (Johnson et al., 2015). For the highest-risk patients, Denver Health funded three high-intensity clinics with small patient panels, such as adults who have significant mental health diagnoses and recent multiple readmissions. Segmentation is not without its practical challenges. First, it is expensive to develop. Denver Health received a $19.8 million grant from the Center for Medicare & Medicaid Innovation (CMMI) in 2012 to support its risk-prediction development process. Second, there is an inherent tension between integration and specialization of services when patients are divided into groups, which could lead to increased fragmentation of care. More analysis is needed to assess the implications of segmentation and identify the best ways to ensure coordinated, patient-centered, and continuous care.

WHAT WORKS? LESSONS FROM THE LITERATURE ON PROMISING MODELS FOR THE HIGH-NEED, HIGH-COST POPULATION

Improvement in the HNHC population has proved difficult to achieve in many instances; however, the evidence shows that a number of care-management models targeting HNHC patients have had favorable results in quality of care and quality of life and mixed results in their ability to reduce unnecessary hospital use or reduce costs of care (Boult et al., 2009; Brown et al., 2012; Hong et al., 2014b; Nelson, 2012). A 2015 review of the literature by Johns Hopkins University researchers identified 13 rigorous studies that reported health care use and spending outcomes for patients who had multiple chronic conditions. Of the 13, 12 reported a significant reduction in hospital use or cost; however, only 2 of the 12 showed significantly favorable results in all three domains of the triple aim: quality of care, patient experience, and use or cost of care (Bleich et al., 2015). There are important issues regarding the sustainability of these models. For example, only half the programs identified were still operating when they were contacted by Johns Hopkins researchers in 2015. To illustrate the variety of interventions that target HNHC patients and have been shown to work, *Table 11-1* presents four examples of successful models. The four were selected because they have generated evidence of improved care, better patient experience, and lower use or cost of care and they show the variety of care settings in which such models can operate, including a primary care practice, the community setting, and a patient's home.

An examination of the care-management models that had favorable outcomes reveals their common features. Common attributes include closely targeting patients who are most likely to benefit from the intervention, comprehensive assessment of patients' risks and needs, specially trained care managers who facilitate coordination and communication between patient and care team, and effective interdisciplinary teamwork (Anderson et al., 2015; McCarthy et al., 2015). An important feature of innovative models is the ability to manage patients in multiple settings because patients are at high risk of moving from primary care to hospital to postacute care site or nursing home. An analysis by Avalere in 2014 showed substantial return on investment in programs that actively managed Medicare patients' transitions between hospital, skilled nursing facility, and home (Rodriguez et al., 2014).

TABLE 11-1 | Examples of Successful Care-Management Models for HNHC Adults

CARE SETTING	PROGRAM/ SPONSOR	TARGET POPULATION	KEY COMPONENTS	RESULTS
Primary care practice	Care Management Plus, Oregon Health and Science University	Age 65 years and older with multiple comorbidities, diabetes, frailty, dementia, depression, and other mental-health needs; entry by referral from primary care provider; model has been adapted to serve non-elderly patients who have complex needs.	Specially trained care managers in primary care clinics perform person-centered assessment and work with families and providers, using a specialized information-technology system to formulate and implement a care plan to ensure continuity and provide coaching and self-care education to patients and families (Bodenheimer and Berry-Millett, 2009).	Controlled study comparing patients receiving care management in seven intervention clinics with similar patients in six control practices within Intermountain Healthcare found decreased hospitalization rates after 2 years for intervention (Dorr et al., 2007) patients and about 20 percent reduction in mortality among all Care Management Plus patients with reduction most pronounced in patients who had diabetes (Dorr et al., 2008).
Home	Independence at Home (Kinosian et al., 2016)	Medicare beneficiaries who have multiple chronic conditions and need assistance with two or more long-term functional limitations (such as walking and eating).	Primary care practices provide home-based primary care to targeted chronically ill beneficiaries for a three-year period, making in-home visits tailored to an individual patient's needs and coordinating care. CMS will track the beneficiary's care experience through quality measures; practices that succeed in meeting these quality measures while generating Medicare savings will have an opportunity to receive incentive payments after meeting a minimum savings requirement.	Enrollees had fewer hospital readmissions within 30 days; had followup contact with their provider within 48 hours of a hospital admission, hospital discharge, or emergency-department visit; had their medications identified by their provider within 48 hours of discharge from the hospital; had their preferences documented by their provider; and used inpatient hospital and emergency-department services less for such conditions as diabetes, high blood pressure, asthma, pneumonia, and urinary tract infection.

CARE SETTING	PROGRAM/ SPONSOR	TARGET POPULATION	KEY COMPONENTS	RESULTS
Community-based	Program of All-Inclusive Care for the Elderly (PACE)	Age 55 years and older with insurance through Medicare or Medicaid, with chronic conditions and functional or cognitive impairments, and living in the service area of a local PACE organization; patients must be certified by Medicaid as eligible for nursing-home level of care and be able to live safely at home with help from PACE.	Each PACE site provides comprehensive preventive, primary, acute, and long-term care and social services—including adult day care, meals, and transportation—to allow patients to live independently in the community; an interdisciplinary team meets regularly to design individualized care plans; clinical staff are employed or contracted by the local PACE organization, which is paid on a per-capita basis and not on the basis of volume of services provided (Beauchamp et al., 2008).	PACE enrollees experienced fewer hospitalizations but more nursing-home admissions, better quality of some aspects of care (such as pain management), and lower mortality than comparison groups (Ghosh et al., 2014); PACE appeared cost-neutral with respect to Medicare and may have increased costs for Medicaid although more research is needed to reflect current payment arrangements (Ghosh et al., 2014); a later study found that PACE may be more effective than home- and community-based waiver programs in reducing long-term nursing-home use (Segelman et al., 2015); higher self-rated PACE team performance and other program characteristics were associated with better enrollee functional health outcomes (Mukamel et al., 2006, 2007.
Transitional care	Naylor Transitional Care Model	Hospitalized, high-risk older adults with chronic conditions.	Multidisciplinary provider team led by advanced-practice nurses engages in comprehensive discharge planning, including 3-month postdischarge followups with frequent home visits and telephone calls; program involves patients and family members in identifying goals and building self-management skills.	Randomized controlled trial found the following 1 year after discharge: • 36 percent fewer readmissions. • 38 percent reduction in total costs. • Short-term improvements in overall quality of life and patient satisfaction (Naylor et al., 2004).

CHALLENGES TO SPREAD AND SCALE

Despite evidence from a number of models that show spending reductions and increased efficiency, several barriers limit the widespread adoption of these programs. The most prominent obstacle is the misalignment of financial incentives. Few programs like accountable care organizations (ACOs) have implemented value-based physician compensation to align with value-based payment; capital and reorganization costs are often borne by the providers, but the savings accrue to the ACO or payer. The financial incentives do not always accrue to the program that undertakes the investment; for example, Medicare typically makes the investment necessary to keep HNHC patients out of nursing homes or long-term care facilities, but the savings accrue to Medicaid and thus are shared by federal and state governments.

Among nonfinancial barriers, professional uncertainty, and lack of training and skill to take on new roles can impede the successful adoption of care management and the necessary accompanying culture change. Training in care coordination, for example, is a necessary addition to the academic curriculum. A lack of interoperability for electronic health record systems precludes integration and coordination throughout the care continuum. Finally, lack of rigorous evidence from multisite interventions—in both the public and private sectors—can make it difficult to determine the generalizability and sustainability of different models or program features in multiple contexts. A shared evaluation framework or common set of outcome measures could help to accelerate testing in both the private and public sectors, which is an important strategy for building a robust evidence base.

VITAL DIRECTIONS

The aging of the population, the shift toward value-based payment, the growth of alternative delivery systems, and the growth of managed care (both Medicare Advantage and Medicaid managed care) are prompting providers and payers to focus their attention on HNHC patients. In anticipation of the new federal administration, we outline a variety of promising policy options that could improve complex care management for people who are at risk of poor outcomes and unnecessary use of health care and high expenditures for it.

Promote Value-Based Payment

A critical strategy to improve care for HNHC patients is to continue to expand the prevalence and improve the effectiveness of value-based payment for risk-bearing organizations, such as ACOs, Medicare Advantage (MA) plans, and risk-based Medicaid managed-care plans. As mentioned above, HNHC patients are the heaviest users of services, and in a fee-for-service environment, there is little incentive for providers to collaborate to help patients who have clinically and socially complex needs. Furthermore, with fee-for-service payment, health systems or hospitals that are developing innovative approaches to help to keep patients healthy or avoid hospitalizations face substantial financial losses. In contrast, capitated payments to a group of providers, such as an ACO or MA plan, give providers an incentive to focus on quality of care and efficiency of services for their patient populations without being preoccupied with generating volume to increase revenue. In 2015, Department of Health and Human Services Secretary Sylvia Mathews Burwell announced the goal of ensuring that 90 percent of Medicare payments be value based by 2018 (Burwell, 2015), and a new administration should continue that policy direction because it could have considerable favorable implications for HNHC patients.

Improve the Design and Implementation of Value-Based Payment

Despite the promise of value-based payment, much evaluation and fine-tuning of new payment approaches are needed to improve its implementation and in particular to understand the implications for patients who have clinically and socially complex needs. However, on the basis of experience with value-based payment thus far, a number of needs for improvement have already emerged. First, there needs to be greater alignment between value-based payments to risk-bearing organizations and value-based payments to individual providers that are part of those organizations. A recent study found that most ACOs and risk-based plans continue to pay their individual clinicians on a fee-for-service basis, and this makes it difficult to translate the ethos of value-based payment to practicing clinicians (Bailit et al., 2015). If the individual providers or practice sites do not feel the shift toward accountability, population health, and value, the diffusion of promising practices or models of care will be slow. Medicare and Medicaid could work more closely with private provider organizations to achieve greater symmetry between organizational and provider payment approaches. It will also be crucial to make sure that the new incentives do not place such undue financial pressure on providers that they compromise care.

Second, value-based payments to providers must account for the different risks that HNHC patients bring to their care and appropriately pay the entities that accept the risks. Most risk-adjustment systems have not done an adequate job of that. Without appropriate risk adjustment, providers face natural pressure either to skimp on care for the sickest patients and the ones who have the most complex conditions or to avoid them entirely. Recently, concern has grown that current risk-adjustment formulas used by the federal authorities do not account adequately for patients' physical, behavioral, and social service needs, which are factors that substantially affect the health of the nation's sickest and poorest patients and the ones who have the most complex conditions (Barnett et al., 2015). Adapting risk-adjustment methods to capture the scope of those patients' risk more accurately will be critical for effective implementation of value-based payment policies.

A third concern is the misalignment between investment and savings. The savings from many complex care management programs often benefit another payer, party, or system even if the group bearing the actual costs is part of a risk-sharing organization. For example, most providers in an ACO, Medicaid managed care plan, or Medicare Advantage network are expected to cover the upfront costs (such as staff training and adjustments of information technology) associated with the program, but savings accrue to the ACO or the plan (Hong et al., 2014a). Even if the savings are shared with the clinician, experience suggests that it can take 3 years for the programs to produce savings, and this lag might discourage providers from investing in the first place. Supplemental payments to providers to support transformational and capital expenditures could help to defray the cost and speed adoption. Alternatively, a partial capitated fee (such as a per-member, per-month supplement) to the site that offers the care management program could cover part of the investment during the transition to value-based compensation.

The discrepancy between payment and savings has serious consequences for patients who are dually eligible for Medicare and Medicaid. In particular, the incentives for managing transitions from a facility to home are not well aligned. Care-coordination or care-transition programs that help to keep this population at home or in the community are often paid for by Medicare. However, the savings, which probably result from a reduction in long-term nursing-home days, accrue to Medicaid. An arrangement would have to be negotiated to figure out how Medicare and Medicaid could share in the savings that result from keeping dually eligible people at home or in community settings.

Increase Flexibility of Accountable Providers to Pay for Nonmedical Services

Another issue is the scope of covered clinical and social services. Unaddressed personal and social needs can increase health care use and costs. Conversely, home meal delivery, which is a low-cost and simple intervention, can reduce hospitalizations and delay nursing-home admissions and thus reduce health care expenditures. In traditional Medicare, the critical component of care-management programs that is often associated with savings—the care coordinator (a social worker or care manager)—is not a covered service. Medicare Advantage does cover a few supplemental services, but the scope and duration are inadequate and disease specific. There is more extensive coverage of supplemental, nonmedical services for Medicaid beneficiaries than for Medicare beneficiaries, but a number of highly effective, low-cost, nonmedical health interventions are excluded. Examples include housing support and reimbursement for community health workers, who provide peer support in chronic-disease self-management and in navigating the system. However, we should be careful not to "medicalize" social services so that everything becomes health care and becomes subject to its rules. Other countries spend considerably more on social services; this allows them to spend less on medical care and can improve outcomes (Bradley and Taylor, 2013).

Provide Intensive Technical Assistance to Providers Regarding Care for High-Need, High-Cost Patients

Once value-based payment incentives are in place to encourage providers to improve care for HNHC patients, health system leaders and clinicians will need technical assistance to design and implement effective programs. Fortunately, the literature provides some guidance. Substantial evidence shows that successful programs effectively target patients who will benefit from interventions. In light of the heterogeneity of the population, public and private insurers may need to adapt benefits, payments, and care models to specific needs of beneficiary groups. Segmenting the high-need population into groups and then targeting the most at-risk patients within the groups will facilitate more successful implementation. Segmentation can also allow for greater person-centered care by eliciting and tailoring care to patients' preferences (Berman, 2012). For Medicare or dually enrolled beneficiaries, functional impairment is an important program eligibility factor to consider because such limitations correlate highly with increases in use, cost, and fragmented care. In the Medicaid context, patients who have substance-abuse disorders or severe and persistent mental health issues substantially increase spending; this suggests potential eligibility for this group of the Medicaid population (Boyd, et. al., 2010).

Give High Priority to Health Information Exchange

The most promising care-management models depend on health information technology for efficient screening and identification of patients for inclusion. Information technology is crucial for enabling patients, caregivers, and providers in different settings and sectors to share critical behavioral, social, and medical information about patients to improve management of their care. Policies to promote interoperability and exchange of information among providers in and outside the health system could have important implications for the adoption and evaluation of promising programs.

Continue Active Experimentation and Support Model Refinement and the Spread and Scale of Evidence-Based Practices

A number of promising models have demonstrated improvements in patient outcomes and reductions in spending, but much of the evidence base draws on studies conducted in few locations, health care settings, or populations. Even when promising models are successfully evaluated, generate favorable mass-media coverage, and generally achieve widespread acclaim, they do not necessarily develop a clear path to sustainability without continuing grant support. More could be done to enable the US health care system to sustain, spread, and scale innovative delivery models. If we cannot solve the related issues of sustainability and scale, we are at risk of repeatedly developing and reinventing small, innovative pilots that go nowhere. First, we need to achieve consensus on the criteria that should be met to declare a model "evidence based" or successful. As a first step toward that goal, the Institute of Medicine released *Vital Signs: Core Metrics for Health and Health Care Progress* in April 2015; it recommended 15 common domains for assessing performance at every level of the health care system (IOM, 2015). Next, payers and delivery-system leaders need to understand how core metrics can be applied to improve care delivery and health outcomes. The Institute for Clinical and Economic Review is developing new analytic tools to produce independent evidence on the effective and relative value of new technologies for families and society; these tools are designed to encourage public discussions about priorities in health care. Similar approaches could be used to assess effects on care-delivery models. Third, health care practitioners need more support to learn how to translate the successful features of evidence-based models. Toward this end, the ACA created the CMMI and Patient-Centered Outcomes Research Institute (PCORI) to promote experimentation to improve care for HNHC patients. The next administration and Congress should continue support for CMMI and PCORI with directions to test the effectiveness of care approaches for HNHC patients and should continue to encourage private-sector engagement.

CONCLUSION

Improving care for HNHC patients is a key lever to bring national health spending to a more sustainable level and accomplish many needed changes in our health care system. There is an opportunity for a new president and the next administration to build on promising models and implement policy changes to improve outcomes for HNHC patients. Our recommendations follow.

- Promote and improve the design of value-based payment.
- Increase flexibility of accountable providers to pay for nonmedical services.
- Provide intensive technical assistance to providers regarding care for HNHC patients.
- Give high priority to health information exchange.
- Continue active experimentation and support for model refinement and the spread and scale of evidence-based practices.

The challenge before us is to apply what we know to improve the health of Americans; this would also contribute to the nation's economy. With the policy opportunities outlined above, we believe that the new federal administration could improve the health and welfare of our nation's HNHC patients considerably.

SUMMARY RECOMMENDATIONS FOR VITAL DIRECTIONS

1. Promote and improve the design of value-based payment.
2. Increase flexibility of accountable providers to pay for nonmedical services.
3. Provide intensive technical assistance to providers regarding care for high-need, high-cost (HNHC) patients.
4. Give high priority to health information exchange.
5. Continue active experimentation and support for model refinement and the spread and scale of evidence-based practices.

REFERENCES

Anderson, G. F., J. Ballreich, S. Bleich, C. Boyd, E. DuGoff, B. Leff, C. Salzburg, and J. Wolff. 2015. Attributes common to programs that successfully treat high-need, high-cost individuals. *American Journal of Managed Care* 21(11):e597–e600.
Bailit, M. H., M. E. Burns, and M. B. Dyer. 2015. Implementing value-based physician compensation: Advice from early adopters. *Health Financial Management* 69(7):40–47.

Barnett, M. L., J. Hsu, and J. M. McWilliams. 2015. Patient characteristics and differences in hospital readmission rates. *JAMA Internal Medicine* 175(11):1803–1812.

Beauchamp, J., V. Cheh, R. Schmitz, P. Kemper, and J. Hall. 2008. *The effect of the Program of All-Inclusive Care for the Elderly (PACE) on quality: Final report.* Washington, DC: Centers for Medicare & Medicaid Services.

Berman, A. 2012. Living life in my own way—and dying that way as well. *Health Affairs* 31(4):871–874.

Bleich, S. N., C. Sherrod, A. Chiang, C. Boyd, J. Wolff, E. DuGoff, C. Salzberg, K. Anderson, B. Leff, and G. Anderson. 2015. Systematic review of programs treating high-need and high-cost people with multiple chronic diseases or disabilities in the United States, 2008–2014. *Preventing Chronic Disease* 12(E197).

Bodenheimer, T., and R. Berry-Millett. 2009. *Care management of patients with complex health care needs.* Princeton, NJ: Robert Wood Johnson Foundation.

Boult, C., A. F. Green, L. B. Boult, J.T. Pacala, C. Snyder, and B. Leff. 2009. Successful models of comprehensive care for older adults with chronic conditions: Evidence for the Institute of Medicine's "Retooling for an Aging America" report. *Journal of the American Geriatrics Society* 57(12):2328–2337.

Boyd, C., B. Leff, C. Weiss, J. Wolff, R. Clark, and T. Richards. 2010. *Clarifying multimorbidity to improve targeting and delivery of clinical services for Medicaid populations.* Trenton, NJ: Center for Health Care Strategies.

Bradley, E. H., and L. Taylor. 2013. *The American health care paradox: Why spending more is getting us less.* Philadelphia, PA: Public Affairs.

Brown, R., D. Peikes, G. Peterson, J. Schore, and C.M. Razafindrakoto. 2012. Six features of Medicare Coordinated Care Demonstration Programs that cut hospital admissions of high-risk patients. *Health Affairs* 31(6):1156–1166.

Brownlee, S., and A. Berman. 2016. *Defining value in healthcare resource utilization: Articulating the role of the patient.* Washington, DC: AcademyHealth.

Burwell, S. 2015. Setting value-based payment goals—HHS efforts to improve U.S. healthcare. *New England Journal of Medicine* 372:897–899.

Cohen, S., and W. Yu. 2012. *The concentration and persistence in the level of health expenditures over time: Estimates for the U.S. population, 2008–2009.* Rockville, MD: Agency for Healthcare Research and Quality.

Dorr, D. A., A. B. Wilcox, S. Jones, L. Burns, S.M. Donnelly, and C.P. Brunker . 2007. Care management dosage. *Journal of General Internal Medicine* 22(6):736–741.

Dorr, D. A., A. B. Wilcox, C. P. Brunker, R.E. Burdon, and S.M. Donnelly. 2008. The effect of technology-supported, multi-disease care management on the mortality and hospitalization of seniors. *Journal of the American Geriatric Society* 56(12):2195–2202.

Druss, B. G.. and E. R. Walker. 2011. *Mental disorders and medical comorbidity.* Princeton, NJ: Robert Wood Johnson Foundation.

Ghosh, A., C. Orfield, and R. Schmitz. 2014. E*valuating PACE: A review of the literature.* Washington, DC: U.S. Department of Health and Human Services, Assistant Secretary for Planning and Evaluation.

Hayes, S., C. Salzberg, D. McCarthy, D.C. Radley, M.K. Abrams, T. Shah, and G.F. Anderson. 2016. *High-need, high-cost patients: Who are they and how do they use health care?* New York: The Commonwealth Fund.

Hong, C., M. K. Abrams, and T.G. Ferris. 2014a. Toward increased adoption of complex care management. *New England Journal of Medicine* 371(6):491–493.

Hong, C. S., A. L. Siegel, and T. G. Ferris. 2014b. *Caring for high-need, high-cost patients: What makes for a successful care management program?* New York: The Commonwealth Fund.

Hughes, J. S., R. F. Averill, J. Eisenhandler, N.I Goldfield, J. Muldoon, J.M. Neff, and J.C. Gay. 2004. Clinical risk groups: A classification system for risk-adjusted capitated based payment and health care management. *Medical Care* 42(1):81–90.

IOM (Institute of Medicine). 2015. *Vital signs: Core metrics for health and health care progress.* Washington, DC: The National Academies Press.

Johnson, T. L., D. Brewer, R. Estacio, T. Vlasimsky, M.J. Durfee, K.R. Thompson, R.M. Everhart, D.J. Rinehart, and H. Batal. 2015. Augmenting predictive modeling tools and clinical insights for care coordination program design and implementation. *eGEMs* 3(1):1–20.

Kinosian, B., G. Taler, P. Bolin, D. Gilden, Independence at Home Learning Collaborative Writing Group. 2016. Projected savings and workforce transformation from converting Independence at Home to a Medicare benefit. *Journal of the American Geriatrics Society* 64(8):1531–1536.

McCarthy, D., J. Ryan, and S. Klein. 2015. *Models of care for high-need, high-cost patients: An evidence synthesis.* New York: The Commonwealth Fund.

Mukamel, D. B., H. Temkin-Greener, R. Delavan, D.R. Peterson, D. Gross, S. Kunitz, and T.F. Williams. 2006. Team performance and risk-adjusted health outcomes in the Program of All-Inclusive Care for the Elderly (PACE). *Gerontologist* 46(2):227–237.

Mukamel, D. B., D. R. Peterson, H. Temkin-Greener, R. Delvan, D. Gross, S.J. Kunitz, and T.F. Williams. 2007. Program characteristics and enrollees' outcomes in the Program of All-Inclusive Care for the Elderly (PACE). *Milbank Quarterly* 85(3):499–531.

Naylor, M. D., D. A. Brooten, R. L. Campbell, G. Maislin, K.M. McCauley, and J.S. Schwartz. 2004. Transitional care of older adults hospitalized with heart failure: A randomized, controlled trial. *Journal of the American Geriatrics Society* 52(5):675–684.

Nelson, L. 2012. *Lessons from Medicare's demonstation projects on disease management, care coordination, and value-based payment.* Washington, DC: Congressional Budget Office.

Rodriguez, S., D. Munevar, C. Delaney, L. Yang, and A. Tumlinson. 2014. *Effective management of high-risk Medicare populations.* Washington, DC: Avalere.

Segelman, M., X. Cai, C. van Reenen, and H. Temkin-Greener. 2015. Transitioning from community-based to institutional long-term care: Comparing 1915(c) waiver and PACE enrollees. *The Gerontologist.* Available at http://gerontologist.oxfordjournals.org/content/early/2015/08/17/geront.gnv106.full (accessed August 31, 2016).

Taylor, L. A., C. E. Coyle, C. Ndumele, E. Rogan, M. Canavan, L. Curry, and E.H. Bradley. 2015. *Leveraging the social determinants of health: What works?* Boston, MA: Blue Cross Blue Shield of Massachusetts Foundation.

Thompson, J. D. 2003. *Organizations in action: Social science bases of administrative theory.* Piscataway, NJ: Transaction Publishers.

AUTHOR INFORMATION

David Blumenthal, MD, is President, The Commonwealth Fund. **Gerard Anderson, PhD,** is Director, Center for Hospital Finance and Management, School of Public Health, Johns Hopkins University. **Sheila P. Burke, MPA, RN,** is Faculty Research Fellow, Malcolm Weiner Center for Social Policy, Harvard John F. Kennedy School of Government, and is Strategic Advisor, Baker Donelson. **Terry Fulmer, PhD, RN,** is President, John A. Hartford Foundation. **Ashish K. Jha, MD, MPH,** is K.T. Li Professor of International Health and Director, Harvard Global Health Institute, Harvard T.H. Chan School of Public Health. **Peter Long, PhD,** is President and CEO, Blue Shield of California Foundation.

12

REALIZING THE FULL POTENTIAL OF PRECISION MEDICINE IN HEALTH AND HEALTH CARE

Victor J. Dzau, MD, Geoffrey S. Ginsburg, MD, PhD, Aneesh Chopra, MPP, Dana Goldman, PhD, Eric D. Green, MD, PhD, Debra G.B. Leonard, MD, PhD, Mark B. McClellan, MD, PhD, Andrew Plump, MD, PhD, Sharon F. Terry, MA, and Keith R. Yamamoto, PhD

Major achievements in scientific research have enabled a new era of health care delivery and treatment. Understanding of the underlying mechanisms of diseases is increasing and allowing scientists to develop new drugs, targeted therapies, and preventive strategies. A new form of health care that is based on data, algorithms, and precision molecular tools has become possible. Precision medicine—an emerging approach that integrates investigation of mechanisms of disease with prevention, treatment, and cure, resolved at the level of the individual subject or patient—has great potential to contribute to solutions for providing high-value health care by improving outcomes while decreasing cost. Despite recent breakthroughs and the growing momentum behind precision medicine, as evidenced by the launch of the US Precision Medicine Initiative (PMI), there remain substantial challenges and barriers to its broad implementation in medical practice, including generating the needed evidentiary support for precision medicine, addressing data–sharing and infrastructure needs, incorporating genomic information into clinical care and research, reconciling the economics of precision medicine, and securing participant engagement and trust. Policymakers will need to address those critical challenges if the full potential of precision medicine is to be realized. Building on the input of national leaders in precision medicine, this paper identifies and explores the challenges to and opportunities to achieve precision medicine and offers specific recommendations to achieve its potential.

OVERVIEW AND STATE OF SCIENCE

Precision medicine is a bold concept that captures and integrates the endeavors and the outcomes of research, health, and health care. The ability to tailor prevention, diagnostics, and therapeutics to individual patients is at the heart of precision medicine. Central to that effort is the ability to assemble a fuller understanding of a patient's health, to share that information (securely) with researchers who are looking for more effective health advice and therapies, and to transition relevant findings back to patients and their providers to improve health outcomes. The aspirations and challenges of precision medicine, as defined and enunciated in the 2011 National Research Council report *Toward Precision Medicine: Building a Knowledge Network for Biomedical Research* (NRC, 2011), encompass—indeed reach beyond—our entire biomedical research, health, and health care enterprise. In the precision-medicine ecosystem, physical and natural scientists and engineers virtually merge their concepts and tools, and they engage with clinicians and social, behavioral, and population investigators to produce and share a computational "learning system"—a knowledge network that aggregates, integrates, accesses, and analyzes information from large patient cohorts, healthy populations, and experimental systems and organisms—to reveal new laboratory-testable hypotheses, to classify diseases by mechanisms, and to provide precise prevention, diagnosis, and treatment options for each person.

Precision medicine, especially as a national or international enterprise, is an audacious aspiration. Consider, however, the potential effects of this endeavor: we would integrate into an iteratively developing knowledge network a working understanding of the logic and mechanisms of biologic processes, thereby contributing continuously and in real time to evidence-based prevention of, treatment for, and cure of chronic, infectious, and rare diseases. Deeper understanding of disease mechanisms would cut drug-development costs by enabling smaller, faster, and more successful clinical trials (as in the case of the approval of Herceptin for breast cancer); reduce the use of prescriptions that are ineffective or produce adverse outcomes (as in the case of Abacvir for HIV); and limit clinical tests that are uninformative for individuals or groups of individuals (as is the case for diagnostic sequencing for rare diseases). Collection and use of data on diverse populations would facilitate and motivate democratization of public health and tailor it to individuals. All those elements working together would yield a healthier, more productive population and drive an overall decline in the slope of the health care cost curve.

We have made great strides in our capacity to initiate the virtuous circle of data collection to health advice and recommended therapies. However, economic, regulatory, social, and technical barriers and challenges must be resolved before the precision-medicine ecosystem can realize its full potential. In creating a more supportive policy environment to overcome the challenges, policymakers will need to work alongside key stakeholder groups—academe, private industry, government, health care providers, patients, and the general public—to engage in more coordinated efforts to establish precision medicine as the driver of our health and health care system.

To empower scientific research and catalyze future innovations in health care, President Obama established a US research program to accelerate progress in the implementation of precision medicine. In his 2015 State of the Union Address, the president announced the launch of the PMI "to bring us closer to curing diseases like cancer and diabetes, and to give all of us access to the personalized information we need to keep ourselves and our families healthier." Ten days later, the president detailed his vision for the initiative at a White House event, placing patients at the center of its design and charging the National Institutes of Health (NIH) with leading a PMI Cohort Program (PMI-CP) and a companion cancer component. The PMI-CP is a monumental and critical effort that offers many promising research opportunities for achieving better health and health care. Given its cutting-edge nature, the PMI-CP will undoubtedly face a number of challenges *(Box 12-1)*. To translate precision medicine into health care, the next administration should consider policies that will facilitate the reduction and eventual elimination of those challenges so that precision medicine can be translated into health care. Critical directions for the advancement of precision medicine include reducing gaps in access to and availability of essential data; establishing data-sharing platforms, incentives, and infrastructure; promoting the use of genomic information in clinical care; creating better economic models for precision medicine; and converting a skeptical patient population to one that is committed and engaged.

KEY ISSUES, BARRIERS TO, AND OPPORTUNITIES FOR PROGRESS

Evidence Generation

Limited evidence that precision medicine improves clinical outcomes, increases cost effectiveness and affordability, and improves quality of care presents a major barrier to its adoption. Before precision medicine can be broadly implemented, there is a need to develop a robust evidentiary foundation of its value. Randomized controlled trials (RCTs) are the gold standard for evidence generation; however, an emerging approach is for health care organizations to collect data as part of continuing clinical care as a means of generating evidence (Ginsburg, 2014)

BOX 12–1

The PMI Cohort Program (PMI-CP)

The PMI-CP aims to establish a national research cohort of 1 million or more Americans, who will share information on their health status and habits, undergo clinical evaluations, provide biospecimens for various analyses, and allow access to their medical records for research. The PMI-CP will generate an unprecedented resource for pursuing research and making major scientific and clinical advances, in addition to the development of new methods for engaging patients as partners in research and in their health care decisions. Key among its strengths is the intent for dynamic governance that includes all stakeholders and is designed to remain agile and responsive to emerging opportunities and experience.

Opportunities
- Enhancing national databases of clinically actionable variants.
- Discovering biomarkers for and developing quantitative estimates of risk for various diseases.
- Identifying the determinants of safety and efficacy of commonly used therapeutics.
- Using home-health and mobile-health (mHealth) technologies to correlate body measurements and environmental exposures with health outcomes.
- Developing new disease classifications and relationships.
- Learning how physicians engage with and use precision-medicine information and what resources are needed to promote high-quality care of patients.
- Developing data-driven models for engaging patients in health care decisions.
- Exploring the use of social-media strategies for communicating with patients and communities about their health care.
- Assessing the evidence on precision medicine in clinical care to inform coverage decisions.

Challenges
- Assimilating, analyzing, and integrating genomic data, electronic medical records (EMRs), data obtained with mHealth devices, and other data on a million or more people.
- Ensuring appropriate participant inclusion with respective to ethnic diversity and other demographics and inclusion of those who are medically disenfranchised, are without EMRs, or lack ready access to the Internet.
- Maintaining momentum on all fronts (for example, funding stability, participant engagement, and provider support) despite the change in administrations.
- Establishing data-driven policies to balance privacy and security concerns with participant and public interests in the sharing of data for research.

on patient and economic outcomes. Although much research is still needed to demonstrate the validity of that method, it holds promise as an approach to address the surging numbers of genomic discoveries, increasing trial costs, and low margins for diagnostic products. As learning health-system models emerge to facilitate evidence creation, the questions become: When should RCTs be required?; and When they are, can they include uniform evidentiary standards and minimum requirements for socioeconomic diversity in addition to the relevant outcomes required for reimbursement reviews and evaluations among payers and regulatory agencies?

The evolving nature of evidence generation for precision medicine will necessitate agreement between stakeholders and policymakers on standards for initial clinical use and on mechanisms for postmarketing collection of data to refine the precision-medicine evidence base. Once a consensus is reached on standards for initial clinical use, regulatory and reimbursement policy can be updated to reflect such standards, contingent on mandatory postmarketing data collection that is required for final approval.

In building the evidence base for precision medicine, postmarket data on diverse populations will have to be collected continuously. Evidence demonstrating the potential of precision medicine to improve care quality and cost effectiveness will take time to develop, and mechanisms must be put into place to ensure continuing evidence generation and assessment. As recommended in the 2016 Institute of Medicine (IOM) report *Biomarker Tests for Molecularly Targeted Therapies: Key to Unlocking Precision Medicine* (IOM, 2016), the development of a rapid learning system for biomarker tests for molecularly targeted therapies would be essential to facilitate knowledge generation, and continuous learning and accelerate the translation of lessons learned into better patient care and improved clinical outcomes. The recommended actions focus on improving the policy environment, data infrastructure, and patient care processes related to biomarker tests for molecularly targeted therapies.

Thoughtful consideration of study designs that are based on the available postmarketing data that support the continued use of various precision-medicine approaches is critical. Precision-medicine evidence generation could be tied to an adaptive approach or pathway for treatment so as to ensure that patients who have unmet needs have access to promising therapies as they become available.

Furthermore, as precision medicine expands into routine clinical use, the evidence supporting its use must come from a broad cross section of the population. Thus, there is a need to develop and implement a series of criteria to indicate when the use of RCTs in precision medicine is required for evidence generation, including uniform evidentiary standards, the minimum requirements for socioeconomic diversity in clinical-trial enrollment, and the relevant outcomes required for reimbursement reviews and evaluations among payers and regulatory agencies. As recommended in the IOM (2016) report, HHS should facilitate a process for the development of common evidentiary standards of clinical utility for biomarker tests for molecularly targeted therapies by convening one or more independent, public–private, multi-stakeholder bodies. These common evidentiary standards would inform the development of an integrated review process for coordinated regulatory, coverage, and reimbursement decisions.

To generate the necessary evidence to assess the health-economic impact of precision-medicine technologies, final regulatory and payer approval could be made contingent on the inclusion of a health-economic impact analysis. Acknowledging that such data, especially longitudinal data, would be difficult to generate within the timeframe of a clinical trial, other approaches could be used to project long-term economic effects, including economic modeling.

Priority considerations for enhancing evidence generation and use include:

- developing and adopting an evidence framework to guide clinical implementation, and then ensure continuing evidence generation, especially in the postmarketing–postapproval setting, for precision-medicine tests and therapies;
- developing and adopting a flexible framework (that ties evidence to the use case) to balance the use of RCTs against "big data" and observational analysis in precision medicine; and
- including health-economic impact analysis (encompassing cost effectiveness and long-term savings) for regulatory and payer approval.

Data Sharing and Infrastructure Needs

The path to precision medicine requires access to large-scale, detailed, and highly integrated patient data to advance our understanding of the genomic, molecular, phenotypic, clinical, and digital signatures of disease. Precision medicine requires not only big data but diverse data. Advancing the field and improving understanding of the complexities of human health and disease will require aligning often-unstructured datasets into a comprehensive knowledge network (NRC, 2011). The vast majority of repositories of research and clinical data cannot now be easily combined with one another. Furthermore, in drug development, pharmaceutical companies could take advantage of clinical trials to explore, learn about, and generate additional hypotheses for collecting data. All too often, clinical trials focus on testing a primary hypothesis and—for reasons related to cost, time, and fear of the unknown—fail to incorporate exploratory genomic, digital, and other measures to help to create the learning necessary to drive precision medicine. As recommended in the 2015 IOM report *Sharing Clinical Trial Data: Maximizing Benefits, Minimizing Risk,* some companies have begun to place clinical-trial data in the public domain; however, data on product failures that would be highly valuable for scientific inquiry are not shared.

Recent progressive policies have facilitated notable progress. At the launch event for the PMI in January 2015, the Obama Administration emphasized that patients should "have access to their own health data—and to the applications and services that can safely and accurately analyze it" (White House, 2015). The administration followed through by regulating electronic health records (EHRs) to offer data access to patient-designated apps and requiring the use of such technology by providers in the Medicare and Medicaid payment incentive programs by 2018. The Office of Civil Rights of the Department of Health and Human Services further clarified that patients have a digital right to access data protected by the Health Insurance Portability and Accountability Act (HIPAA) and can direct it to an end point of their choosing at a marginal cost that can cover only the production of the digital copy (in other words, near zero). Leading health information technology (HIT) vendors publicly pledged to support a "sync for science" program by upgrading their technology in a manner that enables a patient to connect a precision-medicine direct enrollment application to health data otherwise available only via a patient portal.

Considering those developments, we are entering 2017 seemingly far closer to Mitchell Kapor's vision of a "health Internet" (Kapor, 2009), an open platform that would connect providers, payers, and consumers to a growing number of applications, including ones designed for precision medicine. New datasets not traditionally considered part of a health record—digital assessment, intent, and monitoring data—would be available for patients to connect seamlessly via the health Internet to connected, trusted databases that store, analyze, and trigger therapeutic and preventive recommendations. In combination with the Obama Administration's unprecedented efforts to open up health data and focus on aligning payment with improved outcomes, we ought to be entering 2017 with ingredients that enable data-driven, health care delivery models that foster better care for both individuals and communities. To get there, the next administration will need to tackle key challenges that have hindered progress despite unprecedented (often bipartisan) policy commitment. The challenges are discussed below.

The Economics of Health-Data Production

The core of a provider's health care dataset is the complete, digitized longitudinal clinical and administrative records designed in part to meet the needs of payers. Through the Patient Protection and Affordable Care Act, public payers have accelerated a transition from requiring data solely for the purpose of documenting an encounter to measuring outcomes and facilitating better care coordination. That payer-driven demand has sharpened provider focus on the types of health information collected and shared to maximize reimbursement. Previously unstructured data buried in clinical notes, such as smoking status, are now accessible in a form that allows search queries to generate lists of patients who have gaps in care that should be addressed.

Despite wide agreement among public and private payers to drive more outcomes-based payment models, most provider revenue today remains tethered to the fee-for-service model. Thus, the adoption and use of advanced HIT systems capable of performing such queries or publishing such structured data remain challenging. Assuming that precision medicine will achieve better outcomes, any effort to maximize the flow of data for precision medicine should begin by accelerating a shift toward pay-for-value models. That shift would depend on HIT systems to store, share, and provide the very data that support precision medicine.

The Regulation of Data Access, Privacy, and Security

Since the 2009 passage of the Health Information Technology for Economic and Clinical Health Act, we have been on a regulatory "escalator" that has equipped providers with more powerful HIT. But that journey is not yet complete. Under both the "meaningful use" and "advancing care information" Centers for Medicare & Medicaid Services (CMS) incentive programs, providers must use certified technology, but three policy levers deserve further attention if technology is to be aligned with precision-medicine requirements.

First, the Common Clinical Data Set (CCDS) needs to be broadened. Health-records vendors compete, in part, on the value of their underlying data models that can be put to use in achieving a provider's operational needs; to facilitate interoperability among vendors, the administration regulates the transformation of a set of patient data into a more open machine-readable format that is free of intellectual-property (IP) restrictions. An important consideration for the next administration will be the ability of precision-medicine researchers to provide a feedback loop on any necessary expansions or adjustments of the CCDS.

Second, application programming interface (API) access needs to be standardized and expanded. Health-records vendors manage the business and technical models associated with providing third-party applications access to the CCDS via an API, a contract that explains how to access data and logic securely while protecting patient privacy; current policy compels EHR vendors to open developer access to enable connectivity to an app of a patient's choice but leaves open the methods and economic terms. An important consideration will be standardization of those methods among vendors and expansion of patient API access among all regulated HIT systems, including medical devices regulated by the Food and Drug Administration (FDA) and other certified EHR modules.

Third, oversight needs to be strengthened. Two enforcement methods are available to ensure that certified technology delivers information access as tested: surveillance and testing in the field and use of emerging information-blocking tools, including Office of the Inspector General enforcement of antikickback waivers for health systems that subsidize EHR adoption. The next administration should consider more aggressive surveillance to ensure that patients and providers who have application access can query a complete CCDS and that nontechnical barriers, such as cost and burden, are minimized.

Encouraging Further Voluntary Industry Consensus on Standards

Since the Clinton Administration, it has been US policy to leave technical-standards development to voluntary, industry-led bodies that are free to innovate and adjust without undue government interference. In January 2012, the Obama Administration clarified that in some elements of national importance, the government can play a convening role to spur technologic advances in fields that need it and encourage wider adoption (OSTP, 2011). For precision medicine to succeed, adoption of voluntary industry standards will be necessary to ensure that data can be synchronized around the patient, not around the institution that treated the patient for a particular episode or delivered services over the course of an insurance enrollment cycle. If we make the necessary policy adjustments and encourage industry adoption of standards, we will deliver on the promise of using robust and broadly available digital data to discover more appropriate therapies for each individual patient and to ensure that the therapies are delivered via care models that reward delivering better outcomes.

Priority considerations for enhancing evidence generation and use include

- the administration broadening the CCDS to facilitate interoperability among vendors, to create a more open machine-readable format that is free of IP restrictions, and to ensure that patients who have application access can query a complete CCDS with only minimal nontechnical barriers, such as cost and burden;
- the administration standardizing methods among vendors and expanding patient API access among all regulated HIT systems, including FDA-regulated medical devices and other certified EHR modules;

- NIH and health systems driving adoption of voluntary industry standards for structured data or common data elements to be captured in EMRs for synchronizing data around the patient, not around the institution that treated the patient for a particular episode or that delivered services over the course of an insurance enrollment cycle;
- the digital health community (EMR vendors, health systems, and app developers) working toward strengthening digital identities and standardizing how securely identified patients authorize the sharing of health information for precision medicine;
- strengthening consumer protections related to the use (or misuse) of data via patient-designated apps not subject to HIPAA regulation by encouraging industry adoption of a model code of conduct akin to a "digital Hippocratic oath" that can be enforceable by such agencies as the Federal Trade Commission;
- policies promoting incentives to share data among all stakeholders; and
- interagency funding mechanisms (e.g., shared by NIH, the Department of Energy, the Defense Advanced Research Projects Agency, and the National Institute of Standards and Technology) to motivate cross-sector partnerships (.edu, .gov, .com, and .org) that harness intellectual synergies and enable sustainability of infrastructure and activities necessary to realize the full potential of a public benefit from federal investment in precision medicine for biomedical research, public health, and health care.

Integrating Genomic and Other Molecular Data into Clinical Care and Research

Moving genomic and other molecular information into routine health care delivery is critical for a precision-medicine–powered health system. Genomic information is not widely used in clinical care. Some medical centers are incorporating it into clinical research, including the University of Michigan cancer sequencing program (MI-ONCOSEQ), the Geisinger Medicine Institute's MyCode Community Health Initiative in partnership with Regeneron Pharmaceuticals, Inova Translational Medicine Institute, and several research programs supported by the National Human Genome Research Institute, such as Implementing Genomics in Practice (IGNITE), Electronic Medical Records and Genomics Network (eMERGE), and Newborn Sequencing in Genomic Medicine and Public Health (NSIGHT). NIH has also developed the Clinical Genomic Resource (ClinGen) for sharing information about genomic variants and phenotypes and ClinVar, which houses data on evidence of variants of clinical significance associated with disease. The National Cancer Institute (NCI) has launched research programs aimed at identifying the genetic drivers of specific cancers with a goal for developing targeted therapeutics: the Cancer Genome Characterization Initiative, the Cancer Genome Atlas (TCGA), and Therapeutically Applicable Research to Generate Effective Treatments (TARGET). Their data are housed in the newly announced NCI Genomic Data Commons. Together, however, the use of genomic information has been used largely for specific applications—such as diagnosis for severely sick newborns, developmental delay, or unidentified genetic disorders—and to target treatments for some cancers.

In particular, how we think about the genomes of individuals presents a major barrier to the use of genomic information in health care. Medical-genetics experts have promoted thinking of genetic and genomic information as "exceptional" and the idea that it requires great protections. For precision medicine to succeed, we need a fundamental change in medical thinking to move genomics from exceptional to routine information for the understanding of health and health care—to consider a patient's genome sequence as foundational information for health care, just as we consider blood pressure, pulse, temperature, heart rate, height, and weight. We will continue to learn more about the role of genomic variation in health. The American College of Medical Genetics and Genomics has defined 56 genes that have been established as relevant to medical conditions and recommends that variants in these genes be reported whenever clinical exome or genome sequencing is done (Green et al., 2013). As the evidence of the clinical utility of genomic information increases, we need to change how we think about the incorporation and use of this health care information.

A laudable future state of health care would include the effective implementation of precision medicine into learning health systems—health systems that implement genomics, gather data, analyze the data, and then use the results to change care paradigms (IOM, 2015). Genome sequences would be available for most patients and would be integrated into annual testing with other novel platforms (such as metabolic or immune profiling) and into patient-reported information to predict early onset of common and expensive diseases and thus allow prevention or early detection and intervention. All molecular, health care, and patient-reported information would be monitored to identify patterns and outliers, which would be investigated to improve our understanding of health care and health care delivery effectiveness.

Beyond the fundamental issue of changing how we view and use genomic information, key issues for implementation of genomics and its integration into health care include the need to generate additional evidence that demonstrates the clinical usefulness of genomics, the availability and quality of genome-interpretation tools, understanding of how to use genomic information in clinical care, knowing whether genomics will decrease or increase the overall cost of health care and improve outcomes, and public concerns about the potential misuse of genomic information.

Priority considerations for enhancing evidence generation and use include:

- NIH and other agencies engaging communities of stakeholders—diverse participants and providers—in supporting the development of tools and educational resources to promote the integration of precision-medicine information on diverse populations into clinical-practice settings;
- FDA and other regulatory agencies seeking novel pathways to develop and deploy innovative mechanisms to oversee the rapid translation of research findings from precision medicine to health care delivery;
- NIH supporting the development of a national genomic-variant database, which would provide an interpretive resource for precision medicine;
- medical-education oversight bodies, such as the Liaison Committee on Medical Education and the American Board of Medical Specialties, incorporating genomic-education requirements into medical education, residency and fellowship training, continuing-medical-education requirements, and maintenance of certification examinations to ensure a trained workforce and transition to the foundational nature of genomic information for health and health care;
- NIH engaging in collaborations to support the development of a centralized global resource (a toolbox) for the effective integration and use of genomic information in health information systems;
- NIH encouraging the development and dissemination of knowledge about precision medicine by ensuring sufficient resources and funding support for implementation, dissemination, and outcomes research (so-called T3 and T4 domains of translational research) and public and provider education; and
- Congress expanding the Genetic Information Nondiscrimination Act of 2008 to provide full protection against misuse of genomic information for any purpose.

Innovation in Diagnostics, Drug Discovery, and the Economics of Precision Medicine

The challenge in developing new medicines has never been greater than it is today. The aggregate cost of developing a new medicine, in light of attrition rates, has been estimated at $2.7 billion (DiMasi et al., 2016). Extensive investment in research and the large cost of failure, particularly in development, have been used to explain the rising cost of drug discovery. Many reimbursement failures occur because therapies are not substantially different from established medicines; in many other cases, therapies offer benefits to patients but their value cannot be demonstrated experimentally through the comparator studies mandated by health-technology assessment agencies. Precision medicine aims to change the economics of drug and diagnostic development through a deeper understanding of the mechanisms of disease driven by the computational-knowledge network that continuously merges biomedical, clinical, and social and behavioral information. The new knowledge will increase the efficiencies of product development and approval.

Beyond novel targeted therapies, some of precision medicine's greatest benefits may lie in identifying healthy people who are at high risk for disease and for whom efficacious therapies exist. The value to society is twofold: avoiding unnecessary treatment and identifying patients who otherwise would not be treated (Goldman et al., 2013). Depending on the disease, a precision-medicine innovation—one that more accurately identifies people who are at risk for the disease and is coupled to an intervention that reduces incidence even by as little as 10 percent—could generate hundreds of billions of dollars in value in the form of longer, healthier lives enjoyed by the US population (Dzau et al., 2015). The potentially large value generated by personalized diagnostic tests raises the question of why these diagnostic tests have not flourished as rapidly as expected (Aspinall and Hamermesh, 2007).

New diagnostics do not emerge in a vacuum. Rather, they result from investment of capital to finance research and development. The potentially large difference between the value generated by precision diagnostics and the price that they command raises the question of whether innovators have sufficient incentives. That question is particularly relevant for diagnostic tests that are not linked to targeted therapies. Manufacturers of targeted cancer therapies recoup the cost generated by a diagnostic test by charging prices that exceed the costs of production (Yin et al., 2012). With more effective targeting of treatment, the value of a therapy increases. Thus, as long as price and revenue are related to value, there are incentives to develop a companion diagnostic for a targeted therapy.

More broadly, the current reimbursement environment does not reward innovators for the value created by their tests. The development of a precision-medicine–based diagnostic test by one company does not preclude development by others, and this limits economic incentives for test development. Moreover, reimbursement for diagnostics is typically cost based rather than value based. Third-party payers in the United States largely follow the standards set by CMS, which pays for diagnostic tests according to its clinical-laboratory fee schedule. Reimbursement for diagnostic tests is therefore based on Common Procedural Terminology (CPT) codes, which historically set prices according to specific procedures conducted during a test (such as extraction and amplification of DNA). To determine the total price of a diagnostic test, codes for individual procedures were "stacked"; this method decouples price from value. The experience of Oncotype DX® is instructive. Oncotype DX predicts both the recurrence of breast cancer and the likelihood that a patient who has early-stage breast cancer will benefit from chemotherapy. Genomic Health, the manufacturer of Oncotype DX, used a miscellaneous CPT code rather than stacking codes to price its test. Meanwhile, the firm commissioned clinical and health-economic studies to demonstrate the value of its test and, over the course of several years, had obtained nearly complete payer coverage (Gustavsen et al., 2010). Genomic Health also entered into risk-sharing agreements with payers to secure its market price. Although new molecular-pathology codes are replacing older stacked codes, reimbursement is still not systematically related to value and potential downstream cost savings.

The rules for diagnostics stand in marked contrast with reimbursement for novel therapies, which are increasingly reimbursed on the basis of the value—measured according to quality-adjusted life years—that they generate. Ironically, diagnostic tests influence an estimated 60 percent to 70 percent of all treatment decisions but account for only 5 percent of hospital costs and 2 percent of Medicare expenditures; this suggests an imbalance between the value that the diagnostic tests generate and the amount of reimbursement for them (The Lewin Group, Inc., 2005).

Reconciling concerns about rising costs and improving health associated with medical technologies is central to the debate over advancing precision medicine; that is, how can we design reimbursement and regulatory incentives to encourage "valuable" innovation?

Priority considerations for enhancing evidence generation and use include:

- NIH supporting research to assess the value of genomic testing and similar diagnostics in the context of the total cost of lifetime health care and to improve the quality of life and patient outcomes for individuals and populations;
- CMS and the payer community considering that the advancement of precision medicine represents an era of payment reform and that payment reform shifting toward value should incorporate genomic tests;
- the administration taking up patent reform in connection with precision medicine to provide exclusivity for companies that are willing to assume risk in developing precision-medicine approaches; and
- FDA, CMS, NIH, and the Agency for Healthcare Research and Quality developing, adopting, and coordinating an innovative evidence-generation strategy that uses coverage with evidence development, uses data captured in the postmarketing and postapproval setting for precision-medicine tests and therapies, and includes health-economic effect analysis (encompassing cost effectiveness and long-term savings) for regulatory and payer approval.

Participant Engagement and Trust

Like no biomedical science ever before, precision medicine requires participant engagement. For discovery in precision medicine to be accelerated and services based on it to be adopted, people—not just patients—must be involved. That is because, although it is important for some aspects of the science to have data on individuals in the clinical context, it is also important to understand the continuum of health and disease on the basis of data on the experience of many people in diverse communities. Data from self-tracking devices and on the built environment and other nonclinical aspects of people's lives will help to complete the picture essential for precision medicine.

There is a long way to go before participants have a substantive role in precision medicine. In part, the place of participant engagement is not yet accepted because there is no substantial evidence base for its inclusion. That situation is not unlike other aspects of precision medicine, but it has special challenges. Many funders, payers, researchers, and clinicians equate engagement with simple recruitment and retention, but it means much more in this context. It requires relationships with individuals and communities. It requires trust—not only that the people invited to participate should offer trust but that the organizations and entities involved in precision medicine should demonstrate trustworthiness.

There are important resource implications in authentic participant engagement that is based on trust. Trustworthy systems should be transparent and open. Transparency—from simple openness about possibilities, probabilities, and honest presentation of limitations to open science—is expensive. There are no ready-built systems for these activities; they have not been considered essential for research. It is possible that new economies will emerge, but they are not yet apparent. Today's researchers are more likely to use time and funding for other aspects of research and not for recruitment of participants. Further along the continuum, in the realm of the implementation of precision medicine, clinicians involved in gathering data in a learning health care system or implementing new guidelines that result from precision medicine do not have the resources to seek patient-centered outcome reports or to involve patients in decision making—a hallmark of true engagement. Yet there is reason for optimism that these challenges can be overcome through participants' embrace of social media, the Internet, and patient-advocacy groups and their increasing engagement in the conversation on privacy.

Authentic engagement, embedded in trust, must overcome a number of barriers. Participants range in their preferences for engagement from deeply engaged in determining the most relevant questions to not wanting to participate at all. And although there is growing pressure to engage consumers—coming largely from citizen-scientists, community-based participatory researchers, and such nascent entities as the Patient-Centered Outcomes Research Institute—researchers and clinicians have little experience in thinking of participants as partners in these endeavors. Only when the effect of engagement has a solid evidence base will it be supported and even promoted. It will also be critical to increase the literacy of the public in using more accessible methods than are currently imagined or deployed. For needed progress to occur, efforts to advance precision medicine must simultaneously increase the trust felt by the patient population and build the evidence base on the value of authentic engagement.

Priority considerations for enhancing evidence generation and use include:

- NIH working with communities and research networks to establish best practices for engagement of participants and to determine metrics for trustworthiness and participation;
- NIH, FDA, and other agencies piloting open science to make scientific research, data, and dissemination accessible to all levels of society; and
- developing educational programs beginning at early educational stages to ensure genomic literacy, emphasizing precision medicine and related concepts, including the benefits of data sharing.

VITAL DIRECTIONS

Precision medicine is an audacious but necessary aspiration if we are to achieve a health care delivery system that can provide accessible, high-quality, and efficient health care. To move the nation toward achieving the promise of precision medicine, we identify five vital directions *(Figure 12-1)* for the next administration's consideration:

1. **Develop evidence of precision medicine's effect.** Provider and patient adoption and regulatory approval of and reimbursement for precision medicine requires a robust evidentiary framework for evaluation of its effect on outcomes.
2. **Accelerate clinical data integration and assessment.** Advancing precision medicine and achieving a greater understanding of the complexities of human health and disease will require aligning and integrating diverse, often unstructured datasets into a comprehensive knowledge network.

3. **Promote integration of molecular guidance into care.** Moving genomic and other information into routine health care delivery will be critical for integrating precision medicine into health systems. We need to adopt an approach to genetic and genomic information that considers a patient's genome sequence as foundational information for health care.

4. **Develop innovation-oriented reimbursement and regulatory frameworks.** The current reimbursement environment does not reward innovators for the value created by their diagnostic tests. Rather than being value based, reimbursement for diagnostics is typically cost based and discourages the translation of innovative tests and therapies. Incentives to develop the evidence base and the economic model that support precision medicine will be crucial.

5. **Strengthen engagement and trust of the public.** Participant engagement is essential for discovery in precision medicine to be accelerated and for services based on precision medicine to be adopted. Effective engagement will necessitate relationships with individuals and their communities and attaining their trust to overcome existing barriers.

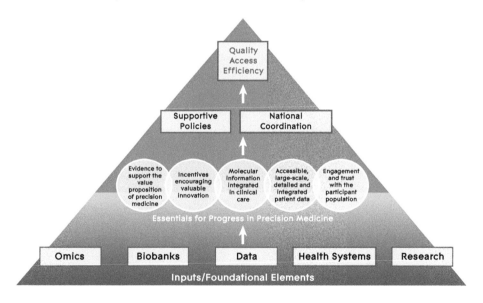

FIGURE 12-1 | The foundational elements of a robust precision-medicine strategy for US health care are in place. Four vital directions for policymakers to follow are offered; they would address key challenges in a strategy to affect quality, access, and efficiency of health care delivery.

SOURCE: Figure adapted from Ginsburg and Dzau, WISH Precision Medicine Report, 2016.

For those vital directions to be followed successfully, the United States will need a coordinated, collaborative effort that brings together the key stakeholders from the public, private, academic, and government sectors. That will require orchestration by a nonconflicted neutral convener. The convener would be charged with coordinating the development of a precision-medicine policy agenda to support the development, implementation, and integration of key precision-medicine infrastructure, data architecture, and tools into health care delivery. For those vital directions to be followed successfully, the United States will need a coordinated, collaborative effort that brings together the key stakeholders from the public, private, academic, and government sectors. That will require orchestration by a nonconflicted neutral convener. The convener would be charged with coordinating the development of a precision-medicine policy agenda to support the development, implementation, and integration of key precision-medicine infrastructure, data architecture, and tools into health care delivery.

SUMMARY RECOMMENDATIONS FOR VITAL DIRECTIONS

1. Develop evidence of precision medicine's effect.
2. Accelerate clinical data integration and assessment.
3. Promote integration of molecular guidance into care.
4. Develop innovation-oriented reimbursement and regulatory frameworks.
5. Strengthen engagement and trust of the public.

REFERENCES

Aspinall, M. G., and R. G. Hamermesh. 2007. Realizing the promise of personalized medicine. *Harvard Business Review* 85(10):108–117.

DiMasi, J. A., H.G. Grabowski, and R.W. Hansen. 2016. Innovation in the pharmaceutical industry: New estimates of R&D costs. *Journal of Health Economics* 47:20–33.

Dzau, V. J., G.S. Ginsburg, K. Van Nuys, D. Agus, and D. Goldman. 2015. Aligning incentives to fulfil the promise of personalised medicine. *Lancet* 385(9982):2118–2119.

Ginsburg, G. 2014. Medical genomics: Gather and use genetic information in health care. *Nature* 508(7497): 451–453.

Goldman, D., C. Gupta, E. Vasudeva, K. Trakas, R. Riley, D.N. Lakdawalla, D. Agus, N. Sood, A.B. Jena, and T. Philipson. 2013. The value of diagnostic testing in personalized medicine. *Forum for Health Economics & Policy* 16(2):121–133.

Green, R. C., J.S. Berg, W.W. Grody, S.S. Kalia, B.R. Korf, C.L. Martin, A.L. McGuire, R.L. Nussbaum, J.M. O'Daniel, K.E. Ormond, H.L. Rehm, M.S. Watson, M.S. Williams, and L.G. Biesecker. 2013. ACMG recommendations for reporting of incidental findings in clinical exome and genome sequencing. *Genetics in Medicine* 15(7):565–574.

Gustavsen, G., K. Phillips, and K. Pothier. 2010. *The reimbursement landscape for novel diagnostics.* Weston, MA: Health Advances.

IOM (Institute of Medicine). 2015. *Genomics-enabled learning health care systems: Gathering and using genomic information to improve patient care and research: Workshop summary.* Washington, DC: The National Academies Press.

IOM. 2016. *Biomarker Tests for Molecularly Targeted Therapies: Key to Unlocking Precision Medicine.* Washington, DC: The National Academies Press.

Kapor, M. 2009. Building the Health Internet. Presented at The Meeting at Harvard on a Health Information Technology Platform, Boston, MA.

The Lewin Group, Inc. 2005. The Value of Diagnostics Innovation, Adoption and Diffusion into Health Care.

NHGRI (National Human Genome Research Institute). 2015. Newborn Sequencing in Genomic Medicine and Public Health (NSIGHT). Available at https://www.genome.gov/27558493/newborn-sequencing-in-genomic-medicine-and-public-health-nsight/ (accessed June 14, 2016).

NHGRI. 2016. Implementing Genomics in Practice (IGNITE). Available at https://www.genome.gov/27554264/implementing-genomics-in-practice-ignite/ (accessed June 14, 2016).

NIH (National Institutes of Health). 2016. About the Precision Medicine Initiative Cohort Program. Available at https://www.nih.gov/precision-medicine-initiative-cohort-program (accessed June 14, 2016).

NRC (National Research Council). 2011. *Toward precision medicine: Building a knowledge network for biomedical research and a new taxonomy of disease.* Washington, DC: The National Academies Press.

OSTP (Office of Science and Technology Policy). 2011. A strategy for American innovation—securing our economic growth and prosperity. Washington, DC: The White House.

The White House. 2015. Fact Sheet: President Obama's Precision Medicine Initiative. Available at https://www.whitehouse.gov/the-press-office/2015/01/30/fact-sheet-president-obama-s-precision-medicine-initiative (accessed June 14, 2016).

Yin, W., J.R. Penrod, R. Maclean, D.N. Lakdawalla, and T. Philipson. 2012. Value of survival gains in chronic myeloid leukemia. *American Journal of Managed Care* 18(11 Suppl):S257–S264.

AUTHOR INFORMATION

Victor J. Dzau, MD, is President, National Academy of Medicine. **Geoffrey S. Ginsburg, MD, PhD,** is Director, Duke Center for Applied Genomics and Precision Medicine, Duke University School of Medicine. **Aneesh Chopra, MPP,** is Cofounder and Executive Vice President, Hunch Analytics. **Dana Goldman, PhD,** is Director and Leonard D. Schaeffer Chair, Schaeffer Center for Health Policy and Economics, Sol Price School of Public Policy, University of Southern California. **Eric D. Green, MD, PhD,** is Director, National Human Genome Research Institute, National Institutes of Health. **Debra G.B. Leonard, MD, PhD,** is Chair of Pathology, University of Vermont. **Mark B. McClellan, MD, PhD,** is Director, Duke-Robert J. Margolis Center for Health Policy and Robert J. Margolis Professor, Duke University. **Andrew Plump, MD, PhD,** is Chief Medical and Scientific Officer, Takeda Pharmaceuticals. **Sharon F. Terry, MA,** is President and CEO, Genetic Alliance. **Keith R. Yamamoto, PhD,** is Vice Chancellor for Science Policy and Strategy, Vice Dean for Research, School of Medicine, University of California, San Francisco.

13

FOSTERING TRANSPARENCY IN OUTCOMES, QUALITY, SAFETY, AND COSTS

Peter J. Pronovost, MD, PhD, FCCM, J. Matthew Austin, PhD, MS, Christine K. Cassel, MD, Suzanne F. Delbanco, PhD, Ashish K. Jha, MD, MPH, Bob Kocher, MD, Elizabeth A. McGlynn, PhD, Lewis G. Sandy, MD, FACP, and John Santa, MD, MPH

Over the past 20 years, the United States has witnessed a shift from little readily available information about the performance of the health care system to the use of a wide variety of measures in different ways by multiple entities (Cronin et al., 2011). The explosion of performance measures and the public reporting of performance have served important functions in raising awareness of deficits in quality and stimulating efforts to close measured gaps (O'Neil et al., 2010). Despite the important gains, serious concerns have been raised about the value of performance measurement in its current state, including the validity and reliability of measures, the burden and complexity of measuring performance, substantial gaps in measuring important aspects of care, and limited evidence regarding the fundamental premise that measurement and reporting drive improvement. The purposes of this paper are to identify the requirements of a valid and useful performance-measurement and performance-reporting system and to suggest a pathway to a better system. The timing of this paper is important inasmuch as the recent goal of moving away from rewarding volume to rewarding value depends on having valid and accurate measures so that the quality of care being delivered can be known and improved.

Transparent reporting of the performance of the health care system is often promoted as a key tool for improving the value of health care by improving quality and lowering costs, although the evidence of its effectiveness in achieving higher quality or lower costs is mixed (Austin and Pronovost, 2016; Hibbard et al., 2005; Totten et al., 2012; Whaley et al., 2014). Transparency can improve value by two key pathways: engaging providers to improve their performance and informing consumer choice (Berwick et al., 2003). With respect to engaging providers, transparency can catalyze improvement efforts by appealing to the professionalism of physicians and nurses and by stimulating competition among them and their organizations (Lamb et al., 2013). With respect to informing consumer choice, public reporting can provide patients, payers, and purchasers with information about performance and enable preferential selection of higher-quality providers, lower-cost providers, or providers that demonstrate both characteristics. Although the potential for informing consumer choice exists, there is limited evidence to support the idea that consumers are using public reports in their current form to make better decisions (Faber et al., 2009; Shaller et al., 2014). We have pockets of success in public reporting that drive improved performance (Ketelaar et al., 2011), including the reporting of the Society of Thoracic Surgeons (STS) registries in cardiac surgery (Shahian et al., 2011a, b; Stey et al., 2015; STS, 2016); the Centers for Disease Control and Prevention's (CDC's) measures of health care–associated infections (CMS, 2016a; Pronovost et al., 2011); measures of diabetes-care processes, intermediate outcomes, and complications (Smith et al., 2012); and the Agency for Healthcare Research and Quality's Hospital Consumer Assessment of Healthcare Providers and Systems (HCAHPS) measure (CMS, 2016b; Elliott et al., 2010). Despite those successes, we have fallen short of the full potential of understanding the performance of the health care system; for example, only a minority of heart-surgery groups have voluntarily reported their performance from the STS registry, and cardiologists do not appear to refer patients to cardiac surgeons who have the best outcomes (Brown et al., 2013).

Health care organizations and providers frequently invest time and energy to improve their performance on reported measures and we should ensure that they are acting on valid information (Winters et al., 2016). That holds true for all types of measures—measures of outcomes (both clinically oriented and patient defined), quality, safety, and costs. The accurate measurement and reporting of health care system performance is important for all stakeholders. Patients, clinicians, payers, and purchasers need measures of absolute and relative performance to facilitate informed choice of providers, innovative benefit designs and provider networks, and alternative payment methods that support quality improvement and greater affordability (Damberg et al., 2011). With transparency of performance results, markets are able to work more effectively; this enables higher-quality providers to attract greater market share, assuming that the incremental revenue to be gained from additional market share is financially beneficial to them. Physicians and hospitals need measures to make treatment decisions and to identify strengths and weaknesses so that they can focus their quality-improvement and performance-improvement activities and monitor progress (Berenson and Rice, 2015). Transparency of performance facilitates identification of exemplary performers, who might, in turn, be emulated by others and encourage learning (Dixon-Woods et al., 2011).

Although transparency is beneficial, it poses risks if the results being shared are not valid (Adams et al., 2010; Austin, 2015; McGlynn and Adams, 2014). There is no standard for how reliable and valid a measure should be before it is publicly reported. Publicly reporting a measure whose reliability and validity are unknown poses risks, including disengaging clinicians from improvement work, and raises potential ethical concerns, such as imposing unjust financial and reputation harm on physicians and provider organizations, misinforming patients about the risks and benefits associated with a treatment option, and guiding patients to riskier rather than to safer care (Winters et al., 2016).

Medicine is based on science, but the science of health care delivery, its measurement, and how to improve it is immature (Marjoua and Bozic, 2012). There are insufficient studies, little research investment, and a lack of agreement on the best way to measure how well health care providers deliver their services (Dixon-Woods et al., 2012). The growth in measurement stems from a wide array of entities' development and use of measures and methods to assess performance, including accreditation organizations (such as the National Committee for Quality Assurance and The Joint Commission), the Centers for Medicare & Medicaid Services (CMS), state Medicaid programs, commercial health plans, consumer review platforms (such as Yelp), and independent parties, ranging from nonprofits to for-profit entities (such as HealthGrades and US News and World Report) (Jha, 2012). The variety of measures and methods and the lack of standards for measures and auditing of data have led to conflicting results in data on quality, safety, patient experience, and cost (e.g., a large proportion of hospitals are rated as top performers by at least one rating program), which potentially confuse those who want to use the data or encourage them to ignore the results altogether because they are incoherent or inconsistent (Austin et al., 2015).

The variety of measures and methods used to measure performance could be a product of different underlying hypotheses and biases (Shwartz et al., 2015). For example, Consumer Reports and the Leapfrog Group both issue patient-safety composites for hospitals (Consumer Reports, 2016; HSS, 2016). The two organizations have chosen to define safety differently: Leapfrog defines safety as "freedom from harm," and Consumer Reports refers to "a hospital's commitment to the safety of its patients." The two organizations have chosen to include different measures in their composites to reflect their chosen definition of the construct (Austin et al., 2015). In this example, both organizations are fully transparent in their methods and underlying constructs, but most often the underlying hypotheses and biases are not transparent, and few are tested. When the data-collection and analytic processes are fully transparent, a robust scientific measurement process is possible. When the underlying hypotheses, assumptions, and biases of measurement methods are not transparent, confusion and misinformation can result.

KEY ISSUES, COST IMPLICATIONS, AND BARRIERS TO PROGRESS

Key Issue 1: The Process of Measuring and Reporting on the Health Care System's Performance is Error Prone and Lacks Standards

The variation in reports about the quality of care can be a function of true variation in quality, of the quality of the underlying data, of the mix of patients cared for by the provider, of bias in the performance measure, and of the amount of systemic or random error (Parker et al., 2012). Data used for performance measurement are often first developed for a different purpose, such as billing or meeting regulatory requirements. If the data were generated for a different purpose, it would not be surprising if they were problematic for "off-label" use (Lau et al., 2015).

There are four key steps in measuring and reporting health care system performance, with an opportunity for error in each step, different entities involved in each step, and no entity entrusted with ensuring the validity of the entire process (*Table 13-1*). The first step of the process is developing and specifying the performance measure. Developing the measure includes deciding what dimension of care is to be measured; when done well, it requires thinking about whether the dimension is a key aspect of care delivery, what evidence supports focusing on that dimension, and the likelihood that existing sources of data can be used to measure the dimension (McGlynn, 2003). Specifying the performance measure includes identifying the measure's population of interest, the outcome or process of interest, and, if appropriate, the model for risk adjustment. Entities involved in measure development include measure developers and professional societies. The National Quality Forum (NQF) uses a multistakeholder, consensus-development process to vet performance measures and endorses the ones that meet the criteria of importance, scientific acceptability, feasibility, and usability (NQF, 2016a). Although that process has helped to improve measures, the criteria are not evaluated in a strict quantitative sense. The NQF does not define specific validity tests for different types of measures, report a measure's validity and reliability, or define specific thresholds for validity and reliability for endorsement. For example, the NQF endorsed the Patient Safety Indicator-90 (PSI-90) measure, for which the

TABLE 13-1 | Steps in the Performance Measurement and Reporting Process and Potential Corresponding Errors

STEPS IN THE PERFORMANCE MEASUREMENT AND REPORTING PROCESS	EXAMPLE OF WHERE ERRORS CAN OCCUR IN THE STEP
Step 1: Developing and specifying the performance measure.	ProPublica's Surgical Scorecard, an on-line report of surgical quality, uses a measure of surgical complications that does not include many common, in-hospital complications that may be important to patients. As a result, this measure has the potential to mischaracterize a surgeon's actual performance. The measure did not undergo the National Quality Forum's formal endorsement process, so those using the measure for improvement or decision making know little about its validity and accuracy.
Step 2: Identifying and collecting the data used to populate the measure.	*US News and World Report* uses a hospital's Medicare data to calculate the Patient Safety Indicators (PSis), a component of its Best Hospitals recognition program. When a patient arrives at the hospital with a preventable harm, that harm is coded as "present on admission" (POA). Events with a POA code are excluded from the PSI calculations. Medicare started requiring POA coding by hospitals in 2007, but hospitals in Maryland, with its Medicare waiver, were not required to include POA codes until 2013. The lack of POA codes for Maryland hospitals in the Medicare data probably penalized those hospitals when Medicare data were used to measure a hospital's quality.
Step 3: Applying the collected data to the specified performance measure.	An examination of common methods for creating physician cost profiles found that the reliability of the measures varied widely by specialty, ranging from 0.05 for vascular surgery to 0.79 for gastroenterology and otolaryngology. Overall, 59 percent of physicians had cost-profile scores with reliabilities of less than 0.70, a commonly used marker of suboptimal reliability. The authors estimated that 22 percent of physicians would be misclassified in a two-tiered system (high cost vs low or average cost). Perhaps this example suggests the importance of having a mechanism to pilot-test measures between their endorsement and their use for public policy (Adams et al., 201 0).
Step 4: Categorizing performance and communicating the results.	Research has demonstrated that many of the current public reports make it cognitively burdensome for the audience to understand the data. For example, a report might share quality information in one place and cost information in another place, rather than assisting the consumer in identifying the "best buy" (Damman et al., 2015; Vaiana & McGlynn, 2002).

SOURCE: Austin, J., G. Young, and P. Pronovost. 2014. Ensuring the integrity and transparency of public reports: How a possible oversight model could benefit healthcare. *American Journal of Accountable Care* 2(4):13–14.

measure developer conducted construct validity testing by examining the association between the composite performance score and hospital structural characteristics potentially associated with quality of care (Owens, 2014). A complementary, and perhaps stronger, approach for demonstrating the construct validity of the score, which is based on administrative data, is to compare the positive predictive value (PPV) of the administrative data with the medical chart. A recent study that examined that approach found that none of 21 PSIs met a PPV threshold of 80 percent; the validity of most of the individual component measures that make up the PSI-90 composite was low or unknown (Winters et al., 2016). In addition, those who measure and report health care performance do not have to use NQF-endorsed measures. How do we ensure the validity and reliability of all performance measures used to hold the health care system accountable? How do we make transparent how "good" the measure is? Is the measure "fit for purpose"? That is, can it be applied as the user intends it to be?

The second step of the process is identifying and collecting the data used to populate measures and ensuring that the data are accurate for the intended purpose. Entities involved in obtaining data for measurement include physicians, hospitals, survey vendors, health systems, and payers. With the exception of data from the National Committee for Quality Assurance (NCQA)—which measures health plans, some clinical registries, and a small number of state health departments that validate health care–associated infection data—few of the data used for performance measurement are subjected to systematic quality-assurance procedures that are specific to the intended use for measurement. Such procedures can include assessment of the extent of missing data or out-of-range values. Challenges include incomplete or fragmented data and providers or sites that differ from one another in coding or recording of data. More is known about variations in claims data because of its longer history of use than about variations commonly occurring in data from electronic medical records (EMRs); EMRs might become a more frequently used data source for quality measurement in the future. The recommendation of systematic quality assurance aligns with the 1998 President's Advisory Commission on Consumer Protection and Quality in the Health Care Industry recommendation that "information on quality that is released to the general public to facilitate comparisons among health care organizations, providers, or practitioners should be externally audited by an independent entity" (AHRQ, 1998). How do we ensure that the data used to populate measures are "good enough"? And how good is "good enough"? NCQA has developed and implemented an auditing process for its Healthcare Effectiveness Data and Information Set (HEDIS) performance measures that could serve as a model for others (NCQA, 2016).

The third step is applying the data to the specified measure. This step is a common source of variation. Multiple sources of data are used for measuring quality, safety, and cost, including claims, medical records, and surveys. Each has strengths and weaknesses that must be considered in the context of a particular measure. Entities that conduct measurement often state that they are using a "standard, endorsed" measure, but in the measurement program there may be minor, or even major, deviations from the endorsed measure, differing inter-pretations of what the measure specifications mean, different sources of data, and "adjustments" of standards for convenience or administrative simplification. For example, NCQA's HEDIS measure of breast-cancer screening attributes patients to clinicians by including patients who had any enrollment, claim, or encounter with a given clinician in the denominator population. A state-based quality collaborative chose to narrow the denominator of this measure to include only patients who had a primary care visit with the measured clinician (NQF, 2016b). Such variation in how the measure is implemented probably means that the validity of the results is unknown and the results are possibly not comparable.

For measures that are publicly reported, the fourth step is creating the public report. Errors at each step in the process cascade and compound, potentially imparting significant biases in published reports. In addition, variations in reporting templates, levels of detail, graphics, and many other factors are sources of variation in look, feel, interpretability, and usability of information. Entities involved in cre-ating reports include government, consumer groups, consumer-oriented websites, news-media organizations, health plans, purchasers, and providers. Approaches to categorizing and communicating results have undergone little systematic evalu-ation (Totten et al., 2012). For example, several researchers raised methodologic concerns about how the results of a recent (2015) ProPublica measure of surgeon quality were constructed and reported, inasmuch as performance categories were determined by using the shape of the distribution of adjusted surgeon complica-tion rates for each procedure and the thresholds chosen did not reflect statistically significant differences from the mean (Friedberg et al., 2015). Questions that still need to be answered about the best way to report results include, Should differ-ences in categories be statistically significant?; Should the differences be clinically or practically significant?; Are users able to interpret the display accurately?; and Should current performance be displayed in the context of a trend over time?

Key Issue 2: The Health Care Measurement and Reporting Enterprise Could Benefit from Standards and a Standard-Setting Organization

In light of opportunities for error in each step of the measurement and reporting process and tensions regarding the release of performance measures of uncertain validity (such as CMS's overall quality "star" ratings for hospitals), standard-setting could stimulate improvements in the integrity of the underlying data and methods used to generate performance measures. One possible oppor-tunity is to learn from financial reporting standards and emulate the Financial Accounting Standards Board (FASB). FASB establishes financial accounting and reporting standards for public and private companies and not-for-profit organizations that follow Generally Accepted Accounting Principles (Pronovost et al., 2007). FASB's mission is to establish accounting and reporting standards whose faithful implementation results in financial reports that provide useful and standard information to investors, creditors, and other providers of capital. FASB develops and issues its standards through a transparent and inclusive process. FASB originated in the early 1970s, when capital-market participants began to recognize the importance of an independent standard-setting process separate and distinct from accounting professionals, so that the development of standards would be insulated from the self-interests of practicing accountants and their clients (FASB, 2016). The standards developed by an "FASB for Health Care" would need to be informed by and to inform a number of stakeholder audiences. The idea of an "FASB for Health Care" has been discussed in many circles for a number of years; now may be the right time for its development. We spent the better part of the last two decades in bringing health care stakeholders along to the ideas of performance measurement and transparency of data. We have reached a shift in the health care environment in which measurement and transparency are now considered the "norm," and this allows us to set priorities for improving the robustness of these systems. In addition, with the current focus on paying for value instead of for volume, an idea that depends on valid performance measures, the need for a robust measurement and reporting process is more important than ever. We may have to settle for imperfect measures in the short term, but having standards for health care performance measures would make it possible to set thresholds for minimum performance of a measure before the measure is used or at least to understand, and make transparent, the imperfectness of the measure.

Key Issue 3: Further Research and Development in Health Care Performance Measurement and Reporting Are Needed

The process of measuring and reporting health care system performance could be thought of as a "system-level" intervention that needs to be studied for efficacy, effectiveness, cost effectiveness, and impact. Questions that still need to be answered include, What are the benefits of and unintended risks posed by public reporting, and do these vary by type of measure?; For which conditions and types of patients is public reporting useful or not useful?; What do we know about the types of public-reporting tools that are useful for different stakeholders and about how and when they should be used?; When is a measure so biased that it risks doing more harm than good?; How do we improve our understanding of how consumers make decisions, given that many consumers already assume care to be of high quality and safe (Hibbard and Soafer, 2010)?; Is the cost of measuring and reporting on quality for an area justifiable?; What attributes of measures engage clinicians to improve?

We need to improve measures and reduce the burden and costs of measurement. We need to produce measures that are useful to patients, particularly measures for conditions that are important to patients; outcomes that matter to patients, such as functional status; and measures of the overall value of the care delivered. The Patient-Centered Outcomes Research Institute (PCORI) has funded some early work in developing measures that are important to patients, but many gaps remain. It is critical to ensure that measures are understandable, impactful, and actionable and that they align with skills and abilities of those who need to use the information. In addition to focusing on new measures, we need to retire measures of low validity, low utility, or low engagement so as to reduce measurement burden. Public and private stakeholders have made little investment in advancing the science of and innovation in performance measurement, and no single entity is responsible for coordinating this work. We lack adequate investment in the "basic science" of measurement development. We lack a safe space for innovation in improving measures (McGlynn and Kerr, 2016), including iterating upon measures between their endorsement by NQF and their use in public reporting and payment. We lack incentives to become a learning health care system that is informed by valid and timely data and is focused on improving. We lack incentives for payers to share their price and quality data with external parties; such sharing might reduce the perceived value of their network discounts. And we lack incentives for consumers to use performance measures inasmuch as out-of-pocket maximums make cost data irrelevant for most care and consumers' inherent trust in the quality of care provided by their doctors and other health care providers may make quality data feel irrelevant (Hays and Ware, 1986). Payers and health care purchasers should continue their efforts to engage patients with these data because they benefit when patients seek higher-quality care, lower-cost care, or both. For a $3 trillion health care system, the costs of investing in a more robust performance-measurement and performance-reporting system, to ensure that we accurately capture and report performance, would constitute a tiny fraction of the total expense and likely reduce costs in the long term.

OPPORTUNITIES FOR PROGRESS AND POLICY IMPLICATIONS

The debate about performance measures has not always been grounded in scientific evidence. Some argue that current measures are good enough, others argue that they are not, and neither side offers evidence on how valid the measures are, how we might make them better, what it might cost to do so, and how valid they need to be. If the health care system is to realize the potential of publicly reporting performance measures, the users and producers of such measures will need to collaborate and gain consensus on those and other key issues.

We can enhance the effectiveness of performance measurement in a number of ways. Transparency of both content and process are foundational for trust and understanding. We need a coordinated policy to fund, set standards for, and support research and innovation in performance measurement in health care just as in the reporting of financial data. As part of a continuously "learning" health care system, in which we constantly assess performance and learn from experience, we need to implement "feedback loops" to understand how to improve the usefulness of measures and to discern unintended adverse or weak effects so that we can create systems by which producers and consumers of measures collaborate, pilot-test, iterate, and ensure the quality and continuous improvement of the entire measurement process (IOM, 2013). The feedback loops can occur at local, regional, and national levels. If lessons are systematically collected and shared, they can serve as a tool for improvement. We need "learning" or innovation laboratories with consumers and producers of measures to explore ways to make measures more useful and less burdensome (McGlynn and Kerr, 2016).

We need better communication with patients to raise their awareness of variation in the quality and costs of care. Few consumers are aware of the variation in quality and costs of care and how they can obtain information about them (O'Sullivan, 2015). For example, in one survey of patients with chronic conditions, only 16 percent to 25 percent of consumers were aware of hospital and physician comparisons on quality, respectively, and fewer (6 percent and 8 percent) had used such information for decision-making (Greene et al., 2015). Engaged consumers can drive health care systems and physicians to report valid measures. We need to engage patients in helping us to define value from their perspective and determining the appropriate selection of measures. We need to engage policymakers in making more data on the performance of our health care system publicly available. Such efforts should garner bipartisan support inasmuch as improving our health care delivery system is a public health issue and market solutions will play an important role in improving quality and reducing costs. We need to coordinate efforts to report the health care system's performance with efforts to improve performance, such as by expanding the use of implementation science, adopting financial incentives, and tapping into the professional motivations of our health care providers (Berwick, 2008; Marshall et al., 2013).

Given those needs, several strategic, specific federal efforts could help. Policymakers could create an independent body to write standards for health care performance measures and for the data used to populate the measures and, when appropriate, could approve standards developed by others. The independent body could finance the work to develop better measures. It would initially be designed to apply to situations in which the performance of individual hospitals or providers is used for accountability, such as public reporting or pay for performance. The structure of the organization ideally would reflect the interests of all stakeholders, it would operate openly and transparently, it would offer the public the opportunity to provide input, and it would evolve. One option would be to build on NQF, which operates in a similar manner. The entity charged with this work ideally would be a private, nongovernment, self-regulating organization, to ensure independence from competing interests. Informed by lessons learned by FASB, the organization might be structured to have a two-level board structure: a board of "standard-writing experts," who would serve terms of 5–7 years, be compensated to attract the brightest minds, and be required to sever ties with industry; and a "foundation board" that would include stakeholders of many types and would oversee the organization and be responsible for fundraising.

To achieve that vision, those leading the effort would need to get stakeholder buy-in and navigate multiple tensions, including tensions between stimulating (not stifling) innovation in measurement and reporting and reflecting the values and preferences of various stakeholders. One specific initial step that could be considered would be for the Department of Health and Human Services to fund a 1-year planning and convening project to engage stakeholders and develop an initial design of a standard-setting body. That would be consistent with the recommendations in the Institute of Medicine's report *Vital Signs* (IOM, 2015).

Other strategic federal initiatives include encouraging the Agency for Healthcare Research and Quality (AHRQ), CDC, and PCORI to fund research on the science and development of performance measures, encouraging CMS to continue its efforts in this regard, and encouraging the multiple federal agencies involved in performance measurement to collaborate. The federal agencies can also support innovation in setting up multistakeholder "learning laboratories," creating feedback loops, and identifying data sources, expertise, and test beds to develop needed measures more quickly. The laboratories could pilot-test and improve measures in the interval between when a measure is endorsed by NQF and when it is publicly reported and used in pay-for-performance programs; this would avoid the current process in which measures are revised after they are implemented (QualityNet, 2016). One approach for a learning laboratory might be to pick a small number of measures and coordinate the reporting and improvement efforts around them.

Federal initiatives should encourage greater transparency and sharing of data. For example, policymakers could prohibit gag clauses that preclude health plans and providers from sharing their data with employers, making it clear that self-insured employers own their claims data and can choose to share them as they see fit and enacting time limits for hospitals to share patient data and payers' claims data to ensure the timeliness of data. Policymakers could strengthen regulations to support the sharing of patients' data with patients themselves; this would reflect the principle that patient data belong to the patient.

The potential effects of those collective efforts should be enhanced quality and safety, reduced costs, enhanced patient choice and satisfaction, enhanced measurement science, and enhanced usefulness and use of performance measures to drive improvements in our health care system. The effects of these efforts can be tracked by monitoring and reporting the degree of transparency in reporting efforts, the progress made nationally on quality and cost, and the shifts in market share toward higher-value providers. To realize those goals, health care needs leadership and trust.

CONCLUSION

Despite important steps toward public reporting of the performance of our health care system, health care performance measurement has not yet achieved the desired goal of a system with higher quality and lower costs. Transparency of performance is a key tool for improving the health care system; however, if transparency is to serve as a tool for improvement, we need to ensure that the information that results from it is both accurate and meaningful.

The measures outlined in the introduction that have been successful—measures of infection associated with health care developed by the Centers for Disease Control and Prevention, measures of diabetes care, and AHRQ's HCAHPS measures—have several common attributes. All were developed with substantial financial investment; they underwent extensive validation, revisions, and improvement; they published information about their validity; and they have wide acceptance among their users. The time is right to evolve a better performance-reporting system. That requires a commitment to the science of performance measurement, which in turn requires imagination, investment, infrastructure, and implementation. Without such commitment, our opportunity to achieve the goal of higher-value care is limited by our inability to understand our own performance.

VITAL DIRECTIONS

The three following vital directions have been identified for improving the health care measurement and reporting systems:

1. **Create a health measurement and data standard-setting body.** Fund a 1-year planning and convening project to engage stakeholders and develop an initial design of a standard-setting body in a way that is consistent with the recommendations in the Institute of Medicine report *Vital Signs: Core Metrics for Health and Health Care Progress* (IOM, 2015). In 2018, on the basis of this initial design, launch an independent body to write standards for health care performance measures and the data used to populate the measures. This helps to ensure that the information we have on the performance of the health care system is valid and accurate. The potential success of payment reform (payment for the value of care, rather than the volume) will be limited if we cannot accurately assess the quality of care being provided. Depending on whether this work is tagged onto existing entities or a new entity is created to accomplish the work, we anticipate that these steps would take 2–5 years to accomplish.

2. **Build the science of performance measures.** Fund research on the science of performance measures and on the best ways to develop them and to pilot-test and improve them and encourage the multiple federal agencies involved in performance measurement to collaborate. That will help to move forward the science of performance measurement and ensure that different entities involved in the work are aligned. We anticipate that significant progress on the funding of research and the alignment of efforts would take 1–3 years to accomplish, with ongoing work thereafter.

3. **Improve the communication of data to patients.** Fund research on how to improve communication with patients about variations in the quality and costs of care, including examining reporting formats and the framework within which consumers make different types of health care choices. For the health care market to work efficiently, we need health care consumers who are knowledgeable about the quality and cost of the services that they seek, including the variation in quality and costs among providers. We anticipate that significant progress on the funding of research could take 1–2 years, with ongoing work thereafter.

SUMMARY RECOMMENDATIONS FOR
VITAL DIRECTIONS

1. Create a health measurement and data standard-setting body.
2. Build the science of performance measures.
3. Improve the communication of data to patients.

REFERENCES

Adams, J., A. Mehrotra, J. Thomas, and E. McGlynn. 2010. Physician cost profiling reliability and risk of misclassification. *New England Journal of Medicine* 362(11): 1014–1021.

AHRQ (Agency for Healthcare Research and Quality and Research (AHRQ). 1998. Summary of recommendations: Providing strong leadership and clear aims for improvement. Available at http://archive.ahrq.gov/hcqual/prepub/recommen.htm (ac-cessed June 14, 2016).

Austin, J. 2015. Why health care performance measures need their own grades. 2015. Voices for Safer Care, Available at https://armstronginstitute.blogs.hopkinsmedicine.org/2015/05/27/why-health-care-performance-measures-need-their-own-grades/ (accessed May 24, 2016).

Austin, J., A. Jha, P. Romano, S. Singer, T. Vogus, R. Wachter, and P. Pronovost. 2015. National hospital ratings systems share few common scores and may generate confusion instead of clarity. *Health Affairs* 34(3):423–30.

Austin, J., and P. Pronovost. 2016. Improving performance on core processes of care. *Current Opinion in Allergy and Clinical Immunology* 16(3):224–230.

Austin, J., G. Young, and P. Pronovost. 2014. Ensuring the integrity and transparency of public reports: How a possible oversight model could benefit healthcare. *American Journal of Accountable Care* 2(4):13–14.

Austin, J., A. Jha, P. Romano, S. Singer, T. Vogus, R. Wachter, and P. Pronovost. 2015. National hospital ratings systems share few common scores and may generate confusion instead of clarity. *Health Affairs* 34(3):423–430.

Berenson, R., and T. Rice. 2015. Beyond measurement and reward: Methods of motivating quality improvement and accountability. *Health Services Research* 50:2155–2186.

Berwick, D., B. James, and M. Coye. 2003. Connections between quality measurement and improvement. *Medical Care* 41(1 Suppl):I30–I38.

Berwick, D. M. 2008. The science of improvement. *The Journal of the American Medical Association* 299(10):1182–1184.

Brown, D., A. Epstein, and E. Schneider. 2013. Influence of cardiac surgeon report cards on patient referral by cardiologists in New York state after 20 years of public reporting. *Circulation: Cardiovascular Quality and Outcomes* 6(6):643–648.

CMS (Centers for Medicare and & Medicaid Services). 2016a. Healthcare-associated infections. Available at https://www. medicare.gov/hospitalcompare/Data/Healthcare-Associated-Infections.html (accessed May 25, 2016).

CMS. 2016b. Survey of patients' experiences (HCAHPS). Available at https://www.medicare.gov/hospitalcompare/Data/Overview.html (accessed May 26, 2016).

Consumer Reports. 2016. How we rate hospitals. Available at http://www.consumer-reports.org/cro/2012/10/how-we-rate-hospitals/index.htm (accessed May 26, 2016).

Cronin, C., C. Damberg, A. Riedel, and J. France. 2011. State-of-the-art of hospital and physician/physician group public reports. Paper presented at the Agency for Healthcare Research and Quality National Summit on Public Reporting for Consumers, Washington, DC.

Damberg, C., M. Sorbero, S. Lovejoy, K. Lauderdale, S. Wertheimer, A. Smith, D. Waxman, and C. Schnyer. 2011. *An Evaluation of the Use of Performance Measures in Health Care.* Santa Monica, CA: RAND Corporation.

Damman, O., A. De Jong, J. Hibbard, and D. Timmermans. 2015. Making comparative performance information more comprehensible: An experimental evaluation of the impact of formats on consumer understanding. *BMJ Quality & Safety* 25(11):860–869.

Dixon-Woods, M., C. Bosk, E. Aveling, C. Goeschel, and P. Pronovost. 2011. Explaining Michigan: Developing an ex post theory of a quality improvement program. *The Millbank Quarterly* 89(2): 167–205.

Dixon-Woods, M., S. McNicol, and G. Martin. 2012. Ten challenges in improving quality in healthcare: Lessons from the Health Foundation's programme evaluations and relevant literature. *BMJ Quality & Safety* 21(10).

Elliott, M., W. Lehrman, E. Goldstein, L. Giordano, M. Beckett, C. Cohea, and P. Cleary. 2010. Hospital survey shows improvements in patient experience. *Health Affairs* 29(11):2061–2067.

Faber, M., M. Bosch, H. Wollersheim, S. Leatherman, and R. Grol. 2009. Public reporting in health care: How do consumers use quality-of-care information?: A systematic review. *Medical Care* 47(1):1–8.

FASB (Financial Accounting Standards Board (FASB). 2016. About the FASB. Available at http://www.fasb.org/jsp/FASB/Page/LandingPage&cid=1175805317407 (accessed May 25, 2016).

Friedberg, M., P. Pronovost, D. Shahian, D. Safran, K. Bilimoria, M. Elliott, C. Damberg, J. Dimick, and A. Zaslavsky. 2015. *A methodological critique of the ProPublica Surgeon Scorecard.* Santa Monica, CA: RAND Corporation.

Greene, J., V. Fuentes-Caceres, N. Verevkina, and Y. Shi. 2015. Who's aware of and using public reports of provider quality? *Journal of Health Care for the Poor and Underserved* 26(3):873–888.

Hays, R., and J. Ware, Jr. 1986. My medical care is better than yours: social Social desirability and patient satisfaction ratings. *Medical Care* 519–525.

Hibbard, J., and S. Sofaer. 2010. *Best practices in public reporting no. 1: how How to effectively present health care performance data to consumers.* Rockville, MD: Agency for Healthcare Research and QualityAHRQ.

Hibbard, J., J. Stockard, and M. Tusler. 2005. Hospital performance reports: impact Impact on quality, market share, and reputation. *Health Affairs* 24(4):1150–1160.

HSS (Hospital Safety Score (HSS). 2016. About the score. Available at http://www.hospitalsafetyscore.org/your-hospitals-safety-score/about-the-score (accessed May 25, 2016).

IOM (Institute of Medicine (IOM). 2013. *Best care at lower cost: The path to continuously learning health care in America.* Washington, DC: The National Academies Press.

Institute of Medicine (IOM). 2015. *Vital signs: Core metrics for health and health care progress.* Washington, DC: The National Academies Press.

Jha, A. 2012. Hospital rankings get serious. An Ounce of Evidence/Health Policy blog. Available at http://blogs.sph.har-vard.edu/ashish-jha/hospital-rankings-get-serious/ (accessed May 25, 2016).

Ketelaar, N., M. Faber, S. Flottorp, L. Rygh, K. Deane, and M. Eccles. 2011. *Public release of performance data in changing the behaviour of healthcare consumers, professionals or organisations.* The Cochrane Library.

Lamb, G., M. Smith, W. Weeks, and C. Queram. 2013. Publicly reported quality-of-care measures influenced Wisconsin physician groups to improve performance. *Health Affairs* 32(3):536–543.

Lau, B., E. Haut, D. Hobson, P. Kraus, C. Maritim, J. Austin, K. Shermock, B. Maheshwari, P. Allen, A. Almario, and M. Streiff. 2015. ICD-9 code-based venous thromboembolism performance targets fail to measure up. *American Journal of Medical Quality* 106286061558354731(5):448–453.

Ketelaar, N., M. Faber, S. Flottorp, L. Rygh, K. Deane and M. Eccles. 2011. *Public release of performance data in changing the behaviour of healthcare consumers, professionals or organisations.* The Cochrane Library.

Marjoua, Y., and K. Bozic. 2012. Brief history of quality movement in US healthcare. *Current Reviews in Musculoskeletal Medicine* 5(4):265–273.

Marshall, M., P. Pronovost, and M. Dixon-Woods. 2013. Promotion of improvement as a science. *The Lancet* 381(9864):419–421.

McGlynn, E. 2003. An evidence-based national quality measurement and reporting system. *Medical Care* 41(1):I1–8.

McGlynn, E., and J. Adams. 2014. What makes a good quality measure? *The Journal of the American Medical Association* 312(15):1517–1518.

McGlynn, E., and E. Kerr. 2016. Creating safe harbors for quality measurement innovation and improvement. *The Journal of the American Medical Association* 315(2):129–130.

NCQA (National Committee for Quality Assurance (NCQA). 2016. HEDIS Compliance Audit Program. Available at http://www. ncqa.org/tabid/205/Default.aspx (accessed June 21, 2016).

NQF (National Quality Forum (NQF). 2016a. What NQF endorsement means. Available at http://www.qualityforum.org/Measuring_Performance/ABCs/What_NQF_Endorsement_Means.aspx (accessed May 25, 2016).

National Quality Forum (NQF). 2016b. Variation in Measure Specifications Project 2015–2016: First draft report. Available at http://www.qualityforum.org/WorkArea/linkit. aspx?LinkIdentifier=id&ItemID=82318 (accessed May 25, 2016).

O'Neil, S., J. Schurrer, and S. Simon. 2010. *Environmental scan of public reporting programs and analysis* (Final Report by Mathematica Policy Research). Washington, DC: National Quality Forum, Washington, DCNQF.

O'Sullivan, M. 2015. *Safety in numbers: Cancer surgeries in California hospitals.* California Healthcare Foundation.

Owens, P. 2014. Letter to NQF Patient Safety Steering Committee members and NQF staff, Subject: PSI 90 for maintenance endorsement. Available at http://www.qualityforum. org/WorkArea/linkit.aspx?LinkIdentifier=id&ItemID=77096 (accessed May 25, 2016).

Parker, C., L. Schwamm, G. Fonarow, E. Smith, and M. Reeves. 2012. Stroke quality metrics systematic reviews of the relationships to patient-centered outcomes and impact of public reporting. *Stroke* 43(1):155–162.

Pronovost, P., M. Miller, and R. Wachter. The GAAP in Quality Measurement and Reporting. 2007. *The Journal of the American Medical Association* 298:1800–1802.

Pronovost, P., J. Marsteller, and C. Goeschel. 2011. Preventing bloodstream infections: A measurable national success story in quality improvement. *Health Affairs* 30(4):628–634.

Pronovost, P, M. Miller, and R. Wachter. 2007. *The Journal of the American Medical Association* 298:1800–1802.

QualityNet. 2016. Specifications manual, Version 5.1. Available at https://www. qualitynet.org/dcs/ContentServer?c=Pa ge&pagename=QnetPublic%2FPage%2FQnetTier3& cid=1228775436944 (accessed July 19, 2016).

Shahian, D., E. Edwards, J. Jacobs, R. Prager, S. Normand, C. Shewan, S. O'Brien, E. Peterson, and F. Grover. 2011a. Public reporting of cardiac surgery performance: part Part 1—history, rationale, consequences. *The Annals of Thoracic Surgery* 92(3): S2-S11.

Shahian, D., E. Edwards, J. Jacobs, R. Prager, S. Normand, C. Shewan, S. O'Brien, E. Peterson, and F. Grover. 2011b. Public reporting of cardiac surgery performance: part Part 2—implementation. *The Annals of Thoracic Surgery* 92(3):S12-S23.

Shaller, D., D. Kanouse, and M. Schlesinger. 2014. Context-based strategies for engaging consumers with public reports about health care providers. *Medical Care Research and Review* 71(5 supplSuppl):17S-37S.

Shwartz, M., J. Restuccia, and A. Rosen. 2015. Composite measures of health care provider performance: A description of approaches. *The Milbank Quarterly* 93:788-825.

Smith, M., A. Wright, C. Queram, and G. Lamb. 2012. Public reporting helped drive quality improvement in outpatient diabetes care among Wisconsin physician groups. *Health Affairs* 31(3):570–577.

Stey, A., M. Russell, C. Ko, G. Sacks, A. Dawes, and M. Gibbons. 2015. Clinical registries and quality measurement in surgery: a A systematic review. *Surgery* 157(2):381–395.

STS (Society of Thoracic Surgeons). 2016. STS public reporting online. Available at http://www.sts.org/quality-research-patient-safety/sts-public-reporting-online (accessed May 25, 2016).

Totten, A., J. Wagner, A. Tiwari, C. O'Haire, J. Griffin, and M. Walker. 2012. Public reporting as a quality improvement strategy. Closing the quality gap: Revisiting the state of the science. Rockville, MD: Agency for Healthcare Research and QualityAHRQ.

Vaiana, M., and E. McGlynn. 2002. What cognitive science tells us about the design of reports for consumers. *Medical Care Research and Review* 59(1): 3–35.

Whaley, C., J. Chafen, S. Pinkard, G. Kellerman, D. Bravata, R. Kocher, and N. Sood. 2014. Association between availability of health service prices and payments for these services. *The Journal of the American Medical Association* 312(16):1670–1676.

Winters, B., A. Bharmal, R. Wilson, A. Zhang, L. Engineer, D. Defoe, E. Bass, S. Dy, and P. Pronovost. 2016. Validity of the Agency for Health Care Research and Quality patient safety indicators and the Centers for Medicare and Medicaid hospital-acquired conditions: A systematic review and meta-analysis. Medical Care 54(12): 1105–1111.

AUTHOR INFORMATION

Peter J. Pronovost, MD, PhD, FCCM, is Senior Vice President for Patient Safety and Quality, and Director, Armstrong Institute for Patient Safety and Quality, Johns Hopkins Medicine. **J. Matthew Austin, PhD, MS,** is Assistant Professor of Anesthesiology and Clinical Care Medicine, Johns Hopkins Medicine. **Christine K. Cassel, MD,** is Planning Dean, Kaiser Permanente School of Medicine. **Suzanne F. Delbanco, PhD,** is Executive Director, Catalyst for Payment Reform. **Ashish K. Jha, MD, MPH,** is K.T. Li Professor of International Health and Director, Harvard Global Health Institute, Harvard T.H. Chan School of Public Health. **Bob Kocher, MD,** is a Partner, Venrock. **Elizabeth A. McGlynn, PhD,** is Director, Center for Effectiveness and Safety Research, Kaiser Permanente. **Lewis G. Sandy, MD, FACP,** is Executive Vice President, Clinical Advancement, UnitedHealth Group. **John Santa, MD, MPH,** is Former Director, Health Ratings Center, Consumer Reports.

14

THE DEMOCRATIZATION OF HEALTH CARE

Paul C. Tang, MD, MS, Mark D. Smith, MD, MBA, Julia Adler-Milstein, PhD, Tom Delbanco, MD, Stephen J. Downs, SM, Giridhar G. Mallya, MD, MS, Debra L. Ness, MS, Ruth M. Parker, MD, and Danny Z. Sands, MD, MPH

The US health care delivery system is in the midst of a transformation. For generations, it was rooted in a transactional, fee-for-service ethos that rewarded mainly interventions to treat individuals for diseases. Today, it aims to emphasize improvement in and maintenance of the health of both individuals and communities. The transformation presents the country with the opportunity to reconsider the role of patients and their families in health. Calls to "empower" patients—to change the traditional hierarchic relationships of health care—are not new but are now far more widespread (Topol, 2015). As in other industries, the availability of information and knowledge resources over the Internet has enabled people to take a more active role in managing their health and their health care and to make decisions that previously required highly trained professionals—in short, has enabled the democratization of health care (IOM, 2013a). Embracing that change not only will improve health outcomes but also will address some of the underpinnings of the continued rise in health care costs and the maldistribution of professional resources.

How can health care be democratized? First, people must have a powerful voice and role in the decisions and systems that affect their health, and they need tools that help them to become far more actively engaged. Second, health professionals and institutions must value social equity and the individual in the context of community. With those principles, we can move from *patient-centered health care*—focused on sickness, medical interventions, and data on the average patient—to *person-centered health care*—motivated by wellness, supportive social conditions, and knowledge about the individual and his or her environments.

Those notions underlie the vision of a culture of health—a society in which all people have opportunities for better health where they live, work, learn, and play. Health is powerfully determined by our environments and our social circumstances—our income, education, housing, transportation, neighborhoods, and social and familial networks. As an example of how social determinants affect health, consider the holistic approach to health taken by Philadelphia's Stephen and Sandra Sheller 11th Street Family Health Services.

Since the late 1990s, the 11th Street clinic has partnered with and served the residents of four public-housing communities, where median family income is $15,000 and 80 percent of the people are covered by Medicaid or are uninsured. Many community members have experienced trauma of various forms, which compounds their acute and chronic health problems. Weaving together services to meet the physical, mental, spiritual, and social needs of patients makes the clinic a standout. During one visit, a 5-year-old can get immunizations and a dental checkup while a teen sibling participates in art therapy as part of an integrated mental health program. Parents and older adults, too, benefit from a variety of resources—including couples and family counseling, mindfulness training, cooking classes, and linkages to housing and food assistance—with comprehensive medical services. The 11th Street model is the exception, not the rule, but the arc appears to be bending in that direction.

We understand increasingly that we cannot achieve the three tenets of the Triple Aim—better health, better patient experience, and lower per capita cost—without the engagement of patients and families. We want people to embrace the transformed models of care and payment that we are building and to change their behaviors in fundamental ways. But, for the most part, our current conversation and actions around engagement focus on how we get people, patients, and families to do what we want them to do. That perspective needs to change if our health care system is indeed to focus more effectively on improving the population's health and health equity. The questions that we should be asking are, How do we build a health system that people *want to and are able to* engage in?; and How do we build a system that defines value through the lens of the people that it serves—a system that helps people to define the health goals that they want to achieve and then supports them in achieving those goals? Engagement must begin with accessible information and knowledge.

Health literacy is fundamental to democratization of health care. Fostering health literacy means aligning the demands and complexities of what is needed for health and health care with the skills and abilities of the public (IOM, 2013b). Hundreds of original research investigations have shown that health disparities depend on people's literacy and numeracy skills, language, education, knowledge, and experience. Health systems routinely impose unnecessary complexity on patients, inasmuch as the design of most health care does not reflect the fact that half of US adults read at or below an 8th- or 9th-grade level. Indeed, the current US health system is too complex to navigate at any educational level. Highlighting patient engagement and allowing it to guide the design and organization of evidence-based health care processes, practices, and research priorities can help to create content that is understandable, is navigable, and reflects patients' needs. Only with a health-literate community can we engage in truly shared decision making.

People make decisions every day that have far greater effects on their health than decisions controlled by the health care system. Patients and their family caregivers are perhaps the most underused resource in improving health status and health care outcomes. The health care system has long been hamstrung by the episodic nature of in-person patient encounters that have generally been required if there is to be payment. Increasingly, however, technology can enable 24/7 contact and much greater levels of self-care. In addition to the health benefits to individuals of a more unified and integrated approach to health care, providing care in less expensive settings on a population scale has economic benefits. The key question is how to realize the substantial economic effects of patients' and caregivers' engaging with the professional health care team to manage patients' health.

Properly and fully engaging individuals and families in managing and improving their health and the health of their communities is foundational to improving the health of Americans. In this paper, we explore a number of topics that are key to democratization of health care and propose policy recommendations to engage America in a journey to better health.

KEY ISSUES

Creating a Culture of Health

Health systems will need to integrate physical health, behavioral health, and social-service delivery further to promote well-being optimally. Effective practice models of integration of primary care with behavioral health exist but have not yet been scaled, because of historical divisions in payment, practice, and culture. New payment models, such as the Centers for Medicare & Medicaid Services Accountable Health Communities, have begun to allow health care dollars to be leveraged for social-service referral, navigation, and collaboration, but these strategies are nascent and need to be thoroughly evaluated. The behavioral-health workforce and social-service system are inadequate, and foundational investment may be required to meet holistic needs identified by the health care system.

It is widely understood that the United States spends far more than any other country on health care services; what is less well appreciated is that many developed countries spend more on social services, which help them to achieve better social and health outcomes (Squires and Anderson, 2015). The current movement from volume-oriented to value-oriented payment provides incentives for health care payers and providers to examine anew how spending on supportive social services centered on the needs of the individual can reduce the need for higher-cost treatment in the medical care system. Poor housing, for instance, has direct effects on health via environmental exposures to (or protection from) lead, mold, vermin, and temperature extremes. Health care systems are beginning to experiment with models for paying for home remediation. The shift to person-centered health care will require a further commitment to communities, cross-sector collaboration, and systemic solutions.

Engaging Individuals and Families

A system that people want to engage in—a truly person-centered and family-centered system—will require a profound change in our health care culture and mind-set and substantial change in payment approaches and care delivery. The most important change must come in how we think about the roles of patients and families. How can we expect to create a person-centered and family-centered system if their voices are not at the table, helping to create and evaluate the system? We must accept, value, and promote genuine collaboration in every dimension of our efforts to transform health care, including not just at the point of care but in design of care processes and payment strategies, governance bodies, policy development, and interfaces with the communities served. Transparency around costs and quality results are foundational to building trusted partnerships with people.

Economic Effects of Engaging Patients and Families

Under the current medical model, providers control both medical advice and the costs of health care. A democratized version of health care would have implications not only for outcomes but for costs. To achieve a state in which patients are more engaged, three key issues must be addressed. First, current patient-engagement efforts are fragmented. Employers, health care providers, payers, and other stakeholder groups are attempting to reach out to patients in different ways to encourage them to engage in a variety of activities: care coordination, wellness promotion, chronic disease management, medication management, and so on. Second, there is little effort to customize engagement strategies to patients' needs, preferences, and motivations. There is insufficient attention, for example, to patient literacy, theories of behavior change, and behavioral economics. Third, patient-engagement efforts have not been integrated into the fabric of everyday life. We ask patients to manage and think about health separately from their social life, daily routines, and the growing technologic infrastructure that supports these activities.

Opportunities for developing evidence about interventions that work and for informing enabling policies exist, for example, in the Center for Medicare & Medicaid Innovation (CMMI) and the Patient-Centered Outcomes Research Institute (PCORI). CMMI and PCORI are in a position to fund demonstrations with the specific goals of coordinating all programs, interventions, and outreach efforts that are targeted at the patient and engaging a patient in a single, cohesive self-management plan. It would be similarly valuable in funding research that examines "translational" barriers to applying the sciences of health literacy, behavior change, and behavioral economics in real-world interventions.

Policy Implications

What policy directions can help us to shift to health partnerships between the care team and patients and a health system that attracts and supports engagement? We need to craft our payment policies to foster a strong foundation of primary care to provide the kind of care that people value. Primary care and the professionals who provide it should be more equitably valued and more adequately compensated. Primary care has enormous potential to enhance engagement and to improve health outcomes, experience, and costs, but payment must be sufficient to support key elements of care that are essential to engagement, namely,

- formation of trusted relationships—the starting point for partnership, engagement, and activation;
- shared care planning and decision making that are not isolated activities but an evolving process that extends to end-of-life care when appropriate;
- adequate clinician time and a team infrastructure for effective coordination and communication during and outside clinical visits;
- recognition of cultural and sociodemographic factors that influence health and health equity; and
- culturally and linguistically appropriate resources that help patients to engage in their health care.

It is equally important to rethink the payment incentives that we create for patients through the design of insurance benefits and to remove financial barriers, such as out-of-pocket costs that deter patients from following recommendations, getting needed care, or pursuing healthier behaviors.

With changes in payment, we need to change the measurement system. Measurement and the information that it generates should be useful to and usable by patients and families. And, patients, families, and their advocates should be integrated as respected partners in measure development and care evaluation. More measures should be developed to use patient-generated data, including patient experience of care and patient-reported outcomes, such as functional status, symptom burden, and quality of life. We need innovative strategies for seamless collection of patient-generated data and for provision of feedback as part of clinical workflow, and we need to make data available quickly so that they can be used to guide clinical improvement.

Changing the payment system will not automatically change how professionals interact with patients. We need to change medical education and training and the approach to licensure and certification of practicing clinicians and health care organizations. The process of valuing individuals, patients, and families as genuine partners in managing health care should begin with provider education and training, including continuing education.

Health Literacy: How Can We Confuse People Less?

A fundamental requirement for greater democratization of health care is greater health literacy among its beneficiaries and participants. Access to and comprehension of information follow the gradient of literacy skills, which are well documented in our nation. In recent studies, patient adoption of "portals" (explained below) was far slower among those who had worse literacy skills. Less-literate older adults were less likely to own a smartphone, use the Internet to access health information, or communicate with health care providers via the Internet (Bailey et al., 2014). As much as 20 percent of our population will probably not contribute actively through personal engagement, because of literacy, language, physical, or mental limitations.

Applying Health Literacy Principles to Policy and Practice

Technologic advances and enthusiastic engagement by innovators and entrepreneurs are moving quickly to make democratization of health care a reality. Policies are needed to address three elements: inclusiveness (with attention to the 20 percent of the population unlikely to participate readily in data input), infrastructure for health democratization (e.g., which data, services, cost and outcome metrics, and privacy protections to include), and user interface design (for easy access, navigation, and clarity).

Examples of Opportunities Related to Existing Legislation

The Patient Protection and Affordable Care Act (ACA). Nearly 36 percent of American adults have low health literacy. As detailed in an Institute of

Medicine workshop summary (*Health Literacy Implications for Health Care Reform*), several ACA provisions directly acknowledge the need for greater attention to health literacy. As regulations are advanced, there are opportunities to ensure that all are able to access, navigate, and use health care in our country. The lens of health literacy can facilitate more effective communication with respect to specifics of coverage expansion (clarity in enrollment processes, network providers, costs and coverage, and use of health insurance), workforce training, and *all* patient information.

The Plain Writing Act of 2010. This act was a mandate for the federal government to use plain writing in documents issued to promote government communication with the public. Federal employees are to be trained in plain writing; senior officials are designated to oversee the act's implementation and a process to gauge compliance. With this federal legislation as background, what are specific opportunities at state and local levels to ensure clarity and foster less confusion as to what all people need to understand and do for their health and health care?

Telehealth

Alternatives to Face-to-Face Encounters

As long as physicians have been treating patients, they have done so mainly in a "visit," an in-person clinical encounter. Those encounters have generally occurred in a physician's office or in an emergency department or other hospital setting (other than house calls, which are not common today). Since the 1990s, some physicians have been using e-mail for communication with their patients (often called e-visits), including communication about clinical issues (in addition to administrative issues), which can help patients to determine their need for a visit or to obviate a visit. The use of ordinary e-mail has been largely eclipsed by the use of secure messaging for many physicians and patients, usually through patient portals as promoted by the Health Information Technology for Economic and Clinical Health Act. E-messaging is extremely efficient and desired by many patients, but it is still underused, and many patients say that their physicians do not respond readily. Secure messaging is asynchronous, so it is appropriate for issues that are nonurgent and not time sensitive. But, sometimes it is more efficient to communicate in real time. For a century, physicians and patients have used the telephone for conversation. Today, we have other real-time communication options for patients (IOM, 2012).

Real-time video communication, often called telemedicine, can ameliorate barriers of space and time spent in traveling to and from a health care professional. It can substitute for face-to-face consultation between providers and patients, and it can make professional collaboration among health care colleagues accessible. Telemedicine has been shown to improve patient access to medical care, especially in underserved areas, and to reduce costs to patients (Berman and Fenaughty, 2005; Hailey et al., 2002; Keely et al., 2013). However, the adoption of such technologies has been hampered by lack of reimbursement and by variations and restrictions in state-by-state licensure rules that have kept physicians from practicing medicine outside the states in which they are licensed.

Patient-Generated Health Data

For many years, physicians have asked patients to monitor their weight, blood pressure, blood sugar, and other characteristics and report them to their physicians or care managers. A burgeoning of connected devices now makes it possible to monitor those entities and more—including physical activity, sleep, and heart rhythm—and to transmit them over the Internet. It can be done actively or passively for patients who are quite ill. As reimbursement is shifting to reward improved outcomes at lower cost, some practices have been gathering patient-generated biometric data, usually as part of a system of managing care that involves nonphysician staff with physicians involved as needed. But, patient-generated health data (PGHD) must go beyond biometric data and encompass patient-reported outcomes, values and preferences, pain scores, and adherence. For PGHD to be incorporated into practice, consideration must be given to

- practice and patient workflow;
- seamless integration into physician-practice tools, such as the electronic health record;
- appropriate incentives; and
- accuracy of the devices.

Patient monitoring in combination with a human component (not as an isolated patient activity) has been shown to improve outcomes, reduce health care costs, and prevent unnecessary hospital admissions (Agboola et al., 2015; Jethwani et al., 2012; Watson et al., 2012).

Policy Issues

To facilitate widespread use of telemedicine, policies that are consistent among states must be developed, for example:

- reimbursement for visits that is based on what was done, not on the channel used to conduct the visits;
- reciprocal state professional-licensure approaches or a federal approach to telehealth licensure;

- simplified, risk-based Food and Drug Administration approval of self-monitoring technologies; and
- increased funding for evaluation of non-visit-based care programs and technologies.

Shared Planning for Health

As in so many other aspects of modern life, transparent communication is helping to inform and rationalize health care. One example of such transparency is OpenNotes (Delbanco et al., 2012), a national initiative funded by several national philanthropies that urges health care providers to offer patients electronic access to the visit notes written by their doctors, nurses, and other clinicians. The goals are to improve communication and to engage patients (and their families) in care more actively. Although it was initiated in primary care, the OpenNotes movement has expanded to include medical and surgical specialties. Mental health professionals are increasingly offering patients their notes as part of the psychotherapeutic process, and fully transparent records are being shared in emergency rooms, on hospital wards, and in intensive-care units. Close to 10 million Americans have access to OpenNotes through patient portals. A growing number of studies indicate, for example, that inviting patients to read their notes may improve medication adherence, help patients to build more trusting and efficient partnerships with the care team for chronic-disease management, and improve patient safety (Bell et al., 2015a). As people become the primary stewards of their own journey through health and illness, striking opportunities for increasingly constructive patient engagement are on the horizon. For example, clinic notes, shaped largely by requirements for fee-for-service billing and, more recently, quality documentation, will need to evolve to play a greater role in informing patients about their health and treatment. And, the OpenNotes movement has demonstrated the potential to improve the accuracy of notes by inviting patients to examine, confirm, and correct physicians' records (Bell et al., 2015a,b)

VITAL DIRECTIONS

1. **Focus health financing on health.** Continue to advance payment-reform policies that provide incentives for providers' comprehensive and long-term thinking about investment to promote health, including increased recognition of primary care as a central tenet of health reform to improve outcomes.
2. **Measure what matters most to people.** Change the system of measuring quality to assess and reward performance on the basis of "measures that matter" to individuals, patients, and families. Fund development of specific measures that matter by the end of 2017, to be implemented in 2018 and affect payment in 2020.

3. **Include needed social services and health literacy in health financing.** Experiment with greater use of Medicare, Medicaid, and private health-insurance funding for social and human services that demonstrate favorable effects on health outcomes or costs. Included in this should be health literacy services to ensure that information, processes, and delivery of health care in all settings align with the skills and abilities of all people.

4. **Streamline access to validated telehealth tools.** Reconcile state-by-state regulatory barriers to telehealth and other online means of providing relevant, convenient, timely information about individuals' health at times of need.

CONCLUSION

There is little disagreement on the substantial potential value of engaging patients and their family caregivers in managing health care. In fact, effective engagement of individuals and their families is key to succeeding under accountable-health models. Today, individual engagement happens in an uncoordinated way that does not take advantage of the scientific findings on how effective engagement must connect with the activities of everyday life. Individuals are facing increasing financial risk associated with health care decisions, but they lack tools for making informed decisions, namely patient-relevant data on options, outcomes, provider performance, and cost. Accelerating changes in health systems and technology support of patient engagement will require bold and deliberate restructuring of the payment system to reward value over volume. Despite widespread agreement on this general direction, wholesale behavior change throughout the health care enterprise awaits precise specifications of measures that appropriately assess whether services provided by health systems improve the health of individuals and communities. Public policies that unambiguously reward improving health will not only make the country's priorities clear but will also motivate health systems to develop innovative solutions aligned with the national move toward a culture of health.

SUMMARY RECOMMENDATIONS FOR VITAL DIRECTIONS

1. Focus health financing on health.
2. Measure what matters most to people.
3. Include needed social services and health literacy in health financing.
4. Streamline access to validated telehealth tools.

REFERENCES

Agboola, S., K. Jethwani, K. Khateeb, S. Moore, J. KveAgboola, S., K. Jethwani, K. Khateeb, S. Moore, and J. Kvedar. 2015. Heart failure remote monitoring: Evidence from the retrospective evaluation of a real-world remote monitoring program. *Journal of Medical Internet Research* 17(4):e101. doi: 10.2196/jmir.4417.

Bailey, S. C., R. O'Conor, E. A. Bojarski, R. Mullen, R. E. Patzer, D. Vicencio, K. L. Jacobson, R. M. Parker, and M. S. Wolf. 2014. Literacy disparities in patient access and health-related use of Internet and mobile technologies. *Health Expectations* 18(6):3079–3087.

Bell, S. K., P. Folcarelli, M. Anselmo, B. Crotty, L. Flier, and J. Walker. 2015a. Connecting patients and clinicians: The anticipated effects of open notes on patient safety and quality of care. *The Joint Commission Journal on Quality and Patient Safety* 41(8):378–384.

Bell, S. K. 2015b. Partnering with Patients for Safety: The OpenNotes Patient Reporting Tool. Poster presentation at the Annual Meeting, Society of General Internal Medicine (SGIM), Toronto, April 2015.

Berman, M., and A. Fenaughty. 2005. Technology and managed care: Patient benefits of telemedicine in a rural health care network. *Health Economics* 14(6):559–573. doi: 10.1002/hec.952.

Delbanco, T., J. Walker, S. K. Bell, J. D. Darer, J. G. Elmore, N. Farag, H. J. Feldman, R. Mejilla, L. Ngo, J. D. Ralston, S. E. Ross, N. Trivedi, E. Vodicka, and S. G. Leveille. 2012. Inviting patients to read their doctors' notes: A year's experience and a look ahead. *Annals of Internal Medicine* 157(7):461–470. doi: 10.7326/0003–4819-157–7-201210020–00002.

Hailey, D., R. Roine, and A. Ohinmaa. 2002. Systematic review of evidence for the benefits of telemedicine. *Journal of Telemedicine and Telecare* 8(Suppl 1):1–7. doi: 10.1258/1357633021937604.

IOM. 2012. *The role of telehealth in an evolving health care environment: Workshop summary.* Washington, DC: The National Academies Press. doi: 10.17226/13466.

IOM. 2013a. *Best care at lower cost: The path to continuously learning health care in America.* Washington, DC: The National Academies Press. doi: 10.17226/13444.

IOM. 2013b. *Health literacy: Improving health, health systems, and health policy around the world: Workshop summary.* Washington, DC: The National Academies Press. doi: 10.17226/18325.

Jethwani, K., E. Ling, M. Mohammed, K. Myint-U, A. Pelletier, and J. C. Kvedar. 2012. Diabetes connect: An evaluation of patient adoption and engagement in a web-based remote glucose monitoring program. *Journal of Diabetes Science and Technology* 6(6):1328–1336. doi: 10.1177/193229681200600611.

Keely, E., C. Liddy C, and A. Afkham. 2013. Utilization, benefits, and impact of an e-consultation service across diverse specialties and primary care providers. *Telemedicine and e-Health* 19(10):733–738. doi: 10.1089/tmj.2013.0007.

Squires, D., and C. Anderson. 2015, October. *U.S. health care from a global perspective: Spending, use of services, prices, and health in 13 countries.* The Commonwealth Fund.

Topol, E. 2015. *The patient will see you now.* New York: Basic Books.

Watson, A. J., K. Singh, K. Myint-U, R.W. Grant, K. Jethwani, E. Murachver, K. Harris, T.H. Lee, J.C. Kvedar. 2012. Evaluating a web-based, self-management program for employees with hypertension and prehypertension: A randomized clinical trial. *American Heart Journal* 164(4):625–631. doi: 10.1016/j.ahj.2012.06.013.

AUTHOR INFORMATION

Paul C. Tang, MD, MS, is Vice President, Chief Health Transformation Officer, IBM Watson Health. **Mark D. Smith, MD, MBA,** is Clinical Professor of Medicine, University of California, San Francisco. **Julia Adler-Milstein, PhD,** is Assistant Professor, School of Information, University of Michigan. **Tom Delbanco, MD,** is Richard A. and Florence Koplaw-James L. Tullis Professor of General Medicine and Primary Care, Beth Israel Deaconess Medical Center. **Stephen J. Downs, SM,** is Chief Technology and Information Officer, Robert Wood Johnson Foundation. **Giridhar G. Mallya, MD, MS,** is Senior Policy Officer, Robert Wood Johnson Foundation. **Debra L. Ness, MS,** is President, National Partnership for Women & Families. **Ruth M. Parker, MD,** is Professor of Medicine, Emory University School of Medicine. **Danny Z. Sands, MD, MPH,** is Senior Vice President, Chief Medical Officer, Conversa Health.

15

WORKFORCE FOR 21ST-CENTURY HEALTH AND HEALTH CARE

Steven H. Lipstein, MHA, Arthur L. Kellermann, MD, MPH, Bobbie Berkowitz, PhD, RN, Robert Phillips, MD, MSPH, David Sklar, MD, Glenn D. Steele Jr., MD, PhD, and George E. Thibault, MD

America's health and health care workforce is made up of people in many occupations, generally categorized as clinicians and people in technical and supporting occupations. Health care accounts for one-fifth of jobs in America; according to the Bureau of Labor Statistics, health care occupations will constitute the fastest-growing occupational segment in the next decade, accounting for one-fourth of new jobs (BLS, 2016). In this perspective, we do not attempt a quantitative assessment of the size or distribution of the American health and health care workforce or of the numerous studies and projections of workforce supply and demand (AAMC, 2016; US nursing workforce, 2014). Rather, we examine the roles, relationships, and capabilities of today's health and health care workforce and how they must evolve to serve the needs of the American people better throughout the 21st century.

Today, our health care system is in the midst of a transition from the traditional fee-for-service approach toward value-based models of care delivery. This reformation of care delivery and management is intended to make care more patient-centric and person-centric while reining in health care costs by keeping people healthy, reducing unnecessary treatment and duplication of services, emphasizing smooth continuity of care within and among sites, and improving the alignment between clinical need and delivery site.

In value-based models, health care providers are paid on the basis of keeping healthy patients healthy while caring for and improving the health of those suffering from acute and chronic illness with cost-effective and evidence-based treatments. Successfully executing those models and achieving the high level of efficiency intended requires not only seamless coordination among care providers but integrated approaches to care centered on the specific needs of individual patients and segments of the patient population that have similar health conditions and characteristics. Health care organizations, assuming the risk for both health outcomes and costs, are increasingly using patient-targeting models (in which the patient population is stratified according to health risk and care use) to deliver efficient and effective care.

It is increasingly clear that the current health care system is not generally organized to serve the many patient subpopulations that exist. Notably, there is neither an operating model nor a financing model that allows a single doctor to discharge adequately and simultaneously the responsibilities of promoting population health, treating major episodes of illness and injury, delivering chronic-disease care optimally, and attending to the special needs of patients at the end of their lives. To deliver efficient and high-quality care, the US health care workforce will need to be organized to be responsive to the needs of individual patients.

To deliver integrated care within these clinical clusters, the US health system will need to recruit, educate, and sustain a diverse health and health care workforce that is comfortable working collaboratively in interdisciplinary teams, is technically skilled, and is adept at harnessing the capabilities of modern health information technology.

In identifying the vital directions for the future of America's health and health care workforce, we examine the vital health and health care needs of broad segments of the American populace with particular attention to characteristics of health status and corresponding health care use:

- People who are generally healthy and experience only intermittent and minor episodes of illness or injury, including those who need maternity and perinatal services for healthy newborns.
- People experiencing acute and major episodes of illness and injury.
- People who have significant chronic medical and behavioral conditions, especially those who have multiple, co-occurring conditions.
- People approaching the end of their natural lifespan who have unique and special health care needs, regardless of their status with respect to a particular diagnosis.

THE POPULATION IN GOOD HEALTH: A WORKFORCE TO KEEP PEOPLE HEALTHY AND TO PROMOTE POPULATION HEALTH

Since 1900, Americans' life expectancy has increased by more than 30 years, more than about three-fourths of which can be attributed to public health (Bunker et al., 1994). In productivity terms, that clearly is an impressive record for public health and prevention and underscores the potential for better health and lower costs. Healthy people consume far less health care than people who are seriously ill or injured. A study published in 2012 determined that half the US population accounts for only 2.7 percent of annual health care expenditures of $1.35 trillion (Cohen, 2014). The healthy half of Medicare beneficiaries uses less than 4 percent of program spending whereas the sickest 5 percent consume 43 percent of program spending (CBO, 2005). A recent population-health study in the province of Ontario, Canada, found a similar distribution of use: the health care expenditures of the healthiest 50 percent of the population accounted for 2.9 percent of overall spending (Wodchis et al., 2016). Moreover, there was stability of that group: only 3.5 percent of the group moved into the top 10 percent of spending in either of the 2 years after the initial study period.

Risks and opportunities are inherent in focusing on the half of the US population that has low health care spending. The "healthy half" is not typically studied, because it does not account for a substantial amount of health care spending per capita, but it does consist of about 162 million people. Promoting and sustaining the health of that group and expanding its size could have dramatic downstream effects on health care spending in the United States (McGinnis et al., 2002). To engage the members of the group and, ideally, to grow their numbers, we need understand the behavioral, biomedical, social, and environmental factors that result in the greatest health benefit. That will enable us to construct a health workforce capable of developing new and effective ways to promote both individual and population health, discourage harmful behaviors, and deliver cost-effective preventive services (IOM, 2003).

Committing to that vision will require a new way of thinking about how we measure and track health status. If we think about health status as an integration of individual-health data and metrics that track the health of populations, much work will be needed to develop and test evidence-based measures of overall health (IOM, 2015a). The goal is to engage not only individuals but also groups and communities in establishing and supporting the services and environments that, early in life, set the stage for long-term health prospects throughout the lifespan (IOM, 2000).

A workforce committed to improving population health will require new roles and expertise outside the traditional boundaries of public health. McGinnis et al. have described the relative contributions of several domains to early mortality in the United States: genetics, 30 percent; social circumstances, 15 percent; environmental exposures, 5 percent; behavioral choices, 40 percent; and shortfalls in medical care, 10 percent (McGinnis et al., 2002). A workforce oriented toward health promotion and health protection will need skills in assessing and addressing social determinants of health, will need knowledge of effective prevention strategies, and will need the ability to communicate (using both traditional and nontraditional media) to engage an increasingly skeptical public.

In addition to population-health skills, the workforce will need preventive-medicine skills. The US Preventive Services Task Force (USPSTF) recommends a variety of tests or examinations that can help to set priorities for the efforts of this future workforce (USPSTF, 2002). For example, the USPSTF recommends mammography for women 40 years old and older every 1–2 years. It also recommends a one-time screening for abdominal aortic aneurysm for men 65–75 years old who have ever smoked. Those recommended screening examinations are now covered by most insurance plans without cost sharing (Health policy brief, 2010). The professional roles associated with keeping people healthy and understanding the risks associated with disease will require expertise in a broad array of topics.

The workforce to assume those roles and provide those services will include not only physicians and nurses but public health and community health workers. Public health is labor-intensive work, especially in low-income and disadvantaged communities. Physicians constitute the most expensive type of health care manpower. In the future, the task of health promotion and protection will increasingly use teams of registered nurses and nurse practitioners, physician assistants, behavioral-health specialists, social workers, informaticists, technologists, pharmacists, nutritionists, and others. New roles may emerge as well. For more than 45 years, Americans have entrusted their prehospital medical care to paramedics and emergency medical technicians, who are remotely supervised by licensed physician medical directors. The day may come when telemedicine-enabled "primary-care technicians" equipped with smartphones or tablet computers work the same way (Kellermann et al., 2013).

Many intermittent illnesses, such as upper respiratory infections, affecting those who are generally healthy are time limited and may be managed by the patient or family with telehealth advice. Locations for accessing services may include the Internet, pharmacy or big-box, retail-based clinics, and urgent-care centers in addition to traditional primary care, hospital outpatient clinics, and health departments. Although members of the healthy population are not heavy users of care, ready access to their medical home should be ensured through telehealth, remotely supervised members of the primary care team, or, if required, office visits. Otherwise, delays in care will undermine patients' confidence in the effectiveness of the health care system and drive them to seek care outside their medical home.

If we want to expand the proportion of the population that remains in good health for the vast majority of their lifespan, we will need to train workforces that are comfortable in working in cooperative teams and at the interfaces of health care, behavioral interventions, social services, and even the justice system. That will require educational pathways and evidence-based practice guidelines to train and support a new generation of health and health care workers—dedicated professionals who are prepared to deliver excellent and affordable preventive care to individuals, families, and entire communities.

THE POPULATION THAT HAS ACUTE ILLNESS OR INJURY: A WORKFORCE TO CARE FOR PEOPLE WHO EXPERIENCE MAJOR EPISODES OF ILLNESS OR INJURY

Despite effective health-promotion and injury-prevention programs, a substantial minority of Americans will continue to experience unexpected serious health events (such as a very premature birth, cancer, or a serious injury due to a fall or car crash). Others will develop one or more common chronic conditions (such as hypertension) that, if improperly managed or ignored, could progress to cardiovascular disease, stroke, cancer, respiratory disorders, or kidney failure. America's future health and health care workforce will need providers who can manage those problems thoughtfully, skillfully, and compassionately without the fragmentation and discontinuities of care that bedevil many health care encounters today.

Some aspects of medical care can be managed only with complex or technically demanding procedures, so we will always need an adequate supply of highly trained and skilled specialist physicians, nurses, and other expert providers. However, there are worrisome signs of a looming shortage of some specialist physicians and a chronic shortage of registered nurses in primary care. Even now, as our nation's population grows and the baby-boom generation ages, increasing numbers of experienced health care professionals are approaching retirement age. It is not clear how we will replace them with the current nursing-school infrastructure (largely a shortage of nurse educators and insufficient clinical placements) and a fixed number of Medicare-funded, graduate, medical-education residency positions. As we proceed further into the 21st century, we will confront an aging population and society's growing expectation of a fully functional, longer life. Those trends foreshadow a continuing need for specialty and subspecialty expertise in the care of patients who have acute illness or severe injury. Educating our future workforce to deal with major illness and injury will continue to be a public necessity regardless of possible changes in how workforce training occurs, where it occurs, and who funds it (IOM, 2014).

Several caveats make the projection of specialty and subspecialty manpower highly uncertain. First, and perhaps most important, there will be continuous reengineering of who does what during episodes of acute care. The historical disciplined-centered argument over which specialty is "in charge" will give way to an approach focused on achieving optimal team performance and reproducible results at the lowest cost. That approach will be increasingly important as payment shifts from fee-for-service reimbursement to paying for bundles (episodes) of work, partial or full capitation, and global budgets.

Second, care that was traditionally confined to hospital venues will expand to include the acute and postacute continuum. That is already happening with outpatient surgery and with prehospital performance of electrocardiography and initiation of acute care by paramedics. In the future, posthospital care will also grow and be delivered by visiting nurses and "community paramedicine." Individual episodes of care, such as joint replacements, are already expanding to encompass preparation before hospitalization, acute care, and rehabilitation after hospital discharge. Care redesign will increasingly engage caregivers who were not previously involved in the acute intervention process. It will also sometimes compel judicious and targeted involvement by highly specialized interventionalists. Those changes will necessarily affect undergraduate and graduate medical and nursing education and increase the importance of training in interdisciplinary practice.

Third, regionalization of care, in which health care institutions within a defined geographic area are centrally organized and managed, may reduce the number of interventional specialists that are needed. If regional health systems and state-based trauma-care and emergency-care networks start to funnel their most challenging cases to a smaller number of high-performing centers, the result may be the high procedural volumes needed to produce more consistent high-quality outcomes than currently occur in many densely served and highly competitive markets (IOM, 2010).

Finally, the relationship between those who give and those who receive care, even in acute-care settings, will evolve as patients become more active participants in their health care. That will affect not only how care is provided but who provides it. It may also influence how much care is deemed worthwhile (not only by providers but by patients and their families). As standardized outcome data become more publicly available and better understood by patients and purchasers, the choice of providers will increasingly be driven by objective information about quality and price rather than by a vague sense of "reputation." That will also require the availability of those who will be able to translate applications of the information and tools for direct personal management of care choice and processes.

All those societal and technologic changes will put pressure on the regulatory and self-regulatory (disciplined-based) structures that until now have effectively maintained the status quo. Regulatory-policy change may be necessary to facilitate needed progress in care delivery. With so many intersecting forces in play, estimating future manpower needs will be a dynamic and ever-more-complex task. We remain convinced, however, that caring for others will continue to be an extraordinarily popular and well-regarded component of our social and economic enterprise.

THE POPULATION THAT HAS CHRONIC DISEASE AND MULTIPLE COMORBIDITIES: A WORKFORCE TO SERVE PEOPLE WHO HAVE CHRONIC MEDICAL OR BEHAVIORAL CONDITIONS

This group includes people who have medical conditions that are not curable but can be treated for and managed so that they can lead productive lives with reasonable hope of normal life expectancy. It includes those who live in a chronic state of difficult life circumstances caused by low income, poor education, unstable housing, food deprivation, obesity, mobility restrictions, and substance abuse.

Although the future "chronic-condition" workforce will have much in common with the workforce that focuses on health promotion, those who focus on chronic-disease care will be expected to develop sustained relationships with chronic-disease patients and family caregivers even in the absence of acute illness or injury. Those relationships matter because patients and family caregivers are essential partners in the caregiving team.

The cases of patients who have chronic conditions are inherently complex. That is particularly true of those who have multiple health problems, those who have comorbid behavioral health issues (mental health or substance-abuse conditions), and those whose conditions are compounded by adverse health determinants. Management of complexity often requires the collective expertise of a team of problem solvers that are attuned to the social, physical, and economic conditions in which their patients live. To meet the needs of the growing number of patients who have multiple chronic conditions or behavioral health issues, we need a health care workforce that looks and behaves differently from the current one and is linked and integrated by team skills, communication strategies, and technology tools in a much more effective fashion.

In 2010, half the US noninstitutionalized adult population had at least one chronic condition, and half of these had two or more chronic conditions (Ward and Schiller, 2013). In 2012, one-tenth of adults said that they felt sad, and one-sixth had felt nervous or restless in the preceding 30 days; these rates were doubled or worse in poor people (Blackwell and Clark, 2014). People who have chronic disease compounded by behavioral health problems are more expensive to treat, and the poor and uninsured are more likely to have both. Having multiple chronic conditions reduces quality of life, but having a comorbid behavioral disorder lowers it substantially more (Mujica-Mota et al., 2015). Many people have demonstrated that outcomes are better if management of physical and behavioral conditions is integrated and care is delivered by a multidisciplinary team (Bodenheimer et al., 2009; Mujica-Mota et al., 2015). Capacity to manage the growth in complex care while holding costs down depends on the development of multidisciplinary teams capable of delivering comprehensive care, particularly in primary care settings (Bodenheimer et al., 2009; Sinsky et al., 2013).

Those findings have important implications for educating health professionals to provide care for our nation's neediest consumers. First, they must be educated interprofessionally to have the skills needed to work effectively in teams and practice collaboratively (Reeves et al., 2013). Accordingly, health professionals in training must have frequent and reinforcing experiences with learners in the other health professions. That is the only practical way to prepare doctors, nurses, and other health professionals to work effectively in teams to deliver the care that patients who have chronic diseases need. Second, those experiences must be less hospital based and instead based more in the community to align with the needs of patients (IOM, 1989, 2014). Training should also be longitudinal and immersive. Third, health-workforce education needs to become more efficient and flexible. Regulations should allow individualization of training, interprofessional teaching, and multidisciplinary supervision to model a future built around collaborative care. In the future, interdisciplinary teams should have these features:

- Continuity should be provided through teams rather than reliance only on individual physicians or nurse practitioners. Within interdisciplinary teams, some members will forge sustained healing relationships with patients, and others will provide episodic support (Leleu and Minvielle, 2013). Information technology will enhance continuity and ensure timely access.
- Work should be distributed on the basis of the skills of the team members. Interdisciplinary teams should ensure a broad scope of practice and provide care in all settings, including patients' homes (Bazemore et al., 2015; Mattke et al., 2015). That means having the best person perform specific tasks, adding more team members when needed, and changing the roles of others (Bodenheimer and Sinsky, 2014).
- Case management should be targeted. The multidisciplinary teams will incorporate staff members who track patients' health care visits and social-service

contacts. They will ensure smooth transitions of care from home to hospital and back again, and they will monitor fragile patients closely by using telehealth-enabled community health workers, primary care technicians, and others who come from the communities that they serve (Kangovi et al., 2014; Kellermann et al., 2013). Recruiting team members who have relevant cultural, linguistic, and interpersonal skills will help teams to foster alliances with the patients, families, and communities that they serve. For that reason, the health care workforce of the future must be more diverse and culturally competent than the current one.

Complex patients require the talents and expertise of many who are inter-connected to work as one team of problem solvers who not only manage patients' medical conditions but also address behavioral health and poor social conditions. Being organized in this way will help the team to improve care for individuals, achieve better health for populations, and lower the cost of care (Berwick et al., 2008).

THE POPULATION FACING DEATH AND DYING: A WORKFORCE TO CARE FOR PEOPLE AT THE END OF LIFE

Sooner or later, each of us faces the reality of death as an inescapable part of the human experience. In the United States, the number of elderly people who have comorbidities, frailties, and co-occurring physical and cognitive disabilities is growing rapidly (IOM, 2015b). Yet many patients who have incurable conditions either have not considered or are unprepared to make decisions about their end-of-life care options. While the education and training of palliative-care and hospice-care professionals have improved greatly in the past two decades, the number of these specialists has remained small, so many patients receive their end-of-life care from other clinicians—typically those who treat advanced illness but lack specialized training in hospice and palliative care (IOM, 2015b). Policies that facilitate the education of providers who work with patients about their end-of-life options and are skilled in delivering palliative medicine and hospice care would offer an important source of comfort and support for patients and loved ones near the end of life.

VITAL DIRECTIONS

As the US health care system transitions to value-based models of care, health care organizations are increasingly turning to population-stratification approaches to deliver care that is targeted, effective, and efficient. The United States will need a workforce that is responsive to that reformation of care delivery and management and that is organized and trained to address the needs not only of individual patients but also of specific segments of the patient population. On the basis of our assessment of the health and health care needs of four critical patient populations—those in good health, those who are facing acute illness and injury, those who have chronic diseases and multiple comorbidities, and those at the end of life—we offer the following vital directions for the future health care workforce:

1. **Assess and ensure the sufficiency of the front-line health care workforce.** American health policy must continue to support a growing health care workforce devoted to keeping people healthy and to promoting population health. The ideal workforce to fulfill this mandate is diverse—geographically, racially, ethnically, and religiously—and multidisciplinary. It consists of physicians, physician assistants, registered nurses, social workers, nutritionists, exercise physiologists, and public health and other health professionals. Organized into multidisciplinary teams, these professionals can use technology to reengineer health care delivery, enhance community-based health practices, extend the reach of clinicians, and increase access to care, particularly in isolated and rural communities. With expanded access to telehealth applications, the healthy population would no longer be constrained to receiving needed services at fixed sites of practice. People who experience minor episodes of illness or injury and who do not require a clinical procedure or access to expensive diagnostic and treatment technology could be managed more conveniently and less expensively close to home. Examples of telehealth services in Arkansas and New Mexico have demonstrated that patients need not travel long distances to achieve optimal primary care outcomes (Arora et al., 2007; Lowery et al., 2014).

2. **Ensure an acute-care workforce that can provide timely accessibility.** The health care workforce serving patients who experience major episodes of illness and injury must reconstitute and reorganize to achieve better outcomes at lower cost. Serving patients who experience major episodes of illness and injury is expensive. It involves clinicians who have received many years of expensive education and training. Often, the care of such patients involves expensive technology, medicines, and long periods of treatment and recovery.

   Reconstitution and reorganization of this segment of the health care workforce should aim to foster the regionalization and better targeting of these services. There is abundant evidence that in treatment of patients who have malignancies, stroke, or cardiac conditions, demonstrable value is associated with bringing patients to the right place at the right time for the right reason quickly and efficiently. Regionalization of care will ensure that this segment of the health care workforce is serving enough patients to sustain skills, achieve optimal outcomes, and support high-quality training programs (IOM, 2010).

3. **Develop the clinical and social service teams required to manage high-need chronic conditions.** The health care workforce serving patients who live with chronic medical and behavioral conditions must be interdisciplinary and team based and be organized around the unique needs and life circumstances of individual patients. Health care professionals serving patients who have chronic medical conditions encounter a more difficult medical-management challenge when the patients live in poverty or have mental health comorbidity. Chronic illness is also more complicated to treat when associated with obesity, substance abuse, or physical disability. Chronic-care management and individual life circumstances are inextricably linked. To serve patients effectively and to achieve optimal health outcomes, the workforce must have the collective education, skills, and capacity to help patients to live with their chronic conditions.

Diverse, interdisciplinary workforce teams that include community health workers, primary care technicians, and other occupational groups are needed for the effective health management of patients who have complex chronic diseases. Ideally, the teams would be characterized by high levels of integration, continuing engagement with patients and family caregivers in the absence of acute episodes, and adoption of home monitoring technologies to prevent expensive hospital admissions and avoidable visits to the emergency department. Practice-support services, in the model of the US Department of Agriculture Cooperative Extension, could facilitate team-based care, and related demonstrations are under way (Bielaszka-DuVernay, 2011; Phillips et al., 2013), as exemplified by the HERO program developed by the University of New Mexico's Health Sciences Center.

4. **Train the caregiver workforce so important at the end of life.** America needs to make a "human" investment in health and health care professionals who serve patients at the end of their natural lifespan.

About 3 million Americans die each year. For too long we have attempted to serve the end-of-life care needs of patients as an extension of the workforce that provides care for those who have advanced illness. Training and supporting more palliative-care and hospice-care professionals would reduce our reliance on health care professionals whose skills and talents are best suited to caring for those who are suffering from acute or advanced illness or chronic disease. With added capacity in palliative care and hospice care, America can provide people with the end-of-life experience that each person desires, more often in a home or other noninstitutional setting.

SUMMARY RECOMMENDATIONS FOR VITAL DIRECTIONS

1. Assess and ensure the sufficiency of the frontline health care workforce.
2. Ensure an acute care workforce that can provide timely accessibility.
3. Develop the clinical and social service teams required to manage high-need chronic conditions.
4. Train the caregiver workforce so important at the end of life.

REFERENCES

Arora, S., K. Thornton, S. M. Jenkusky, B. Parish, and J. V. Scaletti. 2007. Project ECHO: Linking university specialists with rural and prison-based clinicians to improve care for people with chronic hepatitis C in New Mexico. *Public Health Reports* 122(Suppl 2):74–77.

AAMC (Association of American Medical Colleges). 2016. The complexities of physician supply and demand: Projections from 2014 to 2025. Available at http://www.aamc.org/download/458082/data/2016_complexities_of_supply_and_demand_projections.pdf (accessed June 14, 2016).

Bazemore, A., S. Petterson, L. E. Peterson, and R. L. Phillips. 2015. More comprehensive care among family physicians is associated with lower costs and fewer hospitalizations. *Annals of Family Medicine* 13(3):206–213.

Berwick, D. M., T. W. Nolan, amd J. Whittington. 2008. The triple aim: Care, health, and cost. *Health Affairs* 27(3):759–769.

Bielaszka-DuVernay, C. 2011. Vermont's blueprint for medical homes, community health teams, and better health at lower cost. *Health Affairs* 30(3):383–386.

Blackwell, D. L., J. W. Lucas, and T. C. Clarke. 2014. Summary health statistics for U.S. adults: National Health Interview Survey, 2012. In Statistics, Vol. 10. Washington, DC: National Center for Health Statistics.

BLS (US Bureau of Labor Statistics). 2016. *Healthcare occupations: Occupational outlook handbook: U.S. Bureau of Labor Statistics.* Available at http://www.bls.gov/ooh/healthcare/mobile/home.htm (accessed June 14, 2016).

Bodenheimer, T., and C. Sinsky. 2014. From triple to quadruple aim: Care of the patient requires care of the provider. *Annals of Family Medicine* 12(6): 573–576.

Bodenheimer, T., E. Chen, and H. D. Bennett. 2009. Confronting the growing burden of chronic disease: Can the U.S. health care workforce do the job? *Health Affairs* 28(1):64–74.

Bunker, J. P., H. S. Frazier, and F. Mosteller. 1994. Improving health: Measuring the effects of medical care. *The Milbank Quarterly* 72:225–258.

CBO (Congressional Budget Office). 2005. *High-Cost Medicare Beneficiaries.* Washington, DC: Congressional Budget Office. https://www.cbo.gov/sites/default/files/cbofiles/ftpdocs/63xx/doc6332/05–03-medispending.pdf.

Cohen, S. B. 2014, October. The Concentration of Health Expenditures and Related Expenses for Costly Medical Conditions, 2012. Statistical Brief 455, Medical Expenditure Panel Survey. Rockville, MD: AHRQ. Available at https://www.meps.ahrq.gov/mepsweb/data_files/publications/st455/stat455.pdf (accessed August 22, 2016).

Health policy brief: Preventive services without cost sharing. 2010. *Health Affairs.* Available at http://www.healthaffairs.org/healthpolicybriefs/brief_pdfs/healthpolicybrief_37.pdf.

IOM (Institute of Medicine). 1989. *Primary care physicians: Financing their graduate medical education in ambulatory settings.* Washington, DC: National Academy Press.

IOM. 2000. *Promoting health: Intervention strategies from social and behavioral research.* Washington, DC: National Academy Press.

IOM. 2003. *Who will keep the public healthy: Educating public health professionals for the 21st century.* Washington, DC: The National Academies Press.

IOM. 2010. *Regionalizing emergency care: Workshop summary.* Washington, DC: The National Academies Press.

IOM. 2014. *Graduate Medical Education That Meets the Nation's Health Needs.* Washington, DC: The National Academies Press. doi: 10.17226/18754.

IOM. 2015a. *Vital signs: Core metrics for health and health care progress.* Washington, DC: The National Academies Press.

IOM. 2015b. *Dying in America: Improving quality and honoring individual preferences near the end of life.* Washington, DC: The National Academies Press. doi: 10.17226/18748.

Kangovi, S., N. Mitra, D. Grande, M.L. White, S. McCollum, J.Sellman, R.P. Shannon, and J.A. Long. 2014. Patient-centered community health worker intervention to improve posthospital outcomes: A randomized clinical trial. *JAMA Internal Medicine* 174(4):535–543.

Kellermann, A. L., J. Saultz, A. Mehrotra, S. S. Jones, and S. Dalal. 2013. Primary care technicians: A solution to the primary care workforce gap. *Health Affairs* 32(11):1893–1898.

Leleu, H., and E. Minvielle. 2013. Relationship between longitudinal continuity of primary care and likelihood of death: Analysis of national insurance data. *PLoS One* 8(8):e71669.

Lowery, C. L., J. M. Bronstein, T. L. Benton, and D. A. Fletcher. 2014. Distributing medical expertise: The evolution and impact of telemedicine in Arkansas. *Health Affairs* 33(2):235–243.

Mattke, S., D. Han, A. Wilks, and E. Sloss. 2015. Medicare home visit program associated with fewer hospital and nursing home admissions, increased office visits. *Health Affairs* 34(12):2138–2146.

McGinnis, J. M., P. Williams-Russo, and J. R. Knickman. 2002. The case for more active policy attention to health promotion. *Health Affairs* 21:78–93.

Mujica-Mota, R. E., M. Roberts, G. Abel, M. Elliott, G. Lyratzopoulos, M. Roland, and J. Campbell. 2015. Common patterns of morbidity and multi-morbidity and their impact on health-related quality of life: Evidence from a national survey. *Quality of Life Research* 24(4):909–918.

Phillips, R. L., A. Kaufman, J. W. Mold, K. Grumbauch, M. Vetter-Smith, A. Berry, and B. Teevan Burke. 2013. The Primary Care Extension Program: A catalyst for change. *Annals of Family Medicine* 11(2):173–178.

Reeves, S., L. Perrier, J. Goldman, D. Freeth, and M. Zwarenstein. 2013. Interprofessional education: Effects on professional practice and healthcare outcomes (update). *Cochrane Database of Systematic Reviews* 2013(3).

Sinsky, C. A., R. Willard-Grace, A. M. Schutzbank, T. A. Sinsky, D. Margolius, and T. Bodenheimer. 2013. In search of joy in practice: A report of 23 high-functioning primary care practices. *Annals of Family Medicine* 11(3):272–278.

The U.S. Nursing Workforce: Trends in Supply and Education-results in brief. 2014. *American Nurse Today* 9(6) https://www.americannursetoday.com/the-u-s-nursing-workforce-trends-in-supply-and-education-results-in-brief/ (accessed June 14, 2016).

USPSTF (US Preventive Services Task Force). 2016, February. USPSTF A and B recommendations. Available at http://www.uspreventiveservicestaskforce.org/Page/Name/uspsty-a-and--b-recommendations/ (accessed June 14, 2016).

Ward, B. W., and J. S. Schiller. 2013. Prevalence of multiple chronic conditions among US adults: Estimates from the National Health Interview Survey, 2010. *Preventing Chronic Disease* 10:E65.

Wodchis, W. P., P. C. Austin, and D. A. Henry. 2016. A 3-year study of high-cost users of health care. *Canadian Medical Association Journal* 188(3). doi: 10.1503/cmaj.150064.

AUTHOR INFORMATION

Steven H. Lipstein, MHA, is President and CEO, BJC HealthCare. **Arthur L. Kellermann,** MD, MPH, is Professor and Dean, F. Edward Hebert School of Medicine, Uniformed Services University of the Health Sciences. **Bobbie Berkowitz, PhD, RN,** is Dean, School of Nursing, Columbia University. **Robert Phillips, MD, MSPH,** is Vice President, Research and Policy, American Board of Family Medicine. **David Sklar, MD,** is Distinguished Professor Emeritus, Department of Emergency Medicine, University of New Mexico. **Glenn D. Steele Jr., MD, PhD,** is Chairman, xG Health Solutions. **George E. Thibault, MD,** is President, The Josiah Macy Jr. Foundation.

PART III

STRONG SCIENCE AND TECHNOLOGY

16

INFORMATION TECHNOLOGY INTEROPERABILITY AND USE FOR BETTER CARE AND EVIDENCE

Jonathan B. Perlin, MD, PhD, Dixie B. Baker, PhD, David J. Brailer, MD, PhD, Douglas B. Fridsma, MD, PhD, Mark E. Frisse, MD, John. D. Halamka, MD, PhD, Jeffrey Levi, PhD, Kenneth D. Mandl, MD, MPH, Janet M. Marchibroda, MBA, Richard Platt, MD, MS, and Paul C. Tang, MD, MS

Health information technology (HIT) has been seen as a vehicle for improving the quality and safety of health care, for gaining more accountability and value in purchasing, for advancing the role and engagement of consumers in prevention and health decisions, for accelerating discovery and dissemination of new treatments, and for sharpening public health monitoring and surveillance. HIT has had high priority in the health care system under two presidential administrations, and it continues to enjoy strong bipartisan support at the state and federal levels.

When the federal HIT effort was launched in 2004 (The White House, 2004), four overriding national priorities were articulated: providing information tools, such as electronic health records (EHRs), to clinicians for use in patient care; connecting health information so that it follows patients throughout care and can be aggregated to advance health care delivery; supporting consumers with information to help them to manage their care; and advancing public health, clinical trials, and other data-intensive activities. The 2004 HIT plan has been updated three times (in 2009, 2011, and 2015), but the core priorities remain similar.

The first national goal for HIT has been largely realized. Nearly all hospitals use EHRs to manage patient care (ONC, 2015a), as do growing numbers of physician practices, ancillary care facilities, and other sites of care (ONC, 2015b). There is widespread recognition that it is infeasible to operate a complex health care business today without having EHRs and other point-of-care information tools available for clinicians.

The other three goals of the HIT plan have not been realized. Efforts to aggregate and share information for specific patients longitudinally among providers have been aggressively pursued with some success but have been hindered by financial conflicts, proprietary barriers, legacy technology, obsolete regulations, and other challenges. Personalized consumer health information, although enjoying some advances in the form of portals and other online access tools, has not become widely used by consumers for a variety of reasons, including a lack of functionality and interoperability. Likewise, data-intensive sectors of health care—such as clinical trials, public health surveillance, and quality measurement—have not transformed their methods and rules to take advantage of the ubiquity of electronic health information.

Numerous detailed studies have shown how HIT can yield value through information availability, prompts, guidelines, and other decision influencers. However, no studies have shown a favorable aggregated effect of HIT throughout the industry. Indeed, studies in the last decade that have forecasted substantial savings from HIT investment have been called into question as overoptimistic. Yet, nearly all expectations for change in the health care system articulated today rely in some way on HIT and health care information.

As the adoption of EHRs slows and federal incentives through the Health Information Technology for Economic and Clinical Health Act wind down, substantial discussion is under way about how to reset the HIT agenda. Having considered the numerous options for major federal goals for HIT over the next 5 years, we have identified nine central themes in three focus areas:

- **Focus Area 1: Technical underpinnings**
  Key Issue 1: Data standards and achieving interoperability at scale
  Key Issue 2: Interoperability with consumer health technology
  Key Issue 3: Improving patient identification and matching to support interoperability
  Key Issue 4: Service-oriented architectures and Web-based services
- **Focus Area 2: Use cases**
  Key Issue 5: Enfranchising vulnerable populations and improving care for chronic disease
  Key Issue 6: Health data and public health
  Key Issue 7: Accelerating use of aggregated health information and research
- **Focus Area 3: Enablers**
  Key Issue 8: Building a HIT workforce
  Key Issue 9: Creating a trust fabric for health services: privacy and security

Federal policymakers should recognize that information technology will bring massive changes to health care with or without further government action. The changes will be driven by adoption of technology throughout our society, rapid changes in HIT innovation, and economic pressures on health care. Instead of increasing the pace of HIT or picking the more advantageous innovations, policy and policymakers should ensure that the changes that are already under way improve utility and advance the broader principles that the United States maintains for safe, privacy-preserving, equitable, responsive, high-quality, and cost-effective health care.

KEY ISSUES

Data Standards and Achieving Interoperability at Scale

Many have concluded that the Meaningful Use goals of improved quality, safety, and efficiency cannot be reached until more data are shared for more purposes, with sharing integrated into the routine, health care–delivery workflow. As currently designed, HIT and the applicable regulations can slow the routine provision of health care. Enablers of efficiency—such as accurate, transparent, and actionable payer information available at the point of care; the ability to reuse structured health information for health care operations and administration; and documentation well suited for care in the 21st century—could help to achieve efficiency goals. Sharing data more broadly can enhance care coordination, ensuring that patients' lifetime medical records travel among all providers. Redundant and unnecessary testing can be reduced. Physician orders for life-sustaining treatment can be communicated broadly. One estimate suggests that $80 billion could be saved annually if a comprehensive program of EHR data sharing was widely implemented (Hillestad et al., 2005).

Opportunities and Policy Alternatives

Data standards are necessary but not sufficient for interoperability. Supporting infrastructure, policies, and incentives to share data are the rate-limiting elements.

- *Patient identification.* Aggregating patient data among organizations requires uniquely identifying each patient; an exact match of first name, last name, and date of birth is often not specific enough to be useful or safe. The country needs a voluntary national health care identifier, possibly modeled after the Transportation Security Administration Pre Global Entry program, that could provide patients a number to be used among disparate institutions to share their health care information with consent. (See also Key Issue 3.)

- *Provider directory.* There is no national provider directory that contains the electronic addresses of clinicians and hospitals for exchanging health care information, and this complicates the delivery of electronic data. The Centers for Medicare & Medicaid Services could host such an electronic directory, using the National Provider Identifier database as a starting point.
- *Simpler standards for clinical summary exchange.* There are many good standards in health care for clinical summaries, but some are so complex that trained clinical informaticists are needed to generate and parse clinical data summaries. In addition, the available optionality of standards for clinical summaries makes it difficult to engineer a universal import solution. We need a single document standard for clinical summaries with little optionality.
- *Simpler standards for discrete data exchange.* Using simpler standards for discrete data exchange, such as Fast Healthcare Interoperability Resources (FHIR), will enhance data liquidity and enable an ecosystem of new "apps" to evolve. Innovation will accelerate when developers can use agile development methods to create consumer-facing and provider-facing mobile technology that layers onto existing EHRs. The federal government can convene experts and recommend standards that are fit for purpose, but most of the standards' work should take place in the private sector.
- *Data governance.* Every state has different privacy policies that complicate the release and sharing of patient information. We need to rationalize heterogeneous state and local policies for data exchange and use. The federal government could provide a framework or guideline that enables states and localities to reduce the number of variations in data use and reciprocal support agreements. A single national centralized policy is unlikely to be practical in the short term.

Potential Effect and Tracking Benchmarks

The Meaningful Use program was successful in encouraging adoption of EHRs in hospitals and clinician offices, but it did not substantially promote interoperability. If future federal programs focus on enabling infrastructure, creating trust, and streamlining heterogeneous policies, barriers will be reduced and stakeholders will exchange data that support high-value use cases, such as transitions of care, outcomes measurement, and public health reporting. Prescriptive regulations and burdensome certification requirements are not the answer. Creating incentives, such as merit-based payment approaches to use the enablers listed above, will accelerate widespread interoperability.

Overall success can be measured by surveying stakeholders and determining whether their electronic systems are exchanging data in ways that add value in their daily health care activities, including the number of records exchanged by using a national patient identifier, the number of lookups in a national provider-directory infrastructure, the number of new apps available to clinicians that use the standards and support their workflows, and the number of organizations that have successful bidirectional data exchange.

Interoperability with Consumer Health Technology

Historically, health care data systems have been optimized to address specific and localized needs. Administrative data were optimized to reimburse for health care services, medical-records data to document care and to detect adverse drug events, and prescribing and pharmacy systems to fill prescriptions and adjudicate payment. Efforts to standardize health care data have been under way for decades through a number of standards bodies, each addressing different technologies.

Coordination of those efforts has gained momentum only in the last decade as a result of three factors: advances in hardware, software, and network technologies that made interoperability economically feasible; federal mandates, alternative payment models, and programs that support innovative approaches; and public expectations that have led to an array of new consumer-focused products and services seeking to address unmet health needs.

Opportunities

A number of factors, from higher out-of-pocket costs to lack of primary care availability, are driving patient demand for and acceptance of alternative approaches to their care, including the use of retail clinics and a growing catalog of health care products that rely on mobile, "wearable," and home-based technologies. These demands provide both the opportunity and the necessity of a broader view of interoperability among new consumer health technologies and medical devices, traditional and nontraditional health care providers, and other components of our health care system.

Traditional payers and providers face two challenges. They will need to increase their investment in the integration of data to improve care delivery and in measuring the effect of integrated care-management programs. Hospitals in particular will need to focus on ensuring interoperability in their own technologies while addressing postdischarge care in collaboration with payers, families, and other providers. At the same time, payers and providers will need to invest in integration with the emerging consumer health technology market.

Policy Alternatives

Unlike the more traditional, highly regulated health care technologies, new consumer health care products based on mobile or home-based technologies have not yet been constrained by regulatory policies. The new approaches are largely out of the control of any individual entity. Data are managed not by a hospital or health plan but instead by firms new to health care. Security and privacy preservation are not regulated by the Health Insurance Portability and Accountability Act (HIPAA) but instead in accordance with minimal standards set by other agencies. The technologies are driven by consumer demand, not payment mechanisms shaped by federal programs. The market for the new technologies is evolving as buyers and sellers begin to understand their individual and collective value.

Policymakers should create incentive structures that recognize the essential balance between market-based innovations and prescriptive technical standards. We are still experimenting with new approaches, and premature declaration of winners may forestall innovation. Interoperability standards should therefore be incremental so that they can retain a degree of freedom while maintaining core communication standards.

Initially, steps should be taken to ensure that devices at all levels of product maturity are given common data-transmission standards that address public concern about privacy and the market need for effective communication, such as TCP/IP (Transmission Control Protocol and Internet Protocol) with TLS (Transport Layer Security). As new technical innovations and care models become more mature, they should adhere to interoperability standards adopted in hospitals and ambulatory care settings. Respect of data standards is essential for data integration, maintaining data integrity, and ensuring privacy and security. Ultimately, interoperability is a matter of trust best achieved through stronger bonds between informed consumers and their local health care providers.

Standards for application programming interfaces (APIs) into and out of EHRs should be specified. The current HIT certification standards and criteria include certification of an API that enables retrieval of EHR data but that specifies no standards and is not bidirectional. Such standards would support both interoperability among EHRs and interoperability between consumer health technology and EHRs.

Potential Effect and Tracking Benchmarks

Extending interoperability to individuals, their homes, and their personal devices offers the prospect of improvement in health engagement, health behavior, and health-services delivery and the opportunity to measure and improve individual and population health. Benchmarks include the extent to which person-based and mobile technologies can interoperate with one another and with systems used by hospitals and other care providers. Policymakers should proceed cautiously in ways that improve safety and efficiency while markets evolve without impeding innovation that promises even greater long-term benefit.

Improving Patient Identification and Matching to Support Interoperability

Increasing the level of information sharing—supported by the interoperability of systems—requires substantially improved methods for accurately identifying patients and matching their records throughout the health care system. The need for a national strategy for identification and matching has become more urgent in light of the increasingly digitized state of the US health care system and the substantial increase in demands and policies for accelerating electronic information sharing. Actions under way in the private sector can assist in migrating toward a national strategy, but federal action is needed to facilitate accurate identification and matching of patient data to support widespread information sharing and interoperability in the United States.

Opportunities

The most important barrier to a nationwide strategy for patient identification and matching is a law passed by Congress in 1999 that prohibits the US Department of Health and Human Services (HHS) from using any of its funds to develop a unique patient identifier without the express approval of Congress (US Congress, 1998). As a result, HHS has not promulgated policies or standards that would specifically facilitate the matching of patient data among systems. Other barriers to progress include the lack of agreement on and availability of data fields needed for matching and variability in the quality of data used for matching—variability that is due in part to the lack of standards.

The risks associated with the lack of a common patient identification and matching strategy are important. Rates of false-positive and false-negative errors in patient data matching, which a considerable percentage of chief information officers believe exceed the industry standard of 8 percent in their health records (CHIME, 2012), can result in suboptimal care and medical errors. Incorrectly matching a patient to a health record may also have privacy and security implications—such as wrongful disclosure—in addition to the risks associated with treatment that is based on another patient's health information (Bipartisan Policy Center, 2012). The cost and resources associated with addressing matching problems are considerable. One health care system estimated that it could save $4–5 million per year simply by doing a better job of matching records (Conn, 2016). In a recent survey of health information management professionals, 57 percent spent time in sorting through patient-matching duplicates regularly, often weekly (Dooling et al., 2016).

Policy Alternatives

A 2014 report of the Office of the National Coordinator for Health Information Technology (ONC) called for the standardization of specific demographic fields or data elements, the introduction of EHR certification criteria that would require the capture of such data elements according to standards, and broad collaboration on industry best practices to inform policy and practice (Morris et al., 2014). In February 2016, the US Senate Committee on Health, Education, Labor, and Pensions approved S. 2511, the *Improving Health Information Technology Act,* which proposes conducting a Government Accountability Office study to evaluate current patient-matching methods, define additional data elements to assist in matching, agree on a minimum set of elements that need to be collected and exchanged, and require EHRs to have the ability to contain particular fields by using specific standards (US Senate Committee on Health, Education, Labor, and Pensions, 2016).

To accelerate progress toward identification and matching, Congress should continue its efforts to advance accurate patient identification and matching by formally authorizing HHS to adopt and promulgate standards for patient identification and matching. HHS should adopt—through formal rule making—a common set of specific demographic fields or data elements to be used for patient matching in the United States and a common set of standards for such data elements.

Advances in the identification and accurate matching of patient data are also being encouraged by the private sector. The College of Healthcare Information Management Executives (CHIME) recently announced a National Patient ID Challenge with HeroX, offering $1 million in prizes to encourage developers to find a universal solution for accurately matching patients with their health care information (CHIME, 2016). The nonprofit Sequoia Project recently released a framework for cross-organizational patient-identity management (The Sequoia Project, 2016). The private sector should continue to innovate and improve algorithms for matching, building on the common standards adopted by the federal government. Efforts to develop and implement methods for testing and publishing outcomes on the effectiveness of alternative methods should continue.

Potential Effect and Tracking Benchmarks

Advances in patient identification and matching have the potential to reduce the rate of incorrect matching of patients to health records. Likewise, the cost and resources associated with correcting matching problems could be reduced. Those two factors—patient-matching error rates and associated expenditures—could serve as tracking benchmarks for the adoption of patient identification and matching standards.

The lack of a national strategy for identification and matching constitutes a serious barrier to realization of the full value of electronic information sharing to support the delivery of and payment for care, advances in biomedical innovation, and empowerment of patients. The policy suggestions outlined here are politically feasible and achievable in the near term and would have a favorable effect on interoperability and information sharing in the United States.

Service-Oriented Architectures and Web-Based Services

On the whole, the EHR systems in use today are well suited to managing health care reimbursements and meeting certification requirements, but the end users—clinicians and nurses—have found themselves grappling with EHR software often developed during the pre-Internet era. Furthermore, EHRs offer a clinician information entered previously but not the wide array of data and Web-based services (such as advanced decision support) that could and should drive cost-efficient care and decision making (Weber et al., 2014). Realizing a return on the substantial investment in EHRs means unlocking the point of care and opening it up to modern, Web-based software applications, local intranets, and mobile devices and fitting EHRs into a dynamic, state-of-the-art, rapidly evolving information infrastructure.

Opportunities

A truly flexible and adaptable HIT infrastructure becomes possible if the health system can converge on two key forms of interoperability. The first is substitutability—the easy addition of third-party apps to or their deletion from EHRs (Mandl and Kohane, 2009) to permit a tailored end-user experience (Mandl and Kohane, 2012). The second is the adoption of a standardized, service-oriented architecture (SOA) for clinical decision support (CDS) (Loya et al., 2014), which separates CDS rules from the EHR itself and allows recommendations or rules to be added, deleted, or updated through a Web-based service.

An ecosystem of substitutable apps requires standardized, open, and public APIs defining how apps can connect to any EHR or data warehouse (Mandl et al., 2015). The 2015 EHR certification criteria include a requirement for APIs to access EHR data but do not specify standards. An SOA-based CDS standard requires agreement on implementation of EHR triggers that launch decision support and on the mechanism to display advice from the third-party service or to launch an app in response to the trigger.

Policy Alternatives

Standards for APIs that enable EHR query and retrieval of EHR data from web and mobile apps and upload of health data from apps should be incorporated into EHR certification criteria. App developers will be able to build apps that interoperate bidirectionally with EHRs; this will bring greater utility to the apps and greater value to the consumer. (See Key Issue 2.)

Policies should support uptake of the APIs and standards to support SOA CDS. That can happen in three ways: EHR vendors can build specified standards into their products, IT-savvy health care organizations can "retrofit" an API onto existing HIT, and organizations can extract data from EHRs and run an API and CDS on EHR data replicates in a parallel database.

The 2015 edition of the HIT certification standards and criteria specifically embraces the use of APIs as a strategy for engaging patients and for enabling efficient information sharing among providers. But, increased specificity is more likely to produce the desired state—support of a common, public, vendor-agnostic API that allows third-party developers to build external applications and services that integrate with point-of-care HIT products. Rule making under the Merit-Based Incentive Payment System (MIPS) is another opportunity for influence as the Medicare Access and CHIP Reauthorization Act mandates a Meaningful Use component within MIPS.

Potential Effect and Tracking Benchmarks

Those suggestions would build on existing "patient engagement" and "application access" certification criteria, namely, requirements for incorporating APIs into EHRs and enabling a patient to request that his or her data be transmitted to a third party. Fortunately, vendors are taking the initiative with the Argonaut Project (Halamka, 2014) and are actively implementing the "SMART on FHIR" API that manages authorization by using OAuth 2.0 and enables access to a new, openly licensed Health Level Seven draft standard called FHIR (Mandel et al., 2016).

Simply building APIs into EHR products so that data can be called by external applications will improve the current state. But the most important goal is that—as in an "app store"—an app written once will be able to run anywhere in the health care system and that a decision support service will be able to be created once and be called from any care point in the system. Hence, benchmarks should include the number of settings in which a uniform, public API has been implemented and the number of substitutable apps and CDS services created that can run universally. Those efforts will help to create a market in which innovations compete with each other for purchase and use by institutions, providers, and patients. The economies of scale will reduce the cost of care redesign and further promote the markets for new innovations.

Enfranchising Vulnerable Populations and Improving Care for Chronic Disease

Preventing disease by working upstream is more clinically effective and cost effective than a medical model of after-the-fact attention. The current model for health care financing has motivated robust use of interventions, of which 30 percent are unnecessary or potentially harmful (Reilly and Evans, 2009). The aging of our society has created a vulnerable senior population and a liability for unsustainable financial demands.

The Patient Protection and Affordable Care Act (ACA) provides an opportunity for new thinking about managing health and chronic disease. Transforming health care requires more than legislation; it requires a HIT infrastructure that facilitates monitoring, learning about, and predicting the health status of all residents so that we can apply effective preventions and interventions at the appropriate times.

Opportunities

Applying society's resources in the most effective and cost-effective ways requires a global, data-based view of personal and population health. With the opening of federal data sources and the data available through the Internet-of-Things, the opportunity for learning and improvement is more a matter of making sense of the data than of their availability.

The most potent lever for data sharing and use of data for supporting vulnerable populations and individuals is the alignment of incentives for this purpose. The ACA provides authorities that can direct America's resources—public and private—toward improving health and well-being. In 2015, the Secretary of HHS has set a goal of disbursing 50 percent of federal health care reimbursement through value-based payment models (HHS, 2015). As the country orients toward alternative payment models, measuring individual health outcomes and disparities among vulnerable populations is crucial for driving innovation toward outcomes that matter most to individual lives.

Policy Alternatives

Last year, the Institute of Medicine published recommendations on national measures in *Vital Signs: Core Metrics for Health and Health Care Progress* (IOM, 2015). Those measures underpin the logic of a portfolio of actions that should be supported and monitored to the greatest extent possible by EHRs already in place. Further work should be done to ensure that federal public health initiatives can be supported by an expanded HIT infrastructure inasmuch as population health measures are more than the aggregate of individual patient health measures. That backbone of interoperable health information should also evolve to be the backbone of technologies that support vulnerable people in their homes and workplaces with remote physiologic monitoring and an array of "telehealth" services.

Potential Effect and Tracking Benchmarks

Progress would be tracked through performance on quality measures (corresponding to those addressing individual and community health, as detailed in *Vital Signs*) and association with outcomes that matter to patients and consumers. Such progress could be reinforced by payment policies linked to demonstration of successful interoperability.

Health Data and Public Health

The ability of government public health agencies to understand the health of the entire population is limited by a reliance on legacy jurisdictional surveillance systems that have serious lags and are often incomplete. Critically important data on the health of a community are often held in the EHRs of health systems and are not accessible to public health agencies. Public health is community based, and legal barriers can prevent sharing across jurisdictional lines.

New approaches to collaboration regarding data collection, sharing, and analysis will be critical in advancing the general health of a community. That includes a much more profound ability to collect or analyze data than the current capacity of most health departments. In a 2013 survey of local health departments, the National Association of County and City Health Officials found that only 13 percent of the departments were part of health information exchanges and only another 19 percent had plans to be; only 22 percent had EHR capacity, and another 22 percent planned to have it (NACCHO, 2014).

Opportunities

Responsibility for public health and health care data resides primarily at the state and local levels, with federal support from multiple agencies in HHS—such as ONC, the Centers for Disease Control and Prevention (CDC), the Centers for Medicare & Medicaid Services (CMS), the National Center for Health Statistics, the Health Resources and Services Administration, and the Substance Abuse and Mental Health Services Administration—and other federal agencies, such as the Department of Defense, the Department of Veterans Affairs, the Environmental Protection Agency, and the Department of Housing and Urban Development. Jurisdictional law defines how and with whom public health data can be shared and when federal help should be solicited. With widespread adoption of EHR technology, most of the data we need are already available—but not necessarily in a coordinated way and accessible to all who need them. The federal government should work with states to articulate a shared vision regarding who should access various datasets, how datasets should be streamlined, and how all parties should be given incentives to work together to harness the data that are already available and identify new data sources as we broaden our understanding of what contributes to community health (IOM, 2012).

If managed more effectively, federal investment in HIT (whether through ONC or through CMS, which is now actively encouraging states to develop all-payer data systems) and public health surveillance (CDC is the principal funder of state and local surveillance systems) could achieve better outcomes without necessarily requiring new resources. (CDC is beginning a major overhaul of its national surveillance systems and moving toward a cloud-based system that would integrate with EHRs.)

Policy Alternatives

A separation between health care and public health is no longer tenable. Policy initiatives should focus on the following:

- Public health departments need to have the right workforce and technology to advance surveillance and epidemiology functions. CDC should realign its support for state and local health departments to set priorities for foundational capabilities in data (and in related capabilities in communication and policy development) in every jurisdiction (IOM, 2012).
- ONC should set standards for the nation's HIT system that ensure better coordination with public health departments as they develop the capability to work in the HIT system. ONC should continue to work with CDC and other public health agencies to ensure the interoperability of their systems.

Potential Effect and Tracking Benchmarks

Advances in surveillance and epidemiology functions and widespread use of deidentified EHR data for population surveillance would bring a deeper understanding of the health needs of communities and the nation and allow better targeting and alignment of health care and public health dollars to focus on prevention and response. In addition, improvements in the use and coordination of HIT and health data would allow earlier detection of new or reemerging health threats and real-time monitoring of health effects of disasters, which will strengthen the nation's preparedness system.

Tracking benchmarks include the number of local health departments that are participating in health information exchanges and using EHRs and the number that are able to use standardized data from throughout the health system and other local, state, and federal partners.

Accelerating Use of Aggregated Health Information and Research

Routinely collected health information, including EHR and claims data, has great potential for secondary use to support observational and interventional research and to inform policy. National programs that combine information from multiple organizations to assess large populations provide capabilities that have not previously existed to understand patterns and outcomes of medical care and determinants of health conditions and treatment outcomes. Development and maintenance of the infrastructure can be expensive, but the cost of the studies they support can be a small fraction of the costs that would otherwise accrue if each study needed to develop its own data capabilities.

Opportunities

The optimal database design to support care of individual people does not support analyses spanning millions of people, so data must usually be extensively curated and transformed into a new format to make the aggregated data useful for secondary purposes. Even with curation and transformation, it is often necessary to understand both the system of care, including incentives and disincentives to capture specific kinds of events, and the electronic platforms that generated the data. That is especially true for data originating from EHRs, which are typically customized by users in ways that result in the coding of the same health events in different ways. It is often necessary to engage with people who are knowledgeable about the systems that develop specific data to understand whether and how the data can be used for specific purposes.

Protection of people's privacy and of the confidentiality of proprietary information of providers and health systems requires robust protection of information. The challenges are large when datasets involve tens of millions of people. It will be increasingly important to link individuals' data among multiple organizations not only because of the fragmentation of care but also because of the need to make the best possible use of different kinds of data (such as health records, vital statistics registries, and geocoded data).

Policy Alternatives

There has been little change in policy related to the use of HIT in lieu of expensive and rigid trials for demonstrating the safety and efficacy of treatment alternatives. For example, current Food and Drug Administration (FDA) rules severely limit the use of information collected by a medication-taking, smartphone-carrying public in postmarket or phase IV trials. Likewise, little progress has been made in automated syndromic surveillance or occurrence management in public health. Such data collection and surveillance live purely in the realm of state and federal policy and have high priority for federal government action to modernize and streamline regulation and protections to speed discovery through the use of health information.

New policies are needed to encourage the voluntary participation of the public and data holders in national research programs. These include incentives to participate and protections against uses of data in ways that threaten individual privacy or that disadvantage data holders. To be consistent with the HIPAA Privacy Rule and the Common Rule (for the protection of human subjects), holders of data should retain responsibility to ensure that data are used in compliance with applicable jurisdictional law, institutional policy, and individual permissions, including later uses of datasets. The Precision Medicine Initiative of the National Institutes of Health constitutes a bold step toward engaging individuals in helping to accelerate biomedical-knowledge discovery through the use of electronic health information from EHRs and consumer health technology (NIH, 2016).

Two recent kinds of progress should be extended and developed further. The first is the creation of large-scale distributed data systems in which the original holders of data maintain physical and operational control over the data. When the data have been transformed into a standard format, analyses can be performed behind the data holder's firewall. The data holder then returns the results of the analysis, often simple counts or datasets that contain only a few pieces of information. Such a distributed approach eliminates the need to create large, pooled datasets. FDA's Mini-Sentinel project (FDA, 2014) and the Patient-Centered Outcomes Research Network Clinical Data Research Networks are examples of this approach (PCORnet, 2016). The second is the development of advanced methods for analyzing distributed data. Examples are distributed logistic and proportional hazards regression methods. Although the theory for many of these methods has been developed, the methods have not been implemented in a form that allows their deployment in existing large-scale distributed environments.

There is substantial need and opportunity to coordinate federal and private investments in the data infrastructure and governance of cross-network querying capability and in creating a system that will be accessible to many users. Revisions of the Common Rule should specifically allow the use of aggregated health data for research purposes. Coordinated messaging to holders of data and to the public should emphasize the benefits of this use of private data.

Potential Effect and Tracking Benchmarks

We are on the cusp of transforming both public and private capabilities to harness electronic health data to support multiple beneficial purposes. Benchmarks should track the development of a stable funding mechanism, the creation of a system of governance, and the use of messaging about the benefits of using aggregated data for health information and research.

Building a HIT Workforce

Many clinicians learn the mechanics of using IT but lack basic literacy in informatics—the intelligence behind IT. A corollary in medicine would be expecting a physician to learn the mechanics of writing prescriptions without understanding the basics of pharmacology and pathophysiology. The workforce of our 21st-century health care system, awash in data and fundamentally transformed by IT and "big data" analytics, must develop a competence beyond the mechanics of HIT and health information management. Clinicians and other health care workers themselves must become drivers of the "learning health care system." To realize fully the value of HIT and data-driven clinical decision making, we need an educated workforce that understands how to collect and locate, analyze, and use information for health and health care. Educational programs should emphasize the interdisciplinary nature of HIT-enabled care and include not only the technical but the social aspects of connected IT systems. Basic informatics literacy will be critical for the success of HIT in health and health care delivery.

Opportunities

Three kinds of education and training will need to be addressed by inter-disciplinary academic programs and through continuing medical education programs:

- *Basic "informatics literacy"* for all health professionals that goes beyond computer or HIT literacy. Literacy in informatics should become part of medical education, biomedical research, and public health training to give clinicians the skills needed to collect and analyze information and apply it in their practice.
- *Intensive applied informatics training* to improve leadership and expertise in applying informatics principles to the collection and analysis of information and its application to health care problems. This level of training will ensure a supply of qualified professionals for the emerging roles of chief medical information officers, chief nursing information officers, chief clinical informatics officers, chief research officers, and similar roles.
- *Support for education professionals* who will advance the science and train the next generation of informatics professionals in this developing and dynamic field of study.

Policy Alternatives

Adapting current education and training programs will require the commitment of private and nonprofit organizations, and it will demand support from the public sector through smart regulation, consistent funding, and targeted campaigns to promote awareness of training opportunities. Likewise, industry stakeholders, such as health IT developers, will need to partner with academic and nonprofit organizations to develop curricula that ensure that graduates are ready for employment on day one. Specifically, postbaccalaureate and graduate medical education (GME) programs must rethink how informatics is integrated with other clinical domains. Federal GME and indirect medical education payment must similarly be recalibrated to ensure that this integration occurs. CMS should leverage eligibility requirements for Medicare alternative payment models and request that providers include a description of their HIT workforce plan in addition to their leadership and management structure (Leadership and management, 2015) and HIT implementation plan (Required processes, 2015). Without federal funds, programmatic requirements, and commitments from private-sector stakeholders, supply will continue to lag far behind demand for next-generation HIT professionals.

Potential Effect and Tracking Benchmarks

The rise in informatics programs accredited by the Accreditation Council for Graduate Medical Education, the number of graduates of these programs, and the number of board-certified, clinical-informatics subspecialists are important, but insufficient, metrics to monitor. To ensure that a clinical workforce is grounded in basic literacy, we must see an increase in the percentage of medical schools that offer basic informatics course work, and we should develop ways to understand whether frontline clinicians are using technology to optimize care. Surveys among specialty societies and professional organizations regarding their members' training levels and degree of comfort in using technology to optimize care delivery could yield important benchmarks. Another example of how to understand how clinicians are using informatics skills is through their use of data collected by consumer technology to monitor compliance of chronic-care patients. That or similar data use would indicate an increased knowledge of and comfort with informatics.

Creating a Trust Fabric for Health Services: Privacy and Security

Historically, the health care community has viewed information privacy and security as necessary constraints mandated primarily by HIPAA rather than as a business imperative for enabling high-quality care. However, 87 percent of respondents to the 2015 Healthcare Information Management and Systems Society (HIMSS) privacy and security survey indicated that information security had become a critical business priority (HIMSS, 2015). The shift reflects a growing awareness of the need to create a "trust fabric" of trustworthy, defensible, and survivable health systems while enabling the sharing necessary for patient safety, high-quality care, population health, and biomedical knowledge advancement.

Opportunities

The most compelling challenges for health care privacy and security include the following:

- *Cyberthreats.* The Federal Bureau of Investigation has warned of increasing cyber attacks against health care systems and medical devices that are attributed to broad adoption of EHR technology, lax cybersecurity standards, and a higher financial payout for medical records in the black market (FBI Cyber Division, 2014).
- *Identity.* Although federal agencies and other industries specify standard, use case–specific levels of assurance (LOAs) for identity proofing and authentication (NIST, 2013), the health care industry has not done so.
- *Patchwork policy.* State regulations and implementation of HIPAA rules vary. Health research is governed by the Common Rule, consumer health is governed by the Federal Trade Commission, and behavioral health has its own Substance Abuse and Mental Health Services Administration rules.
- *Privacy consciousness.* The fascination with social networking and "connectedness" is evolving into increasing public concern about invasive practices that violate personal privacy. Individuals are demanding the capability to give permission at a highly granular level and to change their permissions. Technology with those capabilities is beginning to emerge in federal health care agencies and the private sector but has not been widely deployed.
- *Health apps.* New certification and Meaningful Use regulations encourage the development of APIs to enable patients to access their EHR data by using apps of their choice, but the regulations raise concerns about a health care organization's responsibilities, vulnerabilities, and liabilities.
- *Encryption.* Health care relies heavily on the TLS protocol, which encrypts data from server to server or server to browser but does not protect data end to end from sender to receiver. An alternative is the Direct secure e-mail protocol, which offers end-to-end protection but is not practical for exchanging large volumes of data, nor has it been widely adopted in the industry (The Direct Project, 2015).

Policy Alternatives

To meet those challenges, we should encourage the industry to establish and support a public–private, health-cybersecurity information sharing and analysis center for industrywide sharing of information about cyberthreats, vulnerabilities, and countermeasures. We should also establish use case–specific LOAs for health care, encourage participation in national initiatives related to identity management, and broadly adopt the principles and strategy of the National Strategy for Trusted Identities in Cyberspace (NIST, 2016).

We should harmonize security and privacy policy for health information among all federal agencies, minimize differences among states and between state and federal regulations, and provide a searchable online resource for federal and state privacy and security rules. We should also encourage broad adoption of Fair Information Practices Principles throughout government and industry while providing examples of surreptitious privacy threats to discourage use by developers and increase consumer awareness.

Federal health care agencies should implement granular and dynamic electronic consent mechanisms. Clarification of organizational responsibilities, vulnerabilities, and liabilities would encourage health care organizations to implement APIs that enable consumer apps to access EHR data. Finally, we should identify, support, and encourage the development and use of encryption solutions that provide end-to-end protection, are easy to implement and use, and are appropriate for the exchange of large volumes of data.

Potential Effect and Tracking Benchmarks

The financial penalty for health care organizations that experience a breach is substantial. In 2015, health care experienced the highest cost per stolen record of any industry, an average of $363 (PR Newswire, 2015). Sharing of threat information and response coordination among health care organizations and among interdependent components of the overall health system is ad hoc at best. The US health system lacks the security and resilience architecture and functional components necessary to withstand an attack on critical health infrastructure (The White House, 2013).

If we create a stronger, more secure, and more resilient critical infrastructure, we will see a reduction in the number of breaches against health care organizations and a reduction in the cost and time needed to recover from a health care breach. Such an infrastructure would include industrywide adoption of high-assurance identity management (e.g., in-person identity proofing and multifactor authentication) for all accesses to clinical and safety-critical information. Patient and safety-critical data would be kept encrypted when not in use, including during storage and continuously during transmission from a sender to an intended recipient, and there would be industrywide engagement in a health care information sharing and analysis center. The proposed changes would also increase consumer trust, giving consumers choices regarding the collection of, access to, and use of their heath information.

CONCLUSION

Creating a longitudinal, complete, and timely record of information for each person has arguably been the most important goal of federal HIT policy and continues to have top priority. The capacity to "interoperate" and share health information is central to realizing the economic and clinical benefits of EHRs and underpins the efficiency of the health care marketplace. A generation of legacy EHRs that lack the design and features needed for interoperation is widely in place, so it will be challenging and potentially expensive to reach this goal.

Progress toward interoperability could be accelerated initially by focusing on high-value use cases, such as transitions of care, outcomes measurement, and public health reporting. Achieving interoperability is like building the interstate highway system: we need to construct on-ramps and off-ramps one at a time, but we also need a master plan.

In the absence of an authoritative private source, the federal government should be highly specific about standards for end-to-end interoperability. Interoperability needs to extend from medical devices to EHR systems. In the absence of interoperability, end-user costs are higher because users are compelled to cobble together inherently noninteroperable systems. In addition to all the risks posed by imperfect interoperation, there is a loss of the value that could be gained through research, care, and public health when these systems interoperate.

Privacy and security risks are increasing as more private and life-critical information becomes available, as health care practitioners increase their dependence on vulnerable technology, and as cyberterrorists become more highly skilled, more determined, and better financed. "Trust" issues and trends span the health care experience. EHRs have become ubiquitous; nearly all health practitioners and hospitals now use the technology. However, cyberthreats are exacerbated by a weak critical security infrastructure and a patchwork security and privacy policy throughout the federal government, between states, and among nations.

There is tension between the clear need for personal health identifiers for seamless interoperability and the need to protect personal privacy. In the era of "big data," the availability of more comprehensive, sensitive, and valuable—but less regulated—data emphasizes the ever-present need for standards for encryption. Genomic (and "multi-omic") data used in personalized medicine lack policies and standards. Consumers are taking more control of their health and increasing the use of personal devices and mobile apps to monitor and improve their health; the data generated should be considered a rich source of information. The ultimate goal of information technology is not only to service patient care in the moment but to also be the underpinning of a continuously learning health system that supports the continuous improvement of health, care, and value.

VITAL DIRECTIONS

1. **Commit to end-to-end interoperability extending from devices to EHR systems.** End-to-end interoperability would advance the longstanding goal to create a longitudinal, complete and timely record of information for each person. Efforts to realize this goal must contend with the existing generation of EHRs that lack the design and features needed to interoperate. A lack of interoperability increases end-user costs, as users are compelled to cobble inherently noninteroperable systems together, and limits the use of these systems for research, care, and public health. In the absence of an authoritative private source, the federal government or a body empowered by the government must be highly specific about standards for end-to-end interoperability.

2. **Aggressively address cybersecurity vulnerability.** Increased reliance on vulnerable technology and the availability of private and life-critical information are increasing privacy and security risk. As cyberterrorists become more highly skilled, more determined, and better financed, we remain exposed due to a weak critical security infrastructure and a patchwork security and privacy policy across the federal government, between states, and among nations. Stronger penalties are needed for hackers and cyberterrorists. Policy should be designed to protect those institutions and entities that meet or exceed applicable laws, policies, and best practices for data protection; appropriate institutional sanctions should be developed for those that fail to meet this minimum standard. Concerted effort is necessary to address the "trust" issues and trends that span the health care experience.

3. **Develop a data strategy that supports a learning health system.** Future federal programs should focus on enabling infrastructure, creating trust, and streamlining heterogeneous policies. This includes making data available for large-scale projects, such as the FDA's Sentinel Initiative, and

for comparative effectiveness trials. However, prescriptive regulations and burdensome certification requirements are not the answer. Rather, policy should enable and promote learning from available data.

SUMMARY RECOMMENDATIONS FOR VITAL DIRECTIONS

1. Commit to end-to-end interoperability extending from devices to electronic health records (EHR) systems.
2. Aggressively address cybersecurity vulnerability.
3. Develop a data strategy that supports a learning health system.

REFERENCES

Bipartisan Policy Center. 2012. Challenges and strategies for accurately matching patients to their health data. Available at http://bipartisanpolicy.org/wp-content/uploads/sites/default/files/BPC%20HIT%20Issue%20Brief%20on%20Patient%20Matching.pdf. (accessed May 3, 2016).

CHIME (College of Healthcare Information Management Executives). 2012. Summary of CHIME survey on patient data-matching. Available at https://chimecentral.org/wp-content/uploads/2014/11/Summary_of_ CHIME_Survey_on_Patient_Data.pdf (accessed May 5, 2016).

CHIME. 2016. CHIME issues national patient ID challenge. Available at https://chimecentral.org/chime-issues-national-patient-id-challenge/ (accessed May 3, 2016).

Conn, J. 2016. Seeking a solution for patient record matching. *Modern Healthcare* January 23. Available at http://www.modernhealthcare.com/article/20160123/MAGAZINE/301239980 (accessed May 3, 2016).

The Direct Project. 2015. Applicability statement for secure health transport, v1.2. Available at http://wiki.directproject.org/file/view/Applicability+Statement+for+Secure+ Health+Transport+v1.2.pdf (accessed May 3, 2016).

Dooling, J., L. Fernandes, A. Kirby, G. Landsbach, K. Lusk, M. Munns, N. Noreen, M. O'Connor, and M. Patten. 2016. Survey: Patient matching problems routine in healthcare. *Journal of AHIMA* January 6. Available at http://journal.ahima.org/2016/01/06/survey-patient-matching-problems-routine-in-healthcare/ (accessed May 3, 2016).

FBI (Federal Bureau of Investigation) Cyber Division. 2014. Healthcare systems and medical devices at risk for increased cyber-intrusions for financial gain. Available at http://www.illuminweb.com/wp-content/uploads/ill-mo-uploads/103/2418/health-systems-cyber-intrusions.pdf (accessed May 3, 2016).

FDA (US Food and Drug Administration). 2014. Mini-Sentinel. Available at http://www.mini-sentinel.org/ (accessed May 5, 2016).

Halamka, J. 2014. Life as a healthcare CIO: The Argonaut Project charter. Available http://geekdoctorblogspot-com/2014/12/the-argonaut-project-charterhtml (accessed May 3, 2016).

HHS (US Department of Health and Human Services). 2015. Better, smarter, healthier: In historic announcement, HHS sets clear goals and timeline for shifting Medicare reimbursements from volume to value. Available at http://www.hhs.gov/about/news/2015/01/26/better-smarter-healthier-in-historic-announcement-hhs-sets-clear-goals-and-timeline-for-shifting-medicare-reimbursements-from-volume-to-value.html (accessed May 5, 2016).

Hillestad, R., J. Bigelow, A. Bower, F. Girosi, R. Meili, R. Scoville, and R. Taylor. 2005. Can electronic medical record systems transform health care? Potential health benefits, savings, and costs. *Health Affairs* 24(5):1103–1117. doi: 10.1377/hlthaff.24.5.1103.

HIMSS (Health Information Management and Systems Society). 2015. 2015 HIMSS cybersecurity survey. Available at http://www.himss.org/2015-cybersecurity-survey (accessed May 3, 2016).

IOM (Institute of Medicine). 2012. *For the public's health: Investing in a healthier future.* Washington, DC: The National Academies Press.

IOM. 2015. *Vital signs: Core metrics for health and health care progress.* Washington, DC: The National Academies Press.

Leadership and management. 2015. 42 CFR § 425.108.

Loya, S. R., K. Kawamoto, C. Chatwin, and V. Huser. 2014. Service oriented architecture for clinical decision support: A systematic review and future directions. *Journal of Medical Systems* 38(12):140. doi: 10.1007/s10916-014–0140-z.

Mandel, J. C., D. A. Kreda, K. D. Mandl, I. S. Kohane, and R. B. Ramoni. 2016. SMART on FHIR: A standards-based, interoperable apps platform for electronic health records. *Journal of the American Medical Informatics Association* 23(5):899–908. doi: 10.1093/jamia/ocv189.

Mandl, K. D., and I. S. Kohane. 2009. No small change for the health information economy. *New England Journal of Medicine* 360(13):1278–1281. doi: 10.1056/NEJMp0900411.

Mandl, K. D., and I. S. Kohane. 2012. Escaping the EHR trap—the future of health IT. *New England Journal of Medicine* 366(24):2240–2242. doi: 10.1056/NEJMp1203102.

Mandl, K. D., J. C. Mandel, and I. S. Kohane. 2015. Driving innovation in health systems through an apps-based information economy. *Cell Systems* 1(1):8–13. doi: 10.1016/j.cels.2015.05.001.

Morris, G., G. Farnum, S. Afzal, C. Robinson, J. Greene, and C. Coughlin. 2014. Patient identification and matching final report. Available at https://www.healthit.gov/sites/default/files/patient_identification_matching_final_report. pdf (accessed May 3, 2016).

NACCHO (National Association of County and City Health Officials). 2014. 2013 national profile of local health departments. Available at http://archived. naccho.org/topics/infrastructure/profile/upload/2013-National-Profile-of-Local-Health-Departments-report.pdf (accessed May 3, 2016).

NIH (National Institutes of Health). 2016. Precision Medicine Initiative Cohort Program. Available at https://www.nih.gov/precision-medicine-initiative-cohort-program (accessed May 5, 2016).

NIST (National Institute of Standards and Technology). 2013. NIST Special Publication 800–63-2: Electronic authentication guideline. Available at http://nvlpubs.nist.gov/nistpubs/SpecialPublications/NIST.SP.800–63-2.pdf (accessed May 3, 2016).

NIST. 2016. National strategy for trusted identities in cyberspace. Available at http://www.nist.gov/nstic/ (accessed May 3, 2016).

ONC (Office of the National Coordinator for Health Information Technology). 2015a. Non-federal Acute Care Hospital Electronic Health Record Adoption. Health IT Quick-Stat 47, June. Available at http://dash-board.healthit. gov/quickstats/pages/FIG-Hospital-EHR-Adoption.php (accessed May 3, 2016).

ONC. 2015b. Office-Based Physician Electronic Health Record Adoption: 2004–2014. Health IT Quick-Stat 50, September. Available at http://dashboard.healthit. gov/quickstats/pages/physician-ehr-adoption-trends.php (accessed May 3, 2016).

PCORnet (National Patient-Centered Clinical Research Network). 2016. Clinical data research networks. Available at http://www.pcornet.org/clinical-data-research-networks/ (accessed May 5, 2016).

PR Newswire. 2015. Ponemon Institute's 2015 global cost of data breach study reveals average cost of data breach reaches record level. Available at http://www.prnewswire.com/news-releases/ponemon-institutes-2015-global-cost-of-data-breach-study-reveals-average-cost-of-data-breach-reaches-record-levels-300089057.html (accessed May 3, 2016).

Reilly, B. M., and A. T. Evans. 2009. Much ado about (doing) nothing. *Annals of Internal Medicine* 150(4):270–271.

Required processes and patient-centeredness criteria. 2015. 42 CFR § 425.112.

The Sequoia Project. 2016. A framework for cross-organizational patient identity management. Available at http://sequoi-aproject.org/framework-for-cross-organizational-patient-identity-matching/ (accessed May 3, 2016).

US Congress. 1998. 1999 Omnibus Appropriations Act. P. L. 105–277, 105th Congr., October 21.

US Senate Committee on Health, Education, Labor, and Pensions Committee. 2016. Improving Health Information Technology Act. S. 2511, 114th Cong.

Weber, G. M., K. D. Mandl, and I. S. Kohane. 2014. Finding the missing link for big biomedical data. *Journal of the American Medical Association* 311(24):2479–2480. doi: 10.1001/jama.2014.4228.

The White House. 2004. Transforming health care: The President's Health Information Technology Plan. Available at https://georgewbush-whitehouse.archives.gov/infocus/technology/economic_policy200404/chap3.html (accessed June 5, 2016).

The White House. 2013. Presidential Policy Directive 21: Critical infrastructure security and resilience. Available at https://www.whitehouse.gov/the-press-office/2013/02/12/presidential-policy-directive-critical-infrastructure-security-and-resil (accessed May 3, 2016).

AUTHOR INFORMATION

Jonathan B. Perlin, MD, PhD, is President, Clinical Services and Chief Medical Officer, Hospital Corporation of America Inc. and Clinical Professor of Medicine and Biomedical Informatics, Vanderbilt University. **Dixie B. Baker, PhD,** is Senior Partner, Martin, Blanck, and Associates. **David J. Brailer, MD, PhD,** is Managing Partner and CEO, Health Evolution Partners. **Douglas B. Fridsma, MD, PhD,** is President and CEO, American Medical Informatics Association. **Mark E. Frisse, MD,** is Accenture Professor, Department of Biomedical Informatics, School of Medicine, Vanderbilt University. **John D. Halamka, MD, PhD,** is Chief Information Officer, Beth Israel Beaconness Medical Center. **Jeffrey Levi, PhD,** is Professor, The George Washington University. **Kenneth D. Mandl, MD, MPH,** is Professor of Biomedical Informatics, Havard Medical School and is Director, Boston Children's Hospital Computational Health Informatics Program. **Janet M. Marchibroda, MBA,** is Director, Health Innovation Initiative, Bipartisan Policy Center. **Richard Platt, MD, MS,** is Executive Director, Harvard Pilgrim Health Care, and Professor and Chair, Department of Population Medicine, Harvard Medical School. **Paul C. Tang, MD, MS,** is Chief Health Transformation Officer, IBM Watson Health.

17

DATA ACQUISITION, CURATION, AND USE FOR A CONTINUOUSLY LEARNING HEALTH SYSTEM

Harlan M. Krumholz, MD, SM, Philip E. Bourne, PhD, Richard E. Kuntz, MD, MSc, Harold L. Paz, MD, MS, Sharon F. Terry, MA, and Joanne Waldstreicher, MD

Increased sharing of health data among all stakeholders in the health system—from patients and advocates to health professionals and medical researchers—is essential for creating a learning health system. Such a system would leverage health data from a variety of sources to meet the challenges of increasingly complex medical decisions and, in the process, create knowledge more efficiently in the service of producing better patient outcomes and less waste. Government agencies, nongovernment organizations (including charitable foundations and disease advocacy organizations), and the research community have taken important strides in recent years toward greater openness of research data and personal health data. In particular, there is increasing movement toward clarifying people's rights to their own health data, promoting standards to ease their access, and providing tools that enable them to exercise their rights. Major challenges remain, however, in overcoming the resistance to data sharing that prevents scientists from learning about clinical trials whose results are unpublished and prevents other people from acquiring and sharing their own health-related data. Those challenges create a need for incentives (financial and otherwise) to create an open-data culture, for changes in laws and regulations to make data sharing easier, for improvement in the infrastructure used for data sharing, and for investment in research to increase data sharing abilities. Policies promoting a more open system should be evaluated to quantify the transition to a data sharing ecosystem and the opportunities to improve its effectiveness in promoting clinical quality, patient choice, and scientific progress. Given the scale of the challenges and the potential rewards, a strategic federal initiative that aligns current and future efforts would be one way to accelerate movement toward a more open, people-centric health system with data sharing at its core.

TOPIC OVERVIEW, ISSUES, AND TRENDS

Health-related and health-research data are vital resources for clinical care, informed clinical choice, quality improvement, drug and device safety, effectiveness assessment, and scientific discovery. *Health-related data* refers to the four major determinants of health: personal, social, economic, and environmental (ODPHP, 2016). Such data are the reagents with which we can produce information to support personal choices about health care, system choices about optimizing medical and public health strategies, and policy choices about laws and regulations. They are the ingredients necessary for medical breakthroughs.

There are formidable impediments—cultural and social as well as technical—to leveraging existing data for the benefit of individuals and society. Because of the incentive structure for data sharing, a prominent impediment is the difficulty in motivating data holders to enable the coalescing and harmonizing of health-related data that reside in disparate venues and formats in the health care and research ecosystems (Murugiah et al., 2016). The ability to access the data is not sufficient to produce benefit; technical advances in analytics and application are also required. Nevertheless, the lack of a way to acquire data easily, securely, and in a useful format is a critical obstacle to producing innovations and improvements in health and health care.

The Institute of Medicine (IOM) (now the National Academy of Medicine) introduced a concept of a learning health system to support transformational change in the fundamental aspects of health and health care (IOM, 2012a). In describing the paradigm shift to a system in which data sharing is the norm rather than the exception, the Office of the National Coordinator for Health Information Technology (ONC), under the aegis of the Department of Health and Human Services (HHS), defines a learning health system as an ecosystem in which all stakeholders can contribute, share, and analyze data and in which continuous learning cycles encourage the creation of knowledge that can be used by a variety of health information systems (ONC, 2015a). A learning health system has the potential to address some of the most pressing challenges of our current system, including the increasing complexity of medical decisions, the inadequacy and sluggish pace of acquiring evidence for guiding care, the systemic waste throughout health care delivery, and health disparities and quality shortcomings despite high spending. A learning health system is also intended to expand capacity for knowledge generation, use health information technology

(HIT) to propel improvement, configure systems for continuous improvement, and engage patients in working toward better outcomes.

Health-related and research-related data are the substrates for both a learning health system and a vibrant research ecosystem. Such systems require rich, detailed health-related data that are primed to be transformed into useful information at the personal and systems levels. The data must be used optimally in the learning health system for the system to generate useful knowledge for researchers and in turn to leverage this knowledge more quickly and effectively in clinical practice. However, a learning health system remains more an aspiration than a consistent achievement, in part because of an inability to leverage relevant data fully.

Our purpose is to identify the principal opportunities to promote sharing, curation, and use of data for a learning health system and the research ecosystem. In particular, we focus on options for a strategic federal initiative, with additional consideration of the role of others. We articulate the aspirations for data sharing initiatives and metrics for tracking. Three overarching vital directions are needed to create a health and research system that is based on data sharing: change the culture and incentive structures of the health system, encourage people's access to their data by leveraging their established rights to their data, and provide seamless means to curate and produce usable data from disparate sources.

PROGRESS

In recent years, policymakers, organizations, and individuals have advanced efforts to promote the culture and infrastructure needed to support the secure accessibility of health and health care data (Ross and Krumholz, 2013). For example, the companies that are part of the Pharmaceutical Research and Manufacturers of America (PhRMA) have committed to sharing their trial data with researchers (PhRMA, 2013).

There is parallel progress in health care. The spread of digital health data has created the opportunity for people to view, download, and transmit their health care data and has introduced the possibility of coalescing data from disparate sources. The adoption of electronic health records (EHRs) was an objective of the Health Information Technology for Economic and Clinical Health (HITECH) Act of 2009 and the Federal Health IT Strategic Plan (Henry et al., 2016; ONC, 2014). In 2011, only 28 percent of hospitals had a basic EHR. By 2015, almost all hospitals (96 percent) had certified EHR record technology.

Many regions of the country have taken substantial steps to promote data sharing and begin the transition to a learning health system. Regional health information exchanges, despite their limitations, represent progress. An example is the MyHealth Access Network, a nonprofit HIT utility in Tulsa, Oklahoma, supported by ONC as part of the Beacon Communities Program (MyHealth Access Network, 2016). MyHealth supports health-data collection by creating a regional health information exchange that as of 2012 contained the medical records of 1.8 million patients (Tulsa Beacon Community, 2012). The system ensures that every health practitioner who sees a patient has access to the patient's full medical history, and it enables doctors seeing the same patient to coordinate care (Kendrick, 2011).

The promulgation of standards, the implementation of appropriate legislation and regulations, the public attention to what ONC termed information blocking, the growth of public activism regarding health information, and technologic advancements have sped changes in expectations and capabilities (NIHOER, 2016; ONC, 2015b). Information blocking was stated in a congressional report by ONC to occur "when persons or entities knowingly and unreasonably interfere with the exchange or use of electronic health information" (ONC, 2015b). Nevertheless, the focus on common data models, interoperability, and application program interfaces (APIs) and authorization protocols are transforming what is possible with regard to secure health-data movement. The common data models are standards to enable different databases to align elements. APIs—which are software programs, protocols, and tools—are making it easier to move information from one location to another. New standards with an API, such as the Fast Healthcare Interoperability Resources (FHIR), hold the promise of accelerating interoperability. Authorization protocols, such as OAuth 2.0, are providing easier and more secure ways to ensure that appropriate people can gain access to data.

The health care and research worlds are also converging with respect to data flow. An example is the Precision Medicine Initiative's introduction of the Sync-for-Science concept. That effort seeks to engage people in acquiring their health-related data, including data from EHRs, and transmitting the data into research databases (PMIWG, 2015).

National legislation and guidance from ONC and HHS are accelerating the transformational change to a digital health-data environment (ONC, 2015a). The 1996 Health Insurance Portability and Accountability Act (HIPAA) made clear that Americans have a right to access their health data, to have an accounting of their health information, and to correct or amend their health information (HealthIT.gov, 2016a). The HITECH Act, a part of the 2009 American Recovery and Reinvestment Act, made clear that Americans have a right to acquire their personal health information (PHI) in an electronic format; as a result, gatekeepers to those data are obliged to provide the data on request (HHS OCR, 2016). The legislation stated that a person can be charged only the labor cost. The HHS

Office for Civil Rights (OCR) guidance states that, "while a covered entity is not required to purchase new software or equipment in order to accommodate every possible individual request, the covered entity must have the capability to provide some form of electronic copy of PHI maintained electronically" (HIPD, 2016). Progress with regard to fees was also made with new guidance from OCR released in early 2016. The guidance now states that "a covered entity may charge individuals a flat fee for all standard requests for electronic copies of PHI maintained electronically, provided the fee does not exceed $6.50, inclusive of all labor, supplies, and any applicable postage" (HIPD, 2016).

ONC released a Shared Nationwide Interoperability Roadmap in 2015 (ONC, 2015a). The short-term goals (for 2015–2017) focus on "sending, receiving, finding, and using priority data domains to improve health care quality and outcomes." The longer-term goals (for 2018–2020) address the need "to expand data sources and users." The even longer-term goals (for 2021–2024) seek broadly to "achieve nationwide interoperability to enable a learning health care system, with the person at the center of a system that can continuously improve care, public health, and science through real-time data access." ONC also released a federal HIT strategic plan for 2015–2020, which stated that the mission is to "improve the health and well-being of individuals and communities through the use of technology and health information that is accessible when and where it matters most" (ONC, 2014).

Many federal agencies are sharing data at an increasing pace. For example, the Centers for Medicare & Medicaid Services (CMS) began releasing data several years ago and has progressed quickly to sharing information of many kinds, including data on hospital discharges, physician volumes, drug prescribing, and durable medical equipment (CMS, 2016; Ornstein, 2016). Moreover, CMS is building APIs that will enable Medicare beneficiaries to connect their CMS data to personal applications in ever easier and more expeditious fashion.

The expansion of alternative payment models (APMs) makes health data sharing more important and creates new incentives to do so. The APMs are likely to grow more rapidly with the advent of the Medicare Access and CHIP Reauthorization Act of 2015, which introduced a Quality Payment Program. APMs serve as an impetus for data sharing, as the move away from a fee-for-service (FFS) model creates a need for longitudinal patient data to enable effective and efficient care over a patient's lifetime. In a FFS model, institutions could get by with data about individual episodes of care; in APMs, institutions increasingly need HIT systems that integrate data over time and enable sharing with other institutions as needed to provide longitudinal care and act to promote health. For example, Blue Cross Blue Shield of Massachusetts launched an APM in 2009 called the Alternative

Quality Contract, which pays a fixed amount, linked to quality measures, for each patient during a specific period. To manage population health with multiple providers in such a system, Blue Cross created a data-reporting system that helps physicians with medical management and provides a mechanism to share best practices and monitor quality measures. The infrastructure in the system could serve as the base for a broader data-sharing system.

Progress is being promoted by many nongovernment organizations. DirectTrust is a nonprofit collaborative that consists of providers that seek methods for a secure, interoperable health information exchange via the Direct message protocols (DirectTrust, 2012). The Argonaut Project is a collaborative effort to facilitate data sharing by using FHIR (FHIR, 2015). The CommonWell Health Alliance is organizing HIT companies and other stakeholders to promote interoperability (CommonWell Health Alliance, no date). Moreover, companies that provide 90 percent of the country's EHRs and several large health systems have signed the ONC Interoperability Pledge and committed to consumer access, no blocking, ensuring transparency, and implementing standards (HealthIT.gov, 2016b).

On the research side, there have been advances in the commitment of influential organizations to mandate data sharing in research. IOM convened meetings over the last several years to discuss data sharing in science and made strong recommendations for promoting progress toward a culture of open science. Many data holders, including PhRMA, are committed to sharing their data, and consortia, individual academic groups, companies, and others have established mechanisms to vet proposals and provide access to their clinical-trial assets (PhRMA, 2013).

Funders are increasingly linking financial support with data sharing. Organizations that include the National Institutes of Health (NIH) and the Patient-Centered Outcomes Research Institute have mandated some forms of data sharing as a condition of funding (Goodman and Krumholz, 2015). They have developed platforms for sharing, are investing in the concept of a data commons, and are committed to testing policy and infrastructure approaches. The Wellcome Trust is seeking to identify structures to enable sharing, stating as its aim "to ensure that the data generated by the research we support is managed and shared in a way that maximizes the benefit to the public" (Wellcome Trust, 2016a). Wellcome is also launching a new publishing platform, which will encourage publication and data sharing (Wellcome Trust, 2016b). Leaders of advocacy organizations have formally convened to propose shared principles that are based on the recommendations.

It is of particular note that in 2014, the Bill & Melinda Gates Foundation promulgated one of the strongest requirements for sharing, making it a contingency of being funded (Straumsheim, 2014). The foundation states that "information generated during the course of our investment activities—in the form of research studies, data sets, evaluation results, investment results, and strategy-related analytics—is significant public good. Access to this information is important for accountability, provides valuable learning to the sectors that we support, will facilitate faster and more well-informed decision making, and contributes to achieving the impact we seek" (Bill & Melinda Gates Foundation, 2016a). The foundation also adopted an open-access policy that "enables the unrestricted access and reuse of all . . . peer-reviewed published research funded . . . by the foundation, including any underlying data sets" (Bill & Melinda Gates Foundation, 2016b).

The International Committee of Medical Journal Editors, on January 20, 2016, released a proposal that could change the landscape of research data sharing (Taichman et al., 2016). The committee stated the belief that there is "an ethical obligation to responsibly share data generated by interventional clinical trials." It proposed requiring authors "to share with others the deidentified individual-patient data (IPD) underlying the results presented in the article (including tables, figures, and appendices or supplementary material) no later than 6 months after publication. The data underlying the results are defined as the IPD required to reproduce the article's findings, including necessary metadata." The committee received more than 300 comments and is considering whether to adopt the policy or modify it.

CHALLENGES

Despite that progress, data sharing is not easy or normative in health care or clinical research. There are daunting obstacles to individuals in accessing their own health care data, let alone data in a useful form. Sharing among researchers, not to mention broader access, is still relatively uncommon, although a recent study provides evidence of its benefit (McKiernan et al., 2016).

Clinicians are often missing clinical information on their patients, and longitudinal information on patients is difficult and expensive to obtain (Smith et al., 2005). Health care systems that seek to improve are stymied by the lack of longitudinal data, which limits them to a partial view of patients. In addition, information on the safety and effectiveness of some approved drugs and devices is incomplete, and this may undermine surveillance efforts (Brookings Institution, 2015).

Scientists are often blocked from accessing research data generated by others even when the work was funded by federal agencies. The IOM report *Sharing Clinical Trial Data: Maximizing Benefits, Minimizing Risks* states the problem succinctly:

"Vast amounts of data are generated over the course of a clinical trial; however, a large portion of these data is never published in peer-reviewed journals" (IOM, 2015a). The consequence of this scientific culture is inefficiency and irreproducibility. The incomplete, inadequate, and even absent harvest of research data, even those generated with public funds, wastes research investment and dishonors the contributions of research participants. Moreover, it slows scientific progress and impedes the self-correcting nature of good science (Silberzahn and Uhlmann, 2015). Academic institutions and their organizations have been relatively quiet about data sharing. For example, the authors of 88 percent of NIH-funded journal articles did not deposit their datasets into known repositories, and this keeps the data "invisible" (Read et al., 2015).

Despite federal regulations, the path to data access is often not easy. Many institutions do not provide seamless ways to transmit or download data. Despite the advocacy of the OpenNotes movement to make clinical notes visible to patients, many institutions do not share this digital information without substantial effort by patients. Some individuals and organizations have formed coalitions to bring attention to the issue, such as Free the Data (free-the-data.org), Get My Health Data (getmyhealthdata.org), and Get My Data (getmydata.org). The coalitions are making slow headway, and there are reports of resistance by those who are concerned that HIPAA prevents people from accessing their health information (which is false) or who are not clear about the various secure transmission mechanisms, such as Direct (DirectTrust, 2012; Evans, 2016; Lohr, 2011). In addition, participants and potential participants in clinical trials are often unable to facilitate sharing of clinical data. Many people do not understand the power of sharing their own health data and are therefore not creating the demand for their data. It is noteworthy that Pfizer now shares data collected in clinical trials with patient participants, both providing patients with nontechnical summaries of trial findings and using Blue Button technology to allow patients to access all collected medical data directly and integrate them into EHRs (Pfizer, 2016).

For any data sharing to be useful, it will first be necessary to ensure that health-data records are trustworthy enough and interoperable among different systems. Improving the quality of notes is also relevant to written records, although some issues are specific to EHRs. There are reports of egregious errors and growing verbiage in electronic medical records, especially as health providers resort to copy-and-paste to fill out the records (Hirschtick, 2006). A 2012 IOM report, *Health IT and Patient Safety: Building Safer Systems for Better Care*, found that poor implementation and use of HIT could lead to new hazards, such as dosing errors or delays in the detection of illnesses (IOM, 2012b). A 2013 report published by members of the American College of Emergency Physicians identified the need for EHR users to have a systematic process to provide comments about potential safety problems and other issues with the EHR systems—a departure from the current system wherein some EHR vendors prohibit users from sharing potential dangers, even in academic publications (Farley et al., 2013). Despite the challenges, there remains much that is trustworthy and reliable in EHRs.

The biggest issue is that progress is not fast enough. For data holders, sharing can represent the loss of a valued asset and the exposure of their work to the scrutiny of others, and the incentives of data holders are not always fully aligned with those of patients and other researchers and physicians. Part of the problem stems from the cost structure, wherein data sharing requires both upfront and continuing spending on infrastructure, administration, standardization, and human resources (Wilhelm et al., 2014). And, of course, data holders face substantial opportunity costs—the time and resources spent on sharing data that would otherwise have gone to conducting new research, running analyses, and generating new data. One particular data-sharing project for Alzheimer's disease research found that 10 percent to 15 percent of total costs and 15 percent of investigators' time was spent on data-sharing activities (Wilhelm et al., 2014). Given that more comprehensive data-sharing projects will impose commensurately higher costs on the data holder and that the benefits will be spread among all parties, some researchers find themselves supporting data sharing for others without sharing their own data.

Many institutional data holders face a public-goods problem with data sharing. Individual data holders will not capture the full social benefits of their own data sharing and will thus underinvest in sharing even as all parties benefit when a single data holder decides to share (Hall, 2014). In the language of economics, data sharing has positive externalities but internalized costs, and this leads to an undersupply of shared data. Mark Hall illustrates that reality with a small-scale example of a patient who has seen four doctors and is heading to a fifth; only the fifth doctor and the patient benefit from the first four doctors' data sharing (Hall, 2014). It cannot be assumed that the five doctors share patients in the same proportion, and the doctors will not necessarily agree to a reciprocal, quid pro quo data-sharing agreement, inasmuch as different doctors have different incentives to share data. Data sharing in connection with clinical trials presents a similar conundrum. A solution to the problem will require a realignment of incentives that enables doctors and researchers to focus on the best outcomes for patients without having to bear a disproportionate share of the costs.

Even those who seek to share data often encounter problems. For example, the IOM committee identified infrastructure, technology, workforce, and sustainability as key challenges in clinical-trial data sharing—issues that apply to all types of health care data sharing (IOM, 2015a). However, the IOM committee that studied the issue could not find a case of "harm" to data holders in data sharing.

In health systems, the sharing of data can enhance options for patients and reduce barriers to changing providers. The issues of access and security are ever-present concerns. The need to respect privacy concerns associated with a person's health-related data and the need to obtain permission, as appropriate, are equally important. The challenge of inadequate metadata, including documentation, impedes progress. Combining datasets that do not have common data models or that have inconsistently applied common models—and duplicative, sometimes conflicting, information—creates problems in use. The timely updating of data that continue to accumulate and the correction of errors remain problematic. High-quality, longitudinal, health-related data remain missing, particularly data generated from devices and responses to patient-reported measures and surveys.

Another issue is the movement of health care data without patients' permission. The Shared Nationwide Interoperability Roadmap states that the goal is a system with the patient at the center (ONC, 2015a). However, massive amounts of data are moving without people at the center. One company claims to have some 300 million EHRs—but without the people's permission (Lohr, 2016). Many companies traffic in a health-data economy, but patients are rarely asked to provide permission for movement of their records. Permission is not always possible, and there are permitted uses and disclosures, but it is possible that there can be greater focus on making it easy for people to be involved in decisions about their data.

The issue of permission is also bound to the issue of combining datasets. A 2012 paper in *Nature Reviews Genetics* identified the need to merge EHR data among regions to maximize the gains for research. The authors argued that true data interoperability would require "the development and implementation of standards and clinical-content models for the unambiguous representation and exchange of clinical meaning" (Jensen et al., 2012). All data-sharing activities today proceed with the institution at the center. As long as Institution A shares data with Institution B without involving the person to whom the data belong, there will be duplicative and incomplete data and difficulty in collecting them longitudinally. However, systems that are centered on the person allow much clearer and cleaner data sharing, much as financial systems allow people to move funds among financial accounts, instruments, and institutions. The person gives permission and manages issues surrounding identity. Such systems in health information management would produce the same benefits.

The size and complexity of the data require new techniques if the data are to yield important insights. Emerging big-data tools, which have proved valuable in other fields, have little utility without useful data. In the research arena, progress is slow; many studies are never published or reported—at least within a reasonable timeframe—and data sharing is an infrequent and often unavailable option (Ross et al., 2012). The computational burden may also be large and require new investment. Data sharing involves considerable costs, such as the costs of developing an infrastructure, curating the data, supporting security measures, and making operations transparent for clinical research sharing. Who would pay for such systems and how the return on investment would be measured are still unclear. Perhaps the most critical issues to be addressed are how the systems can be sustainable and who should bear the burden of the costs.

PRIORITY CONSIDERATIONS

The following considerations apply to the sharing of research data and health-related data (most often with patient permission). The overall goal is to increase the capacity of the health care and medical-research enterprises to enable efficient, secure, and permission-based sharing of data—and for people to be involved, to the extent possible, in decisions about their data. Moreover, in cases in which detailed consent is not possible, there is an imperative to remain attentive to privacy concerns. The considerations are in five main categories: foster a culture of data sharing, improve incentives for data sharing, create legal and regulatory tailwinds for data sharing, strengthen the infrastructure for data sharing, and invest in research and training related to data sharing.

Foster a Culture of Data Sharing

Improvements in data sharing in health care and science start with fostering a culture. For data sharing and its use to spread, the culture of health care and science will need to evolve in such a way that refusal or inability to share is understood as against the best interests of individuals and society. In health care, there should be a broad understanding of the rights of a person to view, download and access, and transmit or share his or her own health data, although it is important to remember that people retain the right not to share data. In research, there should be an understanding that good science and good scientific citizenship require that participant-level data be available for evaluation and reuse. Cooperative efforts among government, academic institutions, industry, consumer-advocacy organizations, and experts in science, health care, and ethics could set common expectations and build on foundational consensus documents, such as those produced by IOM. Statements by HHS Secretary Sylvia Burwell and NIH Director Francis Collins have demonstrated strong support for data sharing (Bowman, 2016; Healy, 2014). Such leadership and expectations need to be internalized throughout the health care and scientific communities.

There is a need to attend to the culture in medicine that has typically marginalized the right of people to be able to access their health records, failed to emphasize the potential for data to create smarter and more responsive health care delivery, and created the notion that investigators have discretion over sharing research results and data. An initiative directed toward fostering a culture of data sharing is warranted. The following proposals would help to kick-start the shift to a culture of data sharing:

- Engage social scientists to define cultural and economic forces that support the status quo.
- Define benefits of data sharing for different stakeholders.
- Identify levers that will change cultural norms regarding data sharing, recognizing that much of that change will come from new incentive models.
- Support working groups to develop clear articulation of the societal value of data sharing.
- Educate the public about data sharing, being attentive to privacy issues, including cases that illustrate the value.
- Define interventions to change the culture regarding data sharing in health care and medical research.

Improve Incentives for Data Sharing

Behaviors that are counter to a culture of data sharing are reinforced by current incentives. Those incentives benefit those who sequester data assets, uphold barriers that prevent people from accessing their records, deny organizations the ability to leverage data, and prevent scientists from sharing data. The evolution to a culture of data sharing will require a shift in the incentives:

- Develop rewards for data sharing and develop penalties for not sharing data.
- Require, to the greatest extent possible, the sharing of trial data with the publication of trial results.
- Encourage publishers to require that data be deposited at the time of publication.
- Provide reimbursement benefit for health systems that facilitate sharing with patients and researchers.
- Provide incentives to companies that have data-sharing programs.
- Give credit for data sharing and downstream use in the process for academic promotion.

- Seek solutions through challenges, such as the HHS Move Health Data Forward Challenge.
- Publicly report metrics on ease of data accessibility for patients at the hospital, health-system, or office level.

Create Legal and Regulatory Tailwinds for Data Sharing

Legal and regulatory actions by the government will be important levers for change. Interest in data sharing is relevant to many federal agencies and departments, including ONC, CMS, the Food and Drug Administration (FDA), NIH, the Health Resources and Services Administration, the Agency for Healthcare Research and Quality, the Department of Defense, the Department of Veterans Affairs, and the Centers for Disease Control and Prevention. The IOM report *Vital Signs: Core Metrics for Health and Health Care Progress* issued a clarion call for coordination and alignment among multiple government agencies in the context of identifying core metrics for measuring health and health care progress (IOM, 2015b). The report argues that opportunities are lost when data collected in one program do not work synergistically with data in another program and when data are not used to create new knowledge. Drawing on the example of the IOM *Vital Signs* report, the alignment of many federal agencies and departments in support of data sharing is critical for providing momentum to change the culture and behaviors in the research environment. In fact, as exemplified in the federal HIT strategic plan, there is already collaboration among federal organizations.

- Establish discussion, including consumers, on permitted uses and disclosures related to which data can be shared without people's explicit permission and provide guidance on informed-consent language.
- Continue to link requirements to facilitate sharing with funding, certification, and approval.
- Continue to promote and harmonize federal standards relevant to data sharing.
- Continue to extend federal standards for ownership, security, and privacy of health care data.
- Continually evaluate regulations, such as those based on HIPAA, following the guidelines of the IOM report *Beyond the HIPAA Privacy Rule: Enhancing Privacy, Improving Health Through Research* (IOM, 2009).
- Require a unique medical-device identifier in every relevant electronic medical record and on administrative claims, building on CMS and FDA recommendations (Rubenfire, 2016).
- Encourage use of standardized authentication systems for patient portal access, using the OAuth 2.0 authorization standard as a model.

- Investigate the value of new approaches, such as FHIR, and promote successful models, highlighting not only the approach but best practices in implementation.
- Promote the provision of information to people about their data rights.
- Develop mechanisms for easy public reporting of instances of information blocking.
- Penalize information-blocking.
- Establish an honor roll for health-related companies that have exemplary sharing policies.
- Penalize academic institutions that do not share data produced with federally funded grants.
- Highlight publicly the data-sharing performance of academic institutions.
- Provide benefits for data sharing in the drug-approval and device-approval process.
- Require data sharing (following the IOM recommendations) for studies that use public funds.
- Support the idea of data sharing related to trials published in journals.

Strengthen the Infrastructure for Data Sharing

As noted in the IOM report, platforms for storing and managing trial data efficiently are inadequate. The lack of infrastructure applies equally to a variety of data assets in health care and science, including personal health information and basic-research data.

- Convene stakeholders and seek common requirements for infrastructure.
- Investigate economies of scale and benefits of competition.
- Define particular needs of different stakeholder groups.
- Identify opportunities for joint ventures between aligned groups, including federal agencies and departments.
- Investigate sustainable business models for data-sharing infrastructure.
- Investigate government solutions for data-sharing infrastructure.
- Define minimal costs of high-quality data sharing in different venues.
- Develop means of promoting FAIR (find, access, interoperate, reuse) principles (Wilkinson et al., 2016).
- Create standards that guarantee people access to their own research data.
- Create standards for informed consent that consider reuse of research data.
- Invest in the human capital necessary to advance an ecosystem that promotes data sharing.

- Continue to open federal databases to the public through APIs such as FHIR (or other suitable means).
- Continue development and dissemination of ontologies (the classes, properties, and relationships between class members with which to model health data sharing).
- Investigate a unique national patient identifier and other strategies to combine a person's health-related data.
- Support the development and implementation of participant-centric data-sharing solutions.

Increase Capability by Investing in Research on Data Sharing

Success in optimizing the organization and use of data to achieve better health and health care will depend on the capability of generating knowledge. The capability to do so will require investment in research that is germane to data sharing. We need to apply what we know while developing more fully the science that underlies successful and sustainable data sharing in health care and science.

The issue of data sharing has technological, computational, organizational, economic, and social dimensions, all of which require study. Research investment should span data science, implementation science, management science, network science, economics, law, and health policy.

Also important is the scope of research in data science. Designing a new assay is considered scientific, but developing a new genomic alignment algorithm or approach for data interoperability is not. To embrace data-driven health care, we need a culture shift in what is considered science, as distinct from infrastructure, from a computational perspective.

- Develop novel approaches to deidentification and privacy concerns.
- Support national surveys of the public's views on data sharing in health care and science.
- Support funding for primary informatics research that is relevant to data sharing.
- Develop analytics suited to shared data and their particular challenges.
- Develop methods that address data access and security.
- Develop methods to enhance data sharing for people who have limited technical ability, health literacy, or access to technology.
- Develop platforms that increase the efficiency and transparency of sharing.
- Develop tools and methods to support infrastructure.
- Test, strengthen, and refine or improve common data models.
- Develop new models of academic credit for sharing data.
- Develop analytics tuned to issues peculiar to data sharing.

- Develop strategies that lower the cost of data sharing.
- Test strategies for enforcing data-sharing policies.
- Investigate benefits, risks, and costs associated with data-sharing, especially as behavior evolves.
- Investigate ethical underpinnings of the imperative to share data for societal benefit.
- Investigate state-based initiatives to assess effects of data sharing, and use states as laboratories.
- Build on evidence-based methods in other fields; pilot-test strategies for engaging the public.
- Evaluate the quality of data being shared and standards for sharing.
- Provide funding mechanisms for data sharing.
- Value those who contribute to data science as we do other researchers and health care professionals.

Options for Strategic Federal Initiatives

Strategic federal initiatives are needed for issues whose substantial consequences span multiple levels of influence. An overarching strategy to promote sharing, curation, and use of data to improve health and health care must address key impediments to progress and promote a view of a better future while articulating the features of that future. The recommendations above focus attention on linchpins in the movement toward data sharing: culture, incentives, infrastructure, and capability. Only the federal government, with its many agencies and departments, can provide the impetus for each of those to enlist the support of other key stakeholders nationwide. Such a pathway would build on successful initiatives that are making data sharing better, faster, and less expensive—strengthening them and enabling data sharing and transparency to be vital parts of efforts to improve health care and science in tandem, invigorating a data economy, and producing marked societal gains. Many of the efforts are already under way in the federal government, and it is important to avoid duplication. Such an initiative could be undertaken by HHS with the US Chief Technology Officer and would be best accomplished as a White House initiative spanning the government. It would also seek to support market forces in leveraging government efforts by creating products that facilitate the use of increasingly available data. The government has the power to recognize achievements, promote education about rights and laws, institute standards, penalize infractions, and protect individuals. This topic is thus primed for a strategic federal initiative, building on and strengthening existing efforts, to accelerate progress toward an era in which digital health-related data could fulfill their role in creating smarter, more personalized health care and more rapid, timely, and efficient science. HHS should conduct participant-centric, citizen science-based pilots based on digital health data to accelerate learning and begin real-world implementation.

POTENTIAL METRICS

Increasing access to health-related data, with people at the center, and producing tools to leverage the data as part of a learning health system could have dramatic effects. The more people own their own health and wellness data, the more likely it is that they will be able to act on them to create better value for themselves. It should be possible to leverage digital data fully to ensure that individual health care decisions are informed by all the data; that, with permission, the data could be used for research and system improvement; and that the data could increase transparency in health care and be an impetus toward improved quality and reduced waste. The potential knowledge trapped within those digital data should be released to propel health care toward more effective and efficient practice in such a way that we could save the time and resources currently devoted to chasing data sources and repeating clinical testing. Medicine would improve if clinicians knew that patients would see their work and could easily share it with other experts for second opinions. Greater data availability could enable people to see how thousands of others who have similar clinical characteristics and backgrounds responded to different treatment paths and then have an evidence-based discussion with their doctors before embarking on a specific treatment plan. It is possible that if people had a say in how their data were used and were positioned to enable higher-quality, more timely, and more comprehensive data to fuel new insights, it could help other people who had similar problems. Health systems and other health care providers could use the data to redesign care and improve results. Scientists could perceive their data as a public good and would share generously, seeking to accelerate progress and finding ways to reward most those who enable others to produce important insights. Savings could be achieved if we sought full harvesting of data generated through research and provided opportunities for reexamination, reanalysis, and reinterpretation of study data to promote public discussion in search of truth. The quality of science could increase if researchers knew that others would view their work, their operating manuals, and their processes.

Interventions that aspire to promote data sharing as a means of improving health care should be evaluated by measures that assess progress toward the goal and monitor for unintended adverse consequences. Leading indicators can signal whether other forces are promoting or impeding progress and results. The metrics should be used to assess progress in enabling people to obtain and use their health data, enabling organizations to share and use their data, and enabling research-ers to report and share their data. The development of metrics requires input from stakeholders, data sources to enable the calculations, and specifications that promote a reflection of the domain under assessment. Details aside, we present below a sampling of metrics that could be used to track progress in data sharing:

- Percentage of late-stage clinical trials by funder with complete and accurate reporting in Clinicaltrials.gov within 12 months and publication within 18 months of completion.
- Percentage of Clinical trials by academic center reported within 12 months and published within 18 months of completion.
- Percentage of nation's hospitals that have Blue Button capability, the ability of patients to view and download their personal health records.
- Percentage of 1,000 largest physician offices that makes it possible for patients to view, download, and transmit their EHR information.
- Percentage of nation's 100 largest hospitals to move data by FHIR API with a common data standard.
- Percentage of patients in nation's hospitals who have patient portals.
- Percentage of hospitals and offices that have high-quality data from patient portals, according to high-quality data standards.
- Percentage of academic institutions that commit to incorporate data sharing into decisions on individual promotions.
- Percentage of academic institutions that have data-sharing initiatives.
- Percentage of federally funded medical-research grantees who report results in a public venue within 12 months of finishing their studies.
- Number of publications per year that are based on NIH-shared datasets.
- Number of publications from prominent data sharing efforts.
- Number of complaints about information blocking and its root causes.
- Number of initiatives for data sharing throughout federal agencies.

CONCLUSION

Data sharing, data curation, and data use for a continuously learning health system hold great potential for promoting better engagement by people in their health and health care, better care, less waste, better outcomes, and greater progress toward medical breakthroughs. To move forward, there are three vital directions. The first is a change in the culture and incentive structure of the health system and research enterprise to move away from a status quo anchored in an environment that offers little opportunity for data sharing. The inefficiencies, errors, restrictions, duplication, and waste imposed by barriers to sharing and use of digital health-related data cost lives and resources. The second direction is to encourage people's access to their data by clarifying and strengthening their rights to their data. This would require changes in regulatory structures and the creation of the tools and infrastructure needed for patients to put their data to work for them. Building on the first two, the third and final direction is to provide seamless means to curate and produce usable data from disparate sources to promote opportunities for improvements in health and health care. Data can fuel the learning health system of the future; but as long as data remain in discrete silos, people will be unable to leverage their own data fully to create maximum value for their own health. Moving toward an enlightened system that grows smarter with the accumulation of data will require unprecedented levels of collaboration among and communication between all stakeholders in the health system. Such a grand strategy for change offers an ideal opportunity for government facilitation and support because these changes are likely to yield an immense return on investment for society.

SUMMARY RECOMMENDATIONS FOR VITAL DIRECTIONS

1. Foster a culture of data sharing.
2. Create the incentives, regulatory alignment, and infrastructure for data sharing.
3. Build the research and federal leadership for continuous improvements in data-sharing capacity.

REFERENCES

Bill & Melinda Gates Foundation. 2016a. Bill & Melinda Gates Foundation open access policy. Available at http://www.gatesfoundation.org/How-We-Work/General-Information/Open-Access-Policy (accessed August 25, 2016).

Bill & Melinda Gates Foundation. 2016b. Information sharing appoach. Available at http://www.gatesfoundation.org/how-we-work/general-information/information-sharing-approach (accessed August 25, 2016).

Bowman, D. 2016. Sylvia Mathews Burwell: Work remains to make healthcare system open. Available at http://www.fiercehealthit.com/story/sylvia-mathews-burwell-work-remains-make-healthcare-system-open/2016-05-10 (accessed August 25, 2016).

The Brookings Institution. 2015. *Strengthening patient care: Building an effective national medical device surveillance system.* Available at http://www.fda.gov/downloads/aboutfda/centersoffices/officeofmedicalprod-uctsandtobacco/cdrh/cdrhreports/ucm435112.pdf (accessed August 25, 2016).

CMS (Centers for Medicare & Medicaid Services). 2016. CMS data navigator. Available at https://dnav.cms.gov/ (accessed August 25, 2016).

CommonWell Health Alliance. No date. Why CommonWell Health Alliance. Available at http://www.commonwellalliance.org/ (accessed August 25, 2016).

DirectTrust. 2012. What is DirectTrust? Available at https://www.directtrust.org/about-directtrust/ (accessed August 25, 2016).

Evans, B. 2016. Barbarians at the gate: Consumer-driven health data commons and the transformation of citizen science. *American Journal of Law and Medicine* 42(4).

Farley, F., K. Baumlin, A. Hamedani, D.S. Cheung, M.R. Edwards, D.C. Fuller, N. Genes, R.T. Griffey, J.J. Kelly, J.C. McClay, J. Nielson, M.P. Phelan, J.S. Shapiro, S. Stone-Griffin, and J.M. Pines. 2013. Quality and safety implications of emergency department information systems. *Annals of Emergency Medicine* 62(4):399–407.

FHIR (Fast Health Interoperability Resources). 2015. The Argonaut Project. Available at http://hl7.org/fhir/2015Jan/argonauts.html (accessed August 25, 2016).

Goodman, S., and H. Krumholz. 2015. Open science: PCORI's efforts to make study results and data more widely available. Available at http://www.pcori.org/blog/open-science-pcoris-efforts-make-study-results-and-data-more-widely-available (accessed August 25, 2016).

Hall, M. 2014. Property, Privacy and the Pursuit of Integrated Electronic Medical Records. Wake Forest University Legal Studies Paper 1334963. doi: 10.2139/ssrn.1334963.

HealthIT.gov. 2016a. Your health information rights. Available at https://www.healthit.gov/patients-families/your-health-information-rights (accessed August 25, 2016).

HealthIT.gov. 2016b. Interoperability pledge. Available at https://www.healthit.gov/commitment (accessed August 25, 2016).

Healy, M. 2014. Big data, meet big money: NIH funds centers to crunch health data. Available at http://www.latimes.com/science/sciencenow/la-sci-sn-big-data-money-20141009-story.html (accessed August 25, 2016).

Henry, J., Y. Pylypchuk, T. Searcy, and V. Patel. 2016. Adoption of Electronic Health Record Systems among U.S. Non-Federal Acute Care Hospitals: 2008–2015. ONC Data Brief 35, May. Available at http://dashboard.healthit.gov/evaluations/data-briefs/non-federal-acute-care-hospital-ehr-adoption-2008–2015.php (accessed August 25, 2016).

HHS OCR (Department of Health and Human Services Office for Civil Rights). 2016. HITECH Act enforcement interim final rule. Available at http://www.hhs.gov/hipaa/for-professionals/special-topics/HITECH-act-enforcement-interim-final-rule/index.html (accessed August 25, 2016).

HIPD (Health Information Privacy Division). 2016. Individuals' right under HIPAA to access their health information 45 CFR § 164.524. Available at http://www.hhs.gov/hipaa/for-professionals/privacy/guidance/access/ (accessed August 25, 2016).

Hirschtick, R. 2006. Copy-and-paste. *Journal of the American Medical Association* 295(20):2335–2336.

IOM (Institute of Medicine). 2009. *Beyond the HIPAA privacy rule: Enhancing privacy, improving health through research.* Washington, DC: The National Academies Press.

IOM. 2012a. *Report brief: Best care at lower cost: The path to continuously learning health care in America.* Available at http://www.nationalacademies.org/hmd/~/media/Files/Report%20Files/2012/Best-Care/BestCareReportBrief.pdf (accessed August 25, 2016).

IOM. 2012b. *Health IT and patient safety: Building safer systems for better care.* Washington, DC: The National Academies Press.

IOM. 2015a. *Sharing clinical trial data: Maximizing benefits, minimizing risk.* Washington, DC: The National Academies Press.

IOM. 2015b. *Vital signs: Core metrics for health and health care progress.* Washington, DC: The National Academies Press.

Jensen, P., L. Jensen, and S. Brunak. 2012. Mining electronic health records: Towards better research applications and clinical care. *Nature Reviews Genetics* 13:395–405.

Kendrick, D. 2011. The Beacon communities at one year: The Tulsa experience. Available at http://healthaffairs.org/blog/2011/06/01/the-beacon-communities-at-one-year-the-tulsa-experience/ (accessed August 25, 2016).

Lohr, S. 2011. U.S. tries open-source model for health data systems. *New York Times,* February 2. Available at http://bits.blogs.nytimes.com/2011/02/02/u-s-tries-open-source-model-for-health-data-systems/ (accessed August 25, 2016).

Lohr, S. 2016. IBM buys medical analytics company for $2.6 billion. *New York Times,* February 19, p. B3.

McKiernan, E. C., P. E. Bourne, C. T. Brown, S. Buck, A. Kenall, J. Lin, D. McDougall, B. A. Nosek, K. Ram, C. K. Soderberg, J. R. Spies, K. Thaney, A. Updegrove, K. H.Woo, and T. Yarkoni. 2016. Point of view: How open science helps researchers succeed. *eLife* 5:e16800.

Murugiah, K., J. D. Ritchie, N. R. Desai, J. S. Ross, and H. M. Krumholz. 2016. Availability of clinical trial data from industry-sponsored cardiovascular trials. *Journal of the American Heart Association* 5(4):e003307.

MyHealth Access Network. 2016. Available at http://myhealthaccess.net/who-we-are/ (accessed August 25, 2016).

NIHOER (National Institutes of Health Office of Extramural Research). 2016. NIH sharing policies and related guidance on NIH-funded research resources. Available at https://grants.nih.gov/policy/sharing.htm (accessed August 25, 2016).

ODPHP (Office of Disease Prevention and Health Promotion). 2016. Determinants of health. Available at https://www.healthypeople.gov/2020/about/foundation-health-measures/Determinants-of-Health (accessed August 25, 2016).

ONC (Office of the National Coordinator for Health Information Technology). 2014. Federal Health IT Strategic Plan: 2015–2010. Available at http://dashboard.healthit.gov/strategic-plan/federal-health-it-strategic-plan-2015–2020.php (accessed on August 25, 2016).

ONC. 2015a. Connecting health and care for the nation. A shared nationwide interoperability roadmap. Available at https://www.healthit.gov/sites/default/files/hie-interoperability/nationwide-interoperability-roadmap-final-version-1.0.pdf (accessed August 25, 2016).

ONC. 2015b. Report on health information blocking. Available at https://www.healthit.gov/sites/default/files/reports/info_blocking_040915.pdf (accessed August 25, 2016).

Ornstein, C. 2016. What Feds' push to share health data means for patients. Available at http://www.scpr.org/news/2016/05/09/60446/what-feds-push-to-share-health-data-means-for-pati/ (accessed August 25, 2016).

Pfizer. 2016. Returning clinical data to patients. Available at http:// www.pfizer.com/research/clinical_trials/trial_data_and_results/data_to_patients (accessed August 25, 2016).

PhRMA. 2013. Principles for responsible clinical trial data sharing. Available at http://www.phrma.org/phrmapedia/responsible-clinical-trial-data-sharing (accessed August 25, 2016).

PMIWG (Precision Medicine Initiative Working Group). 2015. The Precision Medicine Initiative Cohort Program—Building a research foundation for 21st century medicine. Available at http://acd.od.nih.gov/reports/PMI_WG_report_2015-09–17-Final.pdf (accessed August 25, 2016).

Read, K. B., J. R. Sheehan, M. F. Huerta, L. S. Knecht, J. G. Mork, B. L. Humphreys, and NIH Big Data Annotator Group. 2015. Sizing the problem of improving discovery and access to NIH-funded data: A preliminary study. *PLoS One* 10(7):e0132735.

Ross, J. S., and H. M. Krumholz. 2013. Ushering in a new era of open science through data sharing: The wall must come down. *Journal of the American Medical Association* 309(13):1355–1356.

Ross, J. S., T. Tse, D. A. Zarin, H. Xu, L. Zhou, and H. M. Krumholz. 2012. Publication of NIH funded trials registered in ClinicalTrials.gov: Cross sectional analysis. *British Medical Journal* 344:d7292.

Rubenfire, A. 2016. CMS and FDA advocate for device identifiers on claims forms. Available at http://www.modern-healthcare.com/article/20160714/NEWS/160719938 (accessed August 25, 2016).

Silberzahn, R., and E. L. Uhlmann. 2015. Crowdsourced research: Many hands make tight work. *Nature* 526(7572):189–191.

Smith, P., R. Araya-Guerra, C. Bublitz, B. Parnes, L.M. Dickinson, R. Van Vorst, J.M. Westfall, and W.D. Pace. 2005. Missing clinical information during primary care visits. *Journal of the American Medical Association* 293(5):565–571.

Straumsheim, C. 2014. Gates goes open. Available at https://www.insidehighered.com/news/2014/11/24/gates-foundation-announces-open-access-policy-all-grant-recipients (accessed August 25, 2016).

Taichman, D. B., J. Backus, C. Baethge, H. Bauchner, P. W. de Leeuw, J. M. Drazen, J. Fletcher, F. A. Frizelle, T. Groves, A. Haileamlak, A. James, C. Laine, L. Peiperl, A. Pinborg, P. Sahni, and S. Wu. 2016. Sharing clinical trial data: A proposal from the International Committee of Medical Journal Editors. *Annals of Internal Medicine* 164(7):505–506.

Tulsa Beacon Community. 2012. Available at https://www.healthit.gov/sites/default/files/beacon-factsheet-tulsa.pdf (accessed August 25, 2016).

Wellcome Trust. 2016a. Data sharing webpage. Available at http://www.wellcome.ac.uk/About-us/Policy/Spotlight-is-sues/Data-sharing/ (accessed August 25, 2016).

Wellcome Trust. 2016b. Why we're launching a new publishing platform. Available at https://wellcome.ac.uk/news/why-were-launching-new-publishing-platform (accessed August 25, 2016).

Wilhelm, E., E. Oster, and I. Shoulson. 2014. Approaches and costs for sharing clinical research data. *Journal of the American Medical Association* 311(12):1201–1202.

Wilkinson, M. D., M. Dumontier, I. J. Aalbersberg, G. Appleton, M. Axton, A. Baak, N. Blomberg, J. W. Boiten, L. B. da Silva Santos, P. E. Bourne, J. Bouwman, A. J. Brookes, T. Clark, M. Crosas, I. Dillo, O. Dumon, S. Edmunds, C. T. Evelo, R. Finkers, A. Gonzalez-Beltran, A. J. Gray, P. Groth, C. Goble, J. S. Grethe, J. Heringa, P.A.C. 'tHoen, R. Hooft, T. Kuhn, R. Kok, J. Kok, S. J. Lusher, M. E. Martone, A. Mons, A. L. Packer, B. Persson, P. Rocca-Serra, M. Roos, R. van Schaik, S. A. Sansone, E. Schultes, T. Sengstag, T. Slater,

G. Strawn, M. A. Swertz, M. Thompson, J. van der Lei, E. van Mulligen, J. Velterop, A. Waagmeester, P. Wittenburg, K. Wolstencroft, J. Zhao, and B. Mons. 2016. The FAIR guiding principles for scientific data management and stewardship. *Scientific Data* 3:160018.

AUTHOR INFORMATION

Harlan M. Krumholz, MD, SM, is Harold H. Hines, Jr. Professor of Medicine and Epidemiology and Public Health, Yale University School of Medicine. **Philip E. Bourne, PhD,** is Associate Director for Data Science, National Institutes of Health. **Richard E. Kuntz, MD, MSc,** is Senior Vice President, Chief Scientific, Clinical and Regulatory Officer, Medtronic, Inc. **Harold L. Paz, MD, MS,** is Executive Vice President, Chief Medical Officer, Aetna. **Sharon F. Terry, MA,** is President and CEO, Genetic Alliance. **Joanne Waldstreicher, MD,** is Chief Medical Officer, Johnson & Johnson.

18

INNOVATION IN DEVELOPMENT, REGULATORY REVIEW, AND USE OF CLINICAL ADVANCES

Michael Rosenblatt, MD, Christopher P. Austin, MD, Marc Boutin, JD, William W. Chin, MD, Steven K. Galson, MD, MPH, Sachin H. Jain, MD, MBA, Michelle McMurry-Heath, MD, PhD, Samuel R. Nussbaum, MD, John Orloff, MD, Steven E. Weinberger, MD, and Janet Woodcock, MD

This paper describes issues and challenges in inventing and regulating new medicines, vaccines, and devices and in integrating these advances into clinical practices as rapidly as appropriate and possible. It describes the landscape of discovery and invention, evaluation of efficacy and safety, determination of value, and postapproval surveillance and identifies windows of opportunity. It provides the rationale for markedly enhanced patient input throughout the process from target identification to decisions regarding insurance coverage. It describes the role of academe–industry collaboration in speeding the translation of research findings into health benefits and emphasizes the opportunity for medical education at multiple levels to realize the value of therapeutic innovations to society. Finally, it offers high-priority recommendations.

CONTEXT AND TYPES OF OPPORTUNITIES

The pharmaceutical and biotechnology sectors experienced considerable challenges during the first decade of the 21st century. Stagnant research and development (R&D) productivity and the slow pace and high cost of drug development led many to argue for new approaches to discovery, manufacturing, development, and commercialization of new products to meet patients' needs. Estimated costs for bringing a new drug to market through the research, development, and regulatory processes may be as much as $2.6 billion, a substantial increase over the previous decade (TCSDD, 2015). The complexities of the analytics and cost attributions present challenges that are sources of active discussion, but there is no question that the costs are substantial. Furthermore, about 85 percent of therapies fail through early clinical development, and only half those surviving to Phase III will be approved (Ledford, 2011). Some have argued that this "clinical-trial cliff" results from losing a substantial number of good drugs to outdated and impractical clinical-trial designs (Ledford, 2011). Those challenges are forcing all sectors (industry, regulators, academe, government agencies, and patient advocacies) to evaluate opportunities to replace traditional drug-development paradigms with newer and more efficient models (Boname et al., 2016; IOM, 2010; Kaitlin and Honig, 2013).

Favorable trends in new-product approvals and breakthrough therapies over the last few years indicate that efforts to adapt to a new landscape of bioinnovation may be starting to pay off. In 2015, the Food and Drug Administration (FDA) approved 45 novel drugs or biologics, more than the average number approved each year during the last decade (28) while applications for new approvals were steady. More "orphan" drugs for rare diseases are being approved than in previous years, and we are seeing regulatory approval of new treatments for broader conditions, such as various forms of cancer, heart failure, hypercholesterolemia, and infectious disease. Furthermore, the use of expedited regulatory pathways (fast track, accelerated approval, priority review, and breakthrough designation) for therapies (60 percent of novel drugs in 2015) that will offer much to patients in need has accelerated.

In the United States, several initiatives are under way to accelerate pharmaceutical innovation. Eight recommendations in the President's Council of Advisors on Science and Technology 2012 report sought to "double the output of innovative new medicines for patients with important unmet medical needs, while increasing drug efficacy and safety, through industry, academia and government working together to decrease clinical failure, clinical trial costs, time to market and regulatory uncertainty" (PCAST, 2012). The president's ambitious Precision Medicine Initiative (whitehouse.gov/precision-medicine) was kicked off in 2015, and FDA has offered accelerated approval pathways for specialized treatments for rare and life-threatening diseases. Approval of the 21st Century Cures Act by Congress could further speed regulatory approvals for therapies that will have a substantial effect on patients' lives. The Critical Path Institute (https://c-path.org) was established in 2005 with the aim of bringing academic, industry, and regulatory scientists together to improve the drug and device development process. TransCelerate BioPharma (transceleratebiopharmainc.com) is a nonprofit organization whose mission is to foster collaboration throughout the biopharmaceutical R&D community to drive more efficient delivery of effective new medicines to improve the health of people worldwide. Finally, the Innovative Medicines Initiative (imi.europa.eu) is Europe's largest public–private initiative; it was undertaken jointly by the European Union and the pharmaceutical industry to speed the development of better and safer medicines. The number of precompetitive collaborations designed to improve drug development continues to grow, increasing the odds that the future will see improved productivity of innovative therapies.

DISCOVERY OF NEW THERAPIES

Opportunities abound to improve efficiency in the discovery phase of new therapy development, including the following:

- *Target "validation."* New targets for drug development are urgently needed, and the Human Genome Project has provided thousands of potential targets. A precompetitive effort to determine which targets are most likely to produce therapeutic value would benefit all stakeholders and increase the success rate of new drug development.
- *Predictive toxicology and efficacy.* Unexpected adverse effects and lack of efficacy despite promising preclinical results in model systems lead to the failure of most potential drugs to progress to approval. New approaches, including pathway-based systems biology and "organ-on-a-chip" systems, have the potential to deliver more efficient and accurate predictions of safety and efficacy and thus to give drug developers real-time, human-based information with which to develop new therapies; these new approaches should also provide regulators with a better scientific basis on which to make regulatory decisions.
- *Additional uses for existing drugs.* Potentially the most efficient and safest way to develop a new treatment is to use a drug that is already in development or has been approved for another disease (sometimes referred to as repurposing). Use of mechanism-based nosology would facilitate this approach. The recognition that some diseases traditionally thought to be independent are, in fact, mechanistically related provides a transformative opportunity to treat several diseases with drugs that have been approved or are in development (particularly compelling examples are immune-oncology therapies). Applying this principle to all diseases and all drugs would require substantial effort.
- *Combination therapies.* Many disorders—such as infectious diseases, cancers, and hypertension—can require more than one drug for adequate treatment. Methods to identify combinations of drug candidates with improved efficacy and reduced safety risk would leverage the many individual therapies already developed and in development. Dedicated technology development, testing, and clinical-development strategies are needed.

- *New gene-based and cell-based therapies.* A recent scientific renaissance of gene therapy, powerful new gene-editing techniques, and the expanding flexibility of stem-cell technologies have the potential to provide transformational therapeutic approaches that are complementary to small-molecule and protein drugs. Most, however, are in the concept stage, and dedicated effort will be required to translate them to application to human disease.
- *Precompetitive collaboration.* Much of the current work in drug discovery and development is in the most challenging therapeutic sectors, such as neurodegenerative, autoimmune, and inflammatory diseases. In addition, endemic outbreaks of antibiotic-resistant bacteria or viral infections—such as Ebola and Zika, many pediatric diseases, and some rare diseases—still lack consistent R&D efforts. Given the lack of complete knowledge of the pathogenesis of such maladies, it is essential that industry, government, and academe appreciate that neither domain is sufficient alone and that they must work together to achieve the needed breakthroughs. The breakthroughs must be approached through more focused and organized precompetitive collaborations involving industry, government, academia, and other groups. Recent examples of success in the preclinical and clinical spaces include the Accelerating Medicines Partnership (nih.gov/research-training/accelerating-medicines-partnership-amp) in the former and the Alzheimer's Disease Neuroimaging Initiative (adni-info.org) in the latter. Such collaborations also hold promise of providing translational-science tools (such as organs-on-a-chip) that permit extrapolation of preclinical data to the clinic regarding both efficacy and safety.

DEVELOPMENT OF NEW THERAPIES

Over two-thirds of the total cost, in both dollars and time, of the discovery and development of a new drug is embedded in the clinical-testing phase. Hence, it is critical that advances in such arenas as biomarkers, patient-reported outcomes, innovative clinical-trial designs, use of real-world evidence (RWE), and precision medicine be deployed in this phase for optimal advantage.

- *Biomarkers.* Biomarkers are biologic indicators that may provide predictive, diagnostic, prognostic, risk, safety, and treatment monitoring information about a patient's condition or disease. Examples are biochemical, genetic, and imaging data that may identify groups of patients who might respond better to a specific intervention or serve as end points in clinical trials that complement or replace clinical end points. However, there is a paucity of qualified or "approved" biomarkers or combinations of biomarkers that can expedite the drug-development and regulatory process. Hence, there is a critical need for a biomarker-qualification process. That requires an understanding of the context of use followed by a consideration of the benefit:risk ratio of the marker and then an understanding of the kind of evidence standards that are required to "approve" it for use in preclinical and clinical testing. Successful establishment of a biomarker-qualification framework would expedite and promote work by industry, academe, and government—a collaborative effort that is necessary for ultimate progress.

- *Patient-reported outcomes.* Patient focus should be a primary goal of drug development rather than merely a desirable addition. Inclusion of patient-reported outcomes that provide insights into benefit:risk assessment is critical. Patient focus consists not merely of anecdotes but rather of a science of patient input as described later in the section "Educating the Public, Policymakers, and the Mass Media" (see page 385). To achieve that aspiration, the emerging discipline must be developed more rapidly and deliberately.

- *Innovative clinical-trial designs.* The traditional three-phase approach (assess safety, then obtain proof of concept of efficacy and establish a dose range, and then undertake pivotal clinical trials in large populations) may not always be the optimal way to test potential medicines. Adaptive designs blur the distinctions between the phases by using predetermined enrichment schemes bolstered by advanced statistical tools, such as Bayesian statistics and modeling. For instance, a seamless or phaseless clinical-trial approach has been used in recent oncology trials. A clinical trial might be optimized to maximize speed and minimize size. Furthermore, science-based approaches to determine the appropriate representation of females vs males, underrepresented racial and ethnic groups, and so on, should be used in the recruitment of patients for trials. And, pilot experiments are essential in testing new trial designs.

- *Real-world evidence.* It has been traditional practice to consider only information gained through randomized, double-blind, controlled clinical trials (RCTs) in deciding the efficacy or benefit and safety of new therapies. That approach has generally served medicine well. However, the current ability to gather large amounts of data presents an opportunity to gain knowledge about the benefits and safety of drugs in a real-world setting that heretofore was not possible. Indeed, the observational biases that are inherent in the use of RWE might be mitigated on the basis of the size of a cohort and the number of observations. RWE might add important information about medicines not seen with RCTs. Early applications of RWE might be more wisely applied to supplemental applications of approved medicines to diminish safety considerations but could complement RCTs in the future. Deployment of selected pilots in a continuous learning approach to explore the value of RWE in both postapproval and preapproval settings is warranted.

- *Precision medicine.* We have used medicines in a "one-size-fits-all" paradigm too long. That is due largely to lack of knowledge about how to match a specific drug to a specific patient. The identification of groups that might benefit more from a particular drug before clinical testing has already seen applications in oncology and rare diseases in a personalized-medicine approach. In the future, a hypothesis about a population that responds to an intervention more favorably than the rest of the cohort with the disease might be posited and examined. Clinical trials could be smaller and shorter, assuming that the effect size is significantly greater in the relevant group. That would lead to improved efficiency of clinical trials and reduce exposure of subjects who probably would not benefit from a given medicine. Ideally, precise diagnosis mated with precise drugs would result in precision medicine wherein the right patient would receive the right medicine at the right dosage and at the right time.

CLINICAL TRIAL EXECUTION

Beyond innovative designs, there are opportunities for greater efficiency in the execution of clinical trials, as follows:

- *New technology.* Improvements are necessary to streamline the number of required procedures, site qualification, recruitment, safety monitoring, real-time data evaluation, and the informed-consent process. New technologies—such as the use of biosensors, electronic sourcing, risk-based monitoring, electronic medical record (EMR)–linked recruitment tools, and Web-enabled trials— are already being piloted and implemented, positioning the clinical-research enterprise for substantial change. The simple establishment of a single institutional review board for collaborating institutions would speed clinical trials and reduce costs. New technologies alone are insufficient to transform the operating model of clinical trials, but if they are combined with alternative trial paradigms, such as the use of remote clinical-research networks or web-based "virtual" trials, the full cost benefit of new technologies for conducting clinical trials might be realized.
- *Decentralization of clinical trials.* Moving activities away from tertiary care centers and closer to patients in their own communities has the potential to reduce the infrastructure costs associated with drug development dramatically. At the same time, such measures could broaden the participation of untapped

groups of patients and providers who would otherwise not engage in clinical research studies.

- *Pragmatic clinical trials.* Decentralization of clinical trials and the incorporation of new digital technologies would also greatly facilitate the execution of "pragmatic clinical trials" (PCTs), which more directly address the real-world performance of new products compared with traditional RCTs. Pragmatic trials are typically designed to enroll more diverse patient populations in clinical-practice settings where compliance may be highly variable and are often integral to comparative-effectiveness research or large simple trials. Consequently, PCTs come closer than RCTs to addressing whether a product works under diverse practice conditions.

- *Integration with health care delivery.* The integration of clinical research with health care delivery presents another opportunity to transform how clinical studies are conducted, potentially gaining efficiency and reducing cost. By working with providers and information technologists to embed continuous learning, including clinical trials, in information-technology systems, such as EMRs, sponsors of clinical research could serve as a catalyst for creating what the Institute of Medicine has described as a learning health care system whereby care delivery is integrated with knowledge generation (IOM, 2007).

- *Safety assessment.* Sponsors of innovative products that hold promise for addressing unmet needs or represent important improvements over standard of care are increasingly using expedited review processes. Limited patient exposure before market entry raises the question of how to address assessment of the safety profile. Products with novel mechanisms of action can have unforeseen rare but potentially serious adverse effects that might be observed only after a large number of patients have been exposed or after a duration of exposure that exceeds what was studied in preapproval trials. That applies generally but is more acute for products coming to market via an accelerated approval pathway with a limited safety database. Although improvements in predictive toxicology and safety assessment may mitigate the risk of adverse effects to some extent, earlier market entry of innovative products generally means that safety and effectiveness profiles are not fully elucidated. Consequently, an understanding of a potential shift in the benefit:risk ratio in the postapproval setting requires continuous monitoring through such mechanisms as the FDA Sentinel initiative (FDA, 2016a), a distributed data and analytic partner network that allows queries related to medical-product safety and comparative effectiveness and education of patients, the public, and the mass media.

REGULATORY REVIEW

Regulators increasingly will have to respond to the expectations of a wide array of stakeholders outside the biomedical-research community. The current societal imperatives—expediting products for unmet medical needs and generating better evidence to optimize therapy when alternatives exist—will probably strengthen in the next decade. Intensifying interest of patient groups, legislatures, and the mass media will lead to expansion of regulators' tasks in such spheres as global harmonization and "regulatory convergence," access to investigational drugs, use of real-world evidence (RWE) in regulatory decisions, clinical-trial data transparency, and response to outbreaks and pandemics. Regulators increasingly will need to take into account the needs of payers and technology assessors when considering trial design and outcome measures.

- *Regulatory convergence.* The United States has the strongest medical-product regulatory system in the world. As more and more countries try to emulate FDA, we are seeing a proliferation of global regulators and with them greater variety in regulatory standards among countries. The increasing globalization of medical-product development is leading to a stronger push toward worldwide "regulatory convergence." For the past two decades, the International Conference for Harmonisation of Technical Requirements for Pharmaceuticals for Human Use (ICH; ich.org/home.html) has been the vehicle for development of common standards. ICH was convened primarily by the regulators and innovating pharmaceutical industries of three regions—Japan, Europe, and the United States. ICH has recently been re-formed to recognize the global nature and broad scope of drug manufacturing and will have much broader participation by regulators and industry worldwide. Similar efforts are under way with regard to medical devices via such organizations as the International Medical Device Regulators Forum (imdrf.org/index.asp). The harmonization activities are resource intensive. Outside ICH, regulators are working together on greater harmonization of regulatory procedures. The United States is evaluating mutual reliance on manufacturing inspections with the inspectorates of countries in the European Union. FDA has the opportunity to act not only as an active participant in global regulatory convergence but also as a model participant.
- *Closing the knowledge gap between innovators and regulators.* The rate of scientific progress and therapeutic innovation in all sorts of medical products is increasing exponentially. With true innovation, the innovators not only are the leading experts in a specific technology but may be the only people that fully understand all the issues at play. The knowledge gap between innovators

and regulators can lead to delays in allowing pioneering therapies to reach the patients that need them the most. Initial efforts are under way by the FDA Center for Devices and Radiological Health (CDRH) to establish mechanisms to provide additional reviewer training via programs like the Experiential Learning Program (FDA, 2016b) and the Network of Experts (FDA, 2016c). However, they fall short in true technologic innovation, in which specific knowledge may not exist outside the innovators. FDA will need to explore new methods of interacting with sponsor companies and outside experts to understand the technologies that they regulate and the appropriate methods of evaluating them to ensure that US patients have timely access to all approvable therapies.

- *Access to investigational drugs.* Many states have passed "right-to-try" laws that declare a seriously ill patient's right to request an investigational drug without government oversight. FDA approves almost all requests for patient access, but problems persist, including disparities in access to information, shortage of drug supplies, lack of access to an institutional review board, unwillingness of physicians to suggest or take responsibility for administering investigational drugs, and sponsors' inability or unwillingness to create access programs. Nonprofits are making multiple efforts to develop "patient navigator" functions to improve transparency and increase access.

- *Postapproval evaluation of medical products.* It is clear that no matter how high the regulatory bar, premarketing studies are often imperfect in predicting real-world performance in diverse patient populations and care settings. There is great interest in using digital health care data to evaluate the performance of marketed products. The FDA Amendments Act instructed FDA to construct an active drug-safety surveillance system that would use such data. The FDA Sentinel initiative (FDA, 2016a) is operational and contains data on almost 200 million people, mainly from claims. Industry has long used RWE—data from health care settings—to describe unmet medical needs, assess the economic value of drug products, and study disease incidence, prevalence, and natural history. RWD are increasingly used by industry to conduct postmarketing comparative-effectiveness research, to characterize drug benefit:risk profiles, to facilitate postmarketing safety signal identification and evaluation, and to develop quality-of-care measures. FDA is also broadly interested in the use of RWD to generate evidence beyond drug safety. In addition to the studies described above, randomized and other types of interventional trials can be conducted in practice settings by using EMRs to capture results. FDA is exploring linkages between its Sentinel initiative and the National Patient-Centered Clinical Research Network (PCORnet; pcornet.org), which contains

EMR data, and registries and other data sources. Key priorities for the effort, which might involve FDA and possibly academia, include expanding the use and utility of common data models, establishing regulatory standards for data integrity and human-subject protection in real-world trials and data-collection efforts, improving methods for design and analysis, and building regulatory expertise in the mining, interpretation, and use of RWD to enable more timely patient access to innovative therapies.

- *Innovative regulatory policy.* The pace of therapeutic innovation is growing rapidly, often with little corresponding evolution to the dated regulatory paradigm by which the products will be judged. For example, innovation in the combination-product space (the combination of a device with a drug or biologic) has been constrained by a regulatory system that has lacked full transparency and predictability. Recent FDA initiatives to strengthen and improve the known issues with the regulatory review of combination products are a step in the right direction, such as development of the Combination Products Policy Council (FDA, 2016d) and launching of the Lean Management Process Mapping Project (FDA, 2016e), but reveal a fundamental flaw in the current regulatory paradigm, namely, that regulatory processes are not systematically evaluated and improved unless they reach a tipping point. Ideally, medical-product stakeholders would be working in real time to assess and improve regulatory paradigms to ensure that regulatory processes are not adding unnecessary obstacles to patient access to safe and effective innovative products.

PATIENT-CENTERED PRODUCT DEVELOPMENT

Historically, patients have not been engaged in medical-product development beyond their participation in clinical trials. However, the paradigm is changing. Patient input from early-stage R&D through the postapproval period, including insurance-coverage decisions, is increasingly recognized as essential (Norris et al., 2015; Pogorelc, 2013). Many stakeholders—including researchers, drug developers, and FDA—are starting to engage patients to develop mutually beneficial core objectives and ensure greater public acceptance. The mandate of regulators emphasizes needs of and risks to the population, but patients have views of the benefit:risk ratio that emphasize the individual perspective. Those views often differ substantially and need to be reconciled. Engaging patients directly will ensure that medical products are designed to meet their needs and that clinical trials capture information that is relevant and specific to intended end users. Learning and change for all participants in the health ecosystem will be necessary to speed and enable the integration of patient preference into the health care system and overcome the uncertainty and unfamiliarity associated with patient-preference data.

Patient input can help greatly to identify unmet needs and set research priorities by influencing end-point selection and clinical-trial design and conduct; this will result in easier and faster clinical-trial recruitment, less burdensome trials, and the evaluation of outcomes relevant to patients (Hoos et al., 2015). By ensuring that new products reflect patients' needs, stakeholders can avoid expensive errors. For example, billions of dollars were spent on development of Exubera, an inhalable form of insulin, but it was removed from the market after only 1 year when people who had diabetes did not see sufficient benefit from the product (Heinemann, 2008). The result of patient engagement is new treatments that meet patients' needs. The practice of including patient input throughout a product's life cycle is growing and evolving, but many challenges must be overcome to achieve a patient-centered drug-development process, including the following:

- *Incorporating patient input.* Stakeholders vary widely, so there is a clear need to identify appropriate methods, strategies, and approaches to engage with patients. Public–private partnerships could spearhead collaborative efforts to develop methodologic standards for collecting patient input and developing consensus-based guidelines. The engagement rubric released by the Patient-Centered Outcomes Research Institute (PCORI) illustrates how input from patient and stakeholder partners can be incorporated throughout the entire research continuum (PCORI, 2015). The Medical Device Innovation Consortium produced a framework for incorporating patient preferences into regulatory assessments of new medical technology, and the University of Maryland's Center of Excellence in Regulatory Science and Innovation has created a patient-focused drug-development rubric (MDIC, 2015; UMCERSI, 2015). Over the past decade, FDA has launched a number of initiatives aimed at expanding patient engagement to inform medical-product reviews. The Center for Drug Evaluation and Research (CDER) launched the Patient-Focused Drug Development program and the CDRH issued draft guidance on the use of patient-preference information in device approvals and created the Patient Engagement Advisory Committee (Enriquez, 2015; FDA, 2015, 2016f). Similar activity to engage patients is taking place globally, for example, the Patient Focused Medicine Development coalition (patientfocusedmedicine.org) and the Innovative Medicines Initiative (imi.europa.eu) (Hoos et al., 2015; Supple et al., 2015). Those examples demonstrate a growing acceptance of patients as partners in the development and regulatory process and urgency to target research efforts collectively.

- *Building capacity to engage with patients.* There is a need to build patient skills so that they are better prepared to engage and play a more influential role. For example, the Parkinson's Disease Foundation's learning institutes have trained nearly 300 volunteers to play a role at every level in Parkinson's disease research (PDF, 2016). Similarly, the Cystic Fibrosis Foundation has worked with the medical community to establish more than 110 cystic fibrosis care centers nationwide, about 80 of which can conduct clinical trials (IOM, 2012).

- *Establishing FDA guidance.* Despite efforts to increase patient engagement in drug development, regulatory uncertainty is a major barrier to obtaining useful input (Nordrum, 2015). Industry stakeholders believe that for purposes of providing input the best patient is an informed patient. So industry researchers seek greater clarity regarding interactions with patients because of concerns that such communication might be viewed as "promotional." The patient and stakeholder communities have called on FDA to provide guidance about such topics as appropriate industry interactions with patients, incorporation of patient information on product labels, and linking of patient information to benefit:risk assessments (NHCGA, 2015). Without clear FDA guidelines that define appropriate bilateral communication between industry and patients, biopharmaceutical companies will not risk implementing innovative engagement strategies. Conversely, guidelines that are cocreated with measured input from the patient and stakeholder communities will receive greater acceptance and result in better use.

- *Defining value.* Value models have emerged recently as the latest tools for assessing the worthiness of new medical products; however, value is often confused with cost or price and described in narrow terms of cost effectiveness. Cost effectiveness may be an indicator of value from the payer perspective (and can be influenced by discounts, bundling purchases, and a one-size-fits-all population approach), but it is often unrelated to the patient perspective. For patients, value is individualized and may evolve with disease trajectory or the stage of a patient's life. In 2015, several initiatives to calculate value were released (ICER, 2016; MSKCC, 2015; NCCN, 2016; Schnipper et al., 2015), but it is not apparent that individual patients or patient organizations were engaged in their creation or development. A collaborative effort of all stakeholders is recommended to develop an accurate value-model rubric (NHC, 2016).

Priority considerations for increasing patient engagement in developing new treatments include:

- strengthening and expanding initiatives for patient engagement, such as those under way in CDER and CDRH;
- continuously evolving the FDA's Patient-Focused Drug Development program (FDA, 2015) to create opportunities for patients and patient organizations to provide their perspectives to FDA;
- convening FDA and stakeholders, including the patient community, to establish methods for gathering and using patient input in drug development;
- clarifying how FDA will evaluate and measure patient preferences and incorporate them into regulatory assessment;
- helping to educate the patient community about drug development, regulation, and insurance coverage and about mechanisms for participating in patient-engagement efforts; and
- convening the Centers for Medicare & Medicaid Services (CMS) and stakeholders, including the patient community, to gather input for assessing the "value" of new medications and the implications for drug coverage and reimbursement.

SPEEDING THE UPTAKE OF MEDICAL ADVANCES INTO CLINICAL PRACTICE

Within the next decade, whole-genome sequencing and an understanding of the molecular profiles of cancers and therapies targeted to alterations in cancer have the potential to usher in an age of personalized medicine and novel approaches to drug discovery. Despite the promise of exceptional health and health care, we continue to have a disconnect between clinical knowledge and the evidence basis of care on the one hand and the care that is delivered to patients on the other hand. Clinicians, particularly primary care physicians—who are taking on a greater role as coordinators of care—and specialists, are unable to keep up with the explosion of information (over 1 million health-related publications each year). Our health information systems do not provide sufficient clinical support and advanced analytics to guide care or innovative care models. We are living in an age of big data, but we are not optimizing the use of the data. For example, during the 1990s, many women needlessly underwent bone-marrow transplantation for breast cancer before it was shown to be an ineffective treatment.

How do we close the time gap between the development of new evidence and its integration into practice? Several notable approaches that will serve as a framework for the future are under way. They involve the use of RWE and collaborations among sectors of the health care system that will generate knowledge about the best use of drugs, devices, and clinical models of care; cognitive computing to understand the most effective and appropriate interventions for enhanced clinical outcomes; specialists working in their professional organizations to guide clinical care, reduce the current variation in care, and promote evidence-based care; harmonized quality measures and payment instruments; effective leveraging of new organizational structures and their clinical leaders; and the enabling of patients to facilitate shared information and become partners in care.

- *Distributed data networks.* One particularly important example of the more rapid translation of evidence into practice is the FDA Sentinel initiative. Working collaboratively with health care systems, health plans, and manufacturers enables FDA to monitor the safety of newly approved products by using a distributed-data model that can identify, often rapidly, safety issues and extremely rare events. The system creates a federated dataset that enables query of all participating health-plan and delivery-system data, enabling aggregation of data on more than 100 million people. PCORI, through PCORnet, and the National Institutes of Health (NIH) Collaboratory Distributed Research Network are taking similar approaches to engage key providers and advance real-world, observational clinical research.
- *Cognitive computing.* Cognitive computing has been used to identify targeted treatment options for patients who have specific variants of disease. Memorial Sloan Kettering Cancer Center, for example, has been working with IBM's Watson Health (mskcc.org/about/innovative-collaborations/watson-oncology) to enable a new paradigm for cancer care in which patient genomic data can be checked against libraries of clinical-trial data to identify treatment paradigms that are most closely tailored to a patient's particular variant of cancer. To some extent, that automates the process of matching evidence to appropriate practice-based situations in which it can be used and ensures that physicians are informed of the latest advances in science. Those approaches will find their way to consumers as people become more deeply knowledgeable about alternative approaches to care and their preferences for care.
- *Professional standard setting.* The Choosing Wisely campaign (choosingwisely. org), developed by the American Board of Internal Medicine Foundation, exemplifies how the medical profession can best work together to synthesize evidence and drive it into practice. The campaign, aimed at determining approaches to remove waste and ineffective care from our health care system, assembled more than 70 medical-specialty organizations to identify over 300 areas of ineffective clinical care. This resulted in new guidelines about appropriate care. In connection with multiple key stakeholder organizations,

including such leading consumer organizations as Consumer Reports, the new guidelines were made visible within specialties and in general public discourse. Early data suggest that the campaign has been successful in promoting the adoption of new practices and in the discontinuation of ineffective and wasteful practices.

- *Performance and quality standard setting by multiple stakeholder groups and payers.* Harmonization of performance and quality measures by health professionals, CMS and other federal agencies, and private-sector health plans can speed the implementation of new practices by creating clear expectations of practice behavior. For example, more than a decade ago, the National Committee for Quality Assurance established the prescription of beta-blockers after myocardial infarction as an important quality measure—a reflection of the best evidence on managing patients after a heart attack. That practice was eventually widely adopted to the point where nearly 100 percent of myocardial-infarction patients were receiving beta-blockers. The inclusion of quality measures in the Health Information Technology for Economic and Clinical Health Act suggests that health information technology, when combined with a thoughtful approach to quality measurement, can be an important enabler of the rapid integration of evidence and new clinical standards into practice.

- *Institutional and clinical leadership.* As the structure and organization of the health care system evolves from small practices to large integrated practice structures, institutions and their clinical leaders can take an enhanced role in driving new insights into practice. Historically, clinical leaders have not had a strong role in auditing the clinical work of other physicians; physicians have been able to practice according to styles and norms of their choosing. There is a potential enhanced role for clinical leaders in integrated practice settings (large health systems, medical groups, and payer–provider entities) to drive changes into practice. Some risk is associated with it—such as potentially compromising individual clinicians' autonomy—but it has the benefit of a layer of oversight over practice patterns. Clinical leaders could provide value by coaching physicians into new practice paradigms that they might not pursue on their own.

- *The role of patients.* The historical hierarchic nature of the physician–patient relationship is changing. Physicians and patients—particularly those managing chronic illnesses—are increasingly viewed as partners. Patients have a role in speeding the use of innovations in clinical practice both by sharing the innovations with each other and by sharing them with physicians as they learn about them through their experience, the Internet, and other vehicles. The democratization of information has enabled patients to participate in such forums as Patients Like Me (patientslikeme.com), Smart Patients (smartpatients. com), and the ImproveCareNow Network (improvecarenow.org). The cutting-edge information that they acquire can be taken to clinicians who might not be as personally engaged in learning about a particular issue as are the patients. That powerful role reversal has the potential to drive diffusion of information from patient to physician. Physicians then may transform their practice patterns for all the patients that they serve.

- *Health care costs and affordability.* Health care costs are crowding out investment in education, housing, and other social determinants of health and are imped-ing growth of wages. Using resources in the most effective ways will require new approaches to the value of health care and interventions, particularly pharmaceuticals and devices. It is vital to assess overall effects on improved health, reduction in the burden of illness, reduction in health care costs, and assessment of indirect benefits, such as increasing workplace productivity and effects on family caregivers. Such assessments in the case of hepatitis C or Alzheimer's disease will provide a far more encompassing picture than just the cost of specific therapies. Such organizations as the Institute for Clinical and Economic Review and other private-sector initiatives are stepping into the void created when federal agencies (including PCORI, the Agency for Healthcare Research and Quality, and FDA) were directed to exclude con-sideration of cost and value.

- *The role of medical education.* Ensuring that new medical advances are incor-porated into practice in a timely fashion requires identifying the full array of stakeholders that need to be addressed. Practicing physicians are the most obvi-ous group, but the audience is much more extensive, including nonphysician practitioners (such as nurse practitioners and physician assistants), information-technology professionals who support medical practices, office-management staff, practice-based quality-improvement professionals, and payers who often set clinical standards for practice. In addition, it is critical to include future practitioners (such as medical students, residents, and subspecialty fellows) and the academic faculty who train them. Finally, patients must be informed and educated about advances—their appropriate use, value, potential harms, and potential financial obligations that they will have to bear.

- *Mechanisms for delivery of information.* Increasing time pressure on health care practitioners makes it critical that new information be transmitted concisely and that multiple vehicles be used, taking into account the diversity of ways in which health care professionals like to receive information. Although pre-sentations of new research at scientific meetings followed by peer-reviewed journal articles are the traditional critical initial sources of information about advances, practicing clinicians commonly do not have the time to read and absorb the original scientific data. Instead, they often depend on secondary sources in which the information is digested, interpreted, and repackaged. The secondary sources include review articles, point-of-care clinical-decision support resources, specialty society meetings and other continuing-medical-education activities, electronic journal alerts, and professional newsletters. Ultimately, clinical guidelines created by professional societies can help to shape practice patterns, but they are often less timely because of the need to accumulate a sufficient evidence basis and an inherent delay in their development and dissemination. In the future, innovative modes of data retrieval, integration, and dissemination, as exemplified by IBM's Watson Health (ibm.com/smarterplanet/us/en/ibmwatson/health), may become common tools.

- *Training of future physicians.* Attention needs to be paid to teaching new and existing physicians how to integrate new data into practice; indeed, the foundations of future medical practice will be much less about the specific evidence base that is in use today and much more about having the skills, values, and professionalism to continue to refresh one's approach to clinical practice. That is not a new idea, but it will be more important than ever as the evidence base grows exponentially.

EDUCATING THE PUBLIC, POLICYMAKERS, AND THE MASS MEDIA ABOUT CLINICAL DATA AND TRIALS

Many of the efforts and suggestions presented in this paper will not be realized unless the knowledge and understanding of policymakers and the public are enhanced. We believe that strategic federal initiatives to increase understanding about the role of clinical trials, about the need to increase participation, and about the importance of clinical trials to society would constitute a worthwhile investment in the health of Americans.

- *Benefit:risk ratio.* The concept of "benefit:risk" is generally not well understood by patients, payers, and policymakers. Although the public and Congress expect medicines and vaccines to be "safe and effective," they often fail to understand the nature and nuance of these terms in science and medicine. No medicine or vaccine is perfectly safe, and few are universally effective—that is, for all patients who have a given disease. We believe that a better term would be "risk:risk." Each disease increases the risk of some adverse experiences. So does each therapy. Patients and their doctors need to determine on an individual basis whether the risk of the natural progression of the disease is greater than the risks associated with a therapy. If that is not the case, they should not initiate the therapy. Government-sponsored educational programs that target the public, policymakers, and the mass media would probably carry considerable weight.

- *Product liability.* Ramifications of product liability should be addressed to balance the desire to move life-affecting therapies to market faster on the one hand with the protection of patient safety on the other. Striking the right balance is necessary to maintain appropriate incentives for continued innovation in the biopharmaceutical sector.

CONCLUSIONS

This paper is replete with descriptions of actions now under way or recommended that would serve as levers for progress or change in policy. We conclude by reemphasizing a subset of them and highlighting options for strategic federal initiatives. New policies and strategic investment can be leveraged to create value, decrease costs, create jobs, and strengthen global leadership in health innovations by the United States. Progress is already being made to implement the strategies outlined here. Many of the new agents that are in development have the potential to transform or even cure diseases (such as some cancers or hepatitis C, respectively) for which there were no treatments in the past. The success of translational R&D is increasing, and FDA has been rising to the challenge posed by the increasing number of new drug candidates by establishing "breakthrough therapy" and other "fast-track" mechanisms to facilitate the rapid and responsible movement of important advances to patient care.

However, moving such advances to patients as rapidly as possible presents many challenges. Innovative designs for clinical trials can reduce development time and expenses. Such designs are especially effective in demonstrating "proof of concept" and determining efficacy. They can facilitate arriving at "no-go" decisions, thus saving time and money. But, there is no shortcut for assessing safety in humans. Confidence in a given "level of safety" of a drug, vaccine, or device is established by the number of people exposed, the duration of exposure, and, when appropriate, the magnitude of exposure. Shorter trials with fewer participants are inherently linked to a lower level of confidence.

Without understanding of some of the potential compromises that arise from speedier drug-development approaches, earlier regulatory approval that is based on such trials places the inventors of drugs at greater vulnerability in our litigious society, especially when society and the mass media assume that FDA approval means that a new drug is absolutely safe and effective for everyone. The legal and educational issues in this arena would benefit from strategic federal intervention.

Harmonization or convergence of regulation among countries and regions is a pressing need with respect to new medicines, vaccines, and devices. Convergence will reduce development costs, decrease patient exposure to experimental drugs and devices, and speed worthy innovations to those in need globally.

Precision medicine holds great promise. But, as advances in genotyping, proteomics, and so on identify more and more populations in a given disease category, challenges to the business model for biopharmaceuticals increase. For example, although the cost of developing a precise therapy for 10 percent of a disease population is likely to be less than that of developing an agent generated through conventional methods, the accompanying decrease in cost is unlikely to be 90 percent. And, although the value of such precision products is greater, the market will be much smaller than that for products prescribed without "precision" to the general population for a given disease. New approaches to determining value will be essential to provide incentives for drug invention without placing an onerous financial burden on individuals and society.

Antibiotic resistance and bioterrorism are other domains in which the business model is challenging but the needs are essential for the future health of Americans. Population medicine impels us to be good stewards of antibiotics to slow the emergence of antibiotic resistance in pathogens. However, creating antibiotics in the hope that they will be rarely, if ever, used runs counter to the conventional business model. The same conundrum is faced in inventing vaccines and anti-infectives for agents that might be used in bioterrorism. Without government programs to address the need for innovative anti-infectives and vaccines, there is little incentive to invest over the long term, especially if other therapeutic needs do not face this challenge. Given the threat of virulent epidemics and bioterrorism, it might even be possible to address the needs through multinational programs; for example, the United States, Europe, Japan, and other countries could collaborate, dividing the labor and financial costs of programs directed at global solutions.

As discussed earlier, FDA's Sentinel initiative is being used to detect safety signals earlier and with greater sensitivity. There is interest in using the same huge clinical database to obtain RWE of efficacy. But, most clinical databases have flaws. The US government could assemble experts and stakeholders to create measures to improve the databases, set standards, and recommend appropriate methods for specific categories of inquiry.

The complexity of issues in health and medicine that our society needs to address is so enormous that no sector can devise or implement solutions on its own. The negative climate around academe–industry interactions strains current collaborations and inhibits formation of new ones. If this situation persists, the position of the United States versus global competition will be disadvantaged. NIH, FDA, other government agencies, academe, and industry could do more to reaffirm their common goals and encourage scientists, especially younger ones, to work at interfaces of these sectors.

Keeping NIH and FDA strong in leadership and funding will reap rewards in health and finances. Scientific and regulatory efforts in predictive animal models of human toxicity and efficacy and biomarkers for specific diseases, especially in neuroscience (e.g., Alzheimer's disease) and oncology, could speed innovation and diminish risk.

None of the means for speeding and evaluating innovation will improve health without enhancement of avenues for introducing advances into clinical care. Several mechanisms are being tried, and other promising ones are on the horizon. It is important for professionals who provide care to use them, especially in an environment of increasing (appropriate) pressure on physicians to control costs. Cost containment is increasingly incorporated into physician-payment systems. That leads to more pressure to demonstrate the "value" of innovative therapy through comparative-effectiveness (and, when feasible, cost-effectiveness) studies. For innovations to be accepted and prescribed by physicians, their value—not only their effectiveness—must be demonstrated.

With the right policies and investment, there is good reason to believe that innovations will improve the health of Americans and people around the globe while maintaining US leadership and strengthening the US economy.

VITAL DIRECTIONS

1. **Accelerate progress toward real-world evidence generation.** As clinical data move toward universal storage on digital platforms, the possibility exists to reduce the time and expense involved in the development of evidence on the effectiveness, safety, and applicability of medical interventions. Priorities include initiatives to develop data and interoperability standards, and improve data quality and accessibility, capacity to facilitate protected data sharing, and regulatory policies that allow phased introduction with evidence generation.

2. **Invest in and apply the promise of cognitive computing.** With rapidly expanding computing capability to integrate, process, and assess very large databases, opportunities develop for accelerated learning, understanding individual variation, and developing predictive modeling. Priorities include

public–private initiatives targeting the science of large-dataset computing, integrating individually generated data, and communicating results.

3. **Position and equip patients and families as partner stakeholders.** To capture the advantages of the use of patient-generated data to care management and of patient involvement to care outcomes, priorities include initiatives to enable and facilitate the roles of patients and families in all clinical decision making, and to enlist their guidance and involvement in the capture, design, and use of clinical data for new knowledge.

SUMMARY RECOMMENDATIONS FOR VITAL DIRECTIONS

1. Accelerate progress toward real-world evidence generation.
2. Invest in and apply the promise of cognitive computing.
3. Position and equip patients and families as partner stakeholders.

REFERENCES

Boname, M. L., A. W. Gee, and A. B. Claiborne. 2016. *Advancing the discipline of regulatory science for medical product development: An update on progress and a forward-looking agenda: Workshop summary.* Washington, DC: The National Academies Press. Available at http://www.nap.edu/catalog/23438/advancing-the-discipline-of-regulatory-science-for-medical-product-development (accessed March 25, 2016).

Enriquez, J. 2015. FDA forms patient advisory committee for medical device reviews. *Med Device Online,* September 22. Available at http://www.meddeviceonline.com/doc/fda-forms-patient-advisory-committee-for-medical-device-reviews-0001 (accessed March 25, 2016).

FDA (Food and Drug Administration). 2015. Patient Engagement Advisory Committee. Available at http://www.fda.gov/AdvisoryCommittees/CommitteesMeetingMaterials/PatientEngagementAdvisoryCommittee/default.htm (accessed March 25, 2016).

FDA. 2016a. FDA's Sentinel Initiative. Available at http://www.fda.gov/Safety/FDAsSentinelInitiative/default.htm (accessed March 25, 2016).

FDA. 2016b. CDRH's experiential learning program. Available at http://www.fda.gov/scienceresearch/sciencecareeropportunities/ucm380676.htm (accessed March 25, 2016).

FDA. 2016c. CDRH Network of Experts. Available at http://www.fda.gov/AboutFDA/CentersOffices/OfficeofMedicalProductsandTobacco/CDRH/ucm289534.htm (accessed March 25, 2016).

FDA. 2016d. Developing a consensus voice: The Combination Products Policy Council. Available at http://blogs.fda.gov/fdavoice/index.php/2016/04/developing-a-consensus-voice-the-combination-products-policy-council/ (accessed March 25, 2016).

FDA. 2016e. "Leaning in" on combination products. Available at http://blogs.fda.gov/fdavoice/index.php/2016/03/leaning-in-on-combination-products/ (accessed March 25, 2016).

FDA. 2016f. The voice of the patient: A series of reports from FDA's Patient-Focused Drug Development Initiative. Available at http://www.fda.gov/ForIndustry/UserFees/PrescriptionDrugUserFee/ucm368342.htm (accessed March 25, 2016).

Heinemann, L. 2008. The failure of exubera: Are we beating a dead horse? *Journal of Diabetes Science and Technology* 2:518–529.

Hoos, A., J. Anderson, M. Boutin, L. Dewulf, J. Geissler, G. Johnston, A. Joos, M. Metcalf, J. Regnante, I. Sargeant, R. F. Schneider, V. Todaro, and G. Tougas. 2015. Partnering with patients in the development and lifecycle of medicines: A call for action. *Therapeutic Innovation & Regulatory Science* 49:929–939.

ICER (Institute for Clinical and Economic Review). 2016. Value Assessment Framework. Available at http://icer-review.org/methodology/icers-methods/icer-value-assessment-framework/ (accessed March 25, 2016).

IOM (Institute of Medicine). 2007. *Roundtable on evidence-based medicine: The learning healthcare system: Workshop summary.* Washington, DC: The National Academies Press. Available at http://www.ncbi.nlm.nih.gov/books/NBK53494/pdf/Bookshelf_NBK53494.pdf (accessed March 25, 2016).

IOM. 2010. *Transforming clinical research in the United States: Challenges and opportunities: Workshop summary.* Forum on Drug Discovery, Development, and Translation. Washington, DC: The National Academies Press. Available at http://www.ncbi.nlm.nih.gov/books/NBK50888/ (accessed March 25, 2016).

IOM. 2012. *Public engagement and clinical trials: New models and disruptive technologies: Workshop summary.* Washington, DC: The National Academies Press. Available at http://www.ncbi.nlm.nih.gov/books/NBK92104/#ch2 (accessed March 25, 2016).

Kaitlin, K. I., and P. K. Honig. 2013. Reinventing bioinnovation. *Clinical Pharmacology & Therapeutics* 94:279–283.

Ledford, H. 2011. Ways to fix the clinical trial. *Nature* 477:526–528.

MDIC (Medical Device Innovation Consortium). 2015. Patient Centered Benefit-Risk Project Report: A framework for incorporating information on patient preferences regarding benefit and risk into regulatory assessments of new medical technology. Available at http://mdic.org/wp-content/uploads/2015/05/MDIC_PCBR_Framework_Web.pdf (accessed March 25, 2016).

MSKCC (Memorial Sloan Kettering Cancer Center). 2015. Welcome to Drug Abacus. Available at http://www.drugabacus.org/drug-abacus-tool/ (accessed March 25, 2016).

NCCN (National Comprehensive Cancer Network). 2016. NCCN Clinical Practice Guidelines in Oncology (NCCN Guidelines) with NCCN Evidence Blocks. Available at http://www.nccn.org/evidenceblocks/ (accessed March 25, 2016).

NHC (National Health Council). 2016. The patient voice in value: The National Health Council Patient-Centered Value Model rubric. Available at http://www.nationalhealthcouncil.org/sites/default/files/Value-Rubric.pdf (accessed March 29, 2016).

NHCGA (National Health Council and Genetic Alliance). 2015. Dialogue/Advancing meaningful patient engagement in research, development, and review of drugs, September 22. Available at http://www.nationalhealth-council.org/sites/default/files/PatientEngagement-WhitePaper.pdf (accessed March 25, 2016).

Nordrum, A. 2013. FDA and pharmaceutical companies welcome patient voices to new drug development—but will it last? *International Business Times,* September 3. Available at http://www.ibtimes.com/fda-pharmaceutical-com-panies-welcome-patient-voices-new-drug-development-will-it-last-2082262 (accessed March 25, 2016).

Norris, S. M. P., E. Strauss, C. DeFeo, and C. Stroud. 2015. *Financial incentives to encourage development of therapies that address unmet medical needs for nervous system disorders: Workshop summary.* Washington, DC: The National Academies Press. Available at http://www.nap.edu/read/21732/chapter/5 (accessed March 25, 2016).

PCAST (President's Council of Advisors on Science and Technology). 2012. Report to the president on propelling innovation in drug discovery, development, and evaluation. Available at https://www.whitehouse.gov/sites/default/files/microsites/ostp/pcast-fda-final.pdf (accessed March 25, 2016).

PCORI (Patient-Centered Outcomes Research Institute). 2015. Engagement rubric for applicants. Available at http://www.pcori.org/sites/default/files/Engagement-Rubric.pdf (accessed March 25, 2016).

PDF (Parkinson's Disease Foundation). 2016. Training dates and locations. Available at http://www.pdf.org/crli (accessed March 25, 2016).

Pogorelc, D. 2013. What's behind the FDA's push for more patient engagement (hint: it's not that everyone else is doing it). *MedCity News*. Available at http://medcitynews.com/2013/05/whats-behind-the-fdas-push-for-more-patient-engagement-and-its-not-that-everyone-else-is-doing-it/ (accessed March 25, 2016).

Schnipper, L. E., N. E. Davidson, D. S. Wollins, C. Tyne, D. W. Blayney, D. Blum, A. P. Dicker, P. A. Ganz, J. R. Hoverman, R. Langdon, G. H. Lyman, N. J. Meropol, T. Mulvey, L. Newcomer, J. Peppercorn, B. Polite, D. Raghavan, G. Rossi, L. Saltz, D. Schrag, T. J. Smith, P. P. Yu, C. A. Hudis, R. L. Schilsky, and the American Society of Clinical Oncology. 2015. American Society of Clinical Oncology statement: A conceptual framework to assess the value of cancer treatment options. *Journal of Clinical Oncology* 33:2563–2577.

Supple, D., A. Roberts, V. Hudson, S. Masefield, N. Fitch, M. Rahmen, B. Flood, W. de Boer, P. Powell, and S. Wagers. 2015. From tokenism to meaningful engagement: Best practices in patient involvement in an EU project. *Research Involvement and Engagement* 1:5.

TSCDD (Tufts Center for the Study of Drug Development). 2015. *Outlook 2015*. Boston: Tufts University.

UMCERSI (University of Maryland Center of Excellence in Regulatory Science and Innovation). 2015. Assessing meaningful patient engagement in drug development: A definition, framework, and rubric. Available at http://www.pharmacy.umaryland.edu/media/SOP/wwwpharmacyumarylandedu/centers/cersievents/pfdd/mcersi-pfdd-framework-rubric.pdf (accessed March 25, 2016).

AUTHOR INFORMATION

Michael Rosenblatt, MD, is Chief Medical Officer, Flagship Ventures. Portion written while Executive Vice President, Chief Medical Officer, Merck & Co., Inc. **Christopher P. Austin, MD,** is Director, National Center for Advancing Translational Sciences, National Institutes of Health. **Marc Boutin, JD,** is Chief Executive Officer, National Health Council. **William W. Chin, MD,** is Chief Medical Officer, and Executive Vice President of Science and Regulatory Advocacy, Pharmaceutical Research and Manufacturers of America. **Steven K. Galson, MD, MPH,** is Senior Vice President, Amgen, Inc. **Sachin H. Jain, MD, MBA,** is CEO and Chief Medical Officer, CareMore Health Group, Inc. **Michelle McMurry-Heath, MD, PhD,** is Vice President, Worldwide Regulatory Affairs, Johnson & Johnson. **Samuel R. Nussbaum, MD,** is Senior

Fellow, University of Southern California Schaeffer Center for Health Policy and Economics. **John Orloff, MD,** is R&D Biopharmaceutical Executive and former Executive Vice President, Global Head of R&D and Chief Scientific Officer, Baxalta. **Steven E. Weinberger, MD,** is Executive Vice President and CEO, American College of Physicians. **Janet Woodcock, MD,** is Director, Center for Drug Evaluation and Research, Food and Drug Administration.

19

TARGETED RESEARCH:
BRAIN DISORDERS AS AN EXAMPLE

Alan I. Leshner, PhD, Steven E. Hyman, MD, and Story C. Landis, PhD

Much discussion surrounds the question of the most appropriate strategies for bringing the power of science to bear on the nation's pressing problems. Some problems, such as an emerging infectious disease, are urgent and must be addressed immediately. Others, such as the increasing global burden of dementia and other neurodegenerative diseases as populations grow older, become apparent with time but can be just as pressing in their implications. Advances in science and technology are often critical for progress, and circumstances can make it imperative for major science-based initiatives to deal with problems. We argue here that now is the right time for a substantial science-based assault on disorders of the brain. Our thesis is based on the conjunction of a growing worldwide societal burden of brain disorders with scientific opportunity driven by the maturing of neuroscience and related disciplines, by the recent and continuing emergence of relevant tools and technologies, and by the quality and number of personnel in the field.

POLICY STRATEGIES

There is no simple recipe for the planning and conduct of science-based initiatives that would ensure advances in both scientific progress and their application to societal problems. Much, however, has been learned from prior science initiatives. The temptation is always great, particularly when funding is constrained, to focus research funding in explicit or targeted ways, specifying in detail the exact problems to be solved and even the research approach to be taken. But, the history of American science shows that stipulation of details can be counterproductive. What has generally been proved most effective is a combination of approaches to the support of research and development that involves diverse strategies. Moreover, it should be emphasized that increased funding, although almost always a necessary condition for progress, will not by itself yield solutions to critical problems. The science must be tractable—even if difficult—and there must be an appropriate workforce in the field in question or workers willing to enter from related fields. Both those conditions prevailed in the response to HIV/AIDS that began in the 1990s.

In addition to substantial increments in funding, policy and regulatory initiatives may be required to advance relevant science and to apply it effectively to the pressing problems that motivated the investment. Policy initiatives involving regulatory and possibly legislative bodies, the academic and industrial sectors, and journal publishers can markedly increase the likelihood of successful research and societal outcomes. Examples include the sharing of data (in conjunction with appropriate ways of protecting the privacy of individuals), the sharing of methods and key reagents by scientists, increased incentives for scientific rigor (as opposed to premature publication), and decreased barriers to partnerships between academic and industrial researchers that address the issue of conflicts of interest.

If increased funding and appropriate policy interventions set the stage for acceleration of progress, decisions must be made about strategies for funding projects. Different federal agencies use different approaches. One funding approach is largely undirected or unconstrained: almost every technically sound project proposal is considered, and funding decisions are made solely on the basis of scientific merit as determined by peer review. That "unsolicited" approach has been particularly effective for such agencies as the National Science Foundation (NSF), whose mission is the broad support of virtually all fields of basic or fundamental science. NSF-funded research has produced many important discoveries, often with benefits to society that were initially wholly unexpected. An excellent example of such an unexpected benefit is the diverse science underpinning intelligent learning systems, which has led to an enormous number of applications, such as speech-recognition technology and powerful data-analysis tools that are used throughout academe, many industries, and government. A complementary funding approach is to target specific questions or problems that need to be answered or specific technologies that are needed by end users and then to solicit responsive proposals. In its extreme version, the "directed" approach might specify timelines and much detail about the desired products. Such agencies as the Defense Advanced Research Projects Agency (DARPA) typically use this approach, and their efforts have resulted in many important advances, often with clear utility. The National Institutes of Health (NIH) has successfully used a combination of approaches whereby some biomedical research projects are supported as a result of unsolicited proposals and others are supported as a result of targeted requests for applications. Such a hybrid approach is recommended for the initiative proposed here.

A major goal of special initiatives is to draw researchers to work on particularly difficult or urgent questions and challenges. Such initiatives usually direct a substantial stream of targeted funding to a problem. They typically use a variety of approaches, which may ultimately be specified by a funding agency through such mechanisms as requests for applications. Most successful efforts are initially grounded in consultations and workshops among diverse members of the investigator community. One of the largest such efforts was directed against HIV/AIDS. For over 20 years, 10 percent of the NIH budget was set aside to support HIV/AIDS research; some of the research projects were specified by the agency, and others were "bottom-up" projects proposed by members of the scientific community. Because of the size and complexity of the effort, it was overseen by the Office of AIDS Research, which coordinated work among NIH Institutes and ensured that grants made under the rubric of HIV/AIDS research were germane to the problems at hand. That approach contributed substantially to the transformation of HIV infection from a death sentence to a manageable chronic illness and to success in prevention of transmission. NIH recently determined that the challenges that remain with respect to HIV/AIDS—such as understanding viral reservoirs and developing a vaccine—no longer require the longstanding set-aside of funds.

Dedicated funding targeted to a particularly promising basic-science subject resulted in the great feat of sequencing the human genome. It is important to recognize the enormous value that that effort generated: not only was an initial human-genome reference sequence published, but also the development of technologies and computational tools that have revolutionized biomedical science was directly supported and encouraged. The rapid decrease in costs of sequencing DNA and the increase in the ability to analyze and understand the resulting data have led to a truly remarkable acceleration in identification of genetic contributors to many diseases, which, in turn, is beginning to influence diagnostics and discovery of therapies throughout medicine. The return on investment has been extraordinary, not only scientifically but economically: nearly $1 trillion in economic growth for a 178-fold return on investment (Batelle Technology Partnership Practice, 2013).

Another dramatic example is provided by approaches to cancer (an umbrella term for a diverse family of illnesses that have different etiologies, molecular mechanisms, treatment responses, and outcomes). President Nixon declared a War on Cancer in 1971, and cancer research has since periodically received substantial infusions of funds. The increases in funding have undoubtedly contributed to the transformation of some cancers from untreatable, rapidly lethal diseases into chronic conditions that can be managed over increasing periods of survival or, in some cases, cured. Cancer biologists and clinicians faced scientific challenges, but they also benefited from scientific opportunity—direct access to living tumor tissue excised in biopsies or in surgical treatments and in more recent years the ability to sequence the genomes of large numbers of cancer cells from diverse tumor types. In his January 2016 State of the Union address, President Obama announced a new initiative in cancer, a Cancer Moonshot that has such goals as accelerating progress by focusing on preventive vaccines, early detection, immunotherapy, pediatric cancer, and data sharing (Lowy and Collins, 2016).

As we have emphasized, a funding initiative does not by itself make a particular set of scientific problems immediately tractable, nor does it ensure effective handoffs from academic or government scientists to industry or the development of safe and effective preventive interventions or treatments. However, in addition to supporting relevant research directly, funding initiatives can attract established researchers to a field, influence the popularity of a field among trainees, and gain the attention of academic and industrial developers of technology. Those effects have certainly resulted from the initiatives with HIV/AIDS and cancer research. One of the great benefits of the genome project was its focus on supporting technology development even as it changed the size of the market for even more sophisticated DNA-sequencing machines. New federal investment in a field can also lead to reexamination and reform of regulation, such as the passage of the Genetic Information Nondiscrimination Act of 2008, which prohibits the use of genetic information in employment and health insurance.

BRAIN DISORDERS ARE RIPE FOR SPECIAL ATTENTION

The key factors that now motivate a proposal for an initiative on brain disorders are the rapidly advancing tools and knowledge to facilitate understanding of disease mechanisms, a strong and growing scientific workforce in neuroscience, and a substantial mismatch between research investment and unmet medical need, global disease burden, and rising costs to societies (Bloom et al., 2011; Murray et al., 2013). The need for research investment is highlighted by the growing global prevalence and costs of neurodegenerative disorders (Hebert et al., 2013; Hurd et al., 2013) and a large disinvestment by industry in brain disorders since 2010 (Choi et al., 2014) with the possible exception of Alzheimer's disease clinical trials. The withdrawal of industry is, in large part, a consequence of gaps in molecular-target identification and validation and in biomarkers, in contrast with such diseases as cancer that have been the beneficiaries of many initiatives that have brought resources to bear. The consequence for the preponderance of brain diseases—such as autism, epilepsy, depression, schizophrenia, and stroke—is that the translation of emerging neuroscience is impeded. If the current Alzheimer's disease trials fail, even this industry commitment to therapy development will disappear, as did the commitment to stroke therapies after trials failed.

The initiative proposed here would capitalize on new technologies and rapidly emerging scientific discoveries to create a new effort focused on identification and validation of molecular targets and identification of biomarkers. In the language of industry, such efforts would "derisk" brain-disorders research and thus decrease the barriers to reentry for companies. It is clear that new technologies and scientific advances can accelerate therapy development. For example, the use of magnetic resonance imaging to screen potential neuromodulatory treatments for multiple sclerosis has resulted in the successful development of a number of therapeutic agents that slow disease progression. The discovery that dopamine was depleted in Parkinson's disease led to the development of dopamine replacement therapy, and elucidation of the brain circuitry that is perturbed in Parkinson's disease led to treatment with deep brain stimulation that transforms the lives of patients in the middle stage of the disease.

Brain disorders as diverse as autism and Alzheimer's disease are increasingly addressable by biomedical science. That point is critical. The complexity of the human brain and its inaccessibility to direct examination during life have rendered the study of brain disorders extremely challenging, but the last decade has seen the development of diverse technologies that permit a concerted attack on these illnesses. The recognition of the great and growing burden of brain disorders on society and the extraordinary recent progress in brain research and in the development of technologies for such research make the disorders particularly ripe for special attention. An initiative could lead to important improvements in the lives of patients and their caregivers while accruing substantial economic benefits by decreasing levels of disability.

Over 100 million Americans suffer from brain disorders, including mental illnesses, neurologic disorders, and addiction. According to NIH, one-fourth of Americans suffer from a diagnosable mental disorder at some point in their lives. Over 50 million Americans suffer from neurologic disorders, including over 5 million from Alzheimer's disease alone. The World Health Organization's *Global Burden of Disease* study (Murray et al., 2013) showed that brain disorders are the leading cause of disability in the United States; they are also the largest cause of financial loss due to noncommunicable disease. The World Economic Forum and Harvard School of Public Health estimated the global financial cost of mental illnesses in 2010 at US$2.5 trillion per year and the expected cost by 2030 at US$6 trillion. A science-focused initiative would contribute to a great reduction in both personal and financial costs.

It is important to recognize how difficult it has been to carry out the science needed to deal with those disorders effectively and what is involved. Understanding the structure and function of the human brain remains extremely challenging. The human brain is the most complex organ; it has more than 80 billion neurons, and there are 5,000 or more types of neurons and glial cells. Each neuron has about 1,000 connections (synapses) with other neurons, but the range is vast. The roughly 100 trillion synapses in the human brain give rise to the neural circuits that underlie the computations that produce sensation, cognitive function, emotion, motivation, and the control of behavior. Longlasting changes in synaptic connections and circuits are the basis of learning and memory. Abnormalities in the structure and functioning of brain cells, synapses, and circuits are responsible for the diverse symptoms and impairments that result from brain disorders.

Much as Galileo could not have advanced understanding of the solar system without a telescope, new tools developed in the last decade have revolutionized the life sciences in general and neuroscience in particular. They include genomic technologies and computational tools, which resulted in large part from the Human Genome Project; stem-cell technologies; genome engineering tools, such as CRISPR-Cas9; and, of particular importance to neuroscience, rapidly advancing technologies to study and even control activity in the cells and circuits of living brains and to provide useful maps of connectivity, such as those emerging from the Human Connectome Project and from the Allen Institute for Brain Science. The development of transformative tools and technologies, too often neglected, is critical for advances in our understanding of how the brain works and the development of better diagnoses and effective treatments for brain disorders. For example, advanced tools to study the expression of genes in single cells were described last year and are already being applied to the analysis of diverse cell types in the brain, but the actual mapping of particular protein complexes—the intended targets of drugs—to particular neural cell types awaits further development.

Federal funding has rarely been used to support the creation and dissemination of research tools and technologies, although there are notable exceptions, as in the Human Genome Project. Recognizing the great opportunities provided by recent advances in brain research coupled with the critical need for new technologies, a group of federal agencies and private foundations have joined forces and committed funds to the BRAIN (Brain Research through Advances in Innovative Neurotechnologies) Initiative. That initiative, a 12-year public–private partnership, was begun in 2013 and aims to provide the new tools and technologies needed to accelerate understanding of normal and abnormal brain structure and function. The current federal partners include NSF, NIH, DARPA, the Intelligence Applied Research Projects Agency, and the Food and Drug Administration. The private foundations in the partnership include the Howard Hughes Medical Institute, the Simons Foundation, the Allen Institute for Brain Science, and the Kavli Foundation. The collaborative focus of so many participants and funding organizations on developing new technologies and using them to elucidate brain circuitry is unprecedented. The BRAIN Initiative, with its focus on technology development and the normal brain, is essential in elucidating how the brain processes information and initiates behavior, and it should continue to be supported. However, it is only the beginning for understanding brain disorders. To address those, it is essential that newly developed technologies be applied to further understanding of human brain structure and function in health and disease. Moreover, the integration of advances arising from the genetic dissection of brain disorders with the kinds of tools and technologies emerging from the BRAIN Initiative is likely to be critical if gene lists are ultimately to be translated in a manner that improves human health.

ELEMENTS OF AN INITIATIVE ON BRAIN DISORDERS

This proposal is based on the pressing need to improve the prevention of and treatment for early-onset neuropsychiatric and neurodegenerative disorders. The highly damaging effects of these conditions on individuals, families, and society have been well documented by studies of disease burden, direct costs of health care, and economic loss.

Perhaps the greatest impediment to progress in preventing and treating brain disorders has been the incomplete knowledge of normal brain function coupled with slow progress in understanding their detailed pathophysiology, including molecular mechanisms of disease. Much can be learned from how progress has been made in cancer biology, even though diseases of the nervous system bring even greater challenges. Identification of molecular mechanisms and therapeutic targets in cancer has been rapidly advanced by sequencing the genomes of many surgically obtained cancer cells under a variety of large-scale efforts supported by the National Cancer Institute, beginning with the *Cancer Genome Atlas* in 2005. That approach is feasible because of the centrality of highly penetrant acquired mutations in the origin of most cancers notwithstanding the complexities of tumor heterogeneity and of distinguishing the mutations in cancer cells that drive pathogenesis from the welter of passenger mutations.

The identification of molecular mechanisms of pathogenesis in brain disorders has been more difficult. Despite well-known examples of rare monogenic disorders of the nervous system, such as Huntington's disease and rare familial forms of amyotrophic lateral sclerosis, genetic risk factors for the vast majority of psychiatric, neurologic, and addictive disorders are carried by large numbers of modestly penetrant genetic variants. Thanks to the revolution begun by the Human Genome Project, what had seemed an insuperable problem has begun to yield rapidly to modern genomic technologies being brought to bear on specific disorders by large global consortia. Perhaps unrecognized in the broader scientific community, those efforts have achieved remarkable success related to many conditions, including autism, epilepsy, schizophrenia, bipolar disorder, and common, late-onset forms of Alzheimer's disease. Those growing success stories also reveal that the genetic analysis of brain disorders is scalable, and with appropriate organization and good policies (such as requirements for data-sharing within the bounds of protecting subject privacy) additional funding would efficiently advance the pace of discovery and thus accelerate investigations into disease mechanisms (Sekar et al., 2016), the nomination of molecular targets for therapies, and the discovery of candidate biomarkers (Jack and Holtzman, 2013).

It has often been objected that neuroscience has been unable to exploit even Mendelian genetic discoveries for therapies, notably for mutations that alter protein function, such as the gene in which triplet repeats cause Huntington's disease. In fact, the challenge of therapy for Huntington's disease is not dissimilar to that facing therapy for monogenic hematologic disorders, such as sickle-cell disease, in which the causative amino acid variation has been known since the 1950s: both in Huntington's disease and in monogenic hematologic disorders early attempts at gene therapy are proceeding in parallel. The deeper problem that calls for a scientific initiative is how to study pathogenesis of common polygenic brain disorders—how to use rapidly emerging genetic results to inform useful biologic experimentation and ultimately therapy. The problem of polygenicity is, at one level, no different from that in studying immunologic disorders or metabolism—although it is of note with respect to metabolism that essentially all the genetic regulation of body-mass index maps to the brain, not liver, pancreas, gut, or adipocytes.

A focus on brain disorders is warranted by its contribution of lifetime disease burden and by the promising technologic advances created by the BRAIN Initiative and the development of tools that are advancing all biology, such as stem-cell technologies, production of organoids, and genome engineering technologies.

The initiative proposed here is meant to advance and make more widely available platform technologies and data sharing through increased funding and policy initiatives and to enhance collaboration between academe and industry to advance the translation of basic findings as they mature. An example of a successful public–private consortium that could be used as a model for new collaborations is the Alzheimer's disease neuroimaging initiative (ADNI) which played a key role in the identification and implementation of biomarkers for Alzheimer's disease in clinical trials.

Specific components of the initiative proposed here include the following set of actions:

- Encourage and support the formation of new consortia to advance genetic and phenotypic analyses of brain disorders in diverse populations and to collect biospecimens that, among other things, will permit the production of induced pluripotent cell lines and organoids.
- Combine those efforts with policy initiatives to encourage sharing of data, cell lines, and other materials in a manner that is consistent with the protection of privacy. Create infrastructure to support secure data storage, data sharing, and the banking of biologic materials.
- Increase funding for the dissemination of cell lines, animal models, technologies, and software packages. Policy initiatives involving funders and journals are needed to ensure the availability of detailed scientific methods to enhance replicability of results.
- Support completion of the initial goals of the BRAIN Initiative to ensure that the necessary tools and technologies are available to study normal and pathologic brain function, including fundamental understanding of neural-cell types and circuits.
- In parallel, support expansion of the BRAIN Initiative to provide tools and to produce and study both in vitro (cellular, organoid, and explant) models and in vivo models of brain disorders on the basis of insights coming from genetics. Accelerate technology development to study the human brain.
- Support advances in human experimental biology (e.g., using new physiologic and imaging technologies derived from the BRAIN Initiative) to investigate candidate biomarkers coming from genetic analyses and, when possible, disease pathogenesis.
- Encourage and support empirical investigations and ethical analyses to investigate emerging concepts of privacy among cultures and age groups and the risk tolerance of patients and families for participating in genetic and

phenotyping studies that involve longitudinal participation and data sharing (with attendant risks to the privacy of their personal data).

- Support training of clinicians in the interpretation of genetic data and their clinical utility while increasing the number of genetic counselors being trained.
- Facilitate the development of and identify funds for public–private initiatives (using such models as ADNI and the Accelerating Medicines Partnership) on topics that include biomarker discovery and target validation. Development of appropriate policies for partnerships will require involving both regulatory and funding agencies from the outset.
- Explore avenues to facilitate the adaptation of the most promising biomarker candidates for early diagnosis of neuropsychiatric and neurodegenerative disorders to allow interventions at the earliest possible time, when they are most likely to be effective.

SUMMARY RECOMMENDATIONS FOR VITAL DIRECTIONS

1. Create new models for large-scale research consortia and public—private partnerships.
2. Develop new tools and technologies for research.
3. Establish policies and infrastructure for banking of biospecimens, storage of data and software, and their sharing, and develop effective approaches to dissemination of knowledge, tools, and reagents.

REFERENCES

Batelle Technology Partnership Practice, for United for Medical Research. 2013. The impact of genomics on the U.S. economy. Available at http://www.battelle.org/docs/health-and-pharmaceutical/the-impact-of-genomics-on-the-u-s-economy-june-11-final.pdf?sfvrsn=0 (accessed June 6, 2016).

Bloom, D. E., E. T. Cafiero, E. Janeliopis, S. Abrahams-Gesse, L. R. Bloom, S. Fathima, A. B. Geigi, T. Gaziano, M. Mowafi, A. Pandya, K. Prettner, L. Rosneberg, B. Seligman, A. Z. Stein, and C. Weinstein. 2011. *The global economic burden of noncommunicable disease.* Geneva: World Economic Forum.

Choi, D. W., R. Armitage, L. S. Brady, T. Coetzee, W. Fisher, S. Hyman, A. Pande, S. Paul, W. Potter, B. Roin, and T. Sherer. 2014. Medicines for the mind: Policy based "pull" incentives for creating breakthrough CNS drugs. *Neuron* 84:554–563.

Hebert, L. E., J. Weuve, P. A. Scherr, and D. A. Evans. 2013. Alzheimer disease in the United States (2010–2050) estimated using the 2010 census. *Neurology* 80:1778–1783.

Hurd, M. D., P. Martorell, A. Delavande, K. J. Mullen, and K. M. Langa. 2013. Monetary costs of dementia in the United States. *New England Journal of Medicine* 368:1326–1334.

Jack, C. R., Jr., and D. M. Holtzman. 2013. Biomarker modeling of Alzheimer's disease. *Neuron* 80:1347–1358.

Lowy, D. R., and F. S. Collins. 2016. Aiming high—changing the trajectory for cancer. *New England Journal of Medicine* 374:1901–1904.

Murray, C. J., C. Atiknos, K. Bhalia, and US Burden of Disease Collaborators. 2013. The state of US Health 1990–2010. Burden of diseases, risk factors, and injuries. *Journal of the American Medical Association* 310:591–608.

Sekar, A., A. R. Bialas, H. de Rivera, A. Davis, T. R. Hammond, N. Kamitaki, K. Tooley, J. Presumey, M. Baum, V. Van Doren, G. Genovese, S.A. Rose, R.E. Handsaker, Schizophrenia Working Group of the Psychiatric Genomics Consortium, M. J. Daly, M.C. Carroll, B. Stevens and S.A. McCarroll 2016. Schizophrenia risk from complex variation of complement component 4. *Nature* 530:177–183.

AUTHOR INFORMATION

Alan I. Leshner, PhD, is CEO Emeritus, American Association for the Advancement of Science. **Steven E. Hyman, MD,** is Director, Stanley Center for Psychiatric Research, The Broad Institute of MIT and Harvard University. **Story C. Landis, PhD,** is Scientist Emeritus, National Institute of Neurological Disorders and Stroke.

20

TRAINING THE WORKFORCE FOR 21ST-CENTURY SCIENCE

Elias A. Zerhouni, MD, Jeremy M. Berg, PhD, Freeman A. Hrabowski, PhD, Raynard S. Kington, MD, PhD, and Story C. Landis, PhD

Continuing to improve human health at reasonable costs is one of the biggest challenges facing society in the 21st century. Prior scientific advances have led to longer life expectancies, which, in turn, have led to the emergence of chronic diseases often related to aging (IOM, 2001). Our health care system was designed primarily for acute care, whereas today chronic disease is responsible for 80 percent of health care costs (McKenna and Collins, 2010). The current system is characterized by episodic care, fragmentation of services, and a less-than-holistic view of the patient, all of which lead to a growth in inefficiencies and costs (IOM, 2001).

The need for more coordinated and seamlessly integrated multidisciplinary care is obvious. In parallel, advances in our knowledge of biologic systems and their complexity will require an unprecedented convergence of biologic, physical, and information sciences to solve the issues that we face. The life sciences are moving from an era of monodisciplinary and reductionist explorations of the fundamental elements of biologic systems to a multidisciplinary understanding of human biology and the course of disease. Given that evolution, the hope of precision medicine is unlikely to be realized without a transformation in how we educate and train a new generation of physicians, scientists, engineers, and population-health professionals. These experts need to be able to create and implement new ways of tackling complexity with the goal of reducing disease burden at a cost that society can afford.

Today, our biomedical educational and scientific training pathways are fragmented (Kruse, 2013). Young talents are often discouraged because of the longer and uncertain pathways to a successful career, especially when they will be saddled with a much greater debt burden at the end of their studies than was the prior generation.

Over the past 100 years, the United States assumed a global position of unparalleled scientific achievement and has reaped the many health, economic, diplomatic, social, and military benefits of its preeminence. US citizens have been awarded more Nobel prizes in physiology or medicine than those of any other country—by a factor of 3 (Kirk, 2015). Those accomplishments have contributed to remarkable improvements in human health, innovation, and economic success and to a great sense of national pride. Our preeminence, however, is now being challenged by external and internal factors.

> "It is a miracle that curiosity survives formal education."
>
> —Albert Einstein

Other countries are competing more successfully in science and technology. The United States used to be preeminent in attracting the best and brightest in the world to its shores, but that dominance is not as pronounced today. China, for instance, has markedly increased its research and development (R&D) funding and the quality of its top universities (IRI, 2016). As a result, China can increasingly attract its expatriate scientists back to enrich local institutions with world-class talent trained in the United States and Europe, while a well-trained generation of young scientists is emerging from top Chinese universities.

A visit to any US laboratory today reveals the dependence on foreign-trained scientists at postdoctoral levels (Matthews, 2010). At the same time, young and American-trained talented people, who face a financial burden greater than do their colleagues in other countries because of high tuition costs in the United States and consequent high debt, increasingly shy away from scientific endeavors. They see the greatly increased length of training imposed on them by our academic institutions, delay of opportunities to work independently until their late 30s (NAS et al., 2007), and grant funding that is uncertain (Harris and Benincasa, 2014) and highly competitive. It is not surprising that many of the best and brightest view this path as forbidding relative to more lucrative nonscientific careers, less fraught with uncertainty.

With the retirement of the extraordinarily productive current generation of US scientists, our nation will have to plan carefully and act swiftly to continue to attract young people to science and to train and retain a world-class scientific workforce from within its citizenry if it hopes to retain its longstanding advantage. Furthermore, novel training paradigms and multidisciplinary skills that combine life sciences and physical sciences will be essential. For instance, solutions to the most intractable disease problems, such as those related to Alzheimer's disease and diabetes, will require both new scientific discoveries and fundamental and integrative health-system changes if we hope to control the soaring health care costs associated with those problems. The United States will need to create and sustain a competitive and highly skilled new generation of talented people who are unafraid of challenging the status quo and who can create the knowledge and the new industries that can emerge from innovation. In short, if the United States is to maintain leadership in biomedical research and the development and delivery of medical innovation, the training of a new generation of scientists and engineers will need to become as innovative as the science that they are expected to deliver. That must have high priority for the nation.

In brief, our analysis identifies four interrelated key issues that we must address if our scientific workforce is to remain preeminent:

- The lack of high school exposure to cutting-edge science by the best teachers.
- The increasing financial burden of a scientific education with unsustainable student debt that forces many, especially members of underrepresented minorities, to forgo scientific research careers.
- The unjustified lengthening of our postgraduate training system with poorly defined career pathways even for promising scientists, who today do not reach independence until their late 30s.
- The persistence of rigid disciplinary silos that make multidisciplinary training and research unnecessarily difficult.

What needs to change? We must find ways to attract the most talented science, technology, engineering, and mathematics (STEM) students and support them throughout their education and training. To do that, we must create new pathways to help to ensure that they are trained in the skills and knowledge necessary to succeed in 21st-century biomedical and health care sciences.

To understand the problems and plan for the educational revolution that will be required, we need to look at the current systems through the eyes of the young people who are contemplating or navigating a life in science—high school students, undergraduate students, graduate students, and postdoctoral fellows.

THE HIGH SCHOOL EXPERIENCE

Brittany is an entering high school freshman in a small town. She has already been identified as a star student, excelling in her classes and performing well above her peers on standardized tests. She has always loved science and likes to imagine herself working on a cure for cancer. In the coming years, however, she will be faced with biology classes drawn almost entirely from textbooks, lectures about the taxonomic classification of plants and animals, and a brief exposure to basic Mendelian genetics. She will receive little exposure to laboratory work that is not simply "cookbook science," and she will not get any experience in hypothesis-driven research or an opportunity to be creative. In short, her high school biology class will be distressingly similar to that experienced by her parents 2 decades earlier. In class, she yearns for the excitement, the cutting-edge advances, the new science applied to treating disease and saving lives that she sees on television and the Internet. Unfortunately for Brittany, that exciting science is many years away if she continues to tread the traditional academic path. After her freshman year in biology, she will be channeled into chemistry in the 10th grade. Physics will come the year after that. There is a shortage of skilled teachers for more advanced classes. Because of this experience, Brittany, like many of her peers, will most likely have lost enthusiasm for biology by the time she applies to college. She is aware that her cousin in the United Kingdom is simultaneously studying biology, chemistry, and physics in each of the 2 years of her A-level program, giving her an extensive basis in all three subjects before college entry. Like most other high school students, Brittany has not signed up for classes in computer science or engineering and therefore is not acquiring skills essential for a future in research. Most important, she does not understand the consequences of not taking the advanced mathematics required for a career in 21st-century biology. She and her parents do not know that the United States was ranked 27th among Organisation for Economic Co-operation and Development (OECD) countries in the performance of 15-year-olds in mathematics (OECD, 2014)[1]. With most developed countries producing students who have stronger mathematics skills, Brittany's potential to compete at a high level in science may already be compromised unless she can catch up in college. If society is lucky, Brittany will enter a fine undergraduate institution one of whose professors will reignite her interest in biology, and she will be able to catch up to the rest of the world in mathematics. But, it is equally likely that Brittany will veer off the path of science altogether.

THE UNDERGRADUATE EXPERIENCE

Michael is entering a prestigious university as an engineering student. He has already shown an aptitude for mathematics, having won a national competition in high school. He has had little exposure to laboratory science, inasmuch as his time in high school was devoted largely to mathematics courses and the required curriculum. He has taken biology but found its emphasis on rote memorization of facts discovered decades earlier stultifying. Michael has had no exposure to and therefore no interest in research and does not see how his mathematics skills and interest in engineering could be applied to biological research anyway. His college adviser steers him down the path of civil engineering and more advanced mathematics, but fails to recommend that he expose himself to chemistry or large-scale data analysis. In his junior year, Michael learns a bit about molecular biology from his roommate and sees that this field of research is fascinating. He gets a chance to work in a university genetics laboratory over the summer and finds it exciting—some of the required data analyses even allow him to use his advanced mathematics skills. But, when he returns to college for his senior year, he is advised that it is too late to change direction in his undergraduate program and he would be unlikely to be accepted by a premier graduate program in biology given his lack of college courses in the subject. In contrast, he could choose from among a number of well-paying, entry-level jobs as an engineer immediately. His professors tell him that if he does try to pursue a PhD in a biological science, it would be a 4- or 5-year commitment followed by a postdoctoral fellowship (or two), which would require 2–6 more years and give him no guarantee of a job at the end of it. Michael envisions himself getting to the age of 36 years and not having a stable, well-paying job—and carrying the substantial debt incurred by his college tuition. A career as a civil engineer working for a construction company is increasingly attractive.

THE GRADUATE EXPERIENCE

Jamar grew up in the inner city. He is a master's-degree student in a school of social work. He chose this profession because he saw the system failing his family and the families around him. He is particularly interested in the health services for nonworking single mothers. He has done a number of internships as part of his training and sees that community services around the city do not use a standard approach to care. No one seems to know what

> "Study hard what interests you the most in the most undisciplined, irreverent, and original manner possible."
> —Richard Feynman

works. They know what seems to feel good but not what will actually improve the health outcome of mothers and their children. He has a terrific idea for a citywide demonstration–research project to test various models of care delivery empirically. What is more, he intends on using real-world data to test his hypotheses.

He does not, however, have the skills to undertake such complicated analytics and no resources to hire expert help. His faculty adviser is supportive, but grant funding for health services delivery research is limited. He reaches out to the city, the state, and the federal government for funds for research to no avail. When he receives his master's in social work, he finds himself, much to his dismay, in a new job implementing one of the untested service-delivery programs that he had wanted to study. He is destined to spend his career in helping people while having little opportunity himself to develop the evidence so needed to improve the health care system. He sees no path to a PhD.

THE POSTGRADUATE EXPERIENCE

Jose is in medical school and is heading off to a residency in neurology. His parents emigrated from South America when he was a baby, and he is the first person in his family to graduate from college. He is enjoying medical school and working with patients and is doing well. Along the way, he has developed a deep interest in clinical research. He sees the problems that patients are facing and sees that innovation is the only way forward. He has many good ideas for new research projects and is even tinkering with an idea for a new device to help late-stage Parkinson's disease patients ambulate. However, he had to borrow heavily, using student loans to pay for his medical-school tuition, because his parents were not in a position to help him financially, and he has been barely getting by. On graduation and starting his residency, he looks forward to paying down some of his debts—and raising his standard of living a bit and possibly helping his parents financially. As he surveys his career options, however, he is discouraged about the prospects of combining a career in medicine with one in research. Watching the medical-school faculty members around him, he sees them struggling to deliver high-quality care while finding the time to get research grants and conduct the research itself. He begins to think that maybe he should abandon the idea of more research, take his device idea, and just start a company. But, his training and his medical-school mentors have not told him much about the steps needed to move from an idea to a marketable product. He will probably be a successful medical practitioner, but his ideas for innovation will never come to fruition.

THE POSTDOCTORAL EXPERIENCE

Preeti has a PhD and is a postdoctoral trainee in a large medical school. She comes from a family of scientists. Both her parents were trained in India and now have faculty positions in the United States, her father in biochemistry and her mother in nursing. She is in her 4th year of training and has published several important papers. Recently, her intellectual interests have veered away from those of her mentor, who is focused on the role of kinases in heart muscle. Preeti has some innovative ideas about how kinases play a role in muscular dystrophy, but she does not have the computer-science skills that she needs to do the modeling necessary to explore the ideas. She would like to work with a colleague in the computer-science department, but her mentor does not have a grant in this disease field, and Preeti does not have the time or independent resources required to pursue her ideas unless she obtains a faculty position of her own. Her father, who has been a productive scientist for years, just lost his major grant and is having a hard time keeping his laboratory running. Preeti sees the lack of job stability in the academic sector, and it worries her. Meanwhile, her mentor depends on her leadership in the laboratory and wants her to continue to work with him on his projects. She feels stuck. She sees several more years of postdoctoral effort ahead of her and the long odds against gaining a tenure-track position, followed by grant-seeking activities that may or may not bear fruit. She does not know how to look for a job in industry and has never met an industry scientist, so she has no idea whether this is an interesting, let alone viable, career option. She also wants to start a family and is trying to figure out how to fit this into her life plans. She may decide to follow a clearer path to a well-paying and stable career as a financial analyst for a firm that deals in biotech stocks.

KEY ISSUE: THE CHALLENGE OF ATTRACTING AND RETAINING THE BEST AND THE BRIGHTEST IN THE 21ST CENTURY

The stories above highlight the problems faced by aspiring scientists at critical stages of their career development. Those young people all have a fire in the belly that may be extinguished not because of a lack of passion or willingness to work hard but because of environmental circumstances. That is the case even though we have decades of experience in learning how students find their way into science careers. There have been a number of cogent and well-received reports on the nation's scientific workforce (NAS et al., 2007, 2010; NRC, 2012b). As a result of the recommendations in those reports, a number of agencies and even private-sector entities have sought to address some of the challenges we have laid out above. But, the problems persist, and much bolder action is needed.

For high school students, we know about the importance of early school-based research experiences, informal out-of-school science experiences, and motivating information about a career in science (NRC, 2011). Even so, there is little opportunity for students to be exposed to the process of science—exploration, discovery, and validation—as opposed to memorizing previous discoveries. That circumstance limits their understanding of science and dampens their enthusiasm for science as an exciting and creative activity. The current cookie-cutter approach to science education makes it hard to keep the brightest students intellectually engaged and interested in science in general and in biology in particular. Some students may want the opportunity for more rigorous and in-depth learning in their high school years; for example, classes in molecular genetics or neurobiology in high school would undoubtedly ignite young minds. But, state education budgets are shrinking at the very time when more money is needed. More important, state curriculum requirements effectively limit how far students can go in high school (NRC, 2002; Schmidt et al., 2013). The adaptability of the system to the potential of the promising student is the key. Today, it is the student who adapts to a rigid system of programs, rather than the opposite.

Implementing substantial change will require changes in K–12 teacher training. Only a minority of STEM teachers have robust research experience (NAS et al., 2007; PCAST, 2010). Furthermore, the knowledge and skills of STEM teachers, as opposed to teachers in such disciplines as history or English, will rapidly go stale if they are not kept up to date. Few school districts have the resources to send their STEM teachers to annual meetings or continuing education in the form of advanced coursework or bench science (NRC, 2002, 2005a, 2007). As science becomes more complex, the training of the nation's science teachers must keep pace—teachers themselves need more exposure to hypothesis-based thinking, problem solving, mathematics, and computer science in addition to continuous exposure to the evolving knowledge in their fields.

Higher-level mathematics, computer science, and data analytics have become critical for success in most arenas of health research, especially with the rise of genomics and real-world evidence. But, most US students do not even go as far as calculus in high school, let alone to linear algebra or statistics (NAS et al., 2007). The same can be true in college. Statistics is almost absent from curricula, and many students, not recognizing the importance of exposure to such subjects, take as few mathematics and statistics courses as permissible. Moreover, almost no high school or college training in computer science is focused on biology, in which the need for computer science and large-dataset analytic skills is increasing. In middle school, 74 percent of girls express interest in STEM, but when choosing a college major, just 0.4 percent of high school girls select computer science (Girls Who Code, 2016). The number of men and women who have college degrees in mathematics or computer science is a small fraction of the number who are pursuing careers in business administration, and the number of women is much lower than the number of men (NCES, 2014). In addition, the larger problem of attracting members of underrepresented groups, especially minority groups, to careers in science and retaining them must be addressed if we are to take advantage of all America's brainpower. As a country, we are losing many smart young people who could not only become important scientists but bring a richness and diversity of experience and thought to bear on the health challenges of the future.

In college, even when high-level courses in mathematics and computer science are available, they are often rigid and siloed. Curricula are narrowly focused and offer few examples in computer-science classes of how analytic techniques can be applied to modern-day biology, leaving computer scientists largely ignorant about career opportunities in the biomedical workforce. For freshmen still undecided about a career, opportunities for laboratory-based, hypothesis-driven research are sparse. For students with traditional goals, a high mark in organic chemistry has become the Holy Grail of success and serves as a requirement for admission to medical school. Rather than just high marks, the goal of the students should include the development of the problem-solving skills needed in research.

Of all the groups in the biomedical workforce, PhD students are under particular stress in the current environment. Some argue that we are training too many PhDs, others argue that we have too few PhDs in critical fields (Benderly, 2010; Cyranoski et al., 2011; Domer et al., 1996; Trivedi, 2006), and still others suggest that the training is too long and too narrow. The needs of both PhD students and society will be served better by aligning training programs with varied career research options, including "big pharma," biotech, device companies, foundations, government, data-analytics companies, and patient groups.

Despite the growing number of possible careers, we are operating with an outmoded model of training PhDs. It leads to students and postdoctoral scholars who are coming out of their training hoping simply to replicate the careers of their mentors rather than to contribute to the exploration of novel ideas through more diverse careers. Such students finish their training with inadequate exposure to the wider array of career options and the skills that would allow them to make informed decisions about their career paths. It has been suggested that universities and their faculties continue to promulgate that approach because trainees are critical for the productivity of their laboratories. It can be argued that the current postdoctoral system is an apprenticeship program for the benefit of the faculty and results in longer and longer periods of postdoctoral training. Instead, the endgame should be focused on independence as soon as possible rather than having postdoctoral scholars continue to serve as a low-paid labor pool. The current situation is no doubt discouraging to the most creative. It is no surprise that dropping out of college is an increasingly popular recommendation that some entrepreneurs, such as Peter Thiel (Brown, 2014), have made to brilliant students if they are to succeed creatively; Steve Jobs, Bill Gates, and Mark Zuckerberg did not complete their college training, but each has changed the world. Although that recommendation has worked in technology fields, such as computer science, it would not work for such fields as modern biomedical research (NRC, 2005b; Powell, 2015).

Breakthroughs in medicine often move from the bedside to the bench, and this is why the physician–scientist is critical for medical advancement (NIH, 2014). But, there are few formal research-training programs for physicians, especially after residency. The National Institutes of Health (NIH) Medical Scientist Training Program (MD–PhD) (NIH, 2015) has been successful, but many argue that it requires too great an investment of time. Even when physicians try to eke out time for research, health systems end up discouraging such activity in the face of needs to ensure adequate clinical care services and more predictable revenues than those gained from competitive research-grant funding. For example, physician–scientists who have an idea for a product with immediate and direct effects on treatment must often take a leave of absence from the workplace to devote time to such efforts at the risk of damaging their careers.

In the distant past, biomedical scientists could master all the relevant research fields needed to be productive scientists, for example, physiology, pharmacology, anatomy, and genetics. Such scientists toiled away in their academic laboratories, talking to each other in the hallways or at scientific meetings with like-minded academic researchers. And, with that experience, they could be successful in conducting cutting-edge research. Now, to be successful, scientists need to collaborate simultaneously with colleagues in academe, industry, nonprofit organizations, patient groups, and government in the United States and around the world.

The need for collaboration is a result of changes in the health-science research enterprise, which depends increasingly on nontypical biomedical disciplines. Engineering, mathematics, and computational science are now essential. The scientific disciplines, which used to be learned as separate subjects, are increasingly overlapping and complementary. For example, it is now hard to work in genomics without competence in computer-based data analytics. To formulate and test hypotheses, scientists increasingly need to be knowledgeable about and able to apply the skills from not only their own fields but also many other fields. That is particularly true of the emerging discipline of translational research, which sits in the space between basic discovery and "first-in-humans" clinical studies.

Translational research itself has its own methodology (Emmert-Buck, 2014; Fang and Casadevall, 2010; Trochim et al., 2011) and is essential for moving a discovery into an innovation in health care. Today, the most often cited obstacle to the development of novel and more successful therapies is the general lack of a deep understanding of human pathogenesis. For example, after a century, we still do not understand the fundamental causes of diabetes. We can control the disease in some patients, but it progresses inexorably in the large majority of them. The tools and methods arising from the extraordinary progress of the basic sciences—such as genomics, proteomics, and many other advances of the last few decades—need to be applied directly to large patient cohorts who are followed for years. The tools are available, but where are the trained physicians and scientists who will dedicate their lives to such long and difficult explorations and be free of the need to generate large revenues from an increasingly cost-conscious academic health system?

The traditional disciplines of population and behavioral research are also increasingly important. Data from those disciplines have become crucial for even basic science in helping to devise testable hypotheses and identify precisely the patients who would benefit most from existing or new therapies.

The necessity for collaboration is driving new ways of working together. Research has moved from solely a single-investigator model to include team-based science and multidisciplinary and interdisciplinary research. The collaborative approach itself is not based on a single model. For example, team-based research in academe, where the outcome is new knowledge, can be different from team-based research in industry, where the output is a product. Current training programs fail to help young researchers to understand and appreciate the difference between working in academe and working in industry; academe-based training and industry-based training do not comingle enough to allow young researchers to appreciate the differences first-hand. The situation is exacerbated by the perception that industry tends to act primarily in its own interest and often underinvests in R&D. Some argue that industry does not work for the greater good of the scientific enterprise or society. In fact, at a time when public funding for scientists is unstable, it is important to be aware that industry invests much more in R&D than does NIH—by at least $10 billion a year (Powaleny, 2016). The absence of industry experience aggravates the false perception and can keep the best and brightest out of this crucial component of the innovation pipeline. Ironically, it is happening at a time when industry is moving to an external-innovation model, in which much innovation is derived from work with small companies or academics rather than from internal research in industry-owned laboratories.

For all the reasons described above, we need to move from reliance on the old view of scientific training to a new view that takes into account the complexity of biology and the changed environment. No single training pathway is the answer; flexibility and adaptability to the needs of trainees will be essential for success. Most important is the need for incentives for academic institutions to change the scientific culture and be open to new models of training.

That said, large-scale changes in our training systems and infrastructure are probably not all possible at once, certainly not within current national budget constraints. Nevertheless, there are many opportunities for true training innovation. The question is, Which innovations would have the greatest near-term or long-term impact?

At one time, we had only anecdotes to help us to understand how students found their way to careers in scientific research. Today, we have several decades of research to illuminate the importance of early school-based science training, informal out-of-school science experiences, information about careers in science, parental support, and other factors (NRC, 2011). The short scenarios in the section above are intended to be simple illustrations, but available data support the common intuition that students who have access to a robust set of early science experiences are more likely to have scientific careers than are students who do not receive such access (NIH, 2014). As we seek a robust set of pathways into the health-sciences research workforce, how can we ensure that we are supporting students (K–12, undergraduate, and graduate) by making them aware of specific opportunities in the health-sciences research enterprise? How can we be sure that we are reducing barriers to success and linking students to the jobs and careers where there is unmet demand?

In recent years, steps have been taken to correct the cacophony of K–12 educational standards and curricula that characterized the American education system for many decades. The Common Core Standards and the Next Generation Science Standards (NGSS, 2016b) are available for states to use voluntarily. By using them, states can elect to collaborate in curricular materials and student assessments. Such collaboration offers substantial opportunities for cost savings. The standards, although far from perfect, constitute a substantial improvement on what most states had in place before their adoption. The mathematics and science standards (NGA and CCSSO, 2010; NGSS, 2013) will require periodic revision, and the scientific community should remain ready to assist in this process as the National Academy of Sciences did when it played an important role in the draft document that led to the NGSS (NGSS, 2016a; NRC, 2012a).

Exposing students at all levels of education to the wide variety of health-science careers available in industry and policy, as well as academe, will make it easier for them to envision themselves working in these settings. Students able to see themselves in a particular career early are far more likely to prepare themselves for it. Recruitment efforts would benefit from coordinated public–private initiatives. In today's economy, many students (and their parents) are concerned about the availability of well-paying jobs at the end of a particular educational pipeline.

In all sectors and at all levels of biomedical science, there is an urgent need to improve the diversity of the workforce. A diverse scientific workforce will improve our efforts to explore the whole array of health issues that affect our diverse demographics. And, yet, while the number of women in science has been rising in the last 2 decades, the number of minority-group members remains unacceptably low (NSF and National Center for Science and Engineering Statistics, 2015). Clearly, we must do much more to attract and retain underrepresented minorities to STEM education (NAS et al., 2011). Some suggest that despite the desire of many institutions to increase faculty diversity, many minority-group students are unsure how to navigate the job-hiring process or choose to move to higher-paying positions outside academic research. To that end, it may be necessary to develop plans for mentoring for these students to help them to transition from doctoral studies into research positions in the academic workforce.

In sum, changes in high school STEM will require complementary federal, state, and local efforts, perhaps with the new US president working with governors to stimulate new initiatives. That will be especially important in light of budget crunches that force states to cut education budgets. Federal matching grants could be an incentive for states to invest.

What opportunities exist at the undergraduate and graduate levels to address the problems that we have articulated here? For example, should there be a reinvigoration of master's programs, especially in such fields as statistics and computer science, in which a PhD may not be necessary? Should we consider programs similar to those in Europe (Martinho, 2012), where especially talented students go straight from high school to MD or PhD programs or where parts of undergraduate and doctoral training are condensed? It would certainly be feasible to consider national programs, perhaps supported by federal or state grants, which give more undergraduate students summer research experiences. Why not create accelerated pathways for the most gifted students, especially members of underrepresented minority groups, rather than impose the same programs on all, primarily for the purposes of credentialing?

It is undeniable that the debt burden amassed by a student pursuing a high-level credential in science in this country is substantial and is a disincentive to pursuing such a path (Zelser et al., 2013). Is it time to consider debt forgiveness for students completing PhDs in some high-need fields, such as bioinformatics? Another big problem is the lack of faculty (Dinsdale et al., 2015; Sainani, 2015), especially in the United States, to train bioinformaticians and biostatisticians. In the nation's graduate schools, including medical schools, the opportunity to take courses in biostatistics and bioinformatics is limited by the lack of adequate qualified staff to teach them. There is such a high demand for those skills that schools cannot keep up. Would government support for master's-program students, especially in disciplines with shortages, such as biostatistics, help to meet the need for more faculty?

With all the evidence of problems in the system, it should not be surprising that there has been no lack of initiatives aimed at solving at least some of them. But, there has been no comprehensive examination of outcomes. Federal STEM programs have involved projects at different stages of development. For some, innovation and initial prototype development are the goal; for others, scalability and effects need to be evaluated. It is important to understand not only what works but also why it works and what appears not to be working and why. Governmentwide evaluation funds should be used to create an educational knowledge base for the benefit of future programs and interventions. For example, what can be learned from existing undergraduate research programs, including the National Science Foundation (NSF) Research Experiences for Undergraduates program (NSF, 2016b)? How can we build on successful diversity initiatives, such as the NIH Building Infrastructure Leading to Diversity initiative (NIH, 2016a, b), The University of Maryland, Baltimore County Meyerhoff and Howard Hughes Medical Institute–funded adaptation (HHMI, 2014; UMBC, 2016), and relevant NSF programs (NSF, 2016a)? Are there programs that are working well but could be improved, such as NIH's Broadening Experiences in Scientific Training (BEST, 2016), Pathways to Independence (K99-R00) (NIH, 2016e), Early Independence Awards (NIH, 2016d), F32 (NIH, 2016c), and T32 awards (NIH, 2016f)? We need to know which programs should be expanded and which could or should be ended. In creating new programs, one always needs to look for ways to prevent the tendency for programs, once put into place, to stay forever—long past their utility.

The discussion above articulates many of the initiatives that could be considered in an effort to optimize the 21st-century scientific workforce. They have been presented to illustrate the breadth of issues and to draw attention to some solutions that could address them. However, it could be argued that if we try to change everything at once, we will end up changing nothing. Rather, a realistic approach to change is needed—change that will not require wholesale reinvention of the current system. We must focus on the biggest problems and try to make immediate and pragmatic changes, which are likely to promise lasting effects.

POLICY SUGGESTIONS

A visible response to ensure the future competiveness of the country by creating a new generation of innovators in the life sciences is of strategic importance. The life sciences will undoubtedly embody the largest economic opportunity for growth of novel solutions for addressing disease and disability and for control of runaway health care costs and burdens. We do not have the full array of programs that will ensure that the best and brightest pursue, and do not deviate from, careers in biomedical research. We need to ensure that these young people have the opportunity to realize their most creative ideas with all the support and encouragement required. We must work at all levels simultaneously to instigate change. Following are two policy suggestions that taken together could make a critical difference in the nation's ability to tackle the challenges of creating and supporting a truly 21st-century health-science workforce.

A NextGen Opportunity Fund

The president could create a NextGen Opportunity Fund, whose resources come from a 2 percent set-aside from the appropriations of each relevant federal health, science, or education agency, which could rise to as much as 5 percent over the next decade as it is evaluated for impact. Strategic use of the funds would be guided by a presidential panel that comprises heads of federal agencies and divisions, state governors, and representatives of academe, payers, providers, industry, and patient groups. It would function under the aegis of the Office of Science and Technology Policy's National Science and Technology Council Committee on Science. Resources would be used to expand current programs and create newer, more focused opportunities in relevant federal agencies. The goal is to attract the most talented into biomedical research, train them for the 21st century, foster their creativity, and ensure that they become independent researchers earlier. The programs would ensure that the next generation of health scientists is multidisciplinary, collaborative, and working in an environment that fosters their most creative ideas.

The opportunity fund could be used to support existing and new programs at the federal and state levels to train the brightest aspiring scientists with the goal of engaging them in urgent improvement of the nation's health.

The fund should be an incentive for the nation's governors and K–12 educators to ensure that the most talented students are given the opportunity and encouragement to excel (see *Box 20-1* for sample programs). Working with academe and through federal agencies, it should also be used for creating new incentives to shorten the time from undergraduate and graduate training to independence (see *Box 20-2* for sample programs).

All new programs funded in this manner should have a 10-year limit with an opportunity to renew after favorable evaluation.

BOX 20–1
Sample High School Initiatives

- Create biology-related curricula in computer-science classes.
- Create opportunities to take online college courses for credit in such subjects as computer science where appropriate courses or appropriately qualified teachers are not available locally.
- Ensure that all federal science-mission agencies play a formal role in improving the nation's high school education system via appropriate authorizing language.
- Create "science-teaching fellows" who work in high schools with the most talented students.
- Provide more early school-based science training, informal out-of-school science experiences, and information about careers in science.
- Provide federal matching grants as an incentive for state investment in innovative science curricula for the best and brightest.

The Health-Science Corps for the 21st Century

The profile of health scientists will need to be different in the future from today. To that end, an additional policy approach to training the next generation of health scientists could be to create a National Health-Science Corps for the 21st Century. The corps could be funded either from the NextGen Opportunity Fund described above or through appropriations directly to relevant federal agencies and departments. The mission of the corps would be to address the lack of high school exposure to the best science by the best teachers; the unjustified lengthening of our postgraduate training system with poorly defined career pathways even for promising scientists who today do not reach independence until their late 30s; the increasing financial burden of a scientific education with unsustainable student debt levels that forces many, especially members of underrepresented minorities, to forgo scientific careers; and the persistence of rigid disciplinary silos that make the multidisciplinary training and research experience more difficult and longer than necessary.

Admission to the corps would be highly competitive. Such an "army of innovators" would be nurtured at all stages of career development, from high school to early independence. This cohesive program would provide customized opportunities for members of the corps with the singular goal of turning out

BOX 20–2
College and Graduate Initiatives

- Create more master's programs, especially in such fields as statistics and computer science.
- Explore programs in which especially talented students go straight from high school to MD and PhD programs.
- Create programs in which parts of college and doctoral training are condensed.
- Provide debt-forgiveness programs for students who are working toward master's degrees or doctorates in some high-need fields, such as bioinformatics and biostatistics.
- Provide federal training and research support for the best and brightest master's and doctoral students who are interested in health-services research and public health research.
- Create more master's programs, such as programs like the Sloan Professional Science Master's program, focused on multidisciplinary approaches to problem solving.
- Expand on existing industrial postdoctoral and other internship experiences, such as the NIH T32 and F32 training programs.
- Provide incentives to identify the best and brightest members of underrepresented minority groups and women in high school and college.
- Set time limits on institutions for the maximum duration of PhD training.
- Change the Office of Management and Budget indirect-cost calculation for NIH-funded universities on the basis of time to first independent job for postdoctoral fellows.
- Create new mechanisms to promote careers as staff scientists (nontenured with no teaching responsibility) in academic settings.
- Create a new Entrepreneurship Division in NSF or the Department of Commerce to provide postdoctoral fellows with startup funds.
- Provide incentives for 4-year colleges to work with community colleges for early identification of science interest and talent.
- Create new programs for medical students and residents to have the time and resources to conduct research.
- Expand community-college and college programs that create opportunities for exceptional students who have suffered from weak K–12 experiences.
- Create programs to help students, particularly minority-group students, who need guidance on completion of a doctorate or postdoctoral fellowship as to how to navigate the job hiring process.

highly trained independent scientists ready to contribute to improvements in health. The program would address all educational levels, with corps members being admitted to the program as early as high school and as late as postdoctoral fellowship and medical residency. Corps members would be assessed regularly to evaluate progress and success. People entering the corps would be able to participate in advanced curricula designed to speed their trajectory toward becoming independent scientists. For example, new programs might include opportunities for high school students to take college classes in computer science for credit and to do it while replacing, for example, a history requirement. Undergraduate colleges could be required to provide corps members the opportunity to conduct 4 years of hypothesis-driven research with a mentor in an assigned laboratory.

Unlike programs that address different phases of the career pipeline independently, this program would address the big picture by pushing forward at all stages of the scientific workforce simultaneously, ensuring continuity for the best and the brightest as they progress from high school through postdoctoral work and residency. Thus, the program would serve as an umbrella for all phases of science education, training, and early career development. It could draw on and include existing programs as necessary and appropriate.

Relevant agencies, state governors, and the private sector should be responsible for operationalizing the corps, that is, designing the programs that would deliver the expected outcomes. *Boxes 20-1 and 20-2* identify possible initiatives. Plans for evaluation would be designed so that the most effective aspects of the corps could be continued and others discontinued, as needed.

CONCLUSION

The scientific workforce of the 21st century will be different from that of the 20th: it must be more diverse and multidisciplinary. Many workforce initiatives to date have involved directing existing federal and some private-sector investment into agency or foundation initiatives. We have trod that path before. The BIO2010 report (NRC, 2003) and *Rising Above the Gathering Storm* (NAS et al., 2007) both raised many of the issues addressed here.

Efforts to instigate change, however, have been uneven and have lacked cohesiveness. We cannot allow history to repeat itself, so we respectfully put forth these proposals that would immediately and persistently change the training landscape in the United States. The absence of such bold moves would put the nation at risk. Historically, presidents have changed the fortunes of the nation by launching specific initiatives, such as the GI Bill and the space program. We are at a comparable historical juncture with regard to the life sciences in this century.

Motivated and talented human capital is the core determinant of national competitiveness. Nothing is more critical than ensuring that our next generation of health scientists accomplishes even more than the current one. It will require courage, perseverance, and leadership at the highest levels of the nation.

SUMMARY RECOMMENDATIONS FOR VITAL DIRECTIONS

1. Establish a NextGen Opportunity Fund.
2. Create a Health-Science Corps for the 21st Century.

NOTE

1. The results of the 2012 Program for International Student Assessment (PISA) study conducted by OECD-ranked US high school students 27th in mathematics among the 34 OECD member nations. In the same study, US students placed 17th in reading skills and 20th in science. Overall, that means that our high school students score at or below the international mean in the key measures of academic readiness. Shanghai, China (not an OECD member nation), was the top international performer in mathematics. Shanghai's average score placed it more than 2 full school years ahead of the average in Massachusetts (one of the top-performing US states). Setting aside average performance and focusing instead on top-performing students does not provide much solace. About 2 percent of US high school students score at the highest level of mathematical achievement—compared with an OECD average of 3 percent and Shanghai's standout performance of 31 percent. America has to aspire to be more than "average" to have any chance of retaining its position as a world leader in STEM (OECD, 2014).

REFERENCES

Benderly, B. L. 2010. Does the U.S. produce too many scientists? *Scientific American,* February 22. Available at http://www.scientificamerican.com/article/does-the-us-produce-too-m/ (accessed July 13, 2016).

BEST (Broadening Experiences in Scientific Training). 2016. Broadening Experiences in Scientific Training-BEST. Available at http://www.nihbest.org/ (accessed July 13, 2016).

Brown, M. 2014. Peter Thiel: The billionaire tech entrepreneur on a mission to cheat death. *The Telegraph,* September 19. Available at http://www.telegraph.

co.uk/technology/11098971/Peter-Thiel-the-billionaire-tech-entrepreneur-on-a-mission-to-cheat-death.html (accessed July 13, 2016).

Cyranoski, D., N. Gilbert, H. Ledford, A. Nayar, and M. Yahia. 2011. Education: The PhD factory. *Nature* 472(7343):276–279.

Dinsdale, E., S. C. Elgin, N. Grandgenett, W. Morgan, A. Rosenwald, W. Tapprich, E. W. Triplett, and M. A. Pauley. 2015. NIBLSE: A network for integrating bioinformatics into life sciences education. *CBE Life Sciences Education* 14(4):e3.

Domer, J. E., R. F. Garry, P. S. Guth, M. R. Walters, and J. W. Fisher. 1996. On the crisis in biomedical education: Is there an overproduction of biomedical PhDs? *Academic Medicine* 71(8):876–885.

Einstein, A. 2016. AZQuotes.com. Available at http://www.azquotes.com/quote/87375 (accessed July 13, 2016).

Emmert-Buck, M. R. 2014. Translational research: From biological discovery to public benefit (or not). *Advances in Biology* 2014:1–20.

Fang, F. C., and A. Casadevall. 2010. Lost in translation—basic science in the era of translation research. *Infection and Immunity* 78(2):563–566.

Feynman, R. P. 2016. AZQuotes.com. Available at http://www.azquotes.com/quote/343610 (accessed July 13, 2016).

Girls Who Code. 2016. Girls who code—join 40,000 girls who code today! Available at https://girlswhocode.com/ (accessed July 13, 2016).

Harris, R., and R. Benincasa. 2014. U.S. science suffering from booms and busts in funding. *NPR News,* September 9. Available at http://www.npr.org/sections/health-shots/2014/09/09/340716091/u-s-science-suffering-from-booms-and-busts-in-funding (accessed July 13, 2016).

HHMI (Howard Hughes Medical Institute). 2014. Three universities united to replicate and spread successful STEM program. Available at http://www.hhmi.org/news/three-universities-unite-replicate-and-spread-successful-stem-program (accessed July 13, 2016).

IOM (Institute of Medicine). 2001. *Crossing the quality chasm: A new health system for the 21st century.* Washington, DC: National Academy Press.

IRI (Industrial Research Institute). 2016. The 2016 global R&D funding forecast. *R&D Magazine* Winter(Suppl):1–35.

Kirk, A. 2015. Nobel Prize winners: Which country has the most Nobel laureates? *The Telegraph,* October 12. Available at http://www.telegraph.co.uk/news/worldnews/northamerica/usa/11926364/Nobel-Prize-winners-Which-country-has-the-most-Nobel-laureates.html (accessed July 13, 2016).

Kruse, J. 2013. Fragmentation in US medical education, research, and practice: The need for system wide defrag. *Family Medicine* 45(1):54–57.

Martinho, A. M. 2012. Become a doctor in Europe: Objective selection systems. *AMA Journal of Ethics* 14(12):984–988.

Matthews, C. M. 2010. *Foreign science and engineering presence in U.S. institutions and the labor force.* Washington, DC: Congressional Research Service.

McKenna, M., and J. L. Collins. 2010. Chapter 1 in *Current issues and challenges in chronic disease control,* 3rd ed., edited by P. L. Remington, R. C. Brownson, and M. V. Wegner. Washington, DC: American Public Health Association.

NAS (National Academy of Sciences), NAE (National Academy of Engineering), and IOM (Institute of Medicine). 2007. *Rising above the gathering storm: Energizing and employing America for a brighter economic future.* Washington, DC: The National Academies Press.

NAS, NAE, and IOM. 2010. *Rising above the gathering storm, revisited: Rapidly approaching category 5.* Washington, DC: The National Academies Press.

NAS, NAE, and IOM. 2011. *Expanding underrepresented minority participation: America's science and technology talent at the crossroads.* Washington, DC: The National Academies Press.

NCES (National Center for Education Statistics). 2014. Bachelor's, master's, and doctor's degrees conferred by postsecondary institutions, by sex of student and discipline division: 2012–13. Available at https://nces.ed.gov/programs/digest/d14/tables/dt14_318.30.asp (accessed July 13, 2016).

NGA (National Governors Association Center for Best Practices) and CCSSO (Council of Chief State School Officers). 2010. *Common Core state standards for mathematics.* Washington, DC: NGA and CCSSO.

NGSS (Next Generation Science Standards). 2013. *Next Generation Science Standards: DCI arrangements of the Next Generation Science Standards.* Washington, DC: Achieve, Inc.

NGSS. 2016a. Development overview. Available at http://www.nextgenscience.org/development-overview (accessed July 13, 2016).

NGSS. 2016b. Standards by DCI. Available at http://www.nextgenscience.org/overview-dci (accessed July 13, 2016).

NIH (National Institutes of Health). 2014. *Physician-scientist workforce report 2014.* Washington, DC: NIH.

NIH. 2015. Medical Scientist Training Program. Available at https://www.nigms.nih.gov/Training/InstPredoc/Pages/PredocOverview-MSTP.aspx (accessed July 13, 2016).

NIH. 2016a. Building Infrastructure Leading to Diversity (BUILD) initiative. Available at https://www.nigms.nih.gov/train-ing/dpc/pages/build.aspx (accessed July 13, 2016).

NIH. 2016b. Enhancing the diversity of the NIH-funded workforce: Funded research. Available at https://commonfund.nih.gov/diversity/fundedresearch (accessed July 13, 2016).

NIH. 2016c. F32 Ruth L. Kirschstein postdoctoral individual national research service award. Available at https://re-searchtraining.nih.gov/programs/fellowships/F32 (accessed July 12, 2016).

NIH. 2016d. NIH director's early independence award program. Available at https://www.nlm.nih.gov/ep/pathway.html (accessed July 13, 2016).

NIH. 2016e. NIH pathway to independence (PI) award (K99/R00). Available at https://www.nlm.nih.gov/ep/pathway.html (accessed July 13, 2016).

NIH. 2016f. T32 Ruth L. Kirschstein postdoctoral individual national research service award. Available at https://researchtraining.nih.gov/programs/training-grants/T32 (accessed July 13, 2016).

NRC (National Research Council). 2002. *Learning and understanding: Improving advanced study of mathematics and science in U.S. high schools.* Washington, DC: The National Academies Press.

NRC. 2003. Bio2010: *Transforming undergraduate education for future research biologists.* Washington, DC: The National Academies Press.

NRC. 2005a. *America's lab report: Investigations in high school science.* Washington, DC: The National Academies Press.

NRC. 2005b. *Bridges to independence: Fostering the independence of new investigators in biomedical research.* Washington, DC: The National Academies Press.

NRC. 2007. *Taking science to school: Learning and teaching science in grades K-8.* Washington, DC: The National Academies Press.

NRC. 2011. *Successful K-12 STEM education: Identifying effective approaches in science, technology, engineering, and mathematics.* Washington, DC: The National Academies Press.

NRC. 2012a. *A framework for K-12 science education: Practices, crosscutting concepts, and core ideas.* Washington, DC: The National Academies Press.

NRC. 2012b. *Research universities and the future of America: Ten breakthrough actions vital to our nation's prosperity and security.* Washington, DC: The National Academies Press.

NSF (National Science Foundation). 2016a. Programs. Available at http://www.nsf.gov/od/odi/programs.jsp (accessed July 13, 2016).

NSF. 2016b. Research experiences for undergraduates. Available at http://www.nsf.gov/funding/pgm_summ.jsp?pims_ id=5517&from=fund (accessed July 13, 2016).

NSF and National Center for Science and Engineering Statistics. 2015. *Women, minorities, and persons with disabilities in science and engineering.* Arlington, VA: Special Report NSF.

OECD (Organisation for Economic Co-operation and Development). 2014. PISA 2012 results in focus: *What 15-year-olds know and what they can do with what they know.* Paris: OECD Publishing.

PCAST (President's Council of Advisors on Science and Technology). 2010. *Prepare and inspire: K-12 education in science, technology, engineering and math (STEM) for America's future.* Washington, DC: Executive Office of the President.

Powaleny, A. 2016. The catalyst: America's biopharmaceutical industry is central to diverse R&D ecosystem. PhRMA (the Pharmaceutical Research and Manufacturers of America), March 29. Available at http://catalyst.phrma.org/americas-biopharmaceutical-industry-leads-diverse-rd-ecosystem (accessed July 13, 2016).

Powell, K. 2015. The future of the postdoc. *Nature* 520(7546):144–147.

Sainani, K. 2015. The ever-expanding and heterogeneous landscape of bioinformatics education. *Biomedical Computation Review* 11(3):12–19.

Schmidt, W. H., N. A. Burroughs, and L. S. Cogan. 2013. On the road to reform: K-12 science education in the United States. *The Bridge* 43(1):7–14.

Trivedi, B. P. 2006. Are we training too many scientists? *The Scientist* 20(9):42–28.

Trochim, W., C. Kane, M. J. Graham, and H. A. Pincus. 2011. Evaluating translational research: A process marker model. *Clinical and Translational Science* 4(3):153–162.

UMBC (University of Maryland, Baltimore County). 2016. Meyerhoff Scholars Program. Available at http://meyer-hoff.umbc.edu/ (accessed July 13, 2016).

Zelser, K. L., R. J. Kirshstein, and C. Tanenbaum. 2013. *The price of a science PhD: Variations in student debt levels across disciplines and race/ethnicity.* Washington, DC: Center for STEM Education and Innovation at American Institutes for Research.

AUTHOR INFORMATION

Elias A. Zerhouni, MD, is President, Global R&D, Sanofi. **Jeremy M. Berg, PhD,** is Associate Senior Vice Chancellor for Science Strategy and Planning in the Health Sciences, and Visiting Professor of Computational and Systems Biology, University of Pittsburgh. **Freeman A. Hrabowski, PhD,** is President, University of Maryland Baltimore County. **Raynard S. Kington, MD, PhD,** is President, Grinnell College. **Story C. Landis, PhD,** is Scientist Emeritus, National Institute of Neurological Disorders and Stroke.

APPENDIXES

APPENDIX A

VITAL DIRECTIONS STEERING COMMITTEE BIOGRAPHIES

Sheila P. Burke, MPA, RN is Adjunct Lecturer in Public Policy at Harvard Kennedy School's Malcolm Wiener Center for Social Policy. She served as a lecturer and Executive Dean of the school from 1996–2000. Previously she had been Chief of Staff to former senate Majority Leader Bob Dole (1985–1996), a professional staff member of the Senate Committee on Finance (1979–1982), and Deputy Staff Director of that committee (1982 to 1985). From 2000–2007 she served as Undersecretary and then Deputy Secretary of the Smithsonian Institution. She is a member of the National Academy of Medicine, serving on its National Council, and a fellow of the National Academy of Public Administration and the American Academy of Nursing. She serves on the adjunct faculty at Georgetown University and is a Distinguished Visitor at the O'Neill Institute for National and Global Health Law, Georgetown Law Center. She serves on several boards including the Kaiser Commission on the Future of Medicaid and the Uninsured, Ascension Health Care, the Commonwealth Fund, Abt Associates, is a member of the Board of Regents of the Uniformed Services University of the Health Sciences and serves on the Board of Directors of Chubb Insurance. She served as a member of the Medicare Payment Advisory Commission (MedPac) 2000–2007, the Kaiser Family Foundation 1999–2008 where she served as Chair of the Board. Burke, who also serves as a Senior Public Policy Advisor and Chair of the Government and Public Policy practice at Baker Donelson Caldwell & Berkowitz. She holds a bachelor of science from the University of San Francisco in addition to her master's in public administration from Harvard University.

Molly J. Coye, MD, is Executive in Residence at AVIA, the nation's leading network for health systems seeking to innovate and transform. AVIA's mission is to advance care delivery transformation through the effective identification and deployment of digital solutions. By providing strategic focus, process discipline, and a collaborative approach, AVIA delivers measurable results to its Network of more than 20 health system members representing over 325 hospitals. Dr. Coye was previously Social Entrepreneur in Residence for the Network for Excellence in Health Innovation (NEHI), a nonprofit, national health policy institute focused on enabling innovations that provide solutions to the most pressing issues facing our health care system today.

From 2010–2015, Dr. Coye was the Chief Innovation Officer for UCLA Health and headed the Institute for Innovation in Health and the Global Lab for Innovation at UCLA, where she led the health system in identifying new strategies, technologies, products, and services to support the large-scale transformation of healthcare. Today the Global Lab for Innovation at NEHI advances the adoption of high-value innovations that enable dramatic improvements in access to and affordability of health services. Dr. Coye also advises technology developers, investors, national health systems and policymakers about disruptive technologies and business models that accelerate transformation and constrain health expenditures, and serves on the advisory boards of early stage companies and venture and private equity firms investing in health care information technology and services.

Dr. Coye was previously the Founder and CEO of the Health Technology Center (HealthTech), a nonprofit education and research organization established in 2000 that became the premier forecasting organization for emerging technologies in health care. Dr. Coye has also served as Commissioner of Health for the State of New Jersey, Director of the California State Department of Health Services, and Head of the Division of Public Health Practice at the Johns Hopkins School of Hygiene and Public Health. Dr. Coye is an elected member of the National Academy of Medicine, and a member of the Board of Directors of Aetna, Inc., Prosetta Biosciences, Inc., and ACCESS Health International. She has previously served as Chair of the Board of Directors of PATH, one of the largest nonprofit organizations in global health, and on the boards of the American Hospital Association, the American Public Health Association, the American Telemedicine Association, Big White Wall, Cholestech, The California Endowment, and the China Medical Board. Dr. Coye holds MD and MPH degrees from Johns Hopkins University and an MA in Chinese History from Stanford University, and is the author of two books on China.

The Honorable Thomas A. Daschle is the Founder and CEO of The Daschle Group, A Public Policy Advisory of Baker Donelson. The Daschle Group is a full-service strategic advisory firm that advises clients on a broad array of economic, policy, and political issues.

Senator Daschle has participated in the development and debate of almost every major public policy issue of the last three decades. In 1978, he was elected to the US House of Representatives, where he served for eight years. In 1986, he was elected to the US Senate and was chosen as Senate Democratic Leader in 1994. Senator Daschle is one of the longest serving Senate Democratic leaders in history and one of only two to serve twice as both Majority and Minority Leader.

During his tenure, Senator Daschle navigated the Senate through some of its most historic economic and national security challenges. In 2003, he chronicled some of these experiences in his book, *Like No Other Time: The 107th Congress* and *the Two Years That Changed America Forever.* In the 2013 release of *The US Senate: Fundamentals of American Government*, Senator Daschle explores the inner workings of this important part of the legislative branch.

Since leaving the Senate, Senator Daschle has remained an active and learned voice among policymakers. As a well-known expert on health policy reform, he has written two books: *Critical: What We Can Do About the Health-Care Crisis* and *Getting It Done: How Obama and Congress Finally Broke the Stalemate to Make Way for Health Care Reform.*

Senator Daschle has also emerged as a leading thinker on climate change, food security, and renewable energy policy. He serves on both advisory and governing boards of a number of corporate and nonprofit organizations and currently cochairs The Cuba Consortium, an organization dedicated to an improved relationship with the people of Cuba.

In 2007, Senator Daschle joined with former Majority Leaders George Mitchell, Bob Dole, and Howard Baker to create the Bipartisan Policy Center, an organization dedicated to finding common ground on some of the pressing public policy challenges of our time. Senator Daschle is Chair of the Board of Directors at the Center for American Progress and Vice-Chair for the National Democratic Institute. He serves on the board of Edward M. Kennedy Institute and the LBJ Foundation. He also is a member of the Health Policy and Management Executive Council at the Harvard School of Public Health and the Council of Foreign Relations.

Born in Aberdeen, South Dakota, Senator Daschle attended South Dakota State University, graduating in 1969. He then served for three years as an intelligence officer in the US Air Force Strategic Command. Following his military service, he spent five years as an aide to South Dakota Senator James Abourezk. After leaving the Senate in 2005, Senator Daschle joined Alston & Bird LLP as a special policy advisor and then went on to work in the same role at DLA Piper before establishing The Daschle Group in 2014.

He is married to Linda Hall Daschle and has three children and five grandchildren.

Angela Diaz, MD, PhD, MPH, is the Jean C. and James W. Crystal Professor of Pediatrics and Preventive Medicine at the Icahn School of Medicine at Mount Sinai. After earning her medical degree at Columbia University College of Physicians and Surgeons, she completed an MPH from Harvard University and a PhD in epidemiology from Columbia University.

Dr. Diaz is the Director of the Mount Sinai Adolescent Health Center, a unique program that provides comprehensive, interdisciplinary, integrated, medical care, sexual and reproductive health, mental health, dental and optical services to young people. Under her leadership the Center has become the largest adolescent-specific health center in the US, serving more than 10,000 young people every year—for free. The Mount Sinai Adolescent Health Center is a major training site in the field of adolescent health and medicine, with research funded by NIH.

Dr. Diaz is a member of the National Academy of Medicine (NAM), where she sits on its governing council, is a member of the Committee for the Health and Medicine Division, and chairs the Board on Children, Youth and Families at the National Academies of Sciences, Engineering, and Medicine. Dr. Diaz has been a White House Fellow, a member of the Food and Drug Administration Pediatric Advisory Committee, and a member of the Board of Directors of the New York City Department of Health and Mental Hygiene. In 2003, Dr. Diaz chaired the National Advisory Committee on Children and Terrorism for the Department of Health and Human Services. In 2009, she was appointed by Mayor Michael Bloomberg to the New York City Commission for Lesbian, Gay, Bisexual, Transgender and Questioning (LGBTQ) Runaway and Homeless Youth Taskforce.

Dr. Diaz is active in public policy and advocacy in the United States and has conducted many international health projects in Asia, Central and South America, Europe, and Africa. She is a frequent speaker at conferences throughout the country and around the world.

Victor J. Dzau, MD *(Co-Chair),* is the President of the National Academy of Medicine (NAM), formerly the Institute of Medicine (IOM). In addition, he serves as Chair of the Health and Medicine Division Committee of the National Academies of Sciences, Engineering, and Medicine. He is Chancellor Emeritus and James B. Duke Professor of Medicine at Duke University and the past President and CEO of the Duke University Health System. Previously, Dr. Dzau was the Hersey Professor of Theory and Practice of Medicine and Chairman of Medicine at Harvard Medical School's Brigham and Women's Hospital, as well as Chairman of the Department of Medicine at Stanford University.

Dr. Dzau has made a significant impact on medicine through his seminal research in cardiovascular medicine and genetics, his pioneering of the discipline of vascular medicine, and his leadership in health care innovation. His important work on the renin angiotensin system (RAS) paved the way for the contemporary understanding of RAS in cardiovascular disease and the development of RAS inhibitors as widely used, lifesaving drugs. Dr. Dzau also pioneered gene therapy for vascular disease, and his recent work on stem cell paracrine mechanisms and the use of microRNA in direct reprogramming provides novel insight into stem cell biology and regenerative medicine.

In his role as a leader in health care, Dr. Dzau has led efforts in health care innovation. His vision is for academic health sciences centers to lead the transformation of medicine through innovation, translation, and globalization. Leading this vision at Duke, he and his colleagues developed the Duke Translational Medicine Institute, the Duke Global Health Institute, the Duke-National University of Singapore Graduate Medical School, and the Duke Institute for Health Innovation. These initiatives create a seamless continuum from discovery and translational sciences to clinical care, and they promote transformative innovation in health.

As one of the world's preeminent academic health leaders, Dr. Dzau advises governments, corporations, and universities worldwide. He has been a member of the Council of the IOM and the Advisory Committee to the Director of the National Institutes of Health (NIH), as well as Chair of the NIH Cardiovascular Disease Advisory Committee and the Association of Academic Health Centers. He served on the Governing Board of the Duke-National University of Singapore Graduate Medical School and the Board of Health Governors of the World Economic Forum and chaired its Global Agenda Council on Personalized and Precision Medicine. He also served as the Senior Health Policy Advisor to Her Highness Sheikha Moza (Chair of the Qatar Foundation). Currently, he is a member of the Board of Directors of the Singapore Health System, the Expert Board of the Imperial College Health Partners, UK, and the International Advisory Board of the Biomedical Science Council of Singapore. In 2011, he led a partnership between Duke University, the World Economic Forum, and McKinsey, and he founded the International Partnership for Innovative Healthcare Delivery and currently chairs its Board of Directors.

Among his honors and recognitions are the Gustav Nylin Medal from the Swedish Royal College of Medicine; the Max Delbruck Medal from Humboldt University, Charité, and the Max Planck Institute; the Commemorative Gold Medal from the Ludwig Maximilian University of Munich; the Inaugural Hatter Award from the Medical Research Council of South Africa; the Polzer Prize from the European

Academy of Sciences and Arts; the Novartis Award for Hypertension Research; the Distinguished Scientist Award from the American Heart Association (AHA); and the AHA Research Achievement Award for his contributions to cardiovascular biology and medicine. Recently, he was awarded the Public Service Medal by the president of Singapore. He has received nine honorary doctorates.

The Honorable William H. Frist, MD, is a nationally-acclaimed heart and lung transplant surgeon, former US Senate Majority Leader, and chairman of the Executive Board of the health service private equity firm Cressey & Company. He is actively engaged in the business as well as the medical, humanitarian, and philanthropic communities. He is chairman of both Hope Through Healing Hands, which focuses on maternal and child health and global poverty, and SCORE, a statewide collaborative education reform organization that has helped propel Tennessee to prominence as a K12 education reform state.

As a US Senator representing Tennessee from 1994–2006 (the first practicing physician elected to the Senate since 1928), Dr. Frist served on both the Health (HELP) and the Finance Committees responsible for writing all health legislation. He was elected Majority Leader of the Senate, having served fewer total years in Congress than any person chosen to lead that body in history. His leadership was instrumental in the passage of the 2003 Medicare Modernization Act and the historic PEPFAR legislation that provided life-saving treatment globally to over 12 million people and reversed the spread of HIV/AIDS worldwide. He also held seats on the Foreign Relations Committee where he chaired the Subcommittee on Africa, the Commerce Committee, and the Banking Committee.

Currently Dr. Frist serves as an adjunct professor of Cardiac Surgery at Vanderbilt University and clinical professor of Surgery at Meharry Medical College. As a leading authority on healthcare, Senator Frist speaks nationally on health reform, government policy, global health, education reform, and volunteerism. His current board service includes the Robert Wood Johnson Foundation, The Nature Conservancy, Kaiser Family Foundation, Smithsonian Museum of the American Indian, Bipartisan Policy Center, and Nashville Health Care Council. In the private sector, he serves on the boards of Select Medical, Teladoc, AECOM, and others.

Martha E. Gaines, JD, LLM, is Distinguished Clinical Professor and Founder and Director of the interdisciplinary Center for Patient Partnerships at the University of Wisconsin Schools of Law, Medicine, Nursing & Pharmacy. The Center's mission is to disrupt dysfunctional health care by restoring people to the core of care. The Center advocates with patients to get the care they need, while teaching future professionals to see their patients as partners; promotes changes in health care policy at the local, state, and federal levels; and conducts primary, mixed methods research focused on patients' experiences of their care. Students derive from a breadth of disciplines including medicine, nursing, law, health systems, genetic counseling, industrial engineering, and pharmacy, and work in interprofessional teams to provide advocacy services to patients with life-threatening and serious chronic illnesses.

Ms. Gaines's work focuses on consumer engagement and empowerment in health care reform where she has been privileged to collaborate with the Robert Wood Johnson Foundation, the Kaiser Family Foundation, the American Board of Internal Medicine Foundation, the Josiah Macy Jr. Foundation, and the National Cancer Institute among others. She serves on the National Cancer Research Advocates of the NCI, on the Board of the American Academy on Communication in Healthcare, recently cochaired the Josiah Macy Jr. Foundation annual conference "Partnering with Patients, Families, and Communities to Link Interprofessional Practice and Education," and was appointed by the ABIMF to serve on the committee to develop the Charter on Organizational Professionalism for Healthcare Organizations, as a companion to the Charter on Medical Professionalism of the Choosing Wisely Campaign.

Her diverse publications include "Engaging Patients at the Front Lines of Primary Care Redesign: Operational Lessons for an Effective Program," "Medical professionalism from the patient's perspective: Is there an advocate in the house?," "Integrating Compassionate, Collaborative Care (the "Triple C") Into Health Professional Education to Advance the Triple Aim of Health Care," "A Social Compact For Advancing Team-Based High-Value Health Care," "Best Case/Worst Case": Evaluation of a novel communication tool for difficult in-the-moment surgical decisions" and "Moving from tokenism to co-production: implications of learning from patient and community voices in developing patient centred professionalism."

Distinguished Clinical Professor at the University of Wisconsin, Ms. Gaines teaches courses related to consumer issues in health care advocacy and reform, and exploring professionalism for the twenty-first century to graduate students from law, medicine, public health, nursing, pharmacy, genetic counseling, and others.

Ms. Gaines earned her bachelor's degree at Vassar College and holds juris doctorate and master of law degrees from the University of Wisconsin Law School. She is a long-term survivor of metastatic ovarian cancer.

Margaret A. Hamburg, MD, former Commissioner of the US Food and Drug Administration, is Foreign Secretary of the National Academy of Medicine.

In this position, Dr. Hamburg serves as a senior adviser on international matters to the NAM President and Council and as liaison to foreign academies of medicine and science.

Dr. Hamburg was appointed Commissioner of the FDA in May 2009, the second woman to serve in this position. Her past roles have also included senior scientist at the Nuclear Threat Initiative; Assistant Secretary for Policy and Evaluation in the US Department of Health and Human Services; and Commissioner of the New York City Department of Health and Mental Hygiene.

Jane E. Henney, MD, is Home Secretary for the National Academy of Medicine. In this capacity, she assists the NAM President and Council in strengthening and supporting membership activities and participation.

Dr. Henney has held senior leadership positions in both the academic and federal sectors. Among these, she was the Commissioner of the US Food and Drug Administration from 1998 until January 2001; Deputy Director of the National Cancer Institute from 1980–1985; Senior Vice President and Provost for Health Affairs at the University of Cincinnati 2003–2008; Vice President for Health Sciences at the University of New Mexico 1994–1998; and Vice Chancellor for Health Programs and Policy at the University of Kansas Medical Center 1988–1992 and Interim Dean of the College of Medicine 1987–1989.

Dr. Henney was elected to the National Academy of Medicine in 2000. She is a fellow of the American College of Health Care Executives and was elected to membership of both the Society of Medical Administrators and the Medical Administrators Conference. She has received numerous citations and awards for her work. Dr. Henney currently serves on the boards of directors of several not-for-profit organizations and publicly traded companies.

Shiriki K. Kumanyika, PhD, MPH, is Emeritus Professor of Epidemiology in the Department of Biostatistics and Epidemiology at the University of Pennsylvania Perelman School Of Medicine. She has an interdisciplinary background and holds advanced degrees in social work, nutrition, and public health. During her tenure on the Penn Medicine faculty, Dr. Kumanyika also served as the Associate Dean for Health Promotion and Disease Prevention, held a secondary appointment as Professor of Epidemiology in the Department of Pediatrics (Division of Gastroenterology, Nutrition Section), and was affiliated with numerous Penn institutes and centers. She was the Founding Director of Penn's interdisciplinary, multischool Master of Public Health program. Dr. Kumanyika's research focuses on identifying effective strategies to reduce nutrition-related chronic disease risks, with a particular focus on achieving health equity for black Americans. For more than three decades, she has led or collaborated on single- or multicenter, randomized clinical trials or observational studies related to obesity, salt intake, and other aspects of diet. Several of these studies have evaluated interventions to promote healthy eating and physical activity in African American children or adults in clinical or community-based settings.

Dr. Kumanyika founded (in 2002) and continues to Chair the African American Collaborative Obesity Research Network (AACORN) (www.aacorn.org), a national network that seeks to improve the quantity, quality, and effective translation of research on weight issues in African American communities. She has extensive experience in advisory roles related to public health and nutrition policy in the US and abroad. Dr. Kumanyika is a member of the National Academy of Medicine (formerly the Institute of Medicine) and is a past president of the American Public Health Association.

The Honorable Michael O. Leavitt is the Founder and Chairman of Leavitt Partners, where he helps clients navigate the future as they transition to new and better models of care. In previous roles, Mike served as a three-time elected governor of Utah and in the Cabinet of President George W. Bush: first as administrator of the Environmental Protection Agency (2003–2005) and then as Secretary of Health and Human Services (2005–2009). At HHS, he led the implementation of the Medicare Part D Prescription Drug Program. The task required the design, systematization, and implementation of a plan to provide 43 million seniors with a new prescription drug benefit. By the end of the first year, enrollments exceeded projections, prices were lower than projected, and seniors expressed high levels of satisfaction.

Mike's strategic ability can be seen in his redesign of the nation's system of quality and safety standards for imported goods. In the spring of 2006, President Bush assigned him to lead a government-wide response. Within months, he commended a major strategic shift in US policy on import regulation and trade.

Mike is a seasoned diplomat, leading US delegations to more than 50 countries. He has conducted negotiations on matters related to health, the environment, and trade. At the conclusion of his service, the Chinese government awarded him the China Public Health Award—the first time this award has ever been given to a foreign government official.

Mike is, at heart, an entrepreneur. As governor, he organized a group of his colleagues to form Western Governors University. At WGU, degrees are earned based on competency rather than credit hours. WGU now has more than 60,000 students who reside in each of the 50 states and several foreign countries. Enrollment is growing at 35 percent a year. In November 2008,

TIME magazine named WGU "the best relatively cheap university you've never heard of." His book—*Finding Allies, Building Alliances*—was released in September 2013 by Jossey-Bass Publishers and chronicles his expertise and passion for collaboration.

Mark B. McClellan, MD, PhD *(Co-Chair),* is the Robert J. Margolis Professor of Business, Medicine, and Policy, and Director of the Duke-Margolis Center for Health Policy at Duke University with offices at Duke and in Washington, DC. The new Center will support and conduct research, evaluation, implementation, and educational activities to improve health policy and health, through collaboration across Duke University and Health System, and through partnerships between the public and private sectors. It integrates the social, clinical, and analytical sciences to integrate technical expertise and practical capabilities to develop and apply policy solutions that improve health and the value of health care locally, nationally, and worldwide.

Dr. McClellan is a doctor and an economist, and his work has addressed a wide range of strategies and policy reforms to improve health care, including such areas as payment reform to promote better outcomes and lower costs, methods for development and use of real-world evidence, and more effective drug and device innovation. Before coming to Duke, he served as a Senior Fellow in Economic Studies at the Brookings Institution, where he was Director of the Health Care Innovation and Value Initiatives and led the Richard Merkin Initiative on Payment Reform and Clinical Leadership. He also has a highly distinguished record in public service and in academic research. Dr. McClellan is a former administrator of the Centers for Medicare & Medicaid Services (CMS) and former commissioner of the US Food and Drug Administration (FDA), where he developed and implemented major reforms in health policy. These include the Medicare prescription drug benefit, Medicare and Medicaid payment reforms, the FDA's Critical Path Initiative, and public-private initiatives to develop better information on the quality and cost of care.

Dr. McClellan is the founding Chair and a current board member of the Reagan-Udall Foundation for the FDA, is a member of the National Academy of Medicine and chairs the Academy's Leadership Council for Value and Science-Driven Health care, co-chairs the guiding committee of the Health Care Payment Learning and Action Network, and is a Research Associate at the National Bureau of Economic Research. He has also previously served as a member of the President's Council of Economic Advisers and Senior Director for Health Care Policy at the White House, and as Deputy Assistant Secretary for Economic Policy at the Department of the Treasury. He was previously an Associate Professor of Economics and Medicine with tenure at Stanford University, and has twice received the Kenneth Arrow Award for Outstanding Research in Health Economics.

Michael McGinnis, MD, MPP, an active front-line participant in national and international health policy and programs for more than four decades, is currently Leonard D. Schaeffer Executive Officer at the National Academy of Medicine (NAM). He is also an elected Member of the NAM, Executive Director of the NAM Leadership Consortium on Value & Science-Driven Health Care, and founder and facilitator of its Learning Health System initiative. In a tenure unusual for political and policy posts, he held continuous appointment through the Carter, Reagan, Bush, and Clinton Administrations at the Department of Health and Human Services, with policy responsibilities for disease prevention and health promotion. In this capacity, he was founder and steward of various still ongoing programs and policies, including: the *Healthy People* program of national goals and objectives, the HHS/USDA *Dietary Guidelines for Americans*, the U.S. Preventive Services Task Force, and the Ten Essential Services of Public Health. In other appointments, he served as founding director/chair of: the health program group at the Robert Wood Johnson Foundation; the World Bank/European Commission Task Force for Health Reconstruction in Bosnia; the federal Office of Research Integrity, and the HHS Nutrition Policy Board. Early in his career, he served as director of the World Health Organization's smallpox eradication program in Uttar Pradesh, India, and director of the U.S.-Eastern Europe cooperative health research program. Educated at Berkeley (AB), UCLA (MA, MD), and Harvard's Kennedy School of Government (MPP), he is perhaps most recognized for his research and publications on population health and the root sources of morbidity and mortality. Recognitions include the federal Distinguished Service Medal, the 1996 National Health Leader of the Year award, and the 2013 national Public Health Hero award.

Ruth M. Parker, MD, is Professor of Medicine, Pediatrics and Public Health at Emory University in Atlanta, Georgia. She attended Davidson College and the University of North Carolina at Chapel Hill School of Medicine, completed residencies in Internal Medicine and Pediatrics at the University of Rochester, and was a Clinical Scholar at the University of Pennsylvania. For over two decades, her work has focused on research, education, and advocacy efforts to advance our nation's health literacy. She is an author of the Test of Functional Health Literacy in Adults (TOFHLA) and of the definition of health literacy used by Healthy People 2010, the IOM, the NIH, and the Affordable Care Act, as well as many scholarly pieces on health literacy. She is a National Associate of the National Research Council of the National Academy of Sciences, and serves on Advisories to the FDA and PCORI.

Dr. Parker served in leadership roles as a Health Literacy Advocate for professional societies including the AMA and the ACP Foundation. She has consulted with numerous federal and state agencies, professional organizations and members of industry regarding their health literacy efforts. She was a member of the IOM Health Literacy Committee, a member and now Consultant to the Health Literacy Roundtable.

Dr. Parker has received national awards in recognition of her work, including the Silver Achievement Award from the AAMC, the Richard and Hinda Rosenthal Award from the ACP, the Walter C. Alvarez Award from the American Medical Writers Association, the Cecilia and Leonard National Health Literacy Award, and FDA Advisory Committee Service Award.

Lewis G. Sandy, MD, is Executive Vice President, Clinical Advancement, UnitedHealth Group (a Fortune 25 diversified health and well-being company dedicated to helping people live healthier lives). At UnitedHealth Group he focuses on clinical innovation, payment/delivery reforms to modernize our health care system, and physician collaboration. He also is a Principal in the UnitedHealth Center for Health Reform and Modernization, with a focus on payment/delivery innovation and policy. From 2003 to 2007, he was EVP and Chief Medical Officer of UnitedHealthcare, UnitedHealth Group's largest business focusing on the employer/individual health benefits market. From 1997 to 2003, he was EVP of The Robert Wood Johnson Foundation. At RWJF, he was responsible for the Foundation's program development and management, strategic planning and administrative operations. Prior to this, Dr. Sandy was a program VP of the Foundation, focusing on the Foundation's workforce, health policy, and chronic care initiatives. An internist and former health center medical director at the Harvard Community Health Plan in Boston, Massachusetts, Dr. Sandy received his BS and MD degrees from the University of Michigan and an MBA degree from Stanford University. A former RWJF Clinical Scholar and Clinical Fellow in Medicine at the University of California, San Francisco, Dr. Sandy served his internship and residency at the Beth Israel Hospital in Boston. He is a Senior Fellow of the University of Minnesota School of Public Health, Department of Health Policy and Management.

Leonard D. Schaeffer is the founding Chairman & CEO of WellPoint, the nation's largest health benefits company by membership. WellPoint (now Anthem) serves nearly 39 million medical members and has annualized revenues of $78.4 billion. He is currently the Judge Robert Maclay Widney Chair and Professor at the University of Southern California (USC) and is a Senior Advisor to TPG Capital, a private equity firm.

Schaeffer was Chairman & CEO of WellPoint from 1992 through 2004 and continued as Chairman through 2005. In 1986, Schaeffer was recruited as CEO of WellPoint's predecessor company, Blue Cross of California, when it was near bankruptcy. He managed the turnaround of Blue Cross and the IPO creating WellPoint. During his tenure as CEO, WellPoint completed 17 acquisitions and endowed 4 charitable foundations with assets of over $6 billion. Under Schaeffer's leadership, the value of the company grew from $11 million to over $49 billion.

During his tenure, WellPoint was selected by *Fortune* as America's Most Admired Health Care Company for 6 consecutive years; named by *BusinessWeek* as one of the 50 best performing public companies for 3 consecutive years; and identified by *Forbes* magazine as America's best large health insurance company. Schaeffer was selected by *BusinessWeek* as one of the Top 25 Managers of the Year and by *Worth* as one of the "50 Best CEOs in America."

Schaeffer's public service included appointments as Administrator of the federal Health Care Financing Administration (now CMS), Assistant Secretary for Management and Budget of the federal Department of Health, Education and Welfare, Director of the Bureau of the Budget for the State of Illinois, Chairman of the Illinois Capital Development Board, and Deputy Director of the Illinois Department of Mental Health.

Schaeffer is a member of the boards of trustees of USC, RAND, the Brookings Institution, and the board of fellows at Harvard Medical School. He also serves on the boards of directors of Walgreens, Quintiles, and scPharmaceuticals. He is an elected member of the National Academy of Medicine (NAM).

In 2009, Schaeffer established a new research center at USC. The Schaeffer Center for Health Policy and Economics emphasizes an interdisciplinary approach to research and analysis to promote health and value in health care delivery and to support evidence-based health policy. He has also endowed chairs in health care financing and policy at the Brookings Institution, Harvard Medical School, NAM, UC Berkeley, and USC.

Previously, Schaeffer served as President & CEO of Group Health, Inc., EVP & COO of the Student Loan Marketing Association (Sallie Mae), and a Vice President of Citibank.

Glenn D. Steele, Jr., MD, PhD, is the Chairman of xG Health Solutions. From 2001–2015, he served as President and Chief Executive Officer of Geisinger

Health System, an integrated health services organization nationally recognized for the development and implementation of innovative care models.

Glenn previously served as Dean of the Biological Sciences Division and the Pritzker School of Medicine and Vice President for Medical Affairs at the University of Chicago, as well as the Richard T. Crane Professor in the Department of Surgery. Prior to that, he was the William V. McDermott Professor of Surgery at Harvard Medical School, President and Chief Executive Officer of Deaconess Professional Practice Group, Boston, Massachusetts, and Chairman of the Department of Surgery at New England Deaconess Hospital, Boston, Massachusetts. Glenn is past Chairman of the American Board of Surgery. His investigations have focused on the cell biology of gastrointestinal cancer and precancer, and most recently on innovations in healthcare delivery and financing. A prolific writer, he is the author or co-author of more than 488 scientific and professional articles.

A member of the National Academy of Medicine, Glenn serves as a member of the Roundtable on Value and Science-driven Healthcare, the Committee on the Governance and Financing of Graduate Medical Education, the Vital Directions for Health and Health Care Steering Committee, and previously served on the Committee on Reviewing Evidence to Identify Highly Effective Clinical Services (HECS). A fellow of the American College of Surgeons, he is a member of the American Surgical Association, the American Society of Clinical Oncology, and Past President of the Society of Surgical Oncology.

Glenn serves on the following boards and national committees: Vice Chair, Health Transformation Alliance; Director, Cepheid; Director, City of Hope; Member, Emory University's Healthcare Innovation Program (HIP) External Advisory Board; Director, Ingenious Med; Member, Institute for Healthcare Optimization Advisory Board; Director, PTC Therapeutics; Director, Stratus Video Interpreting; Member, the Peterson Center on Healthcare Advisory Board; Director, the State Health Care Cost Containment Commission; and Director, Wellcare Health Plans Inc.

Glenn received his bachelor's degree in history and literature from Harvard College and his medical degree from New York University School of Medicine. He completed his internship and residency in surgery at the University of Colorado, where he was also a fellow of the American Cancer Society. He earned his doctorate in microbiology at Lund University in Sweden.

Pamela Thompson, MS, RN, is Chief Executive Officer Emeritus of the American Organization of Nurse Executives (AONE). Prior to her appointment, she served 16 years as AONE CEO and Senior Vice President Nursing/Chief

Nursing Officer of the American Hospital Association. She was responsible for the management and administrative leadership of AONE, as well as the AHA Workforce Initiative and addressing issues specific to strengthening the health care workforce and the redesign of patient care delivery.

Before joining AONE, Thompson was Vice President of Children's Hospital, Obstetrics, Psychiatric Services, and Strategic Planning at Dartmouth-Hitchcock Medical Center in Lebanon, New Hampshire.

Thompson served as the chair of the National Patient Safety Foundation (NPSF) Board of Directors, was a member of the Lucien Leape Institute of NPSF and the NPSF Board of Advisors. Thompson was also Chair of the New Hampshire Hospital Association board of trustees and the New Hampshire Foundation for Health Communities, as well as Past President of the New Hampshire Organization of Nurse Executives. Thompson was a founding member of the Behavioral Health Network in New Hampshire and served as Chairman of the Board.

Thompson is the recipient of numerous awards including the American College of Healthcare Executives 2009 Edgar C. Hayhow Award for an article she co-wrote about the results of a national survey on chief nursing officer retention and turnover. She also received the California Association of Nurse Leaders Lifetime Achievement Award and National League for Nursing's President's Award.

She earned her master of science degree from the University of Rochester, New York and her bachelor of science degree from the University of Connecticut. Thompson is a fellow of the American Academy of Nursing.

She resides in Manassas, Virginia, with her husband, Bob.

Elias A. Zerhouni, MD, is President, Global R&D, at Sanofi since 2011. A native of Algeria where he received his basic education and training, his academic career was spent at the Johns Hopkins University where he is currently Professor of Radiology and Biomedical Engineering. He served as Chair of the Russell H. Morgan Department of Radiology and Radiological Sciences, Vice Dean for Research and Executive Vice Dean of the Johns Hopkins School of Medicine from 1996 to 2002.

From 2002 to 2008 he served as Director of the National Institutes of Health of the United States of America. From 2009 to 2010 he was Senior Fellow at the Bill and Melinda Gates Foundation and served as US presidential Envoy for Science and Technology. He has authored or co-authored over 200 scientific publications, holds several patents, and has founded or co-founded several companies.

He is a member of the board of the Lasker Foundation. He is a member of the US National Academies of Medicine and of Engineering and the French Academy of Medicine and is a recipient of the French Legion of Honor medal.

APPENDIX B

RELATED PUBLICATIONS FROM THE NATIONAL ACADEMIES OF SCIENCES, ENGINEERING, AND MEDICINE

Better Health and Well-Being

Systems Strategies for Better Health Throughout the Life Course

- National Academies of Sciences, Engineering, and Medicine. 2016. *The Role of Public-Private Partnerships in Health Systems Strengthening: Workshop Summary*. Washington, DC: The National Academies Press. doi:https://doi.org/10.17226/21861.
- Institute of Medicine and National Research Council. 2015. *Measuring the Risks and Causes of Premature Death: Summary of Workshops*. Washington, DC: The National Academies Press. doi:https://doi.org/10.17226/21656.
- Institute of Medicine and National Research Council. 2015. *Investing in the Health and Well-Being of Young Adults*. Washington, DC: The National Academies Press. doi:https://doi.org/10.17226/18869.
- Institute of Medicine. 2015. *Vital Signs: Core Metrics for Health and Health Care Progress*. Washington, DC: The National Academies Press. doi:https://doi.org/10.17226/19402.
- Institute of Medicine and National Research Council. 2014. *New Directions in Child Abuse and Neglect Research*. Washington, DC: The National Academies Press. doi:https://doi.org/10.17226/18331.
- Institute of Medicine. 2014. *Investing in Global Health Systems: Sustaining Gains, Transforming Lives*. Washington, DC: The National Academies Press. doi:https://doi.org/10.17226/18940.
- Institute of Medicine. 2014. *Capturing Social and Behavioral Domains in Electronic Health Records: Phase 1*. Washington, DC: The National Academies Press. doi:https://doi.org/10.17226/18709.

- Institute of Medicine. 2014. *Capturing Social and Behavioral Domains and Measures in Electronic Health Records: Phase 2.* Washington, DC: The National Academies Press. doi:https://doi.org/10.17226/18951.
- Institute of Medicine. 2013. *Best Care at Lower Cost: The Path to Continuously Learning Health Care in America.* Washington, DC: The National Academies Press. doi:https://doi.org/10.17226/13444.
- Institute of Medicine. 2013. *Digital Data Improvement Priorities for Continuous Learning in Health and Health Care: Workshop Summary.* Washington, DC: The National Academies Press. doi:https://doi.org/10.17226/13424.
- Institute of Medicine. 2013. *Core Measurement Needs for Better Care, Better Health, and Lower Costs: Counting What Counts: Workshop Summary.* Washington, DC: The National Academies Press. doi:https://doi.org/10.17226/18333.
- Institute of Medicine and National Research Council. 2013. *U.S. Health in International Perspective: Shorter Lives, Poorer Health.* Washington, DC: The National Academies Press. doi:https://doi.org/10.17226/13497.
- National Research Council. 2011. *Explaining Divergent Levels of Longevity in High-Income Countries.* Washington, DC: The National Academies Press. doi:https://doi.org/10.17226/13089.
- Institute of Medicine. 2010. *The Healthcare Imperative: Lowering Costs and Improving Outcomes: Workshop Series Summary.* Washington, DC: The National Academies Press. doi:https://doi.org/10.17226/12750.
- Institute of Medicine. 2011. *Digital Infrastructure for the Learning Health System: The Foundation for Continuous Improvement in Health and Health Care: Workshop Series Summary.* Washington, DC: The National Academies Press. doi:https://doi.org/10.17226/12912.
- Institute of Medicine. 2000. *From Neurons to Neighborhoods: The Science of Early Childhood Development.* Washington, DC: The National Academies Press. doi:https://doi.org/10.17226/9824.
- Institute of Medicine. 1988. *The Future of Public Health.* Washington, DC: The National Academies Press. doi:https://doi.org/10.17226/1091.

Addressing Social Determinants of Health and Health Disparities

- National Academies of Sciences, Engineering, and Medicine. 2017. *Accounting for Social Risk Factors in Medicare Payment.* Washington, DC: The National Academies Press. doi:https://doi.org/10.17226/23635.
- National Academies of Sciences, Engineering, and Medicine. 2017. *Communities in Action: Pathways to Health Equity.* Washington, DC: The National Academies Press. doi:https://doi.org/10.17226/24624.

- National Academies of Sciences, Engineering, and Medicine. 2016. *A Framework for Educating Health Professionals to Address the Social Determinants of Health*. Washington, DC: The National Academies Press. doi:https://doi.org/10.17226/21923.
- National Academies of Sciences, Engineering, and Medicine. 2016. *Accounting for Social Risk Factors in Medicare Payment: Criteria, Factors, and Methods*. Washington, DC: The National Academies Press. doi:https://doi.org/10.17226/23513.
- National Academies of Sciences, Engineering, and Medicine. 2017. *Accounting for Social Risk Factors in Medicare Payment*. Washington, DC: The National Academies Press. doi:https://doi.org/10.17226/23635.
- National Academies of Sciences, Engineering, and Medicine. 2017. *Accounting for Social Risk Factors in Medicare Payment*. Washington, DC: The National Academies Press. doi:https://doi.org/10.17226/23635.
- National Academies of Sciences, Engineering, and Medicine. 2016. *Framing the Dialogue on Race and Ethnicity to Advance Health Equity: Proceedings of a Workshop*. Washington, DC: The National Academies Press. doi:https://doi.org/10.17226/23576.
- National Academies of Sciences, Engineering, and Medicine. 2016. *Advancing Health Equity for Native American Youth: Workshop Summary*. Washington, DC: The National Academies Press. doi:https://doi.org/10.17226/21766.
- National Academies of Sciences, Engineering, and Medicine. 2016. *Ensuring Quality and Accessible Care for Children with Disabilities and Complex Health and Educational Needs: Proceedings of a Workshop*. Washington, DC: The National Academies Press. doi:https://doi.org/10.17226/23598.
- National Academies of Sciences, Engineering, and Medicine. 2016. *Innovations in Design and Utilization of Measurement Systems to Promote Children's Cognitive, Affective, and Behavioral Health: Workshop in Brief*. Washington, DC: The National Academies Press. doi:https://doi.org/10.17226/23543.
- National Academies of Sciences, Engineering, and Medicine. 2016. *Identifying Opportunities for Prevention and Intervention in the Youth Depression Cascade: Workshop in Brief*. Washington, DC: The National Academies Press. doi:https://doi.org/10.17226/23397.
- National Academies of Sciences, Engineering, and Medicine. 2016. *Opportunities to Promote Children's Behavioral Health: Health Care Reform and Beyond: Workshop in Brief*. Washington, DC: The National Academies Press. doi:https://doi.org/10.17226/23545.
- Institute of Medicine. 2012. *How Far Have We Come in Reducing Health Disparities? Progress Since 2000: Workshop Summary*. Washington, DC: The National Academies Press. doi:https://doi.org/10.17226/13383.

- Institute of Medicine. 2012. *An Integrated Framework for Assessing the Value of Community-Based Prevention.* Washington, DC: The National Academies Press. doi:https://doi.org/10.17226/13487.
- Institute of Medicine. 2011. *The Health of Lesbian, Gay, Bisexual, and Transgender People: Building a Foundation for Better Understanding.* Washington, DC: The National Academies Press. doi:https://doi.org/10.17226/13128.
- Institute of Medicine. 2011. *State and Local Policy Initiatives to Reduce Health Disparities: Workshop Summary.* Washington, DC: The National Academies Press. doi:https://doi.org/10.17226/13103.
- Institute of Medicine. 2010. *Future Directions for the National Healthcare Quality and Disparities Reports.* Washington, DC: The National Academies Press. doi:https://doi.org/10.17226/12846.
- Institute of Medicine and National Research Council. 2009. *Focusing on Children's Health: Community Approaches to Addressing Health Disparities: Workshop Summary.* Washington, DC: The National Academies Press. doi:https://doi.org/10.17226/12637.
- Institute of Medicine. 2009. *Toward Health Equity and Patient-Centeredness: Integrating Health Literacy, Disparities Reduction, and Quality Improvement: Workshop Summary.* Washington, DC: The National Academies Press. doi:https://doi.org/10.17226/12502.
- Institute of Medicine. 2003. *Unequal Treatment: Confronting Racial and Ethnic Disparities in Health Care (with CD).* Washington, DC: The National Academies Press. doi:https://doi.org/10.17226/12875.

Preparing for Better Health and Health Care for an Aging Population

- National Academies of Sciences, Engineering, and Medicine. 2016. *Families Caring for an Aging America.* Washington, DC: The National Academies Press. doi:https://doi.org/10.17226/23606.
- National Academies of Sciences, Engineering, and Medicine. 2016. *Health Literacy and Palliative Care: Workshop Summary.* Washington, DC: The National Academies Press. doi:https://doi.org/10.17226/21839.
- National Academies of Sciences, Engineering, and Medicine. 2016. *Assessing the Impact of Applications of Digital Health Records on Alzheimer's Disease Research: Workshop Summary.* Washington, DC: The National Academies Press. doi:https://doi.org/10.17226/21827.
- National Academies of Sciences, Engineering, and Medicine. 2017. *Strengthening the Workforce to Support Community Living and Participation for Older Adults and Individuals with Disabilities: Proceedings of a Workshop.* Washington, DC: The National Academies Press. doi:https://doi.org/10.17226/23656.

- National Academies of Sciences, Engineering, and Medicine. 2016. *Policy and Research Needs to Maximize Independence and Support Community Living: Workshop Summary.* Washington, DC: The National Academies Press. doi:https://doi.org/10.17226/21893.
- National Academies of Sciences, Engineering, and Medicine. 2015. *Understanding Pathways to Successful Aging: How Social and Behavioral Factors Affect Health at Older Ages: Workshop in Brief.* Washington, DC: The National Academies Press. doi:https://doi.org/10.17226/21815.
- Institute of Medicine and National Research Council. 2015. *The Future of Home Health Care: Workshop Summary.* Washington, DC: The National Academies Press. doi:https://doi.org/10.17226/21662.
- Institute of Medicine. 2015. *Cognitive Aging: Progress in Understanding and Opportunities for Action.* Washington, DC: The National Academies Press. doi:https://doi.org/10.17226/21693.
- National Research Council. 2013. *New Directions in the Sociology of Aging.* Washington, DC: The National Academies Press. doi:https://doi.org/10.17226/18508.
- Institute of Medicine and National Research Council. 2013. *Fostering Independence, Participation, and Healthy Aging Through Technology: Workshop Summary.* Washington, DC: The National Academies Press. doi:https://doi.org/10.17226/18332.
- Institute of Medicine. 2015. *Dying in America: Improving Quality and Honoring Individual Preferences Near the End of Life.* Washington, DC: The National Academies Press. doi:https://doi.org/10.17226/18748.
- National Research Council. 2012. *Aging and the Macroeconomy: Long-Term Implications of an Older Population.* Washington, DC: The National Academies Press. doi:https://doi.org/10.17226/13465.
- Institute of Medicine. 2012. *Nutrition and Healthy Aging in the Community: Workshop Summary.* Washington, DC: The National Academies Press. doi:https://doi.org/10.17226/13344.
- National Research Council. 2011. *Health Care Comes Home: The Human Factors.* Washington, DC: The National Academies Press. doi:https://doi.org/10.17226/13149.
- Aging In Asia (2010)
- National Research Council. 2003. *Elder Mistreatment: Abuse, Neglect, and Exploitation in an Aging America.* Washington, DC: The National Academies Press. doi:https://doi.org/10.17226/10406.
- *Chronic Disease Prevention: Tobacco, Physical Activity, and Nutrition for a Healthy Start*
- National Academies of Sciences, Engineering, and Medicine. 2017. *Exploring Strategies to Improve Cardiac Arrest Survival: Proceedings of a Workshop.* Washington, DC: The National Academies Press. doi:https://doi.org/10.17226/23695.

- National Academies of Sciences, Engineering, and Medicine. 2016. *Review of WIC Food Packages: Proposed Framework for Revisions: Interim Report.* Washington, DC: The National Academies Press. doi:https://doi.org/10.17226/21832.
- Institute of Medicine. 2015. *Public Health Implications of Raising the Minimum Age of Legal Access to Tobacco Products.* Washington, DC: The National Academies Press. doi:https://doi.org/10.17226/18997.
- Institute of Medicine. 2015. *Assessing the Use of Agent-Based Models for Tobacco Regulation.* Washington, DC: The National Academies Press. doi:https://doi.org/10.17226/19018.
- National Research Council. 2015. *Understanding the U.S. Illicit Tobacco Market: Characteristics, Policy Context, and Lessons from International Experiences.* Washington, DC: The National Academies Press. doi:https://doi.org/10.17226/19016.
- Institute of Medicine. 2015. *Physical Activity: Moving Toward Obesity Solutions: Workshop Summary.* Washington, DC: The National Academies Press. doi:https://doi.org/10.17226/21802.
- Institute of Medicine. 2015. *Review of WIC Food Packages: An Evaluation of White Potatoes in the Cash Value Voucher: Letter Report.* Washington, DC: The National Academies Press. doi:https://doi.org/10.17226/20221.
- Institute of Medicine and National Research Council. 2015. *A Framework for Assessing Effects of the Food System.* Washington, DC: The National Academies Press. doi:https://doi.org/10.17226/18846.
- Institute of Medicine and National Research Council. 2014. *Sports-Related Concussions in Youth: Improving the Science, Changing the Culture.* Washington, DC: The National Academies Press. doi:https://doi.org/10.17226/18377.
- Institute of Medicine. 2013. *Educating the Student Body: Taking Physical Activity and Physical Education to School.* Washington, DC: The National Academies Press. doi:https://doi.org/10.17226/18314.

Improving Access to Effective Care for People Who Have Mental Health and Substance Use Disorders

- National Academies of Sciences, Engineering, and Medicine. 2016. *Measuring Recovery from Substance Use or Mental Disorders: Workshop Summary.* Washington, DC: The National Academies Press. doi:https://doi.org/10.17226/23589.
- National Academies of Sciences, Engineering, and Medicine. 2016. *Measuring Trauma: Workshop Summary.* Washington, DC: The National Academies Press. doi:https://doi.org/10.17226/23526.
- National Academies of Sciences, Engineering, and Medicine. 2016. *Measuring Specific Mental Illness Diagnoses with Functional Impairment: Workshop*

Summary. Washington, DC: The National Academies Press. doi:https://doi. org/10.17226/21920.

- National Academies of Sciences, Engineering, and Medicine. 2016. *Measuring Serious Emotional Disturbance in Children: Workshop Summary*. Washington, DC: The National Academies Press. doi:https://doi.org/10.17226/21865.
- National Academies of Sciences, Engineering, and Medicine. 2016. *Ending Discrimination Against People with Mental and Substance Use Disorders: The Evidence for Stigma Change*. Washington, DC: The National Academies Press. doi:https://doi.org/10.17226/23442.
- National Academies of Sciences, Engineering, and Medicine. 2015. *Mental Disorders and Disabilities Among Low-Income Children*. Washington, DC: The National Academies Press. doi:https://doi.org/10.17226/21780.
- Institute of Medicine. 2015. *Psychosocial Interventions for Mental and Substance Use Disorders: A Framework for Establishing Evidence-Based Standards*. Washington, DC: The National Academies Press. doi:https://doi.org/10.17226/19013.
- Institute of Medicine. 2012. *The Mental Health and Substance Use Workforce for Older Adults: In Whose Hands?*. Washington, DC: The National Academies Press. doi:https://doi.org/10.17226/13400.
- National Research Council and Institute of Medicine. 2009. *Preventing Mental, Emotional, and Behavioral Disorders Among Young People: Progress and Possibilities*. Washington, DC: The National Academies Press. doi:https://doi.org/10.17226/12480.
- Institute of Medicine. 2006. *Improving the Quality of Health Care for Mental and Substance-Use Conditions: Quality Chasm Series*. Washington, DC: The National Academies Press. doi:https://doi.org/10.17226/11470.

Advancing the Health of Communities and Populations

- National Academies of Sciences, Engineering, and Medicine. 2017. *Communities in Action: Pathways to Health Equity*. Washington, DC: The National Academies Press. doi:https://doi.org/10.17226/24624.
- National Academies of Sciences, Engineering, and Medicine. 2017. *A National Strategy for the Elimination of Hepatitis B and C: Phase Two Report*. Washington, DC: The National Academies Press. doi:https://doi.org/10.17226/24731.
- National Academies of Sciences, Engineering, and Medicine. 2017. *Community Violence as a Population Health Issue: Proceedings of a Workshop*. Washington, DC: The National Academies Press. doi:https://doi.org/10.17226/23661.
- National Academies of Sciences, Engineering, and Medicine. 2016. *A Framework for Educating Health Professionals to Address the Social Determinants of Health*. Washington, DC: The National Academies Press. doi:https://doi. org/10.17226/21923.

- National Academies of Sciences, Engineering, and Medicine. 2016. *Advancing the Science to Improve Population Health: Proceedings of a Workshop.* Washington, DC: The National Academies Press. doi:https://doi.org/10.17226/23541.
- National Academies of Sciences, Engineering, and Medicine. 2016. *Metrics That Matter for Population Health Action: Workshop Summary.* Washington, DC: The National Academies Press. doi:https://doi.org/10.17226/21899.
- National Academies of Sciences, Engineering, and Medicine. 2016. *How Modeling Can Inform Strategies to Improve Population Health: Workshop Summary.* Washington, DC: The National Academies Press. doi:https://doi.org/10.17226/21807.
- National Academies of Sciences, Engineering, and Medicine. 2016. *Making Eye Health a Population Health Imperative: Vision for Tomorrow.* Washington, DC: The National Academies Press. doi:https://doi.org/10.17226/23471.
- National Academies of Sciences, Engineering, and Medicine. 2016. *Eliminating the Public Health Problem of Hepatitis B and C in the United States: Phase One Report.* Washington, DC: The National Academies Press. doi:https://doi.org/10.17226/23407.
- National Academies of Sciences, Engineering, and Medicine. 2016. *Exploring Data and Metrics of Value at the Intersection of Health Care and Transportation: Proceedings of a Workshop.* Washington, DC: The National Academies Press. doi:https://doi.org/10.17226/23638.
- National Academies of Sciences, Engineering, and Medicine. 2016. *The Private Sector as a Catalyst for Health Equity and a Vibrant Economy: Proceedings of a Workshop.* Washington, DC: The National Academies Press. doi:https://doi.org/10.17226/23529.
- National Academies of Sciences, Engineering, and Medicine. 2016. *Framing the Dialogue on Race and Ethnicity to Advance Health Equity: Proceedings of a Workshop.* Washington, DC: The National Academies Press. doi:https://doi.org/10.17226/23576.
- National Academies of Sciences, Engineering, and Medicine. 2016. *Improving the Health of Women in the United States: Workshop Summary.* Washington, DC: The National Academies Press. doi:https://doi.org/10.17226/23441.
- National Academies of Sciences, Engineering, and Medicine. 2016. *Recent Fertility Trends in Sub-Saharan Africa: Workshop Summary.* Washington, DC: The National Academies Press. doi:https://doi.org/10.17226/21857.
- Institute of Medicine. 2015. *Financing Population Health Improvement: Workshop Summary.* Washington, DC: The National Academies Press. doi:https://doi.org/10.17226/18835.

- Institute of Medicine. 2015. *Spread, Scale, and Sustainability in Population Health: Workshop Summary*. Washington, DC: The National Academies Press. doi:https://doi.org/10.17226/21708.
- Institute of Medicine. 2015. *The Role and Potential of Communities in Population Health Improvement: Workshop Summary*. Washington, DC: The National Academies Press. doi:https://doi.org/10.17226/18946.
- Institute of Medicine. 2015. *Exploring Opportunities for Collaboration Between Health and Education to Improve Population Health: Workshop Summary*. Washington, DC: The National Academies Press. doi:https://doi.org/10.17226/18979.
- National Academies of Sciences, Engineering, and Medicine. 2015. *Sharing Research Data to Improve Public Health in Africa: A Workshop Summary*. Washington, DC: The National Academies Press. doi:https://doi.org/10.17226/21801.
- Institute of Medicine. 2012. *An Integrated Framework for Assessing the Value of Community-Based Prevention*. Washington, DC: The National Academies Press. doi:https://doi.org/10.17226/13487.
- Institute of Medicine. 2012. *Primary Care and Public Health: Exploring Integration to Improve Population Health*. Washington, DC: The National Academies Press. doi:https://doi.org/10.17226/13381.

High-Value Health Care

Benefit Design to Promote Effective, Efficient, and Affordable Care

- National Academies of Sciences, Engineering, and Medicine. 2016. *Hearing Health Care for Adults: Priorities for Improving Access and Affordability*. Washington, DC: The National Academies Press. doi:https://doi.org/10.17226/23446.
- National Academies of Sciences, Engineering, and Medicine. 2015. *Improving Diagnosis in Health Care*. Washington, DC: The National Academies Press. doi:https://doi.org/10.17226/21794.
- Institute of Medicine. 2015. *Integrating Research and Practice: Health System Leaders Working Toward High-Value Care: Workshop Summary*. Washington, DC: The National Academies Press. doi:https://doi.org/10.17226/18945.
- Institute of Medicine. 2015. *Vital Signs: Core Metrics for Health and Health Care Progress*. Washington, DC: The National Academies Press. doi:https://doi.org/10.17226/19402.
- Institute of Medicine. 2012. *Perspectives on Essential Health Benefits: Workshop Report*. Washington, DC: The National Academies Press. doi:https://doi.org/10.17226/13182.
- Institute of Medicine. 2012. *Essential Health Benefits: Balancing Coverage and Cost*. Washington, DC: The National Academies Press. doi:https://doi.org/10.17226/13234.

- Institute of Medicine. 2010. *Value in Health Care: Accounting for Cost, Quality, Safety, Outcomes, and Innovation: Workshop Summary.* Washington, DC: The National Academies Press. doi:https://doi.org/10.17226/12566.
- Institute of Medicine. 2002. *Fostering Rapid Advances in Health Care: Learning from System Demonstrations.* Washington, DC: The National Academies Press. doi:https://doi.org/10.17226/10565.

Payment Reform for Better Value and Medical Innovation

- Institute of Medicine. 2016. *Collaboration Between Health Care and Public Health: Workshop Summary.* Washington, DC: The National Academies Press. doi:https://doi.org/10.17226/21755.
- Institute of Medicine. 2014. *Conflict of Interest and Medical Innovation: Ensuring Integrity While Facilitating Innovation in Medical Research: Workshop Summary.* Washington, DC: The National Academies Press. doi:https://doi.org/10.17226/18723.
- Institute of Medicine. 2013. *Best Care at Lower Cost: The Path to Continuously Learning Health Care in America.* Washington, DC: The National Academies Press. doi:https://doi.org/10.17226/13444.
- Institute of Medicine. 2013. *Variation in Health Care Spending: Target Decision Making, Not Geography.* Washington, DC: The National Academies Press. doi:https://doi.org/10.17226/18393.
- Institute of Medicine. 2010. *The Healthcare Imperative: Lowering Costs and Improving Outcomes: Workshop Series Summary.* Washington, DC: The National Academies Press. doi:https://doi.org/10.17226/12750.
- Institute of Medicine. 2007. *Rewarding Provider Performance: Aligning Incentives in Medicare.* Washington, DC: The National Academies Press. doi:https://doi.org/10.17226/11723.

Competencies and Tools to Shift Payments from Volume to Value

- National Academies of Sciences, Engineering, and Medicine. 2016. *Accounting for Social Risk Factors in Medicare Payment: Identifying Social Risk Factors.* Washington, DC: The National Academies Press. doi:https://doi.org/10.17226/21858.
- National Academies of Sciences, Engineering, and Medicine. 2016. *Accounting for Social Risk Factors in Medicare Payment: Criteria, Factors, and Methods.* Washington, DC: The National Academies Press. doi:https://doi.org/10.17226/23513.
- National Academies of Sciences, Engineering, and Medicine. 2016. *Systems Practices for the Care of Socially At-Risk Populations.* Washington, DC: The National Academies Press. doi:https://doi.org/10.17226/21914.

- Institute of Medicine. 2015. *Vital Signs: Core Metrics for Health and Health Care Progress.* Washington, DC: The National Academies Press. doi:https://doi.org/10.17226/19402.
- Institute of Medicine. 2010. *The Healthcare Imperative: Lowering Costs and Improving Outcomes: Workshop Series Summary.* Washington, DC: The National Academies Press. doi:https://doi.org/10.17226/12750.
- Institute of Medicine. 2013. *Best Care at Lower Cost: The Path to Continuously Learning Health Care in America.* Washington, DC: The National Academies Press. doi:https://doi.org/10.17226/13444.

Tailoring Complex Care Management, Coordination, and Integration for High-Need, High-Cost Patients

- Institute of Medicine. 2015. *Vital Signs: Core Metrics for Health and Health Care Progress.* Washington, DC: The National Academies Press. doi:https://doi.org/10.17226/19402.
- Institute of Medicine. 2013. *Delivering High-Quality Cancer Care: Charting a New Course for a System in Crisis.* Washington, DC: The National Academies Press. doi:https://doi.org/10.17226/18359.
- Institute of Medicine. 2015. *Dying in America: Improving Quality and Honoring Individual Preferences Near the End of Life.* Washington, DC: The National Academies Press. doi:https://doi.org/10.17226/18748.
- Institute of Medicine. 2013. *Best Care at Lower Cost: The Path to Continuously Learning Health Care in America.* Washington, DC: The National Academies Press. doi:https://doi.org/10.17226/13444.
- Institute of Medicine. 2012. *Living Well with Chronic Illness: A Call for Public Health Action.* Washington, DC: The National Academies Press. doi:https://doi.org/10.17226/13272.
- Institute of Medicine. 2011. *Digital Infrastructure for the Learning Health System: The Foundation for Continuous Improvement in Health and Health Care: Workshop Series Summary.* Washington, DC: The National Academies Press. doi:https://doi.org/10.17226/12912.
- Institute of Medicine. 2011. *HIV Screening and Access to Care: Health Care System Capacity for Increased HIV Testing and Provision of Care.* Washington, DC: The National Academies Press. doi:https://doi.org/10.17226/13074.
- Institute of Medicine. 2010. *The Healthcare Imperative: Lowering Costs and Improving Outcomes: Workshop Series Summary.* Washington, DC: The National Academies Press. doi:https://doi.org/10.17226/12750.
- Institute of Medicine. 2001. *Crossing the Quality Chasm: A New Health System for the 21st Century.* Washington, DC: The National Academies Press. doi:https://doi.org/10.17226/10027.

- Institute of Medicine. 2001. *Improving the Quality of Long-Term Care.* Washington, DC: The National Academies Press. doi:https://doi.org/10.17226/9611.

Realizing the Full Potential of Precision Medicine in Health and Health Care

- National Academies of Sciences, Engineering, and Medicine. 2016. *Biomarker Tests for Molecularly Targeted Therapies: Key to Unlocking Precision Medicine.* Washington, DC: The National Academies Press. doi:https://doi.org/10.17226/21860.
- National Academies of Sciences, Engineering, and Medicine. 2016. *Relevance of Health Literacy to Precision Medicine: Workshop in Brief.* Washington, DC: The National Academies Press. doi:https://doi.org/10.17226/23538.
- National Academies of Sciences, Engineering, and Medicine. 2016. *Deriving Drug Discovery Value from Large-Scale Genetic Bioresources: Proceedings of a Workshop.* Washington, DC: The National Academies Press. doi:https://doi.org/10.17226/23601.
- National Academies of Sciences, Engineering, and Medicine. 2016. *Applying an Implementation Science Approach to Genomic Medicine: Workshop Summary.* Washington, DC: The National Academies Press. doi:https://doi.org/10.17226/23403.
- Institute of Medicine. 2015. *Improving Genetics Education in Graduate and Continuing Health Professional Education: Workshop Summary.* Washington, DC: The National Academies Press. doi:https://doi.org/10.17226/18992.
- Institute of Medicine. 2015. *Genomics-Enabled Learning Health Care Systems: Gathering and Using Genomic Information to Improve Patient Care and Research: Workshop Summary.* Washington, DC: The National Academies Press. doi:https://doi.org/10.17226/21707.
- National Research Council. 2011. *Toward Precision Medicine: Building a Knowledge Network for Biomedical Research and a New Taxonomy of Disease.* Washington, DC: The National Academies Press. doi:https://doi.org/10.17226/13284.

Fostering Transparency in Outcomes, Quality, Safety, and Costs

- National Academies of Sciences, Engineering, and Medicine. 2015. *Improving Diagnosis in Health Care.* Washington, DC: The National Academies Press. doi:https://doi.org/10.17226/21794.
- Institute of Medicine. 2015. *Vital Signs: Core Metrics for Health and Health Care Progress.* Washington, DC: The National Academies Press. doi:https://doi.org/10.17226/19402.
- Institute of Medicine. 2013. *Best Care at Lower Cost: The Path to Continuously Learning Health Care in America.* Washington, DC: The National Academies Press. doi:https://doi.org/10.17226/13444.

- Institute of Medicine. 2013. *Core Measurement Needs for Better Care, Better Health, and Lower Costs: Counting What Counts: Workshop Summary.* Washington, DC: The National Academies Press. doi:https://doi.org/10.17226/18333.
- Institute of Medicine. 2011. *For the Public's Health: The Role of Measurement in Action and Accountability.* Washington, DC: The National Academies Press. doi:https://doi.org/10.17226/13005.
- Institute of Medicine. 2010. *The Healthcare Imperative: Lowering Costs and Improving Outcomes: Workshop Series Summary.* Washington, DC: The National Academies Press. doi:https://doi.org/10.17226/12750.
- Institute of Medicine. 2007. *Preventing Medication Errors.* Washington, DC: The National Academies Press. doi:https://doi.org/10.17226/11623.
- Institute of Medicine. 2006. *Improving the Quality of Health Care for Mental and Substance-Use Conditions: Quality Chasm Series.* Washington, DC: The National Academies Press. doi:https://doi.org/10.17226/11470.
- Institute of Medicine. 2006. *Performance Measurement: Accelerating Improvement (Pathways to Quality Health Care Series).* Washington, DC: The National Academies Press. doi:https://doi.org/10.17226/11517.
- Institute of Medicine. 2005. *Quality Through Collaboration: The Future of Rural Health Care.* Washington, DC: The National Academies Press. doi:https://doi.org/10.17226/11140.
- Institute of Medicine. 2004. *Patient Safety: Achieving a New Standard for Care.* Washington, DC: The National Academies Press. doi:https://doi.org/10.17226/10863.
- Institute of Medicine. 2004. *Keeping Patients Safe: Transforming the Work Environment of Nurses.* Washington, DC: The National Academies Press. doi:https://doi.org/10.17226/10851.
- Institute of Medicine. 2003. *Priority Areas for National Action: Transforming Health Care Quality.* Washington, DC: The National Academies Press. doi:https://doi.org/10.17226/10593.
- Institute of Medicine. 2003. *Health Professions Education: A Bridge to Quality.* Washington, DC: The National Academies Press. doi:https://doi.org/10.17226/10681.
- Institute of Medicine. 2002. *Leadership by Example: Coordinating Government Roles in Improving Health Care Quality.* Washington, DC: The National Academies Press. doi:https://doi.org/10.17226/10537.
- Institute of Medicine. 2002. *Fostering Rapid Advances in Health Care: Learning from System Demonstrations.* Washington, DC: The National Academies Press. doi:https://doi.org/10.17226/10565.

- Institute of Medicine. 2001. *Crossing the Quality Chasm: A New Health System for the 21st Century.* Washington, DC: The National Academies Press. doi:https://doi.org/10.17226/10027.
- Institute of Medicine. 2000. *To Err Is Human: Building a Safer Health System.* Washington, DC: The National Academies Press. doi:https://doi.org/10.17226/9728.

Democratization of Health Care

- National Academies of Sciences, Engineering, and Medicine. 2017. *Health Insurance and Insights from Health Literacy: Helping Consumers Understand: Proceedings of a Workshop.* Washington, DC: The National Academies Press. doi:https://doi.org/10.17226/24664.
- National Academies of Sciences, Engineering, and Medicine. 2016. *Health Literacy and Palliative Care: Workshop Summary.* Washington, DC: The National Academies Press. doi:https://doi.org/10.17226/21839.
- National Academies of Sciences, Engineering, and Medicine. 2016. *Integrating Health Literacy, Cultural Competence, and Language Access Services: Workshop Summary.* Washington, DC: The National Academies Press. doi:https://doi.org/10.17226/23498.
- Institute of Medicine. 2012. *The Role of Telehealth in an Evolving Health Care Environment: Workshop Summary.* Washington, DC: The National Academies Press. doi:https://doi.org/10.17226/13466.
- National Academies of Sciences, Engineering, and Medicine. 2016. *Health Literacy and Palliative Care: Workshop Summary.* Washington, DC: The National Academies Press. doi:https://doi.org/10.17226/21839.
- Institute of Medicine. 2015. *Informed Consent and Health Literacy: Workshop Summary.* Washington, DC: The National Academies Press. doi:https://doi.org/10.17226/19019.
- National Academies of Sciences, Engineering, and Medicine. 2015. *Health Literacy and Consumer-Facing Technology: Workshop Summary.* Washington, DC: The National Academies Press. doi:https://doi.org/10.17226/21781.
- Institute of Medicine. 2015. *Transforming Health Care Scheduling and Access: Getting to Now.* Washington, DC: The National Academies Press. doi:https://doi.org/10.17226/20220.
- Institute of Medicine. 2014. *Health Literacy and Numeracy: Workshop Summary.* Washington, DC: The National Academies Press. doi:https://doi.org/10.17226/18660.
- National Academies of Sciences, Engineering, and Medicine. 2017. *Health Insurance and Insights from Health Literacy: Helping Consumers Understand: Proceedings of a Workshop.* Washington, DC: The National Academies Press. doi:https://doi.org/10.17226/24664.

- Institute of Medicine and National Research Council. 2011. *Child and Adolescent Health and Health Care Quality: Measuring What Matters*. Washington, DC: The National Academies Press. doi:https://doi.org/10.17226/13084.
- Institute of Medicine and National Research Council. 2011. *Improving Access to Oral Health Care for Vulnerable and Underserved Populations*. Washington, DC: The National Academies Press. doi:https://doi.org/10.17226/13116.
- Institute of Medicine. 2009. *Race, Ethnicity, and Language Data: Standardization for Health Care Quality Improvement*. Washington, DC: The National Academies Press. doi:https://doi.org/10.17226/12696.
- Institute of Medicine. 2013. *Best Care at Lower Cost: The Path to Continuously Learning Health Care in America*. Washington, DC: The National Academies Press. doi:https://doi.org/10.17226/13444.
- Institute of Medicine. 1990. *Healthy People 2000: Citizens Chart the Course*. Washington, DC: The National Academies Press. doi:https://doi.org/10.17226/1627.

Workforce for 21st-Century Health and Health Care

- National Academies of Sciences, Engineering, and Medicine. 2016. *Assessing Progress on the Institute of Medicine Report The Future of Nursing*. Washington, DC: The National Academies Press. doi:https://doi.org/10.17226/21838.
- National Academies of Sciences, Engineering, and Medicine. 2016. *Approaches to Universal Health Coverage and Occupational Health and Safety for the Informal Workforce in Developing Countries: Workshop Summary*. Washington, DC: The National Academies Press. doi:https://doi.org/10.17226/21747.
- National Academies of Sciences, Engineering, and Medicine. 2016. *Health Literacy and Palliative Care: Workshop Summary*. Washington, DC: The National Academies Press. doi:https://doi.org/10.17226/21839.
- Institute of Medicine. 2014. *Assessing Health Professional Education: Workshop Summary*. Washington, DC: The National Academies Press. doi:https://doi.org/10.17226/18738.
- National Academies of Sciences, Engineering, and Medicine. 2016. *Envisioning the Future of Health Professional Education: Workshop Summary*. Washington, DC: The National Academies Press. doi:https://doi.org/10.17226/21796.
- Institute of Medicine. 2014. *Graduate Medical Education That Meets the Nation's Health Needs*. Washington, DC: The National Academies Press. doi:https://doi.org/10.17226/18754.
- Institute of Medicine. 2011. *The Future of Nursing: Leading Change, Advancing Health*. Washington, DC: The National Academies Press. doi:https://doi.org/10.17226/12956.

- Institute of Medicine. 2010. *Redesigning Continuing Education in the Health Professions.* Washington, DC: The National Academies Press. doi:https://doi.org/10.17226/12704.
- Institute of Medicine. 2009. *The U.S. Oral Health Workforce in the Coming Decade: Workshop Summary.* Washington, DC: The National Academies Press. doi:https://doi.org/10.17226/12669.
- Institute of Medicine. 2008. *Retooling for an Aging America: Building the Health Care Workforce.* Washington, DC: The National Academies Press. doi:https://doi.org/10.17226/12089.
- Institute of Medicine. 1988. *The Future of Public Health.* Washington, DC: The National Academies Press. doi:https://doi.org/10.17226/1091.

Strong Science & Technology

Information Technology Interoperability and Use for Better Care and Evidence

- National Academies of Sciences, Engineering, and Medicine. 2016. *The Promises and Perils of Digital Strategies in Achieving Health Equity: Workshop Summary.* Washington, DC: The National Academies Press. doi:https://doi.org/10.17226/23439.
- National Academies of Sciences, Engineering, and Medicine. 2015. *Health Literacy and Consumer-Facing Technology: Workshop Summary.* Washington, DC: The National Academies Press. doi:https://doi.org/10.17226/21781.
- Institute of Medicine. 2013. *Digital Data Improvement Priorities for Continuous Learning in Health and Health Care: Workshop Summary.* Washington, DC: The National Academies Press. doi:https://doi.org/10.17226/13424.
- Institute of Medicine. 2012. *Health IT and Patient Safety: Building Safer Systems for Better Care.* Washington, DC: The National Academies Press. doi:https://doi.org/10.17226/13269.
- Institute of Medicine. 2011. *Digital Infrastructure for the Learning Health System: The Foundation for Continuous Improvement in Health and Health Care: Workshop Series Summary.* Washington, DC: The National Academies Press. doi:https://doi.org/10.17226/12912.
- Institute of Medicine. 2010. *Clinical Data as the Basic Staple of Health Learning: Creating and Protecting a Public Good: Workshop Summary.* Washington, DC: The National Academies Press. doi:https://doi.org/10.17226/12212.
- National Research Council. 2009. *Computational Technology for Effective Health Care: Immediate Steps and Strategic Directions.* Washington, DC: The National Academies Press. doi:https://doi.org/10.17226/12572.
- Institute of Medicine. 2009. *Health Literacy, eHealth, and Communication: Putting the Consumer First: Workshop Summary.* Washington, DC: The National Academies Press. doi:https://doi.org/10.17226/12474.

- National Research Council. 2007. *Improving Disaster Management: The Role of IT in Mitigation, Preparedness, Response, and Recovery.* Washington, DC: The National Academies Press. doi:https://doi.org/10.17226/11824.

Data Acquisition, Curation, and Use for a Continuously Learning Health System

- Institute of Medicine. 2015. *Integrating Research and Practice: Health System Leaders Working Toward High-Value Care: Workshop Summary.* Washington, DC: The National Academies Press. doi:https://doi.org/10.17226/18945.
- Institute of Medicine. 2013. *Digital Data Improvement Priorities for Continuous Learning in Health and Health Care: Workshop Summary.* Washington, DC: The National Academies Press. doi:https://doi.org/10.17226/13424.
- Institute of Medicine. 2013. *Observational Studies in a Learning Health System: Workshop Summary.* Washington, DC: The National Academies Press. doi:https://doi.org/10.17226/18438.
- Institute of Medicine. 2012. *Health IT and Patient Safety: Building Safer Systems for Better Care.* Washington, DC: The National Academies Press. doi:https://doi.org/10.17226/13269.
- Institute of Medicine. 2012. *Informatics Needs and Challenges in Cancer Research: Workshop Summary.* Washington, DC: The National Academies Press. doi:https://doi.org/10.17226/13425.
- Institute of Medicine. 2011. *Digital Infrastructure for the Learning Health System: The Foundation for Continuous Improvement in Health and Health Care: Workshop Series Summary.* Washington, DC: The National Academies Press. doi:https://doi.org/10.17226/12912.
- Institute of Medicine. 2011. *Future Opportunities to Leverage the Alzheimer's Disease Neuroimaging Initiative: Workshop Summary.* Washington, DC: The National Academies Press. doi:https://doi.org/10.17226/13017.
- Institute of Medicine. 2010. *Clinical Data as the Basic Staple of Health Learning: Creating and Protecting a Public Good: Workshop Summary.* Washington, DC: The National Academies Press. doi:https://doi.org/10.17226/12212.

Innovation in Development, Regulatory Review, and Use of Clinical Advances

- National Academies of Sciences, Engineering, and Medicine. 2016. *Advancing the Discipline of Regulatory Science for Medical Product Development: An Update on Progress and a Forward-Looking Agenda: Workshop Summary.* Washington, DC: The National Academies Press. doi:https://doi.org/10.17226/23438.
- National Academies of Sciences, Engineering, and Medicine. 2016. *Strategies for Ensuring Diversity, Inclusion, and Meaningful Participation in Clinical Trials:*

Proceedings of a Workshop. Washington, DC: The National Academies Press. doi:https://doi.org/10.17226/23530.

- Institute of Medicine. 2015. *Sharing Clinical Trial Data: Maximizing Benefits, Minimizing Risk.* Washington, DC: The National Academies Press. doi:https://doi.org/10.17226/18998.
- Institute of Medicine. 2012. *Public Engagement and Clinical Trials: New Models and Disruptive Technologies: Workshop Summary.* Washington, DC: The National Academies Press. doi:https://doi.org/10.17226/13237.
- Institute of Medicine. 2010. *Redesigning the Clinical Effectiveness Research Paradigm: Innovation and Practice-Based Approaches: Workshop Summary.* Washington, DC: The National Academies Press. doi:https://doi.org/10.17226/12197.
- Institute of Medicine. 2010. *Transforming Clinical Research in the United States: Challenges and Opportunities: Workshop Summary.* Washington, DC: The National Academies Press. doi:https://doi.org/10.17226/12900.
- Institute of Medicine. 2007. *The Learning Healthcare System: Workshop Summary (IOM Roundtable on Evidence-Based Medicine).* Washington, DC: The National Academies Press. doi:https://doi.org/10.17226/11903.

Targeted Research: Brain Disorders as an Example

- National Academies of Sciences, Engineering, and Medicine. 2016. *Biomarker Tests for Molecularly Targeted Therapies: Key to Unlocking Precision Medicine.* Washington, DC: The National Academies Press. doi:https://doi.org/10.17226/21860.
- National Academies of Sciences, Engineering, and Medicine. 2016. *Neuroscience Trials of the Future: Proceedings of a Workshop.* Washington, DC: The National Academies Press. doi:https://doi.org/10.17226/23502.
- Institute of Medicine. 2015. *Policy Issues in the Development and Adoption of Biomarkers for Molecularly Targeted Cancer Therapies: Workshop Summary.* Washington, DC: The National Academies Press. doi:https://doi.org/10.17226/21692.
- National Academies of Sciences, Engineering, and Medicine. 2015. *Enabling Discovery, Development, and Translation of Treatments for Cognitive Dysfunction in Depression: Workshop Summary.* Washington, DC: The National Academies Press. doi:https://doi.org/10.17226/21745.
- Institute of Medicine. 2015. *Developing a 21st Century Neuroscience Workforce: Workshop Summary.* Washington, DC: The National Academies Press. doi:https://doi.org/10.17226/21697.
- Institute of Medicine. 2013. *Neurodegeneration: Exploring Commonalities Across Diseases: Workshop Summary.* Washington, DC: The National Academies Press. doi:https://doi.org/10.17226/18341.

- Institute of Medicine. 2010. *Rare Diseases and Orphan Products: Accelerating Research and Development.* Washington, DC: The National Academies Press. doi:https://doi.org/10.17226/12953.
- Institute of Medicine. 2008. *Neuroscience Biomarkers and Biosignatures: Converging Technologies, Emerging Partnerships: Workshop Summary.* Washington, DC: The National Academies Press. doi:https://doi.org/10.17226/11947.
- Institute of Medicine. 2008. *From Molecules to Minds: Challenges for the 21st Century: Workshop Summary.* Washington, DC: The National Academies Press. doi:https://doi.org/10.17226/12220.

Training the Workforce for 21st-Century Science

- National Academies of Sciences, Engineering, and Medicine. 2016. *Developing a National STEM Workforce Strategy: A Workshop Summary.* Washington, DC: The National Academies Press. doi:https://doi.org/10.17226/21900.
- National Academies of Sciences, Engineering, and Medicine. 2016. *Barriers and Opportunities for 2-Year and 4-Year STEM Degrees: Systemic Change to Support Students' Diverse Pathways.* Washington, DC: The National Academies Press. doi:https://doi.org/10.17226/21739.
- National Academies of Sciences, Engineering, and Medicine. 2017. *Communicating Science Effectively: A Research Agenda.* Washington, DC: The National Academies Press. doi:https://doi.org/10.17226/23674.
- Institute of Medicine. 2015. *Developing a 21st Century Neuroscience Workforce: Workshop Summary.* Washington, DC: The National Academies Press. doi:https://doi.org/10.17226/21697.
- National Research Council. 2015. *Preparing the Workforce for Digital Curation.* Washington, DC: The National Academies Press. doi:https://doi.org/10.17226/18590.
- National Research Council. 2015. *Enhancing the Effectiveness of Team Science.* Washington, DC: The National Academies Press. doi:https://doi.org/10.17226/19007.
- National Research Council. 2015. *Enhancing the Effectiveness of Team Science.* Washington, DC: The National Academies Press. doi:https://doi.org/10.17226/19007.
- National Research Council. 2012. *Education for Life and Work: Developing Transferable Knowledge and Skills in the 21st Century.* Washington, DC: The National Academies Press. doi:https://doi.org/10.17226/13398.
- Institute of Medicine. 2012. *Strengthening a Workforce for Innovative Regulatory Science in Therapeutics Development: Workshop Summary.* Washington, DC: The National Academies Press. doi:https://doi.org/10.17226/13283.

- National Research Council. 2012. *Using Science as Evidence in Public Policy*. Washington, DC: The National Academies Press. doi:https://doi.org/10.17226/13460.
- National Research Council. 2011. *Research Training in the Biomedical, Behavioral, and Clinical Research Sciences*. Washington, DC: The National Academies Press. doi:https://doi.org/10.17226/12983.
- Institute of Medicine. 2009. *Ensuring Quality Cancer Care Through the Oncology Workforce: Sustaining Care in the 21st Century: Workshop Summary*. Washington, DC: The National Academies Press. doi:https://doi.org/10.17226/12613.
- National Research Council. 2010. *Exploring the Intersection of Science Education and 21st Century Skills: A Workshop Summary*. Washington, DC: The National Academies Press. doi:https://doi.org/10.17226/12771.

APPENDIX C

VITAL DIRECTIONS FOR HEALTH AND HEALTH CARE: A NATIONAL CONVERSATION

Symposium Agenda

September 26, 2016 | Washington, DC
National Academy of Sciences Building
2101 Constitution Avenue NW

8:00 AM   Registration/Breakfast available

8:55 AM   Welcome and Introductions

Michael McGinnis, National Academy of Medicine

9:00–9:15 AM   The Need for Vital Directions in U.S. Health and Health Care

Mark McClellan, Vital Direcitons Co-Chair, Duke University

9:15–9:30 AM   Vital Directions Initiative Framework and Approach

Victor Dzau, Vital Directions Co-Chair, National Academy of Medicine

HIGH-VALUE HEALTH CARE

9:30–9:35 AM   Introduction from panel moderator

Sheila Burke, Harvard Kennedy School

9:35–10:35 AM   **Panel discussion**

Marc Boutin, National Health Council
Richard Gilfillan, Trinity Health
Peter Orszag, Lazard
Lewis Sandy, UnitedHealth Group

10:35–11:30 AM   **Audience discussion with panel**

11:30 AM–12:45 PM   **Lunch, Great Hall**

STRONG SCIENCE AND TECHNOLOGY

12:45–12:50 PM   **Introduction from panel moderator**

Elias Zerhouni, Sanofi

12:50–1:50 PM   **Panel discussion**

Alan Leshner, American Association for the Advancement of Science
Jonathan Perlin, Hospital Corporation of America
Ellen Sigal, Friends of Cancer Research
Janet Woodcock, US Food and Drug Administration

1:50–2:45 PM   **Audience discussion with panel**

2:45–3:00 PM   **Break**

BETTER HEALTH AND WELL-BEING

3:00–3:05 PM   **Introduction from panel moderator**

Meg Gaines, University of Wisconsin Law School

3:05–4:05 PM   **Panel discussion**

Georges Benjamin, The American Public Health Association

Molly Coye, AVIA
John Dreyzehner, Tennessee Department of Health
Howard Koh, Harvard T.H. Chan School of Public Health, Harvard Kennedy School

4:05–5:00 PM   Audience discussion with panel

5:00–5:30 PM   Summary remarks

Sheila Burke, *Meg Gaines*, and *Alan Leshner*

5:30 PM   Closing remarks

Mark McClellan and *Victor Dzau*

5:45 PM   Adjourn

CPSIA information can be obtained
at www.ICGtesting.com
Printed in the USA
FSHW01n0227040518
47646FS